CYTOLOGY AND CYTOGENETICS

CARL P. SWANSON

William D. Gill Professor in Biology
The Johns Hopkins University

Englewood Cliffs, N. J.

PRENTICE-HALL, INC.

1957

To

Karl and Hally Sax

Preface

This book brings together in integrated fashion the findings of cellular morphology, behavior, physiology, and biochemistry, which have been grouped under the general term "cytology," and then considers these data in their relation to inheritance and evolution. A number of approaches can be made, and no two authors are likely to agree completely on the order of presentation, the topics to be emphasized, or the examples used for illustration. It is hoped, however, that the contents of the book reflect more than just the author's preferences and interests, and that the coverage, particularly at the experimental level, will convey to the reader the exciting and stimulating discoveries that have come to light in recent years.

The cytologist is customarily thought of as a morphologist, and this point of view is still a legitimate one. As the microscopic and submicroscopic aspects of cellular structure and function are revealed by new techniques and instruments, it becomes increasingly evident that the spatial organization of the cell and its parts, even to the molecular level, is never haphazard. Regulated organization is a prerequisite to regulated function, and these conditions hold even though the living cell is a dynamic and fluid system rather than a static and fixed one. It is at this level that cytology and cellular physiology become virtually indistinguishable. We cannot yet claim with assurance that any biological problem has been reduced to its molecular dimensions and activities, but rapid and almost revolutionary advances place us on the threshold of a newer biology, where the architecture and functions of the cell in metabolism, inheritance, and evolution can be visualized in chemical terms.

The cytologist has had a closer relationship, and one of longer standing, with the geneticist than with the chemist and cellular physiologist. In addition to being the vital unit of biological organization, the cell is also the physical bridge between generations. Its structure and behavior, particularly of the nucleus and the chromosomes, determine exclusively the patterns of inheritance, and an understanding and an appreciation of them in both normal and abnormal forms provides a physical counterpart to studies at the chemical level. Our attention, therefore, becomes focused on the chromosome and its component parts, the genes, and the problem posed is: how do the chemical substances that make up the chromosomal fabric duplicate themselves within a very narrow margin of error once in each cell generation, govern the immediate activities of the cell, control the transmission of hereditary factors, and provide the variability that is acted upon by evolutionary forces? It is not yet possible to discuss this problem in chemical terms alone, nor is it possible to consider the chromosomes apart from their cellular environment; hence, we must content ourselves with an examination of whatever data are at hand, whether physical or chemical.

There is urgent need for a book that asks what has and what has not been done, and ascertains the directions in which current and future research will lead us. To phrase the problem differently, we ask ourselves the questions "What is the chromosome?" "What does it do?" and "Why does it do what it does?" keeping always in mind, of course, that these events and activities take place within an organized cellular environment. To answer these questions, we must consider not only the cytological and cytogenetical aspects of higher forms of life, but also those of microorganisms and viruses, even though the organization and state of their hereditary material is still obscure. The reader will observe that few definitive answers can be given, but it is believed that these discussions will be useful to those working in the immediate fields of cytology, genetics, and evolution, and also to those in the areas of cellular physiology, embryology, systematics, medical research, and plant and animal breeding.

The contents fall naturally into three parts. The first, covering the first four chapters, provides an introduction to historical aspects and to a consideration of cell structure, cell division and syngamy, and the chromosome theory of inheritance. A brief review of Mendelian principles is also included. The second part, Chapters 5 through 12, examines in detail chromosome structure and behavior, with emphasis given to those experimental studies of the last decade that have been most influential in establishing a sound physical and chemical basis for interpretation. The third part, Chapters 13 through 17, deals with the evolution of cytological systems. The numerous references will enable the reader to pursue any of the topics discussed to whatever depth or breadth is desirable.

In presenting this work, it is my pleasure to acknowledge assistance that has been invaluable during its preparation. Professor M. M. Rhoades has read the manuscript in its entirety and has been a constant source of encouragement and help. Any errors or misinterpretations of fact or theory are, however, my sole responsibility. The photographic assistance of Mr. Charles Weber and the stenographic work of Miss Sallie Hemry and Miss Josephine Shyers have greatly lightened my burdens. Many others have been generous in permitting me to make use of unpublished or copyrighted illustrations; citations accompany each figure to indicate its source. To all of these individuals, and to the cited publishing houses, I am grateful indeed.

I would be remiss if I did not also acknowledge my debt to my immediate family, my university, my colleagues, and my students. Their encouragement and support has been most necessary and at all times steadfast and helpful.

CARL P. SWANSON

Contents

CHAPTER 1

Introduction

Any science may be likened to a river. It has its obscure and unpretentious beginning; its quiet stretches as well as its rapids; its periods of drought as well as of fulness. It gathers momentum with the work of many investigators and as it is fed by other streams of thought; it is deepened and broadened by the concepts and generalizations that are gradually evolved. Along its course it may be tapped by other disciplines, and its waters made to irrigate large areas of experiment and practice. Eventually it ceases to become narrowly restricted in a channelized course, and its substance becomes part of a larger and more comprehensive body of thought—in this instance, biology.

Cytology, the study of cells, had its beginning in 1665 when the Englishman, Robert Hooke, first saw the cells of cork, describing them as "empty vessels." Then followed a long series of studies that pointed to the cell as the unit of biological organization, an idea crystallized early in the nineteenth century by the formulation of the Cell Theory. With Virchow's statement in 1858 that cells arise only from pre-existing cells (the Theory of Cell Lineage), the stream of research took a turn that brought it into alliance first with embryology, and then, at the turn of the twentieth century, with genetics. In more recent years, the development of biochemistry and of new physical and chemical microtechniques have led to an outburst of interest in cytochemistry, and in the ultra-fine structure of cells, with the result that cytology and cellular physiology are no longer to be regarded as distinct and separable disciplines. This broadened stream of thought has in turn irrigated other biological sciences—for example, systematics, evolution, and plant and animal breeding—as well as stimulating far-reaching revisions of concepts in such areas of thought as sociology and philosophy.

In discussing cytology from an historical point of view, it has been customary to distinguish the classical period of the nineteenth century, during which the foundations of cytology were being laid, from the modern period which was ushered in with the rediscovery of Mendelian principles by deVries, Tschermak and Correns in 1900. For present purposes, it is more illuminating to think of cytology as beginning with a prolonged *descriptive period* that developed during the 1880's into the modern *experimental period*.

1

THE DESCRIPTIVE PERIOD

The cytologist is essentially a morphologist; like the histologist and the anatomist, he tries to make sense of the structure of things. The structure of cells being inaccessible to ordinary senses, the birth and the growth of cytology have been linked with the development of optical systems of high magnifying and resolving power. It was, of course, a microscope that enabled Hooke first to see and describe cork cells in 1665.

Despite the increasingly detailed observations made possible during the next century and a half by improved microscopes, and by more refined techniques, cytology earned recognition as a special branch of morphology only after the formulation of ideas unique to it. The first of these was the Cell Theory, generally associated with the names of Schleiden and Schwann, and outlined by Schleiden in 1838 in his famous *Beiträge zur Phytogenesis*.

Mirbel, Turpin, Meyen, and von Mohl already had clearly recognized the cell's central importance in the organization of both plants and animals, and in a very general way they had understood that cells were produced by a process of division (Conklin 1939a, b). Schleiden's formal support of it led to the acceptance of the Cell Theory, and the next major advance was Virchow's Theory of Cell Lineage, put forward in 1858. Virchow's observation gave the Cell Theory its impact in terms of heredity, development and evolution, for if present cells have come from pre-existing cells, then all cells trace their ancestry back to the first-formed cell in an unbroken line of descent.

These theories provided the impetus for the study of cell division in detail. Bütschli's investigations, particularly those concerned with the maturation and fertilization of the egg, initiated a decade of great importance. From that time, 1876, the meaning of cell division, and its many implications, became clear. O. Hertwig showed that fertilization of the sea urchin egg involved a union of the nuclei of egg and sperm; Strasburger demonstrated that the principle held also for plants. Flemming in 1882 described the details of the mitotic figure, applied the name "chromatin" to the stainable portions of the nucleus, and discovered the fact that chromosomes split in a longitudinal fashion during cell division. Waldeyer introduced the name *chromosome* in 1888. In 1884 Van Beneden and Heuser showed that longitudinal halves of the chromosomes passed to daughter cells during division, and in the same year Van Beneden pointed out that in fertilization the chomosomal contributions of egg and sperm to the zygote were numerically equal. On a theoretical level Roux and Weismann, in particular, interpreted these discoveries in terms of their hereditary and evolutionary implications, and the concept gradually developed that heredity was a consequence of the genetic continuity of cells by division. The germ cells constituted the physical bridge between generations.

It is these investigators, together with several others we are about to consider, who must rightly be designated the early fathers of nuclear cytology, much as Johann Gregor Mendel, in the modern sense, was the first geneticist (Wilson 1925; Sharp 1934).

THE EXPERIMENTAL PERIOD

The beginnings of experimental cytology were initiated in 1887 by O. and R. Hertwig through their analytical studies of fertilization. This, too, was the year in which the first of Boveri's celebrated *Zellstudien* appeared (Goldschmidt 1916). Descriptive cytology continued, and still continues, to be an important aspect of research, but these critical publications set the stage for work that integrated cytology with embryology, genetics, and evolution.

During the early phase of the experimental period, from 1887 to 1900, cytology was very closely allied with experimental embryology. The favorite objects of study were eggs of sea urchins and Ascaris, beginning with the Hertwigs' study of the developmental behavior of fragmented and enucleated sea urchin eggs. Wilson and Conklin in this country, and Boveri, Roux, Driesch, and others in Europe, studied cell lineages, cleavage patterns, blastomere-organ correspondence, and the prelocalization of embryonic parts as a function of the differentiation of the cytoplasmic ground substance in the egg. This work revealed that all of the early nuclei of an embryo, even in those forms (such as Nereis and Cerebratulus) that were characterized by a highly determinate type of cleavage, possessed an equal hereditary potency, and that in later stages there was a regulation of parts through cell interactions. To explain these observations, Weismann and his followers postulated that certain hereditary materials present originally in the fertilized egg (and preserved undiluted through the germ line) were elaborately distributed to separate places in the body where they governed the development of particular cells and organs. Driesch, interpreting the same facts, developed his vitalistic concept of an "entelechy"—a mysterious non-mechanical force that provided for a continuous and harmonious developmental process throughout the life of the organism. Both hypotheses have since been abandoned.

But advances in experimental embryology did not overshadow studies of the nucleus. By 1885 Weismann, Strasburger, Köllicker, and O. Hertwig had independently concluded that the recently found chromatin was the physical basis of inheritance. Boveri, following Rabl, brought forth in 1888 his ideas on the individuality of the chromosomes, a subject he was later to pursue at greater lengths by a study of multipolar mitoses in dispermic eggs. With Wilson and Van Beneden he pointed out the importance of Flemming's discovery: the continuity of the centrosomes, determining also the origin of these bodies and their role in fertilization. Through study of the fertilization of enucleated eggs of one species of sea urchin by the sperm of another species, Boveri was led to believe that the pluteus larvae showed paternal characteristics, indicating the influence of the nucleus in inheritance and development. These experimental studies began to provide piecemeal data that supported Roux's earlier (1883) hypothesis that not only the chromosomes, but the individual parts of each chromosome (the genes in linear order?), were important in determining the individual's development, physiology, and morphology.

It was E. B. Wilson, a superb synthesizer as well as a stimulating teacher and investigator, who by 1896 had been able to organize the cytological and embryological knowledge of his day in his classic *The Cell in Development and Inheritance* (Muller 1949). Mendel's principles of genetics were still to be rediscovered, but the beginnings of cytogenetics and of the Chromosome Theory of Inheritance were clearly outlined by Wilson in his statement that the visible chromomeres on the chromosomes were in all probability much larger than the "ultimate dividing units," and that "these [ultimate] units must be capable of assimilation, growth, and division without loss of their specific character." We would now add to this statement only that the units must also be capable of change (mutation) without impairment of duplication. A particularly modern note is also struck with the suggestion by Driesch, that these units of assimilation (we would now call them genes) exert their influence upon cells through the production or control of distinctive enzymes.

With thought taking this turn, it is little wonder that the opportune rediscovery of Mendelism at the turn of the century by de Vries, Tschermak, and Correns initiated a second phase of experimental cytology, the alliance this time being with genetics. From this union emerged *cytogenetics,* a hybrid science inheriting from genetics a point of view that was quantitative and physiological, and from cytology one that was qualitative, physical, and descriptive.

By 1925, when the third edition of Wilson's *The Cell in Development and Heredity* was published, the factual threads of genetics and cytology had been woven into a durable and logically beautiful fabric: the Chromosome Theory of Inheritance. Many of the finer details were added later (1910–20) by the Drosophila workers of the Morgan school. The discovery in 1933 of the usefulness in cytogenetic research of the giant chromosomes in the salivary gland cells of Drosophila, the recognition of the value of heteroploidy and polyploidy as cytogenetic tools, and the use of maize in cytogenetics studies have provided, and are still providing, additional avenues of approach to an understanding of the chromosome in cell division as well as in heredity (Schrader 1948). These have served to bolster, as well as to elaborate, the Chromosome Theory of Inheritance. (These findings will be considered in later chapters.)

A third phase of experimental cytology, an extension of earlier work, is the current one. It was becoming increasingly evident that the major problems of cytogenetics were

(1) the nature of the gene,

(2) its manner of self-reproduction, and

(3) its mode of action in character determination.

The answers to these problems, which still remain to be provided, seemed to depend on a more detailed knowledge of chromosome mechanics, chemistry, and physiology. The cytogeneticist therefore turned to the physical and chemical sciences for new tools and new techniques that might furnish new approaches when further progress through conventional means seemed blocked. New tools, such as the electron microscope and the phase-contrast microscope, were being perfected, but more important was the development of new techniques.

Muller and Stadler, independently, in 1927 and 1928, demonstrated that x-rays could increase many-fold the mutation rate of organisms, and it soon became evident that a means was available for the production of an almost unlimited number of gene and chromosome changes, which could be utilized in the study of a wide variety of cytogenetic problems. This discovery was followed by the work of Caspersson, who, in 1936, drew attention to the fact that a quantitative and qualitative probing of the living as well as of the fixed cell could be carried out by means of ultraviolet spectroscopy. Certain molecules exhibit a characteristic absorption of specific wavelengths of light, and he showed that the nucleoproteins of the chromosome absorbed highly in the region of the short ultraviolet spectrum. Supplementary techniques of specific staining, enzymatic digestion of chromosomes, and newer methods of cellular fractionation through centrifugation, have provided, if not clear-cut answers, at least an appreciation of the complexities of the cellular chemistry associated with chromosome behavior and gene action.

In thus separating experimental cytology into three periods characterized by alliance first with embryology, then with genetics, and then with physics and chemistry, emphasis has obviously been given only to dominant trends. Cytology itself, as a science that seeks to understand the cell as a physical, chemical, and biological unit of organization, has moved steadily forward, and each new alliance with related sciences has served to strengthen and broaden our knowledge.

NEWER TOOLS OF CYTOLOGY

Early researchers in cytology made use of fixation procedures, stains of various kinds and degrees of specificity, and standard optical systems using sources of visible light for illumination (Fig. 1–1). There is no need to describe these in detail here since they are adequately treated in other readily available books. It should be pointed out, however, that with the development of aplanatic condensers, apochromatic objectives, and compensating oculars, the light microscope by the beginning of our own century reached near perfection. The wavelength of light used was found to be the limiting factor in resolving power; an increase in resolution could be obtained only by the employment of more discriminating sources of illumination.

The present-day cytologist has a more diversified arsenal of weapons. The newer instruments fall into three groups: (1) those that give an increased resolution, (2) those that provide for identification of cellular structures by their differential absorption of specific wavelengths of light, and (3) those that by differential contrast highlight structural features in systems that would otherwise be optically homogenous.

The electron microscope. A considerable increase in resolving power has been made possible by the development of the electron microscope (cf. Wyckoff 1949). We have noted that the wavelength of the light with which objects are illuminated sets an absolute lower limit for discriminatory vision. Objects whose diameters are less than one-half the wavelength of light cannot be resolved, i.e., cannot be seen as distinct from each other. Theoretical considerations as well as practical testing support this conclusion. Since blue light has a wavelength of approximately 4000 Angstroms (0.4 microns or 400 millimicrons), the light microscope, under the most favorable optical conditions, cannot discriminate two objects separated from each other by a distance of much less than 0.2 microns. Ultraviolet light, being of shorter wavelength, can extend somewhat the lower limits of resolution, but the increase is not appreciable.

One type of electron microscope circumvents such optical barriers by passing electrons through the object studied to a sensitive photographic plate. Differential opacities within the object are reflected in the differential pattern of the electrons that succeed in passing through. The electrons customarily employed in present-day electron microscopes have a wavelength of less than 0.05 A. Because of their electrical charge, they can be brought to focus by electrical or magnetic fields (Fig. 1–1), thus comprising a resolving system capable of revealing the internal structure of molecules. The magnification possible is a function of the voltage, since the amount of voltage used to propel an electron determines its wavelength. The transmission-type electron microscope, under ideal conditions, can resolve structures 8 A apart, a hundredfold increase over that possible with the best light microscope. The field emission microscope makes use of a very fine needle cathode, the tip of which can be coated with a monolayer of the atoms or molecules to be studied (Müller 1953). Individual atoms can be so resolved, and their spatial arrangement in molecues determined.

Although it has revealed much about the structure of living things (Fig. 1–2), two difficulties limit the use of the electron microscope in chromosomal studies. First, the electrons must pass through an evacuated system, which requires that the preparations be thoroughly dried; and, second, the weak penetrating power of the electrons demands extraordinarily thin preparations (0.1 micron or thinner). Recently developed techniques of cutting and embedding permit the preparation of ultra-thin sections, but the few studies made to date on chromosomes have not been particularly revealing.

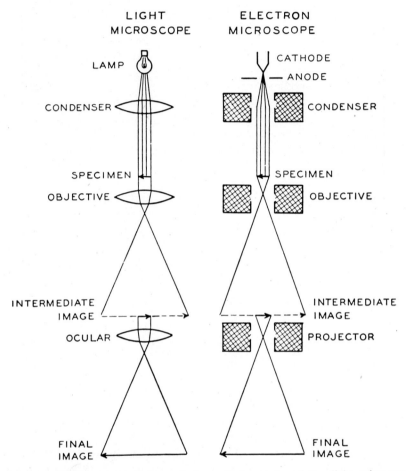

Fig. 1–1. Schematic comparison of the optical systems of the light microscope and the transmission-type electromagnetic electron microscope (Wyckoff 1949, with the permission of Interscience Publishers, Inc.).

The x-ray microscope. At present only in its infancy as a research tool, the x-ray microscope offers certain advantages. The penetrating power of x-rays is such as to permit observation on relatively thick biological preparations surrounded by water vapor or gas. The importance of this technique, when perfected, can readily be appreciated. However, x-rays bear no electrical charge, and must be brought to focus by reflecting mirrors, with the result that the resolving power of the x-ray microscope is thought

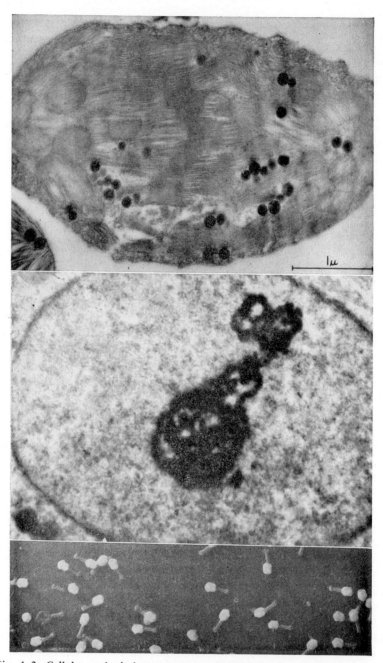

Fig. 1–2. Cellular and viral structures as revealed by the electron microscope. Top, chloroplast of the plant Aspidistra showing the laminated grana embedded in a less well-ordered stroma. The laminations in this particular chloroplast have a periodicity of 250 A. The dark bodies are osmiophilic granules (Frey-Wyssling 1955, after Steinmann). Middle, nucleus of a mouse fibrocyte showing the fibrous nature of the nucleolus and, occasionally, the double nature of the nuclear membrane (courtesy of Dr. Emil Borysko). Bottom, shadow-graphs of the T_2 bacteriophage (bacterial virus) which infects *E. coli*. The head is hexagonal in shape (courtesy of Dr. Roger Herriott).

to be considerably less than that obtainable with the electron microscope. Points 70 A apart can theoretically be resolved by means of the mirror system of focussing, a twenty-fivefold increase over the light microscope (Kirkpatrick 1949).

A more recently developed x-ray microscope makes use of the fact that x-rays can be deflected at various angles by a regular grating such as that present in a crystal, the image formed being characteristic of the crystal. Certain manipulations permit the images of atoms to be obtained— sulfur and iron have been photographed—magnifying the atoms 300,000 times (Anonymous 1951). The usefulness of this tool for biological research, however, is restricted to crystalline structures or molecules.

The phase-contrast microscope. Heterogeneous systems—for example, a living cell—may appear optically homogeneous because the light transmission of the component parts is quantitatively equal. Structural details that may be present consequently pass unnoticed. Differences in optical paths—a reflection of the structures' indices of refraction multiplied by the distance the light travels in traversing the object—may also be of insufficient magnitude to enable the observer to discriminate structure in a heterogeneous system. But differences in transmission and phase (optical path) can be advantageously converted into intensity differences (Fig. 1–3).

Where the differences in transmission are great, direct lighting, as in the ordinary light microscope, is sufficient for contrast; where transmission is similar, but optical path differences are great, oblique or dark field illumination becomes effective. When both of these differences are slight, suitable phase or absorption distributions can be introduced into an optical system to alter and amplify the contrast. The phase-contrast microscope utilizes such an optical system to suppress unwanted details and to emphasize others (Richards 1946; Bennett et al. 1951). Its value for the study of single layers of living or unstained cells is obvious (Fig. 1–4), but its usefulness is not so narrowly restricted. Many fixed and stained preparations often yield clearer images when viewed in the phase microscope than in the light microscope, particularly those preparations that are very lightly stained.

Spectrophotometers. It has become increasingly evident that the chemical constituents and activities of living cells, when accurately known, can provide valuable clues for interpreting the cells' structural and behavioral characteristics. For an intelligent integration, both structural and functional data must be had from identical preparations. It is desirable therefore to obtain the chemical data before sacrificing the cell for structural details. The simplest and most elegant method is by means of light, which, during the periods of exposure, does not damage the cell. The degree of accuracy is determined by the precision with which one can make absorption spectra of the cellular components.

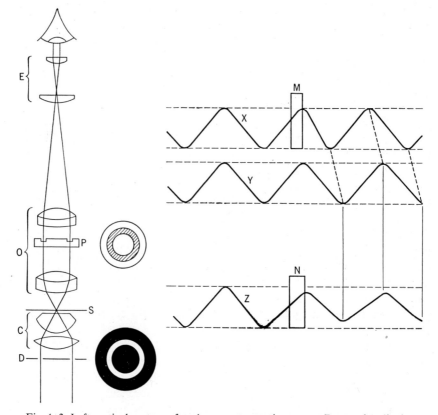

Fig. 1–3. Left, optical system of a phase-contrast microscope. D, annular diaphragm in front of the focal plane of condenser, C; P, annular phase plate in objective, O. The image of D is made to coincide with the annular groove on P (Barer 1955, by permission from *Analytical Cytology,* by R. C. Mellor; copyright, 1955. McGraw-Hill Book Co., Inc.). Top right, ray of light (X) passing through a region of greater optical path (M) is slowed down with the result that the peaks and valleys are behind and out of phase with those of ray Y which has not been impeded. Bottom right, a similar ray of light (Z) passing through a region of greater absorption (N) is reduced in amplitude but remains in phase with Y. The phase microscope converts these differences into visible intensity differences (after Richards 1946).

In this type of research, microscopes with a high resolving power have been combined with spectroscopic devices for measuring the absorption spectra of single cell preparations. The ultraviolet microscope, equipped with quartz lenses, has been found to be extremely useful, since the nucleic acids and proteins, which make up the chromosome and which are found in particulate structures of the cytoplasm, absorb highly in the short ultraviolet (between 2000 and 3000 A) in a most characteristic and selective fashion. For the investigation of molecular systems that absorb in the visible light spectrum, the light microscope can be similarly employed as a microspectrophotometer (Fig. 1–5). The techniques used have been

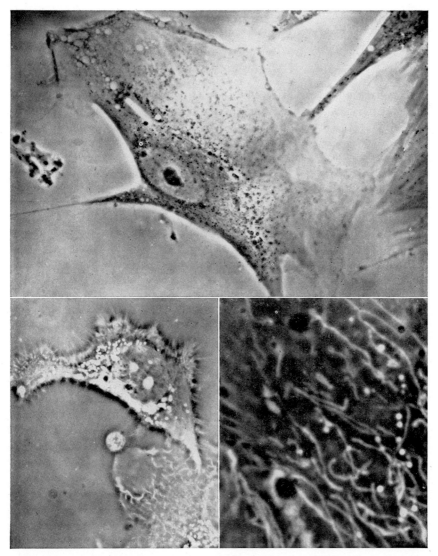

Fig. 1–4. Living cells photographed through the phase-contrast microscope. Top, normal human cervical epithelium (high dry objective); bottom left, malignant (Hela strain) human cervical epithelium (low dry objective); bottom right, portion of a cell of the Hela strain showing the threadlike mitochondria (oil immersion objective) (courtesy of Dr. G. O. Gey).

shown to be technically sound, both as to quantitative and qualitative measurements of cellular components (Pollister and Ris 1947; Caspersson 1950; Pollister and Ornstein 1955; Kurnick 1955).

The recent development of reflecting objectives provides a more flexible system for microspectroscopic studies. Mirrors are used rather than conventional lenses, and the uniqueness of the system is that any wavelength of light from the short ultraviolet to the infrared can be passed through a specimen without change of focus or lens.

NEWER TECHNIQUES OF CYTOLOGY

Recent decades have also witnessed the development of new techniques for studying cell and chromosome structure and function. The chromosomes have been more intimately studied in a quantitative and qualitative chemical manner through enzymatic digestion, more specific staining procedures, and mass analysis. The cytoplasm and the nucleus have been more minutely fractionated and analyzed by refined methods of differential centrifugation and extraction. Not only x-rays but other types of radiation, both ionizing and photochemical, have been found to be effective in inducing a wide gamut of chromosomal and genic variation, and to this group of mutagenic agents has been added a large number of chemical compounds that produce similar effects.

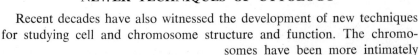

Fig. 1–5. Simplified diagram of the optical system of a microspectrophotometer. The phototube may be replaced by a photographic plate if the degree of darkening of an emulsion is to be used as an index of light transmission (Commoner 1948).

At a somewhat more biological level, methods of hybrid and population analysis have shed much light on the problems of speciation and evolution of cytological systems, while the techniques of microbial and viral genetics permit more exacting quantitative investigations of organisms that can be readily grown in vast numbers. The bacteria and fungi have also proved to be more useful than the cells of higher organisms for the analysis of genetically-determined chemical pathways of metabolism. (Each of these aspects will be discussed more fully in later chapters.)

THE GOAL OF CYTOLOGICAL INVESTIGATIONS

The establishment of such well-defined subsciences as physiological and biochemical genetics, cytochemistry, and cytogenetics, which at first might suggest an ever-narrowing specialization, actually foreshadows approaching unity. Within this seeming diversity it is recognized that structure and function must be considered together before an individual or a cell can be completely understood either as a member of a population or as a factor in future generations.

There is, of course, the hope that among the atoms and molecules making up organic matter there will be discovered the forces, processes, and interactions that convert the inanimate to the animate. The demonstration that active, infective particles of tobacco mosaic virus may be reconstituted from its inactive non-infective protein and nucleic-acid constituents appears to be a step in this direction (Fraenkel-Conrat and Williams 1955).

Since the structures of the cell can by certain disciplines be resolved to molecules, we postulate—and seek—an explanation of cell functions in molecular terms. Such a mechanistic approach may seem unnecessarily limited, but it is the only approach open to experimental science, which recognizes, and can deal with, only those phenomena that are measurable.

However, any optimism regarding the reduction of life processes to absolute molecular realities must be tempered by the realization that few biological problems—and few problems in any scientific discipline—at the present time can be considered completely solved. Thus the discussions that follow are at best only guideposts to the future.

CHAPTER 2

The Generalized Cell

The Cell Theory of Schleiden and Schwann, crudely crystallized in 1838 from the ideas of that time, characterized the cell as the structural unit of organization of living systems. Wilson in 1925 was thus led to state, "Long ago it became evident that the key to every biological problem must finally be sought in the cell; for every living organism is, or at some time has been, a cell."

The assumption has been made, and has not been experimentally disproved, that the plant or animal body is nothing more than the sum of its parts working in unison. But a profound and complex embryological problem still demands explanation: the problem of how cellular coordination is achieved in multicellular organisms. Embryological cell division somehow leads, through differentiation, interaction, and organization, to what we come to regard in form and function as a living organism (Fig. 2–1).

In multicellular species the individual cell, while exhibiting all or most of those characteristics that in aggregate constitute life itself, does not lead an independent existence. Its activity is merged with and governed by the organism as a whole. This integration becomes more pronounced as the cell undergoes differentiation, for specialization is generally accompanied by loss of functional flexibility and by a greater degree of dependence. But despite the amazing array of specialized forms that cells, both plant and animal, can take, it is only rarely that the structural features of the cell are obliterated. Only among such groups of species as the algal Siphonales, which are coenocytic, does one encounter difficulty in applying the Cell Theory rigorously, but these coenocytes may well have developed from ancestral cellular forms.

The *general applicability* of the Cell Theory provides the initial basis upon which experimental cellular biology rests. This deserves special emphasis. Essential for critical experimental studies is a constancy of materials. We find that the Cell Theory defines the cell as the structural entity of organization; the Theory of Cell Lineage defines its origin; and subsequent cytogenetic studies, clarifying the genetic implications of cell division, have defined a population of cells having a common origin as a *genetically homozygous group*. The experimentalist, who takes these facts for granted, is thus assured, except for the rare occurrence of mutations, of a pure

14

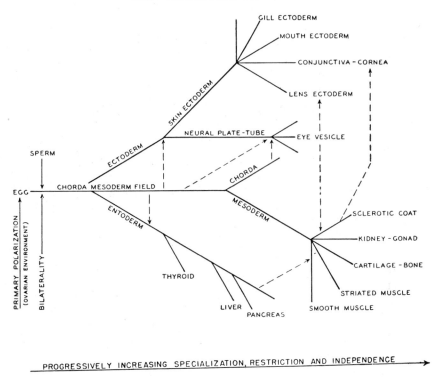

PROGRESSIVELY INCREASING SPECIALIZATION, RESTRICTION AND INDEPENDENCE ⟶

PROGRESSIVE NARROWING POTENTIALITIES

Fig. 2–1. A diagrammatic representation of the pattern of progressive differentiation from the unfertilized egg to the more mature tissues in a multicellular organism (courtesy of Dr. B. H. Willier).

line of cells or organisms which will respond in like fashion to like environmental conditions and thus guarantee reproducible results. The significance of this to cellular biology can scarcely to overemphasized, for the biologist is as dependent upon the genetic purity of his laboratory organisms as the chemist is upon the purity of his reagents.

There remains the possibility that the singular position of the cell in biological organization may be challenged. An increasing knowledge of the viruses poses a problem that may or may not be academic. The crystalline viruses, conforming to the definition of living organism in that they reproduce themselves and mutate, are nevertheless, according to the usual criteria, non-cellular. Simple in structure when compared with even the most primitive of cells, the crystalline viruses are yielding biochemical and physiological information that aids in the interpretation of cellular phenomena—but whether, in the organic world, there exists, or ever did exist, a graded series of life forms from the non-cellular to the cellular, is a question that cannot be answered at present. It is hoped, however, that because their chemistry and biological action resemble that of the genes, a detailed knowledge of virus structure, reproduction, host relationship, and "metabolism" will permit a better understanding of the mechanism of gene action within the individual cell.

The bacterial viruses, more generally known as *bacteriophages,* constitute a possible bridge between the crystalline viruses and the more definitive cellular forms. Electron microscopy studies (Fig. 1–2) indicate that those infecting the colon bacterium, *Escherischia coli,* possess an outer protein membrane; this suggests a primitive cellular structure. But knowledge of their internal organization is at present too meager for us even to hazard a guess about their possible structural relationships with higher forms of life, even though genetically they behave very much like the higher organisms.

While we recognize the existence of "living non-cellular organisms," we should not lose sight of the fact that in the vast majority of organisms the cell still constitutes the basic structure of organization. Wilson's statement remains as valid today as it was in 1925. It will, therefore, not be out of place in this discussion of nuclear cytology and cytogenetics to devote some space to the cell as a whole, and to its extra-nuclear components.

There probably exists no "typical" cell. All cells, however, have certain features in common.

The cell, or *protoplast,* may be defined as *a piece of nucleated cytoplasm surrounded by a cell wall or membrane, existing singly or in groups, and containing structures of various sorts* (Fig. 2–2). It is known, of course, that certain existing cells do not fit this general description. For example, in the later stages of its life the red blood cell of the human body lacks a nucleus, but this is obviously a special adaptation from an earlier nucleated condition. The living sieve cells of the phloem of most angiosperms are similarly without a nucleus, although they originally possessed one; here the adjacent companion cells, which remain nucleated, apparently take over whatever nuclear functions are necessary for the continued existence of the sieve cells. The blue-green algae also lack a definitive nucleus in the usual sense. Various nuclear stains reveal a chromatin network, which undergoes cyclic change as the cells divide, and which undoubtedly serves as a primitive type of nucleus. The bacteria were once thought to be of a like nature, but recent evidence shows that a clearing of the cytoplasm by enzymatic action, followed by staining with the usual nuclear dyes, reveals a nucleus-like structure in all the forms of bacteria so far studied. There is considerable dispute as to the chromosomal organization in bacteria (DeLamater 1951; Bisset 1951, 1955), but the genetic behavior of the bacteria strongly points to a nuclear complexity comparable to that of higher plants and animals (Lederberg 1948, 1955). Whether chromosomal structures exist in the bacteriophages and the larger

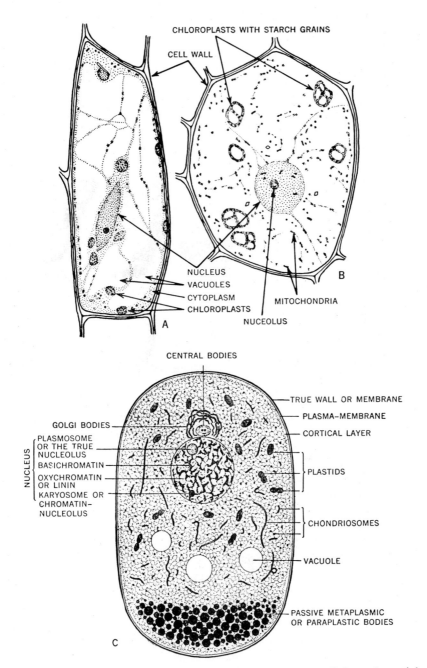

Fig. 2–2. Examples of generalized cells. A, parenchymatous cell from the petiole of a sugar-beet leaf; B, parenchymatous cell from the stem of tobacco; C, generalized cell exhibiting various organelles and labelled according to the terminology of the early cytologists (A and B, reprinted with permission from Esau, *Plant Anatomy*, 1955, John Wiley & Sons, Inc.; C, from Wilson, *The Cell in Development and Heredity*, copyright 1925, and used with the permission of The Macmillan Co.).

viruses is undetemined (genetic linkage groups are known), for electron microscopy in its present state of development is not sufficiently discriminatory to do more than to shadowgraph cells of this type without revealing much in the way of inner details (Fig. 1–2).

Also diverging from the definitive cell with its single nucleus, but diverging in another direction, is the coenocytic type of alga or fungus, and the syncytial arrangement found in some animals such as the rhizopods. Partition walls may give segmented structures here, but each segment contains many nuclei. From a structural if not from a functional point of view, it is problematical whether or not these segments can be considered true cells.

Disregarding the above exceptions, all cells contain a nucleus as well as most, if not all, of the following structures: cell wall, plasma membrane, cytoplasm, centrosome (absent in many plant cells), vacuoles, mitochondria (chondriosomes), plastids (if plant cells), and Golgi material. Each of these structures may readily be demonstrated by the use of certain fixatives and stains, and each undoubtedly has its particular function in the cell's economy. Living cells are conservative in that they probably retain no structures that are without functional importance, with the consequence that even though the functions of some of the intracellular structures are still more or less unsolved enigmas, their presence must be accepted as morphological evidence of some physiological role in cell metabolism.

In terms of intracellular complexity the Protozoa probably have reached the highest expression, for within the confines of a single cell may be found an extraordinary diversity of structures for ingestion, egestion, division, and locomotion. These organisms, however, probably represent special cases of evolutionary divergence and they will be discussed only when they contribute to an understanding of general cytology.

CELL WALLS

Each plant cell is limited at its outer perimeter by a cell wall. This wall may be thick or thin, smooth or sculptured, and it may be impregnated with cellulose, lignin, salts of various kinds, or fatty substances such as suberin and waxes.

In most tissues, and especially in those of higher plants possessing a vascular system for the conduction of water and nutrients, the cell wall is the chief supporting framework for the living protoplasmic system. Strands of protoplasm, or *plasmadesmata,* although difficult to demonstrate, are thought to pass from cell to cell to provide a continuous protoplasmic network throughout all the living portions of the plant. Animals, on the other hand, being supported for the most part by some sort of exo- or endoskeleton, generally possess cells that are characteristically free of plant-style cell walls, the outer boundary of the cell being delimited by a delicate membrane so thin that the protoplast appears naked.

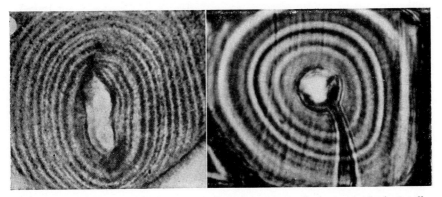

Fig. 2–3. Transverse sections of expanded secondary walls in matured plant cells. Left, light and dark areas result, respectively, from loose or closely aggregated microfibrils of cellulose arranged in a concentrically lamellated pattern (Bailey 1939); right, lamellated structure due to varying intensities of lignification (Bailey and Kerr 1937).

Cell walls are a secretion product of the cytoplasm. In the thick secondary walls of some plant cells there occur many concentric rings of cellulosic deposition of varying densities or porosities (Fig. 2–3). The various thicknesses make it possible to "cross-date the daily growth rings" much as one can cross-date the annual growth rings of trees to interpret annual environmental fluctuations. The denser portions (dark) are laid down during the day, the more porous rings (light) during the night, the width of the rings fluctuating with the environment. In other cells, a ramifying radial pattern may be found.

The matured plant cell wall—considering here those of the vascular plants, which have been most thoroughly investigated—consists of three distinct and definable regions: the middle lamella, the primary wall, and the secondary wall (Fig. 2–4).

The *middle lamella,* or intercellular substance, is of a pectinaceous material, the calcium or magnesium pectate being deposited in the fluid cell plate as the division processes near completion. This layer is shared by adjoining cells. It differs from the other wall components in its staining capacity and light-refracting qualities, and it may be readily dissolved by strong acids to free the cells. In woody tissues it often becomes heavily lignified.

The *primary wall* is the first deposition product of the protoplast. It, too, is pectinaceous, but also contains hemicelluloses and noncellulosic polysaccharides. The hemicelluloses cannot be demonstrated michrochemically in the primary wall, but their presence is inferred from x-ray diffraction patterns and from the fact that the wall shows a birefringence, the cellulose being in the form of a fine framework of cohesive chains. Waxes may also make up part of the framework.

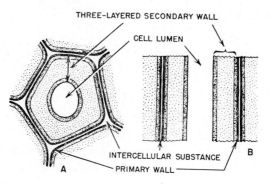

Fig. 2–4. Typical wall structure of matured and lignified plant cells. A, transverse view; B, longitudinal view (Reprinted with permission from Esau, *Plant Anatomy*, 1955, John Wiley & Sons, Inc.).

Since the primary wall is present in dividing cells, it is believed that a dedifferentiation can take place, thus reversing the changes that initially built it up.

Free of pits or irregular thickenings except where the plasmadesmata pass through it, the primary wall is capable of great extensibility. The cotton hair, for example, which is a single cell, elongates from an initial length of 40 microns to as much as 40 mm., a thousandfold increase directly traceable to the elasticity of the primary wall. Because of their somewhat similar chemical makeup the middle lamella and the primary wall are difficult to distinguish. They are frequently referred to, collectively, as the primary wall. Their separate origins, however, indicate that they do not constitute a single structural unit.

The *secondary wall,* characteristically composed of cellulose, hemicelluloses, and polysaccharides, but modified by various additional depositions and thickenings determined by the ultimate function and position of the cell, provides the chief supporting structure for plants. It is laid down after the cell ceases to elongate, and the changes appear to be irreversible. The chemistry and molecular orientation of its elements are extraordinarily complicated, but through the use of microchemical and optical methods much has been learned. Frey-Wyssling (1948), Preston (1952), and Esau (1953) provide excellent summaries of this subject, and it is unnecessary here to consider the topic further.

Zoologists are not in the habit of referring to the outer limits of cells as "walls," and with good reason, for "walls" in the sense of sharp delimiting boundaries do not as a rule occur in animal tissues. The material surrounding, and secreted by, the cells is more commonly called the *interstitial substance.*

In origin the interstitial substance corresponds to the primary and secondary walls of plant cells, but it generally lacks their characteristic layered organization. In such supporting tissues as bone and cartilage, the cells are surrounded by a continuous, more or less amorphous, matrix. In cartilage, this material may be traversed by collagenous fibrils either having a random orientation or gathered in a definite pattern into bundles. In bone, the interstitial substance is impregnated with calcium salts.

Most animal cells, however, are simply limited by a *plasma membrane,* the living outer membrane surrounding the cytoplasm. This membrane is reasonably elastic and is capable of repair. Its toughness, however, varies among the cell types. Thus liver or lymphoid cell membranes of many species are easily distintegrated by grinding, while the membranes of, for example, chicken tumor cells, can resist lengthy maceration with fine sand.

Animal cells possess no middle lamellae, but in place of this structure they secrete an intercellular cement, which, like the middle lamella, serves to bind the cells together. This cement differs from the middle lamella both in its origin and in its chemical structure; it is like the interstitial substance in that it is a secretion product of the cytoplasm.

From a genetic point of view comparatively little is known about cell walls. Maize geneticists have made extensive use of a marker gene, *bm* (brown midrib), which in a homozygous or hemizygous condition causes the usually green walls of the cells along the midribs of maize leaves to turn brown. In cotton much of the breeding work being carried on is directly concerned with genetic factors that determine not only the length of the cotton fiber, but also the orientation of the micelles of cellulose within the cell wall (for this determines the strength of the fiber).

Genes that affect the production of auxin, a plant hormone, also influence indirectly the behavior of the cell walls, since the extensibility of the primary wall is governed to a large extent by the action of auxin. In maize a recessive gene *na* (nana) speeds up the oxidation of auxin to such a high rate that insufficient amounts of it are available to produce the normal degree of cell elongation; the resulting dwarf plants scarcely grow more than two feet high (van Overbeek 1935). "Lazy" strains of maize, characterized by an apparent inability of the stalk to remain erect, result from a gene-determined condition causing an abnormal distribution of auxin. Ordinarily, auxin distribution is governed by gravity, but in "lazy" maize, the auxin distribution is indifferently related to gravity, and the plants may lie flat or even bend downward (van Overbeek 1938). Cell elongation would account for the differential behavior.

Anderson and Abbe (1933) have described wall formation in a homozygous recessive mutant of *Aquilegia vulgaris,* the garden columbine.

Known as variety *compactas,* the mutant is dwarf, brittle, and much more thickly branched than the parent species. A precocious secondary thickening of the cell walls causes an early cessation of stem elongation. Side

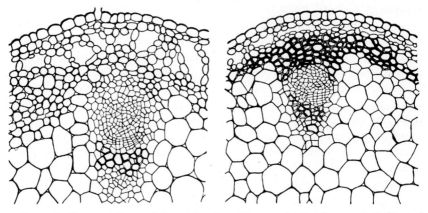

Fig. 2–5. Cross sections of the peduncles of young buds of normal (left) and mutant (right) plants of Aquilegia. The mutant form shows the precocious development of a sclerenchymatous sheath (dark, thick-walled cells) overlying the fibrovascular bundle (Anderson and Abbe 1933).

branches appear, but these too fail to elongate normally, and the result is a bushy, compact growth. The cell types particularly affected are those of the sclerenchymatous sheath capping the vascular bundles, and the earliness at which wall thickening occurs is the only apparent departure from normal development (Fig. 2–5). The physiological circumstances responsible for this departure from normality are not known.

THE CYTOPLASM

A large portion of a cell in an active meristematic or embryonic state consists of a relatively homogenous fluid, the *cytoplasm.* Bounded at its outer perimeter by a thin *plasma membrane,* which lies against the cell wall, or which in animals forms the outer boundary of the cell, the cytoplasm is limited at its inner boundaries by similar membranes wherever it comes in contact with the nucleus or the vacuoles.

These membranes are active, living portions of the cell. They are selectively permeable, the passage of solutes through them depending upon the size and nature of the penetrating molecule, the nature of the membrane, and the physiological condition of the cytoplasm within.

Although generally invisible in the light microscope, the presence of the plasma membrane can be demonstrated by plasmolysis or by inward pressure from a microneedle. A release of pressure allows the membrane to assume its former position without damage. Minor rupturing of the membrane causes no permanent damage, repair being immediately effected by the underlying cytoplasm.

Structurally, the plasma membrane is of a double lipid-protein character. The lipoidal nature of the membrane accounts for the ready penetration of fatty substances into the cell. The membrane's elasticity, however, requires the presence in it of a fibrous element, and this probably consists of a protein network of some sort.

Chemically, the cytoplasm is a system of amazing complexity and structure. Considered by some to be colloidal, and by others to have, in addition, a fibrous structure of submicroscopic protein chains and membranes which make up an endoplasmic reticulum (Claude 1956; Sjöstrand 1956a), its structure need not be considered here to any extent except to point out that in it are found the enzymes that catalyze the innumerable chemical reactions that take place in the cells. In most, if not all, instances, these enzymes are found in or on the particulate bodies that are in the cytoplasm. The cytoplasm—or perhaps, more properly, the protoplasm—is unique in that it can reproduce itself out of the dissolved organic and inorganic substances that it takes into itself, a phenomenon that is one of the primary attributes of living organisms.

The cytoplasm does not, and cannot, long continue to exist apart from the nucleus. Harvey (1936) has shown that an enucleated sea-urchin egg can be stimulated to divide until it has reached a mass of 500 cells. But the cells (more properly described as segments of cytoplasm) do not differentiate, and they soon die, indicating the essentialness of the nucleus for growth and development.

Together the nucleus and the cytoplasm form an integrated physiological system—the cell—and events occurring in one undoubtedly exert an influence on the other. Considered separately, however, the cytoplasm is the immediate environment in which the nucleus is embedded, and it is the substratum through which the genes within the nucleus exert their effects upon the cell as a whole. This has been strikingly demonstrated by the experiments of Hämmerling (1953) on *Acetabularia* (Fig. 2–6).

Acetabularia is a large one-celled alga possessing a rhizoid in which the nucleus is situated, and a cap that characterizes the species. Hämmerling showed that if the cap of one species was grafted upon the rhizoid of another, the cap would assume the species characteristics corresponding to the nucleus in the rhizoid. The cytoplasm was apparently without influence in determining the characteristics of the cap despite the transfer of much cytoplasm in the grafting process.

On the other hand, the increasing interest of the geneticist in the cytoplasm during the past decade indicates that the cytoplasm cannot be disregarded as barren genetic ground (Caspari 1948). Such terms as *plasmagene* and *cytogene* have been coined to designate cytoplasmic units which, like the nuclear genes, are believed to be self-duplicating and capable of determining hereditary characteristics. The term *plasmon* refers, collectively, to the entire cytoplasmic constellation of hereditary units, par-

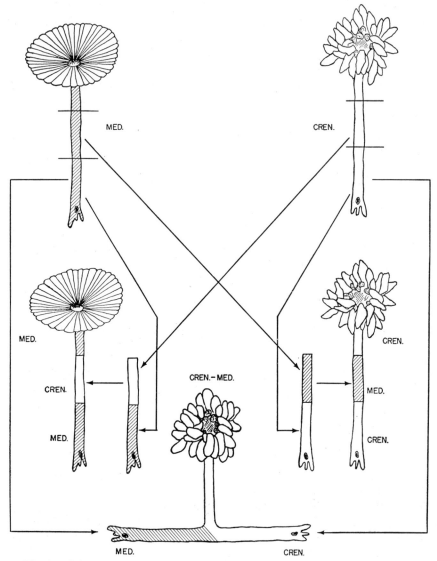

Fig. 2–6. Diagrammatic representation of the influence of the nucleus on development in Acetabularia. Stalk segments of *A. mediteranea* grafted onto nucleus-
containing rhizoids of *A. crenata,* and vice versa, produce caps characteristic of the
species contributing the nucleus. When two nucleus-containing rhizoids are grafted
together, the cap consists of loose rays as in *A. crenata,* but their points are more
rounded as in *A. mediteranea* (after Hämmerling 1953).

ticularly as demonstrated by the work of von Wettstein (1928) on interspecific and intergeneric crosses in the bryophytes, where a certain degree
of autonomous hereditary potentiality appears to be possessed by the
cytoplasm regardless of the genotype of the nucleus.

A note of caution, however, has recently been injected into the discussions revolving around cytoplasmic inheritance (Schultz 1952). Two apparently clear-cut demonstrations of cytoplasmic inheritance, that of male sterility in maize (Rhoades 1933) and that of the kappa factor in *Paramecium aurelia* (Sonneborn 1943), have yielded to somewhat different explanations. The kappa factor has been shown by Preer (1948, 1950; Preer and Stark 1953) to be a microscopically visible particle whose characteristics approach those of a rickettsia-like organism, and which behaves in some strains of Paramecium as a benign infectious agent whose maintenance within the cell is gene-controlled, but whose presence cannot be genically or cytoplasmically initiated. In other strains the kappa factor leads to cell death. The male sterility factor in maize, control of which could not be traced to any nuclear gene, has been thought by Gabelman (1949) to be particulate in nature, but this now seems unlikely. It is more probable that cytoplasmic male sterility in maize—there are several different strains known—involves an interaction of nucleus with cytoplasm since genes are known which insure pollen fertility even though present in sterile cytoplasm.

The two examples just cited indicate that the distinction between plasmagenes and cytoplasmic viruses is a matter of definition. Their differences in origin, that is, internal versus external, cannot provide a clear-cut basis for distinction, because through the process of evolutionary adaptation a symbiotic condition could easily have become an established but not necessarily, for the host, an inviolate relationship. The clear-cut existence of plasmagenes must therefore remain in doubt. At the same time, however, it must be recognized that other cytoplasmic structures such as the plastids appear to be capable of mutation and autonomous action. This subject will be discussed later in the chapter.

In the absence of definite proof of the existence of plasmagenes, the cytoplasm can best be viewed as the cellular clay that is molded into shape by the nucleus. The end product, which is the cell, achieves its final delineation not only by the molding process but also by the sum total of the ingredients that enter into its makeup. The quality of the clay must, on the basis of current information, be considered as gene-determined, although modified by what the environment can contribute to it. An inventory of the cellular ingredients may or may not yield chemical differences traceable back to genetic differences; it will *not* yield information as to the molding processes simply because such a catalogue cannot suggest the spatial and temporal interactions that take place. The manner by which genes act in attaining phenotypic expression constitutes one of the major problems of genetics. A variety of attacks have been made on the problem, but none has yielded a complete analysis, from gene to end product, in terms of chemical reactions.

Beadle and his associates (Baedle 1945) have approached the problem by inducing in the red bread mold, *Neurospora crassa,* mutations that effect biochemical reactions (Wagner and Mitchell 1955). They have demonstrated that, insofar as amino-acid and vitamin synthesis is concerned, mutations can block known reaction pathways, leading to an inability of the cells to produce essential material for growth (Fig. 2–7). It

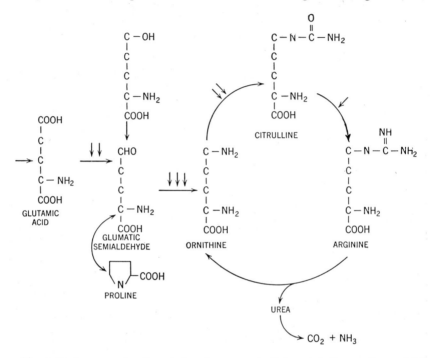

Fig. 2–7. An example of a chain of gene-controlled metabolic reactions which take place in the wild-type strains of Neurospora. Vertical arrows on the reaction arrows denote mutant genes which block the chain of events at particular points to prevent further synthesis. The mutant genes behave as lethals on an unsupplemented medium, but their action may be overcome by supplying necessary substances to the right of the genetic block (Wagner and Mitchell 1955).

is thought that these stepwise reactions are enzymatically controlled, and that the genes in turn control the enzymes. Whether the relationship between a particular gene and a particular enzyme is direct or indirect has not yet been entirely clarified.

The chemical processes so controlled take place initially within the limits of the cell, but the ultimate phenotypic expression may or may not be so spatially restricted. For example, the gene for yellow body color in *Drosophila melanogaster* can be detected in single cells, while the action of the gene in the mouse, leading through a pituitary deficiency to dwarfism, involves the entire body.

To solve these problems, we must understand the action of nuclear genes in determining the structure and function of cells. The many interrelated cellular processes to be understood make our progress in this direction slow. Figure 2–8 provides a graphic description of how the interrelated genetic and environmental factors might be coordinated to determine the definitive characteristics of an organism.

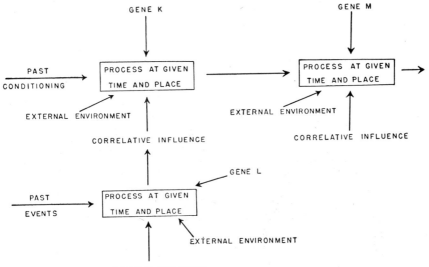

Fig. 2–8. An example of the possible relation of genetic and intra- and inter-cellular environmental factors to any developmental process. The coordinated action of all factors and processes would determine, at any given stage in development, the form and functions of an organism (after Wright 1934).

To the embryologist the cytoplasm presents a more varied picture in that visibly differentiated regions of eggs have long been recognized. In some marine invertebrates the cytoplasmic localization of the potential germ track may be visible before the newly fertilized egg has yet begun to divide. The formation of quite different organ systems from cells of presumably similar genetic constitution, and the inherent harmony of the parts of an organism regardless of its stage of development, also point to the cytoplasm as a delicately balanced and integrated system whose functions vary with the environment within and without the developing multicellular organism. It is known that hormones and inductors of one sort and another, in both plants and animals, contribute to this pattern of growth and differentiation, but again, as in physiological genetics, present knowledge of the interrela-tionships of the mechanisms involved is fragmentary.

MITOCHONDRIA

Lying free in the cytoplasm of non-dividing cells, and taking the form of rods or spherical granules, are minute structures, the *mitochondria* (Fig. 2–9). Ranging from granules 4 to 5 microns in diameter or in length down to submicroscopic particles many of which can be seen only by dark field illumination, they are found in all types of living cells (Hackett 1955; Palade 1952, 1953; Sjöstrand 1956b). In fibroblasts, they may be seen, following Janus green staining, as long, slender filaments several times the length of the cell. Although the form and size which the mitochondria assume may vary greatly within a single multicellular organism, their morphological features are fairly constant for any particular type of cell. The activity of the cell may, however, determine their shape. In senescent cells they may gradually disappear.

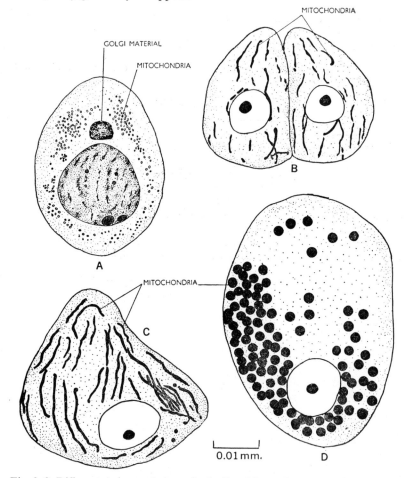

Fig. 2–9. Different shapes and sizes of mitochondria as they appear in: A, primary spermatocyte of the rat; B, mammalian kidney cells; and C, D, liver cells of the turtle in different phases of cellular activity (Gresson 1948, with the permission of the University Press, Edinburgh).

In living cells the mitochondria exhibit a pronounced Brownian movement. It has been generally believed that they are randomly distributed throughout the cytoplasm, but they are frequently found aggregated around the nuclei of actively metabolizing cells, and they may take a definite orientation suggesting that they parallel the lines of flow or diffusion that apparently traverse the cytoplasm (Pollister 1941).

During cell division the mitochondria may undergo definite maneuvers. In the spermatocytes of many animals they show an attraction to the centrosome, becoming locally aggregated in a thick mass (Fig. 2–10). In plants a definite aggregation may occur around the polar caps. As cell division proceeds, the mitochondria behave variously, depending upon the organism. In certain insects they form a mantle about the spindle, the process of furrowing dividing them more or less equally between the two daughter cells. In the scorpion Centrurus, a ring of mitochondrial material

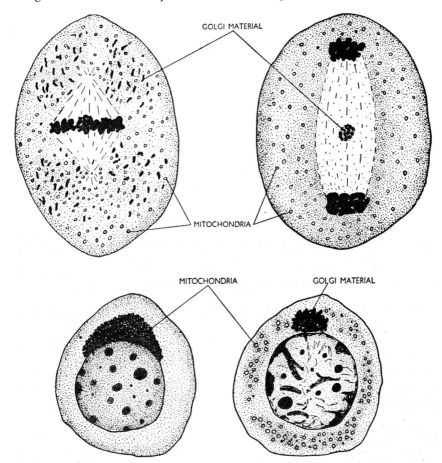

Fig. 2–10. Distribution of mitochondria and Golgi material in various cells. Metaphase I (top left) and anaphase I (top right) in the spermatocytes of the rat; very early prophase I (bottom left and mid-prophase I (bottom right) in the spermatocytes of the pig (Gresson 1948).

is formed which eventually comes to lie between the two anaphase groups of chromosomes, the ring being then cleaved in two by the furrow (Wilson 1925). A ring of mitochondria is also formed in the sporocytes of the fern *Onoclea sensibilis,* but instead of lying as it does in Centrurus, it encircles the spindle at the equatorial plate where the cell plate cleaves it into two rings (Marengo 1949).

The origin of the mitochondria is in doubt. Since they range down to a submicroscopic level, a study of their origin poses technical difficulties which have not been overcome. A number of studies have indicated that the mitochondria can increase in number by a process of simple division. Whether they can have a *de novo* origin has not been settled, although at the present time this seems an unlikely suggestion.

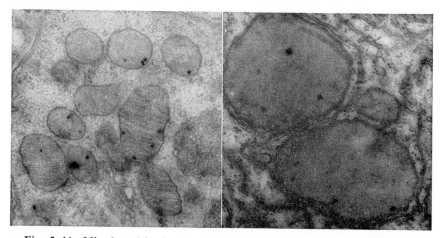

Fig. 2–11. Mitochrondria from epithelium cells of the mouse. Those at the right reveal the internal cristae, those at the left show no internal differentiation. Whether the cristae appear and disappear according to the metabolism of the mitochondrai remains to be determined (courtesy of Dr. E. Borysko).

The mitochondria are heavier than the cytoplasm, being thrown during centrifugation to the cell's basal portion. Structurally they appear to possess a cortex of lipo-protein surrounding an inner core of protein, while internally projecting walls (the cristae mitochondriales) penetrate the center to give each particle a greatly increased surface area (Figs. 2–11, 2–12). It would be a mistake, however, to consider that the mitochondria have a static structure, for studies of living cells (Fig. 1–4) indicate that shape and size can shift rapidly, suggesting a more fluid structure than that inferred from electron microscopy.

A thorough study has been made of the chemical nature of the mitochondria. Claude (1941, 1946, 1949, 1951) found, through differential centrifugation, that it is possible to separate out from tissue homogenates two main particulate cytoplasmic components. The largest of these are

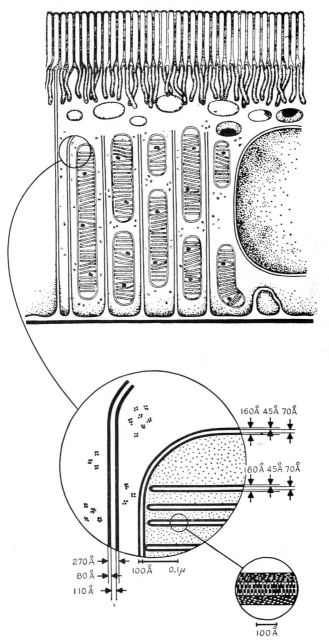

Fig. 2–12. Structure of mitochondria in a cell of the convoluted tubule of the mouse kidney. Top: nucleus to the right, brush border above, and mitochondria between intracellular cytoplasmic membranes. Middle: enlargement of the circled area of the top figure, showing the intracellular cytoplasmic membrane, and a portion of a mitochondrium with its internal cristae. Bottom: enlargement of a crista showing its layered protein-lipoid structure, with the protein being outside, the lipoid layer internal. Dimensions in Angstrom units are given (Sjöstrand and Rhodin 1953).

31

mitochondria and secretory granules, ranging from 0.5 to 2 microns in diameter. The latter, known as *Bensley granules,* are probably specialized mitochondria, although other large granules also are found. The mitochondria are characterized by a limiting semi-permeable membrane which enables them to respond osmotically to changes in salt concentration. Chemically they contain lipids (25–30 percent by weight of which two-thirds are phospholipids), nucleotides, flavins, and nucleic acid of the ribose type, as well as a number of important enzymes: cytochrome oxidase, succinoxidase, cytochrome c, d-amino acid oxidase, various phosphotases, the fatty-acid oxidases, and other enzymes of the Krebs cycle system. The mitochondria, obviously, are active sites of electron transfer and oxygen utilization as well as being the structural entities within which considerable portions of the cell's metabolic and synthetic processes are carried out. Whether all of the enzymes are found in each mitochondrion, or whether several kinds of mitochondria exist, is not known, but treatment of yeast cells with certain acridines destroys part of the chemical activity of the cell known to be associated with mitochondria (Ephrussi and Hottinguer 1951).

The smaller granules, called *Claude's particles* or *microsomes,* range from 60 to 200 millimicrons in diameter and are consequently invisible in the light microscope. They constitute the chromophilic background of the cytoplasmic ground substance and are not homogeneous in nature, several types having been described. From studies made with the electron microscope, Palade and Siekevitz (1956) consider that they are attached to, or are a part of, the endoplasmic reticulum (Fig. 2–13). They have not been shown to possess a limiting membrane although they become hydrated in hypotonic solutions, and they do not have projecting cristae in their interior. Forty percent of their weight is lipid, of which two-thirds is phospholipid, while a large portion (60%) of the ribose nucleic acids of the entire cell is concentrated in them. No special functions are known for this cytoplasmic fraction, although esterase,

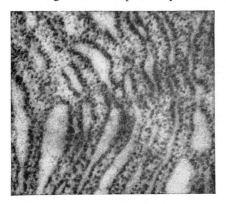

Fig. 2–13. The structure of the cytoplasm of rat liver cells as revealed by electron microscopy, showing the endoplasmic reticulum with its more or less characteristic orientation, and the attached particles (microsomes) which are between 100 and 200 A in diameter (Palade 1955, and used with the permission of the Rockefeller Institute for Medical Research).

DPN-cytochrome reductase, and thromboplastic activity have been reported. The fact that, by weight, they constitute about one-fifth of the cell mass suggests that they must play an important role in the cell's normal activity, while the high concentration of ribose nucleic acids is indicative of active protein synthesis.

THE NUCLEUS

In cells that have been stained, the most conspicuous body within the protoplast in the nucleus. Generally exhibiting in actively dividing cells a spherical shape, it may, in some differentiated tissues, assume a variety of forms. The polymorphonucleated leucocytes of the human blood take their name from their much-lobed nuclei, and the nuclei of cells in the spinning glands of the larval forms of many insects are much branched and lobed.

In the living cell, the interphase nucleus may show the same optical properties as the surrounding cytoplasm, making the structural details of the nucleus hard to see. The refractability of the nucleus increases, however, when the cells enter the division phase, permitting studies to be made of nuclear behavior in the living state. The stamen hairs of Tradescantia, the neuroblast cells and spermatocytes of the grasshopper, and various animal cells in tissue culture, have been successfully used for this purpose. The phase-contrast microscope has proven to be an admirable tool for such studies.

The stainability of the nucleus is due to *chromatin,* a material that readily combines with such standard dyes as haematoxylin, carmine, crystal violet, orcein, methyl green, and basic fuchsin. Its reaction with basic fuchsin, a phenomenon better known as the *Feulgen* or *nucleal reaction,* results from the fact that basic fuchsin has a specific affinity for the exposed aldehyde groupings of hydrolyzed desoxyribosenucleic acid that form a large portion of the chromatin. The chromatin is the hereditary material of the nucleus, and it appears as a fine network, or *reticulum,* in the stained non-dividing cell. The remainder of the nucleus is filled with a non-staining, colorless fluid called the nuclear sap, or *karyolymph.*

The use of fixatives and stains renders nuclear structures so much clearer than those in the living state that most cytological studies have been made on materials treated to show particular structures. Although there is good reason for believing that the chromatin of an interphase nucleus is in such a dispersed and hydrated condition as to "fix" improperly, it has been shown that the fixation of cells in division gives a reasonable picture of chromatin structure. This is also supported by phase-microscopy studies of living cells.

The stained nucleus reveals, in addition to the chromatin reticulum, dark rounded bodies, one or more per nucleus (Fig. 2–2). These are the *nucleoli* (singular, *nucleolus*). Their staining indicates that they are rich in histones, a low-molecular-weight protein, and in ribosenucleic acid. The nucleoli are also known to be attached to specific regions of the chromatin, regions that in some manner act as organizers for the nucleolar material.

Electron photomicrographs reveal that structurally they may have a fibrous internal nature, although it has not been demonstrated that this is true for all nucleoli, or for all stages of nucleolar development.

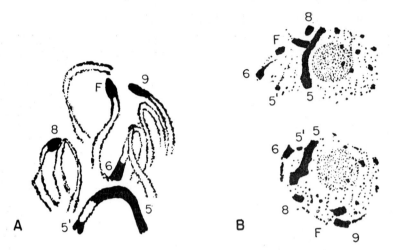

Fig. 2–14. Heteropycnosis in the chromosomes of the bryophyte, *Pellia epiphylla.* A, phophase; B, late teophase. The pycnotic state, identified by numbers, persists into interphase to form what were formerly called pro-chromosomes (Heitz 1928).

Other bodies may also be found in the interphase nuclei of some species. They are often several in number, and the name *prochromosomes* was applied to them because it was thought that they were the precursors to the *chromosomes,* structures into which the chromatin resolves itself during division. It is now generally recognized that the prochromosomes—or *chromocenters* as some authors have labelled them—are specialized portions of the chromatin, which, unlike the remainder of the chromatin, stain deeply during interphase. They are readily demonstrated in the vegetative cells of many plants such as the bryophyte Pellia (Fig. 2–14), tomato, and *Impatiens,* as well as in early meiotic stages of many organisms. Such a condition is known as *heteropycnosis,* a condition also displayed, for example, by the X-chromosome in the spermatocytes of the grasshopper. This out-of-phase phenomenon is characteristic of a particular type of chromatin called *heterochromatin,* and evidence indicates that the heterochromatin is comparatively devoid of the usual type of gene found in the *euchromatin,* which makes up the greater portion of most chromosomes. That it is not genetically inactive, however, is shown by the sex-determining nature of such chromosomes as the X in grasshoppers, as well as by other actions to be discussed in later chapters.

The nucleus has long been considered the control center of the cell, with the genes exerting their effects in elaborate coordination with each other. It is also generally conceded that the so-called "resting state" of the nucleus is really its active genetic stage insofar as its influences on differentiation and development are concerned. Yet, to the physiologist, the nucleus is a rather barren waste land; excepting the morphological changes the chromosomes undergo during cell division, it has been rather unapproachable experimentally. This is because the nucleus, in reacting to experimental agents, also reacts to an altered cytoplasm, and the resultant phenomena must be judged accordingly.

Some facts, however, have been gathered since techniques of cell maceration and differential centrifugation permit the isolation of nuclei free of cytoplasm (Dounce 1954). Such nuclei react osmotically, as does the nucleolus, shrinking or swelling as the tonicity of the cytoplasm varies; they do so less than the cytoplasm, so they must consequently be more viscous, as other experimental methods such as centrifugation have indicated. The nucleus, unlike the cytoplasm, is never vacuolated, although it appears that the nucleolus may become so. The nuclear membrane is incapable of repairing itself when injured as the plasma membrane readily does. This may possibly be due to the structure of the membrane, some investigators considering it to be only a phase boundary. Electron microscopy shows the membrane to have a definite structure, however. On the other hand, the nuclear membrane, whatever its nature, is positively charged, while the chromosomes are negatively charged as shown by their behavior when placed in a magnetic field.

A number of enzymes have been found in isolated nuclei, but they are not as numerous or as diverse as in the cytoplasm, nor are they any different in nature from those already known as cytoplasmic enzymes.

PLASTIDS

Within the cells of green plants are found conspicuous structures whose importance for the continuation of organic existence can scarcely be overestimated. These are the *chloroplasts,* which are intimately concerned with the process of photosynthesis (Mühlethaler 1955). Their shape and size, which vary widely, are characteristic of the species in which they occur, although in any particular species chloroplasts are not necessarily present in all tissues (Fig. 2–15).

Plastids other than chloroplasts also exist. The colorless *leucoplasts* are found in many tissues that are not exposed to light; in the potato tuber, for example, they become specialized *amyloplasts,* which serve to condense hexose sugars into starch. This function is not by any means confined to the leucoplasts. The specialized chloroplasts of the parenchymatous sheath cells of the maize leaf, as well as other members of the subfamily Panicoideae of the grasses, elaborate starch, but apparently do not function in photosynthesis (Rhoades and Carvalho 1944). The starch grains appear to be formed in vacuoles within the plastid, and a single plastid may have as many as forty starch grains. The chromoplasts of fruits and flowers con-

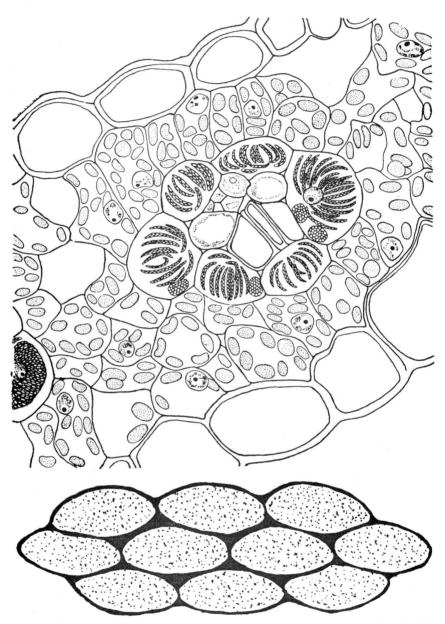

Fig. 2–15. Plastids in the maize leaf. Above, ellipsoidal starch-containing plastids in the single-layered parenchyma surrounding the vascular bundle, and the more characteristically shaped plastids in the outer palisade cells; below, an ellipsoidal plastid showing the arrangement of starch grains. Each platid contains approximately 20 grains (Rhoades and Carvalho 1944).

tain pigments such as carotene and xanthophyll which are also found in chloroplasts where they are apparently involved, along with the chlorophyll complex, in photosynthetic processes. The *elaioplasts,* which appear to elaborate oil, are probably specialized leucoplasts.

The various types of plastids are apparently homologous with each other, and transformation from one type to another can occur. The amyloplasts, for example, of a growing potato tuber exposed to sunlight soon develop chlorophyll to function as chloroplasts. Within the cell, the plastids behave as self-perpetuating, although not necessarily autonomous, bodies which segregate in a more or less random fashion during cell division. Where but a single plastid is found in each cell, as in many of the algae, the plastid divides in two along with the nucleus and the cytoplasm. In the higher plants, the chloroplasts increase in number by a process of simple division, which, however, is not correlated in time with the division of the cell as a whole.

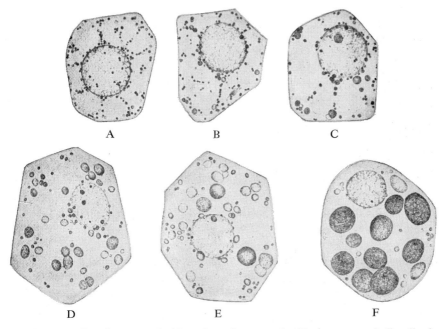

Fig. 2–16. Development of chloroplasts from proplastids in a mesophyll cell of maize (Eames and MacDaniels 1947, after Randolph).

Some controversy exists as to the relationship of the plastids to other cytoplasmic components. Structures called *proplastids* show a gradation up to the size range of normal plastids (Fig. 2–16), indicating that the plastids arise from smaller particles. The origin of the proplastids remains in doubt, but one belief is that they are homologous with, or derived from, mitochondria, which are of similar shape and size. This belief is supported in part by the similar chemical composition of plastids and mitochondria. Like mitochondria, the plastids, in addition to their pigments, are largely made up of lipoprotein. Chloroplasts from spinach leaves yield 56 percent protein and 32 percent lipids (Frey-Wyssling 1948), figures which do not differ greatly from data on the chemical makeup of mitochondria. Furthermore, the plastids also are rich in enzyme systems, with polyphenol oxidases, dehydrogenases, cytochrome oxidase, phosphorylase and catalase, among others, having been identified (Weier and Stocking 1952). These structures, on the other hand, contain little or no ribosenucleic acid which is so richly present in mitochondria and microsomes. This evidence, together with the knowledge that mutated plastids can pass from one generation to another unchanged, suggests either that they are not homologous with mitochondria or that they are not generated anew from some less differentiated cytoplasmic particle in each cell generation.

The interest of the cytogeneticist in plastid structure and behavior centers around the fact that there exists a great variety of chlorophyll variations and variegation. In addition to providing useful genetic markers they also serve a useful purpose in determining whether the plastid can function as an autonomous body in the cytoplasm, or whether it is always under genic control. Many of the chlorophyll variations in maize, which have been studied genetically, and which range in leaf color from white through yellow to various shades of green, follow a simple Mendelian inheritance pattern, and it appears that the mutant genes create a cytoplasmic condition that is unfavorable for the full development and functioning of the plastids. Plastid size is generally, but not invariably, correlated with chlorophyll production (Schwartz 1949).

The proplastids appear to be normal in the various mutant types, but the specific genotype can lead both to chlorophyll deficiencies and to abnormal plastids through either developmental delay or degeneration.

Recent studies on the structure of chloroplasts indicate that, like the mitochondria, they have a complex internal organization (Figs. 1–2, 2–17). (Leyon 1956; von Wettstein 1954, 1956; Leyon and von Wettstein 1954; Steinmann and Sjöstrand 1955; Stubbe and von Wettstein 1955). The body of the plastid is made up of disc-like structures, the grana, which consist of parallel laminations. These appear to arise from the aggregation of lamellae which come into being during the development of the plastid, and they lie embedded in a less well ordered stroma. It seems probable that the chlorophyll in the plastids is spread over the surface of the lamelae to give a vastly increased surface area to this organelle, and thus increase its photosynthetic efficiency.

Of particular interest is the effect of mutations on plastid structure (Fig. 2–17). In barley (von Wettstein 1956), the normal plastids have an organized system of stroma and grana. An albino mutant fails to develop beyond a certain stage, and lacks the stroma and grana. A yellow-green mutant, *xantha 3,* develops somewhat further, but in place of the ordered

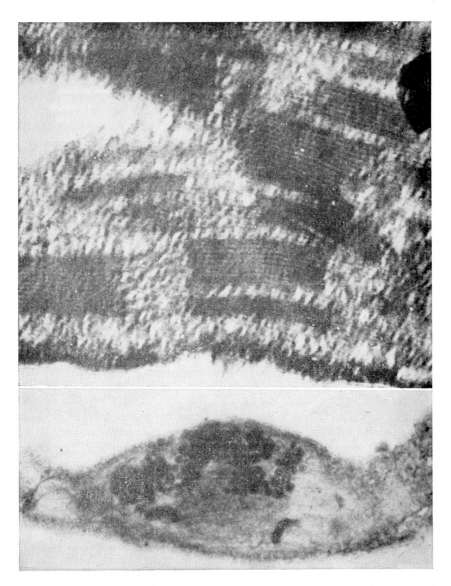

Fig. 2–17. Electron micrographs of barley chloroplasts. Above, small portion of a normal, fully developed chloroplast showing the lamellated structure of the disc-shaped grana and the somewhat less ordered stroma. The distance between lamellae is about 30 A. The blank space to the left was occupied by a starch grain. Below, a chloroplast from a yellow-green *(xantha 3)* mutant in which development is arrested, the grana and stroma have failed to form, and a mass of osmiophilic granules has collected (courtesy of Dr. D. von Wettstein).

pattern of internal structure is a heavy concentration of osmiophilic granules. The granules appear normally during development, but never in such large numbers, and it has been suggested that they represent some by-product of a chemical reaction in the plastid that can proceed no further. If this is true, the granules provide a morphological counterpart of a bio-chemical block in a chain of reactions. In Oenothera (Stubbe and von Wettstein 1955), a yellow-green mutant of the *suaveolens*-type develops normal-appearing plastids in young leaves, but as the leaves mature these disintegrate and do not function properly.

These studies indicate that electron microscopy provides a powerful means for tieing structure and function together in a more meaningful manner, and it would be extremely interesting to have similar studies carried out on the wealth of chlorophyll mutants that have been recognized in maize.

The chlorophyll variegations that follow a non-Mendelian type of in-heritance have recently been reviewed by Rhoades (1946). These include, among others, the well-known "status albomaculatus" type described by Correns in *Mirabilis jalapa,* in which, regardless of the color of the pollen parent, green branches give rise to green offspring, white to white, and variegated to green, white, and variegated.

Two interpretations of this phenomenon are possible. It can be assumed that two kinds of plastids occur, one green and one white, and that somatic segregation of the plastids gives rise to the green and white areas on the plant. The plastids pass to the offspring only through the embryo sac of the mother. Baur has used this hypothesis to explain the periclinical chimeras found in *Pelargonium zonale,* an hypothesis supported in this case by cytological studies in this species, and more recently, in *Antirrhinum majus* (Maly and Wild 1956). Two kinds of plastids have not been found in Mirabilis, however, and Correns believed that a cytoplasmic condition was responsible for the "status albomaculatus" type of inheritance. If this be true, it becomes necessary to assume that a cytoplasmic component controlling plastid behavior is capable of somatic segregation. Whether one terms this component a plasmagene, a virus, or some other equally elusive structure, is at the present time a matter of choice. Proof is difficult in any case, although, as discussed earlier in the section on cytoplasm, the identi-fication of particulate factors as the basis of cytoplasmically determined behavior in several organisms should serve as a point of reference for a reinvestigation of chlorophyll variegations.

Rhoades' (1946) studies on the iojap (*ij*) gene in maize, however, suggest that the plastid can mutate and, thereafter, reproduce its altered self. Homozygous *ij* plants are green-and-white striped. Yellow stripes occur when mesophyll cells with normal-sized plastids overlie colorless layers containing undeveloped plastids. These mesophyll plastids are paler than normal plastids in a totally green area, and it appears that a diffusible substance can enter the mesophyll from the colorless area to impair chlorophyll development in normal cells. The action of the *ij* gene thus seems to be on the cytoplasm rather than directly on the plastid. However, Rhoades has been able to show, through appropriate breeding techniques, that the "mutated" plastids do not revert to normal even when the normal alleles of *ij* are present. The plastid appears, therefore, to be, in some instances at least, capable of permanent alteration (Rhoades 1954). As such it can be considered an autonomous entity—the *plastogene*. This is strongly supported by Renner's (1934, 1936) Oenothera studies. Renner was able to demonstrate that the plastids from one species could exist with the nuclei, and in the cytoplasm, of other species through many generations, and still be recovered without change in specific properties. On this basis, the nuclear gene cannot be considered the only particulate structure capable of mutation. Furthermore, if plastids arise from mitochondria, the latter, too, should be subject to permanent alteration to provide the cytoplasm with transmissible hereditary units of a particulate nature.

GOLGI MATERIAL

Treatment of animal cells by techniques that deposit osmium or silver in the form of a dark precipitate generally brings out a series of lobed bodies or a reasonably continuous network of strands (Fig. 2–10). These are, collectively, the *Golgi material,* so named after its discoverer. Its conspicuous presence in secretory cells, and the fact that it shows a relationship to secretory activity, strongly suggest that it may be concerned with the elaboration or the collection of substances within the cell. It has also been stated that these bodies may provide condensation membranes that absorb various materials for use, perhaps, in the synthetic functions of the cell.

Vitamin C is found associated in fairly high concentrations within the Golgi material in differentiating embryonic cells that are actively synthesizing materials, and it has been proposed that this storage of Vitamin C is possible because the Golgi material provides in the cytoplasm a segregated area of high reducing capacity, which prevents the oxidation of the synthetic materials when the metabolism of the cell is increased (Bourne 1951).

Like the mitochondria, the Golgi material is chemically lipo-protein in structure; and where distinct bodies are found they appear to consist of an outer cortex and an inner core. They are similarly distributed to daughter cells in mitosis in a roughly quantitative fashion.

In plant cells, distinct Golgi material is lacking, and it is doubtful whether it exists in plants at all. The affirmative position is held by some investigators who feel that the Golgi material is in some manner associated with the formation of vacuoles.

But Palade and Claude (1949) have recently taken a position that throws doubt upon the reality of the Golgi material even in animals. These investigators consider the Golgi material to be a myelin (lipid) artifact developed gradually during the fixation procedures that must be used to demonstrate their presence. They have succeeded in showing that there are refractory droplets or inclusions present in living cells within the so-called "Golgi zone," and that these under the influence of ethanol as well as of the usual Golgi fixatives can be transformed into polymorphic structures similar to those that take a Golgi stain. The droplets are more numerous in actively metabolic cells than in quiescent ones, just as the Golgi material has been shown to be. The fact that the droplets are of a myelin nature lead Palade and Claude to state that the hypotheses concerning the functional significance of the Golgi material in cell metabolism have no valid basis. Regardless, however, of whatever metabolic function, or lack thereof, the droplets play in the economy of the cell, the fact that they have a distribution and abundance that can be correlated with cellular activity provides the cell with a structural feature that can be recognized when properly stained. Whether this morphological entity is called a myelin figure or Golgi material seems somewhat arbitrary, particularly since Sjöstrand and Hanzon (1954) have shown that the Golgi material, consisting of membranes, ground substance, and granules, is demonstrable by electron microscopy.

VACUOLES

Conspicuous in the cytoplasm of plant cells, less so in animal cells, are the *vacuoles,* which contain a fluid, the *cell sap.* They are relatively small or even absent in actively dividing cells, but once a cell has passed into a state of differentiation an enlargement and a coalescence of vacuoles— as for example, in the cells of a typical parenchyma—lead to the disposition of the cytoplasm and the nucleus to the periphery of the cell.

Bounded by a membrane called the *tonoplast,* the sap vacuoles contain organic acids, salts, sugars, and pigments in solution. Guilliermond (1941) considers the vacuoles to be colloid systems with a strong imbibing capacity. As such, they are not considered to be a living portion of the protoplasm, but rather a dumping ground for reserve materials and waste products. Active interchange of materials with the cytoplasm undoubtedly occurs across the tonoplast and the plasma membrane adjacent to it.

The origin of vacuoles in plants is somewhat obscure although it is generally agreed that, unlike the mitochondria, plastids, and Golgi material, the vacuoles can arise *de novo,* i.e., they can form spontaneously rather than from some pre-existent vacuole. The experiments of Pfeffer, which indicated that crystals of asparagin within a plasmodium can give rise to vacuoles, suggest that any colloidal or hydrophilic substance in the cytoplasm can be the precursor to a vacuole. In many protozoa, vacuoles are pinched off at the bottom of the gullet, after having collected ingested food particles such as bacteria. The vacuoles later secrete waste products to the outside, and it has been frequently noticed that they possess the power of rhythmical pulsation.

The interest of the plant geneticist in vacuoles arises from the fact that in the cell sap are contained some of the pigments and co-pigments that determine flower, leaf, and fruit color. The flavones and the anthocyanins, which are oxidative products of flavones, are characteristic of these water-soluble pigments. The former determines the yellow color of certain flowers such as the snapdragon, Antirrhinum. The flavones and flavonol derivatives are found in relatively dilute quantities, however, and they are frequently masked by other pigments in the cell sap as well as in the plastids.

The anthocyanins, which are abundantly present in the vacuoles of cells of the seed plants, determine the red, blue, and purple colors of leaves, flowers, fruits, and even stems. The specific color may be determined by one or more of three factors: the pH of the cell sap, the specific type of anthocyanin molecule present, and the amount of anthocyanin per vacuole. Each of the three factors has been shown to have a genetic basis. As pH indicators, the anthocyanins are bluer at higher pH levels than at lower ones. In Primula a pair of genes determines the pH of the petal cells, the recessive form of the gene determining a pH of 6.0 to give a blue flower and the dominant form acting to produce a pH of 5.3 to give a magenta flower (Haldane 1954). Certain genes are also known which change the structure of the anthocyanin molecule (Fig. 2–18). The number and position of the OH, CH_3, and sugar radicals are under genetic control, and with each change a shift occurs in the color of the anthocyanin.

THE CENTROSOME

Adjacent to the outer side of the nuclear membrane of the cells in many animals and in some lower plants is an area that is actively concerned with the process of cell division. This is the *centrosome*. In non-dividing cells, it appears as a clear area in which is sometimes embedded a tiny dark-staining granule, the *centriole*. The centriole when present may be single or double. During active cell division, the centrioles come to lie at either end of the nucleus where they form the gelation centers from which arise the astral rays, as well as the fibers that make up the spindle.

The cells of higher plants, as a rule, do not possess a centrosome such as that exhibited by animal cells, although some of the more primitive forms, such as the mosses, ferns, cycads, and ginkgo, reveal its presence during differentiation of the motile male gametes. The centrosome appears to have a determining role in the formation of the flagellar structures, where the centriole assumes the form of a *basal granule*. The centriole may be missing in some fungi, present in others, and the same holds true

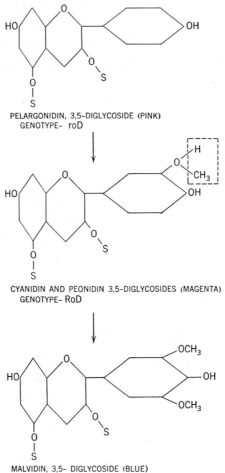

PELARGONIDIN, 3,5–DIGLYCOSIDE (PINK)
GENOTYPE- roD

CYANIDIN AND PEONIDIN 3,5-DIGLYCOSIDES (MAGENTA)
GENOTYPE- RoD

MALVIDIN, 3,5- DIGLYCOSIDE (BLUE)
GENOTYPE-ROD OR rOD

Fig. 2–18. An example of gene-determined anthocyanin derivatives in the Cape primrose, Streptocarpus. Gene *D* causes the derivative molecules to be almost exclusively of the diglycoside type, while the recessive *d* permits a mixture of mono- and diglycosides. Monoglycosides would possess only the sugar (S) radical to the right, the left position being occupied by an OH radical. Gene *R* causes a hycroxylation or a methylation at the 3 position in the side phyenyl ring to give the cyanidin or peonidin derivatives, while genes *R* and *O,* in combination, lead to methylation in both the 3 and 5 positions to give a malvidin derivative. The top configuration results when *r* and *o* are in a homozygous recessive state (after Wagner and Mitchell 1955).

for the algae. In place of the centrosome, dividing cells of the higher plants show a *polar cap,* a clear area which, according to some investigators, is derived from the karyolymph that filters through the nuclear membrane as the membrane shrinks inward at the poles. Its relationship or homology with the animal centrosome is problematical, although presumably it is active in the formation of the spindle.

Because of the need for a detailed discussion of the role of the centrosome in cell division, further consideration will be deferred until a later chapter.

CHAPTER 3

Cell Division and Syngamy

Two processes govern and insure the continuation of species from one generation to the next. In broad terms, these are the *union of cells* and the *division of cells.* The latter process is characteristic of all cellular organisms, while the former is found in those organisms that produce sexual cells, or gametes.

In unicellular organisms, the division of cells is a process of asexual reproduction. It leads simply to an increase in the total number of individuals. In multicellular forms, cell division is an aspect of growth, and it is generally accompanied by cellular enlargement and differentiation.

The union of cells, or *syngamy,* is a portion of the process of sexual reproduction. It involves the union of gametes which, depending on the species, may be morphologically similar or dissimilar. In the higher plants and animals, the actual fusion may be restricted to the nuclear portions of the cell, the cytoplasmic portions of the male cell being largely discarded in the process. A complete fusion of both cells, however, takes place in many species of algae and fungi.

Associated with syngamy is a modified type of division called *meiosis,* which, in a genetic sense, is its equal and opposite, for while syngamy increases the number of chromosomes through the fusion of nuclei, meiosis by a special type of division reduces this number.

A detailed knowledge of the three processes is a necessary prerequisite to an understanding of heredity. An interpretation of the mechanics of cell fusion and division shows the transmission of hereditary traits to have a physical basis of structure and function that is, in its constancy and regularity, nothing short of remarkable. This chapter will deal with the descriptive phases of cell division, meiosis, and syngamy, together with their genetical significance. A detailed analysis of the events that take place will be deferred to later chapters.

MITOSIS

The body of an adult man consists of approximately 10^{14} cells. Not only must these be formed and differentiated in the span of time that the body requires to reach mature proportions, but there must be a constant replacement of cells that have passed through their life cycle and disintegrated.

The problem of replacement is particularly well illustrated by the erythrocytes of the human. According to measurements made by labeling them with radioactive isotopes, these have a relatively short life of some 100 days. Released from blood-forming tissues, they lose their nuclei as they pass into the blood stream. There they function for a time and then die, being replaced by newly formed cells that maintain the cell number at a reasonably constant level.

The cornea of the mammalian eye is another tissue that illustrates the constant need for cell replacement. As the outer cells of the cornea die and are sloughed off, newly formed cells from the underlying layers, which are in a state of constant division, move into position to take their place.

Thus within any organism that grows or requires repair, mitosis goes on at a rate, and for a period of time, determined by the demands of the organism, its genetical constitution, its age, and the environmental conditions. The rate of division is probably higher in the blood-forming tissues than in the cornea because of a greater need for replacement, and both tissues have a higher rate than the kidney or liver which, by comparison in terms of an overturn of cells, are relatively static organs.

The time during which cell division increases an organism to adult proportions is, to a very great extent, determined by its mature size. The mouse, the man, and the whale are all mammals, and their cells are of approximately the same dimensions; their differences in size are due to differences in cell number and to the length of time during which cell multiplication (for purposes of growth rather than replacement or repair) takes place.

Cell division in a number of ways varies widely from one species to another, but the essential processes and consequences are basically similar in all organisms: it provides a means for an increase in the number of cells or organisms, and, in its exactitude, it effects a qualitative and quantitative distribution to daughter cells of the essential particles of heredity—the genes, which are carried in the chromosomes.

For the sake of convenience, the process of cell division has been divided into five stages: *interphase, prophase, metaphase, anaphase,* and *telophase* (Figs. 3–1 and 3–2). However, it should be recognized that, although the various stages are readily identifiable by certain appearances or landmarks, cell division is a dynamic and a continuous process, each step passing almost imperceptibly into the next. This has been clearly demonstrated by motion pictures of cells in division. Metaphase and anaphase stand out as the most sharply discontinuous stages and as a result are the most easily defined. The entire process may be separated into *karyokinesis,* or nuclear division, and *cytokinesis,* or cytoplasmic division. The term *mitosis,* which is synonymous with karyokinesis, has frequently been applied to cell division as a whole, but in the strict sense of its original meaning it should include only the division of the nucleus.

Interphase. Cells in interphase, or the *resting* stage, are characterized by a nucleus that shows little or no definable structure, except for the nucleoli and the prochromosomes. Both of these are seen as dark staining bodies, the nucleolus as a rule being the more pronounced.

Fig. 3–1. Diagrammatic representation of the stages of somatic cell division. A, very early prophase; B, early prophase; C, mid-prophase; D, late prophase; E, metaphase; F, anaphase; G, telophase; H, interphase. The nucleolis are shown as stippled structures, and the cell plate as indicated in G would form only in plant cells.

The nucleus in the living state is optically homogeneous, and in a fixed condition takes very little stain, which probably means that the nucleic acids of the chromosome are too diffused to absorb much dye. The chromosomes, as a result, are extremely thin and tenuous, giving rise to a faintly staining network. It is likely that the high hydration of the chromosomes at this time also reduces their staining capacity. This condition led to the belief that the chromosomes disappeared as structural entities during interphase, but such is now thought to be highly unlikely. The presence of prochromosomes is one indication of their continued persistence. Further evidence of the intact presence of chromosomes during interphase is that whole chromosomes may be extracted from various animal cells during their interphase. Others believe that in the intact cell the chromosomes in interphase are "unfixable," with the exception perhaps of the prochromosomes, and that structures seen during interphase are artifacts of fixation. However, it has been demonstrated that by the proper adjustment of salt concentration in a medium containing grasshopper cells, the interphase chromosomes can be made to stand out sharply in the living nucleus (Ris and Mirsky 1949). Since the process is reversible, there can be little doubt that the lack of visible structure in the nucleus in interphase is no proof of the loss of integrity of the chromosomes.

Prophase. Prophase is said to be initiated at the moment when the chromosomes become visibly distinct. Prior to this an enlargement of the nucleus occurs by an uptake of water. The chromosomes become increasingly more stainable as prophase proceeds. It is believed that the increasing visibility of the chromosomes involves their progressive dehydration, since the metaphase chromosomes appear to contain considerably less water than those of the interphase nucleus. Of equal importance, however, is the fact that the chromosomes shorten and become of greater diameter. This contraction gives the chromosomes a more compact surface for the attachment of the chromatin dyes. Their increased density in the living state is shown by their more pronounced visibility when viewed in the phase microscope.

From the beginning of prophase the chromosomes are longitudinally double, each half being called a *chromatid*. The chromatids are closely appressed to each other throughout their length and are, at the same time, twisted around each other much as are the strands in a length of woolen yarn. Such a twisting of paired chromatids is known as *relational coiling* (Fig. 3–3).

Evidence exists indicating that the chromosome may be even further subdivided, i.e., into half-chromatids. The chromosome, as early as the preceding anaphase, exhibits in good preparations a longitudinal duality and the prophase chromosome appears to possess a quadripartite nature, i.e., it is made up of at least four separate strands, or *chromonemata* (singular, *chromonema*). Such fine details are difficult to see in most organisms except such forms as the Protozoa; evidence other than observational comes largely from x-ray and ultraviolet studies, which indicate that half-chromatids can be broken by these radiations (Swanson 1947;

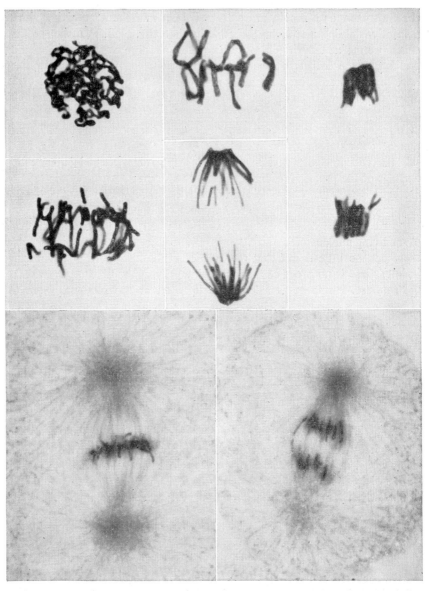

Fig. 3–2. Mitosis in the roottips of *Vicia faba* (upper group) and in the whitefish *(Coregonus sp.)* (lower group). Upper left, early to mid prophase; below it, lateral metaphase; upper middle, early anaphase; below it, late anaphase; upper right, early telophase just before formation of the nuclear membranes; lower left, lateral metaphase with astral rays and spindle showing; lower right, early anaphase. The cells of Vicia are Feulgen stained, and only the chromosomes show; in the lower middle and the upper right the secondary constriction (nucleolar organizer region) in the long chromosomes is clearly evident (courtesy of Mr. T. Merz).

Crouse 1954; Sax and King 1955). Regardless of these interpretations relating to the multi-stranded state of the chromosome, one significant fact is definitely established, namely, that in cell division *the functional unit of the chromosome is the chromatid.*

As prophase progresses the chromosomes become shorter, thicker, and more distinct. Some uncertainty exists as to whether or not an active contraction of the chromonemata reduces their over-all length, but whether this is so or not, the greater portion of the shortening of the chromosomes can be accounted for by the establishment of a coiled structure within each chromatid (Fig. 3–3). Beginning as a rather fuzzy-looking irregularity along the length of the chromatids, the coils eventually take on a regular, smooth appearance akin to that of the coils of a wire door-spring. The number of these coils, or *gyres,* varies widely, being dependent upon the length of the chromosome and the diameter of the individual gyres. In passing from early to late prophase, the coils' number decreases as their diameter increases. Consequently the chromosome undergoes a process of despiralization. The period of initial coiling, when the coils of smallest diameter first appear, has been called the period of *spiralization.*

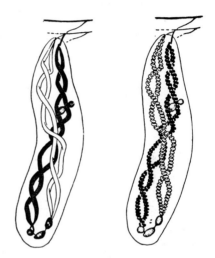

Fig. 3–3. Relational coiling of chromatids (with and without major coils showing) in the protozoan, *Holomastigotoides tusitala* (Cleveland 1949).

The chromosomes during prophase are wound in a thread-like and apparently haphazard fashion throughout the nucleus. They do not, as a rule, come in contact with each other. There appears to be a tendency for them to maintain a certain minimum separation, a condition that may be due to a generalized repulsion between chromosomes. In animal cells the shortened chromosomes have a tendency to migrate to the nuclear membrane where they remain until the membrane undergoes dissolution. This phenomenon is not characteristic of plant chromosomes, which appear to remain more evenly spread throughout the nucleus until metaphase. This evenness may be illusory, however, for Vanderlyn (1948), in his detailed study of mitosis in the onion roottip, considers that the chromosomes are typically associated with the nuclear membrane, with the centromeres and blocks of heterochromatin providing the principal points of contact.

Several other prophase phenomena accompany the shortening of the chromosomes. If one or more nucleoli are present, they can be seen to diminish in size, generally disappearing before the onset of metaphase. In some organisms the nucleoli persist throughout the mitotic period, dividing at anaphase more or less into equal halves, or passing undivided to one or the other of the poles.

In animal cells the centrosome undergoes a series of changes preparatory to exercising its function in cell division. In earliest prophase it lies against the nuclear membrane, and within the centrosome the centriole, if present, can be seen as a divided deeply staining granule. The centrosome divides into two portions each containing a single centriole. These halves migrate along the nuclear membrane in opposite directions, stopping when they lie approximately 180 degrees from each other. The final location of the centrioles determines the position of the poles of the spindle.

Metaphase. The disappearance of the nuclear membrane usually brings prophase to an end although some of the Protozoa may carry out the entire mitotic cycle as an intranuclear phenomenon, and without breakdown of the nuclear membrane (Fig. 3–4). In higher forms the spindle soon appears, and metaphase is initiated.

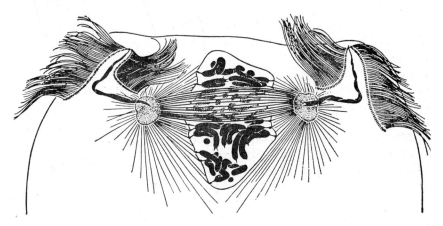

Fig. 3–4. Mitosis in the protozoan, Barbulanympha. Astral rays, emanating from long centrioles, fuse to form a central spindle; other similar rays become extranuclear chromosomal fibers which connect with the intranuclear chromosomal fibers at the nuclear membrane (Cleveland 1938).

The spindle, whose structure and origin may vary widely, serves to bring the chromosomes onto the *metaphase,* or *equatorial, plate* as the first step in the separation of the daughter chromatids. This movement has been separated by Darlington (1937) into three components, the *congression* of the chromosomes from their widely spread condition within the nucleus to a position of equilibrium between the two poles, and their later *orientation* and *distribution* on the plate. The first movement is apparently the result of an interaction between the poles of the spindle (or the centrioles) and the constricted area of the chromosome, which can be clearly seen in some metaphase chromosomes. This interaction brings the chromosomes to a position of equilibrium midway between the poles. The constriction of the chromosomes has been variously named, with the terms *centromere* and *kinetochore* being most generally applied. (Because of its wider usage, the term *centromere* will be used here.) The orientation of chromosomes on the plate is such as to arrange the centromeres in the longitudinal axis of the spindle, while the chromatid arms project at either side. Thus the centromere is the only portion that need be in association with the spindle.

The distribution of the chromosomes on the metaphase plate may be entirely random, or there may be a special arrangement (Fig. 3–5). In most plant mitoses, the chromosomes are scattered in an apparently haphazard arrangement, yet each at a distance from the others as though some form of repulsion kept them from overlapping. On the other hand, some animal cells, such as those in the regenerating tail of the salamander, exhibit a *hollow* or *central* spindle with the centromeres fastened to the spindle's outer edge, the arms of the chromosomes extended outside into the cytoplasm, and the center of the spindle empty.

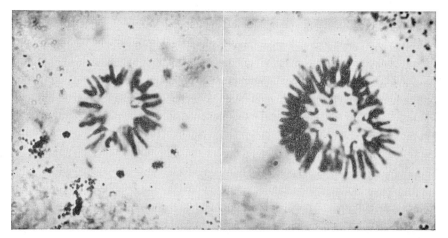

Fig. 3–5. Diploid (left) and tetraploid (right) cells in the axolotl at the metaphase stage and showing the form of the hollow spindle. In the tetraploid cell the chromosomes are too numerous to be contained at the edge of the spindle, and are forced into its interior (courtesy of Dr. G. Fankhauser).

The distribution of the chromosomes on the plate is determined by the manner in which the spindle comes into existence. The centrioles, as they migrate to their positions, and before the nuclear membrane disappears, form astral rays in the cytoplasm; the astral rays, at the time of membrane dissolution, overlap and coalesce to form a central core of continuous fibers (see below) which the chromosomes do not penetrate. Whether the outer core of the spindle is of nuclear or of cytoplasmic origin is not known, but it is to this portion that the chromosomes become attached.

Where the chromosomes are haphazardly arranged on the plate, the spindle originates as the chromosomes congress, and they consequently are spread throughout its central area.

Darlington (1937) disagrees with this interpretation. As a result of studies of abnormal mitoses in Fritillaria, a liliaceous species, where all transitions in chromosome distribution on the spindle are to be observed, he postulates that the distribution is determined by polar repulsions of the centromeres. Weak repulsions would give a random arrangement, while a stronger polar repulsion would push the chromosomes to the periphery of the spindle. Unfortunately, no experimental confirmation of this hypothesis is possible with present-day techniques.

The chromosome at metaphase consists of two tightly coiled chromatids, lying side by side, and attached to the spindle by the centromere whose location within each chromosome is constant. If long, the chromatids may be relationally coiled about each other. The centromere may occupy a median, a sub-median, or a sub-terminal location. These chromosomes, in anaphase, show a V, J, or rod shape as they move to the pole with the centromere leading. The centromere at metaphase is undivided, or if divided, the two portions are enclosed within a structure that behaves singly.

Radiating from the poles to the centromeres are the *chromosomal spindle fibers,* while from pole to pole extend the *continuous fibers.* The latter are derived from the overlapping of astral rays and are of cytoplasmic origin. This is strikingly seen in certain Protozoa (Fig. 3–6), but it could be true only in animal cells since astral rays are not characteristic of plant cells.

A distinction has been made between two types of mitosis on the basis of the kind and origin of spindle elements (cf. Schrader 1953). *Direct mitosis* is supposed to take place when the connection between centromere and pole is by means of the chromosomal spindle fibers, *indirect mitosis* when only the continuous fibers are present. The continuous fibers are found exclusively in those spindles that are derived from cytoplasmic materials before breakdown of the nuclear membrane, and it is to these that the centromeres become attached at the periphery of the spindle (Fig. 3–7). The chromosomal fibers, which may be of nuclear as well as of cytoplasmic origin, apparently are the result of an interaction between the centromere and the pole, for these fibers attach at no other place. Many cytologists, however, believe that all mitoses are direct, and that chromosomal spindle fibers always connect the centromeres with the poles.

Not only are there fibers within the spindle, but many fibrous rays extend into the cytoplasm from the poles. These are the *astral rays,* which form, collectively, the *asters.* It appears that these result from an interaction between the proteins of the cytoplasm and the centrosome, and it has been suggested (Pollister 1941) that rather than being fibers they

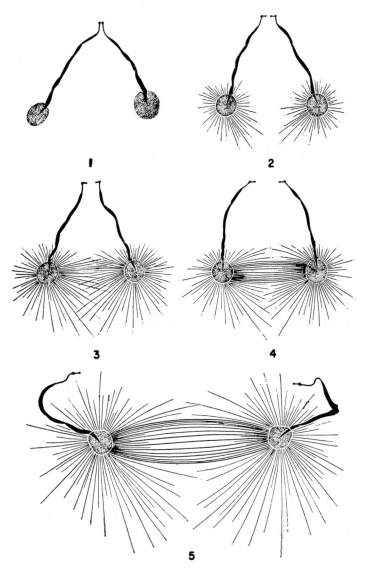

Fig. 3–6. Developmental stages of the spindle as they occur in the protozoan, Barbulanympha. The straplike appendages are the slender centrioles which vary from 15–30 microns in length; the centrosomes are the spherical portions at the terminal ends of centrioles, through which the astral rays pass (Cleveland 1938).

are actually lines of flow strikingly displayed because of the orientation of particles at their margins; but it is also likely that the proteins making up the rays are oriented in a radial direction from the centrosome. The cytoplasm appears to be more fluid in these regions, but the fact that

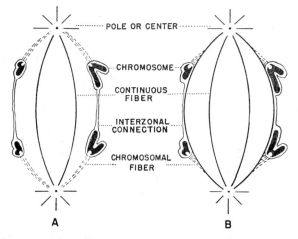

Fig. 3–7. Two types of spindles as seen in anaphase. A, direct type, with the spindle fibers connecting the chromosomes directly with the poles; B, indirect type, with the chromosomes connected with the continuous fibers (Schrader 1953, with permission of the Columbia University Press).

spindles can be isolated without appreciable loss of form (Mazia and Dan 1952) discounts Pollister's earlier suggestion.

Anaphase. Metaphase passes into anaphase at the time when the centromere becomes functionally double, and the chromatids begin to move toward the poles. This movement, which is complex and which may vary from organism to organism, first separates the chromatids at the centromere, with the arms of the chromatids being passively dragged along. Should a chromosome lacking a centromere find itself on the spindle, its movement is either governed by flow currents along the spindle, or it fails to show any movement, remaining as an inert structure in the vicinity of the equatorial plate. Such behavior strikingly emphasizes the role of the centromere as an organ of movement.

The later movement of the chromatids, which can now be considered *daughter chromosomes,* is aided in some organisms by an elongation of the spindle. The two movements eventually move the chromosomes to the polar regions where they stop. The chromosomes consequently have longitudinally separated to give two groups of like genetic constitution.

Telophase. The period of regrouping of the chromosomes into a nuclear structure within a membrane constitutes telophase. This reorganization may be slight in rapidly dividing tissues where one mitosis follows another with little or no delay, but if considerable time elapses between divisions, the chromosomes loosen their coils, lose their stainability, and finally take on the appearance of an interphase nucleus. The nucleoli and the prochromosomes, if present normally, once more make their appearance.

Cytokinesis. While this reorganization proceeds and, indeed, even in the later stages of anaphase, the process of cytoplasmic division is taking place. Since this differs considerably in plant and animal cells, a separate consideration of each is warranted. In some organisms, it should be noted —as for example in the coenocytic algae and fungi—cytokinesis does not follow division of the nucleus, with the result that the thallus becomes multinucleate. The two processes, karyokinesis and cytokinesis, are therefore separate and distinct, although generally coordinated in most kinds of cells. That cytokinesis can occur without the presence of a nucleus has been demonstrated in sea urchin eggs. Fragments of cytoplasm from which the nucleus has been removed can be stimulated to divide until a mass of some 500 cells is achieved (Harvey 1936). The inference to be drawn, therefore, is that the two processes have arisen independently in evolution, and the selective value of their coordinated timing has been sufficiently great to have established it as a regular phenomenon in dividing cells.

In plant tissues, for example in a growing roottip, cytokinesis is accomplished by the formation of a *cell plate*. As the two telophase nuclei are being reorganized, the equatorial region of the spindle widens into the *phragmoplast* (Fig. 3–8). If viewed from the poles this appears to be a hollow ring-like structure. In lateral view, the phragmoplast is somewhat doughnut- or barrel-shaped. It increases its diameter as cytokinesis continues until it reaches the lateral walls, where it disappears. Prior to its disappearance a thin line of droplets or granules (in lateral view, or a membranous layer in polar view) forms across the center opening of the phragmoplast, this widening in area as the phragmoplast widens, and eventually cutting the cell in two. This membrane is the 'cell plate. It is apparently derived initially from the spindle, and later from the cytoplasm, and it becomes the middle lamella after impregnation with pectin. The two daughter cells form a plasma membrane around each of the enclosed protoplasts, and the primary cell wall thickens through deposition of materials secreted by the cytoplasm. In elongated cells of the *lateral cambium* of the higher plants, where the plane of division is in the longitudinal axis of the cell, the phragmoplast persists and grows for a considerable time after reorganization of the telophase nuclei has ceased.

Cytokinesis in animals proceeds by a process of *furrowing* (Fig. 3–2). Whereas in plants the cell plate develops from the spindle area outward, furrowing originates as an indentation of the outer membrane at the position of the equatorial plate, this indentation gradually moving inward to cleave the cell into daughter halves. The two daughter cells may be equal in size, as is generally true for cell division in plants, or they may be quite unequal, as, for example, in the division of the neuroblast cells of the grasshopper embryo. The process may also be quite varied, depending upon whether the dividing cell is isolated from others, or remains in contact with adjacent cells. Gray (1931) is thus led to distinguish between *disjunctive* and *astral* cleavage.

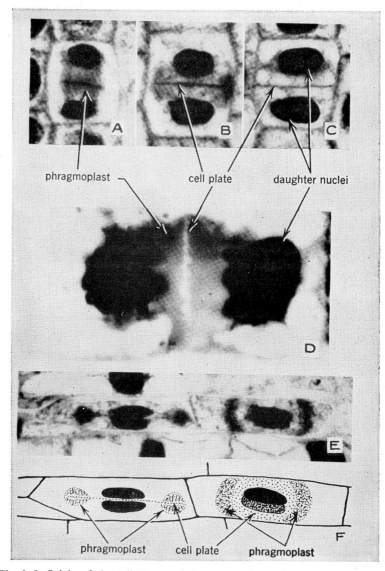

Fig. 3–8. Origin of the cell plate and the appearance and behavior of the phrag-moplast. A–C, successive stages in roottip cells of Allium; D, cell plate in a roottip cell of Narcissus where it appears as if formed from a coalescing line of vacuoles; E and F, side and surface views of the developing phragmoplast (reprinted with per-mission from Esau, *Plant Anatomy,* 1955, John Wiley & Sons, Inc.

Disjunctive cleavage occurs in isolated cells such as leucocytes, or in cells in tissue culture. No appreciable changes in the shape of the dividing cell take place until anaphase when the cell elongates along the mitotic axis, and there is an active "bubbling" of the cytoplasm of the polar regions.

The bubbling, which consists of the repeated projection and withdrawal of protoplasmic blisters, lasts for three or four minutes, while the constriction of the cell becomes pronounced. The two daughter cells then proceed to move away from each other, leaving fine hyaline strands of cytoplasm between them. The significance of the bubbling, although quite characteristic of such cells, is not understood, although it is believed to be related to chemical changes which influence the elasticity of the plasma membrane.

Astral cleavage is characteristic of marine invertebrate eggs, the spherical cell dividing to give two equal *blastomeres*. Such eggs possess a cortical layer, the hyaloplasm, which surrounds them peripherally. Good evidence indicates that a flowing of the hyaloplasm into the area of cleavage at the time of cell elongation plays a role in the cytokinetic process, but uncertainty exists as to the significance of the process. The asters likewise are involved in the phenomenon, judging from the changes in size and shape they undergo, but again the interpretations that can be made are admittedly speculative. Immersion in water that is calcium-free or contains ether will alter, respectively, the behavior of the hyaloplasm or the asters to the point where cell division is altered or prevented.

Time sequence of mitosis. The speed with which the mitotic cycle is completed varies enormously, the time depending upon the organism, the tissue, the temperature, and other environmental agents.

The division cycle in the neuroblast cells of the grasshopper embryo is completed in approximately eight hours at 26° C (Carlson 1941, 1954). Figure 3–9 indicates the relative time occupied by the various stages at 38° C, when the length of time is reduced to three and one-half hours. Such a relative time sequence probably holds very well for many types of cell division, although the actual time consumed in the total process differs from organism to organism. In bacteria, for example, a culture in the logarithmic phase of growth will divide every 20 minutes. Tradescantia stamen-hair cells, according to Bĕlăr, complete division in 340 minutes, whereas others have found time intervals of 135 minutes at 10° C, 75 minutes at 25° C, and 30 minutes at 45° C for the same material. The division in the microspore of Tradescantia takes approximately 30 hours at a temperature of 30° C. Tissue cultures of animal cells divide in 16 to 40 minutes at 37° C, with 10 to 12 hours elapsing between successive divisions (Fischer 1946).

The major difficulty in determining durations of mitosis lies in the inability of the observer to detect accurately the onset of the process, but in general it can be stated that metaphase and anaphase are the shortest stages, telophase next, with prophase being relatively prolonged.

Significance of mitosis. The exact longitudinal division (or reproduction) of the chromosome into chromatids, and the meticulous distribution of the chromatids to daughter cells, insures that the daughter cells will have,

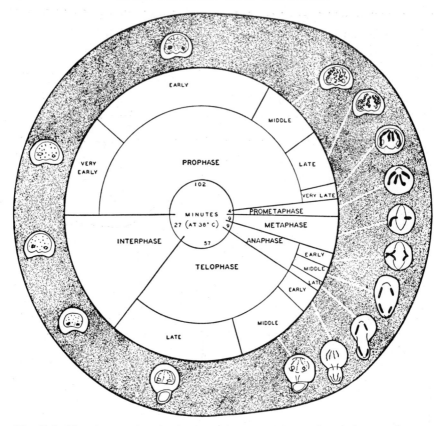

Fig. 3–9. The time cycle of mitosis in the neuroblast cells of the grasshopper, *Chortophaga viridifasciata,* at 38°C. (Carlson 1948).

quantitatively and qualitatively, the same genetic constitution as the original cell from which they arose. Lineal heredity is established, whether it be from cell to cell, or organism to organism. In this manner the constancy of species is maintained, a truly remarkable phenomenon when one considers the enormous numbers of cell divisions involved in the perpetuation of present-day species from the time of their inception.

However, accidents can occur. Failure of cytokinesis or karyokinesis, spontaneous fragmentation of chromosomes, and unequal segregation of daughter chromatids may be found in any tissue or group of cells, but in general these are relatively rare happenings. If taking place in cells of the germ line, they may give rise to variations of potential evolutionary value, and it cannot be doubted that such fortuitous changes do occasionally become perpetuated, leading to diversity within species.

Experimentally, cell division may be varied almost at will, but under the range of environmental conditions to which most organisms are exposed, the process exhibits a remarkable constancy. In the roottips of some plants, cell division is regular at 0° C as well as at 40° C, although the tempo of division will vary. The warm-blooded animals show a lesser degree of tolerance, however, cell division ceasing at temperatures below 24° C or above 46° C (Fischer 1946).

Why do cells divide? An answer to this question is very greatly needed at the present time, for it would provide a much clearer understanding of the basic cause, or causes, of malignant growth, which is generally characterized by the cells involved dividing at an abnormally rapid rate. No clear solution of the underlying mechanism of cell division has been advanced, although a substance *kinetin* has been isolated which fosters cell division when present in extremely minute quantities. Indeed, the physiology of the cell during division is but poorly understood.

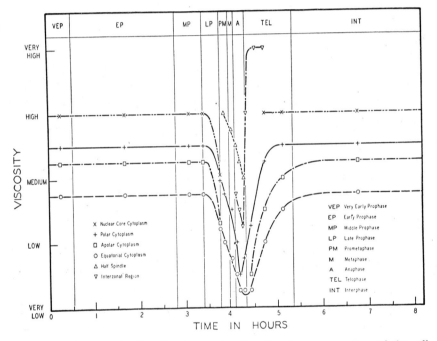

Fig. 3–10. Curves showing the changes in viscosity of various regions of the cell from very early prophase to the succeeding interphase. The degree of viscosity was determined by the rapidity of Brownian movement (Carlson 1946).

Heilbrunn and Wilson (1948) have shown that the viscosity of the cell varies with the stage of division, being lowest at metaphase, and highest immediately before the spindle is formed; the spindle appears, therefore, to be a dehydrated portion of the cell, comparable, perhaps, to the spindle-shaped structures, or tactoids, that result from the gelation of some types of proteins. This pattern of viscosity holds for various parts of the cell, although to varying degrees (Fig. 3–10). There can be little doubt that viscosity changes occur during mitosis, and that these play a role in cleavage, spindle formation, and other phenomena, but the interrelationships are not yet fully understood.

MEIOSIS

When it became evident through the studies of O. Hertwig and Strasburger that the essential factor in both plant and animal fertilization was the fusion of gametic nuclei of paternal and maternal origin, and, through the work of other investigators, that the dividing nuclei of a particular species possessed a definite and constant number of chromosomes, it followed that there must be a mechanism of compensation that would provide for a reduction in chromosome number to offset the increase brought about through syngamy. Van Beneden, in 1883–84, established a factual basis for a solution of the problem by demonstrating that, in the fusion of egg and sperm, equal numbers of chromosomes were contributed by the parents to the offspring. The contribution of each parent, therefore, was a single, or *haploid* set of chromosomes, to give in the zygote a double or *diploid* set. All cells of the offspring that were subsequently derived from the zygote by mitotic division possessed a diploid set of chromosomes, with each chromosome represented twice.

Weismann, in 1887, recognizing not only the problem presented but the fundamental significance of these cytological discoveries toward a solution of the problem, postulated, without being fully aware of the mechanism involved, that a reduction in chromosome number takes place in the germ cells of both plants and animals in such a manner as to separate the diploid chromosomes into two haploid groups without the longitudinal division of each chromosome taking place. His prediction has been fully verified, and reduction division, or meiosis, is to be found coexistent with functional bisexuality.

Meiosis, therefore, is a special kind of cell division, and it is the antithesis of fertilization in that it halves the number of chromosomes. It consists essentially of two nuclear divisions which follow each other in rapid sequence. The first involves the separation of chromosomes that had, in prophase, paired with each other. One chromosome of each pair is of maternal, the other of paternal, origin, and their separation leads to the formation of haploid nuclei. The second division involves the longitudinal separation of chromatids in each of these two haploid nuclei, with the result that four haploid nuclei are produced. Accompanied by appropriate divisions of the cytoplasm, and with subsequent modifications of these cells, the asexual spores or the sexual gametes are formed. The entire process is complicated in detail, and varies widely from species to species.

In most animals, meiosis occurs just prior to fertilization, and results in the formation of sexual cells, the sperm and eggs. Their union in fertilization gives a diploid zygote, and through cleavage, a diploid body.

The time relationships between meiosis and fertilization vary, however, in plants. In some algae and fungi, meiosis immediately follows fertilization, and the resultant products, which are haploid asexual spores, germinate, each growing into a haploid thallus. This structure, the *gametophyte*, produces gametes by mitosis, and the zygote resulting from their union undergoes reduction division without further growth. There develops, consequently, no diploid body.

The higher plants, including here the mosses, ferns, and seed plants,

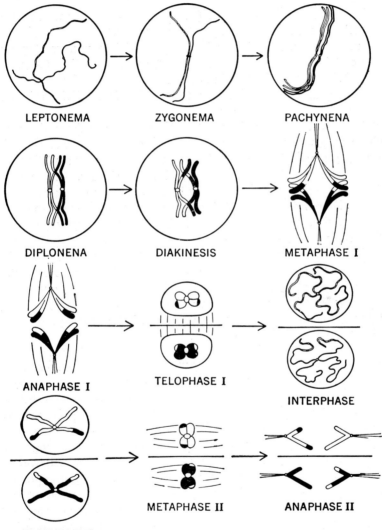

Fig. 3–11. Diagrammatic representation of the stages of division in meiosis I and II. The terms *leptonema, zygonema, pachynema,* and *diplonema* are employed instead of the more conventional, but incorrectly used, leptotene, zygotene, pachytene, and diplotene (Rhoades 1950).

as well as some of the algae, possess a similar life cycle with the exception that the diploid zygote undergoes mitotic division to produce the diploid *sporophyte*. The sporophyte, in turn, develops specialized structures, the *sporangia*, in which meiosis takes place. Thus a diploid plant body intervenes between fertilization and meiosis, giving the forms of plant life with which most of us are familiar. The gametophyte, in the course of evolution of the higher plants, has become reduced in structural complexity and has lost its independent existence at the same time that the sporophyte has gained in size and dominance. (The student unfamiliar with these details can find them outlined in any botany textbook.)

For convenience, meiosis has been separated into various stages that possess certain characteristics permitting of easy recognition (Figs. 3–11 and 3–12). Prophase, the stage in which the most profound, and genetically the most significant, modifications take place, is subdivided into five separate stages.

Leptonema. This stage does not differ appreciably from the earliest prophase stages in mitosis except that the cells and nuclei of meiotic tissues are generally larger than those of the surrounding somatic tissues. The chromosomes, too, are longer and more slender. Unlike mitotic chromosomes, along their length may be seen a series of bead-like structures called *chromomeres,* which insofar as can be determined are constant in number, size, and position (Fig. 3–13). This constancy enables the cytologist to make a good use of them as landmarks for the identification of particular chromosomes. Belling (1931) estimated that in Lilium there are between 1500–2500 chromomeres in the whole chromosome set. He considered them at that time to be the loci of the genes with one gene per chromomere, but it has since been demonstrated in maize not only that there is more than one gene per chromomere, but that the genes exist as well in the interchromomeric regions.

The arrangement of chromosomes in the leptotene nucleus is not always random. In the microsporocytes of Lilium the chromosomes are densely clumped to one side, leaving the remainder of the nucleus clear. The meaning of this arrangement, called *synizesis,* is not clear, although it is probably related to another phenomenon which is more typical, particularly in the spermatocytes of many animals. In these cells the chromosomes are *polarized,* their ends being drawn together at that side of the nucleus where the centrosome is located, and the remaining portions of the chromosomes extending into the center of the nucleus. Such a polarization, which may persist until pachynema, cannot have arisen as the result of a premeiotic telophase orientation, for this would orient the centromeres rather than the ends. There appears to be a definite attraction of some sort between the ends of the chromosomes and the centrosome to bring about polarization, and the less frequent presence of polarization in higher plants may possibly be explained by the absence of a definite centrosome.

Zygonema. The pairing, or *synapsis,* of chromosomes in intimate association begins in zygonema. Since, to a diploid offspring, each parent has contributed a haploid set of chromosomes, and since the chromosomes contributed by the sperm are, with certain exceptions such as the sex chromosomes, identical with those contributed by the egg, all diploid cells possess pairs of similar, or *homologous, chromosomes.* These chromosomes pair lengthwise with each other in a pattern characteristic of the species. Polarization possibly facilitates the initial union of the homologues.

As Darlington (1935) had demonstrated in Fritillaria, synapsis may begin at any of several places along the length of the chromosome; it may be *proterminal,* beginning at the ends and proceeding toward the centromere; it may be *procentric,* beginning at the centromere and proceeding toward the ends; or it may be *intermediate,* beginning at random, or in several regions at once. In any event, synapsis, when once initiated, proceeds in zipper-like fashion to bring the homologous chromosomes together along their entire length. The synaptic force still remains to be explained in physical terms, but there can be no doubt as to its reality.

A study of triploid organisms possessing three sets of homologous chromosomes has shown that, although all three homologues may synapse with each other, at no place along the chromosomes is the association more than two-by-two. The three homologues are never associated together in a three-by-three arrangement in meiotic cells.

Pachynema. If zygonema is considered to be the period of active pairing, *pachynema* is the stable stage. If parts of chromosomes are still unpaired by pachynema, they continue to remain so. The chromosomes, which are visibly thicker, appear to be present in the haploid number, but each thread can be recognized as two chromosomes closely appressed. These pairs are referred to as *bivalents.* In some species the homologues are relationally coiled about each other, but it is not known whether this occurs in all organisms. The nucleolus is particularly evident at this stage, and certain of the chromosomes are attached to it (Fig. 3–14). Pachytene may be quite prolonged, as in maize, and it consequently provides one of the more easily recognized landmarks of meiotic prophase.

Diplonema. Longitudinal separation of the paired chromosomes initiates diplonema (Fig. 3–13). At the same time the longitudinal duality of each chromosome becomes clearly evident, revealing that each bivalent consists of four chromatids. As the pairing relationships of pachynema lapse, the homologues move apart from each other. The separation is generally not complete, however, for the paired chromosomes are held together at one or more points along their length (Fig. 3–15). The bivalents, as a consequence, take on the appearance of a cross if there is one point of contact, a loop if there are two points of contact, or a series of loops if there are three or more points of contact. Each point of contact is a *chiasma* (plural, *chiasmata*), and in clear preparations of diplotene stages

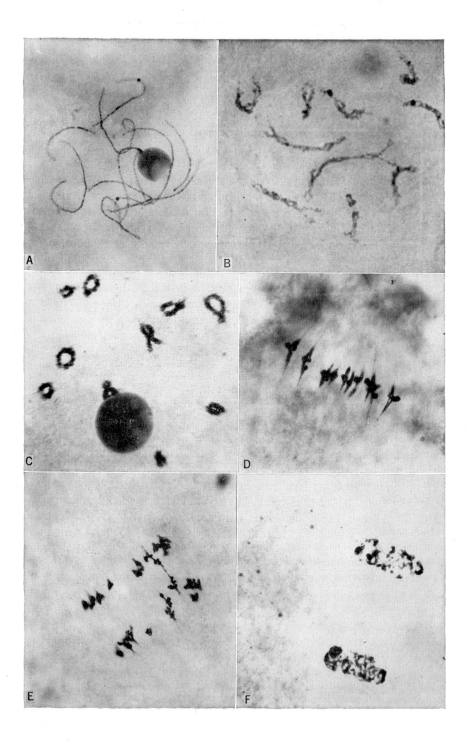

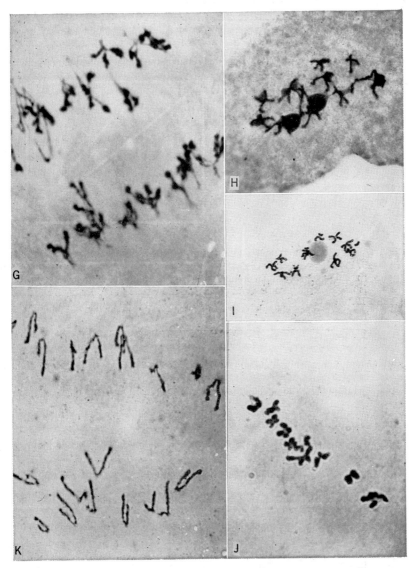

Fig. 3–12. Meiosis in the microsporocytes of maize. Leptonema and zygotnema are not illustrated since in this organism they are difficult stages to photograph well. A, pachynema, with the nucleolus attached to chromosome 6 at the dark-staining nucleolar organizer, and with conspicuous knobs on chr. 7 (top) and chr. 5 (lower center); B, diplonema, with the paired homologues beginning to open out; C, diakinesis; D, metaphase I; E, anaphase I, with one pair of chromosomes separating late; F, interphase; G, anaphase I, with the chromosomes somewhat more despiralized than in E; H, early prophase II, with the dark-staining bodies being matrical material; I, late prophase II, at a somewhat lower magnification; J, metaphase II; K, anaphase II (Rhoades 1950).

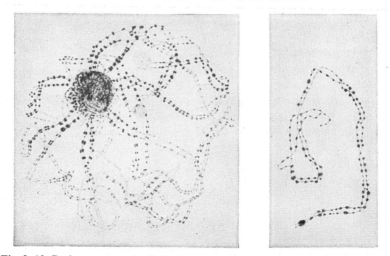

Fig. 3–13. Pachytene or early diplotene stages in microsporocytes of Trillium showing pairing relationships between homologues and chromomere patterns. The large, dark body is the nucleolus, and several chiasmata are visible in the left figure (Huskins and Smith 1935).

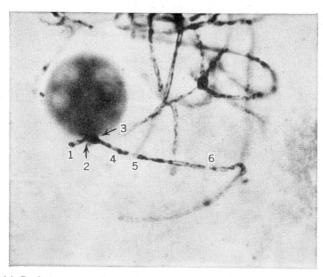

Fig. 3–14. Pachytene stage in a microsporocyte of maize, showing chromosome 6 attached to the nucleolus. The number 3 indicates the dark-staining nucleolar organizer, and 1 the terminal chromomere; 2, 4, 5 and 6 are other recognizable regions (McClintock 1932).

it can be seen that two of the chromatids, one from each chromosome, cross over. Since the two sister chromatids of any chromosome do not separate laterally from each other, the chiasma is a point of exchange that preserves the bivalent structure. The nature of the chiasma and the mechanism of chiasma formation have been actively investigated and discussed, but except for the pointing out that chiasmata are, in general, the cytological expression of genetical crossing over, the subject will be deferred until a later chapter in order to give it the detailed consideration that it requires for clarification.

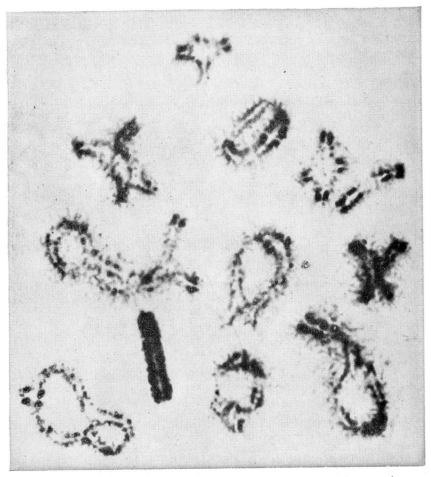

Fig. 3–15. Diplonema or early diakinesis in a spermatocyte of a grasshopper, *Schistocerca gregaria.* The unpaired X-chromosome is seen as a deeply stained rod (Tjio and Levan 1954).

The number and approximate positions of the chiasmata are variable, being dependent upon the species in question and the length of the chromosomes. Longer chromosomes usually have more chiasmata than short chromosomes, but even the short ones appear to be able to form at least one per bivalent. In some species, the chiasmata are more frequent at the ends of the chromosomes, appearing therefore to be *terminal* in position.

Interstitial chiasmata may be found anywhere along the arms of the chromosomes, and it is thought that terminal chiasmata must have had an interstitial origin after which the chiasmata moved to a terminal position. This movement, which takes place up to metaphase, has been called *terminalization* (Fig. 3–16). Interstitial chiasmata may be localized near the centromere, as in *Allium fistulosum* and in some species of grasshoppers, or, as is more general, they may be distributed at random. As many as twelve have been counted in the long chromosomes of *Vicia faba,* the broad bean.

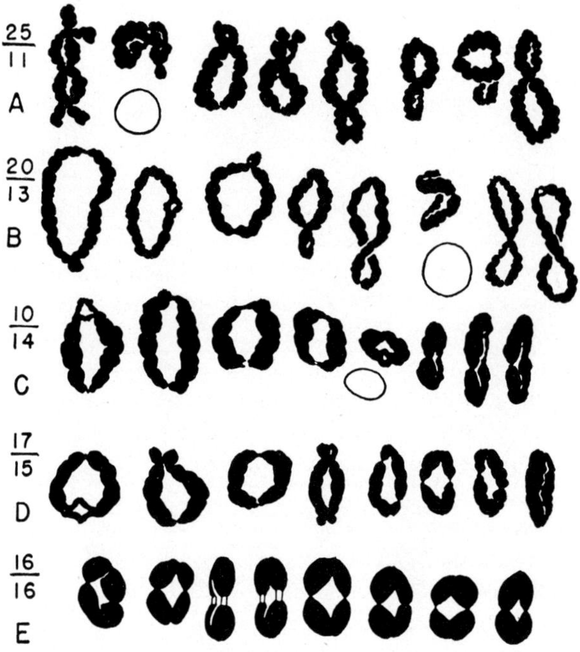

Fig. 3–16. Meiotic chromosomes of *Campanula persicifolia,* showing the changes in chromosome shape from diplonema (A) to metaphase (E) as terminalization goes to completion. The number of chiasmata, total and terminal, in each nucleus are given for each stage; the nucleolus is indicated as an open circle (Gairdner and Darlington 1931).

During diplonema the chromosomes are actively shortening, and their coiled nature is apparent. A difference of opinion exists among cytologists as to the time the coiling begins, some considering that the chromosomes begin to coil as early as leptonema, but the coils may be seen with certainty at diplonema. Various pretreatment techniques employing KCN, ammonia vapors, and heat can be used to demonstrate their presence more clearly. The development of the coil obviously reduces the over-all length of the chromosomes. During this time the nucleolus may become diminished greatly in size, although it continues to remain attached to its particular chromosome or chromosomes.

A somewhat modified type of diplotene behavior is found in the oöcytes of the frog and in some fishes, and in the spermatocytes of certain insects. The chromosomes, on entering diplonema, become quite diffuse and difficult of observation, and it is believed that instead of contracting through the development of a coiled structure, they loosen up and lose their sharp stainability. In most instances the diffusion of chromatin is correlated with a growth of the cytoplasm; the phenomenon is more generally observed in eggs that go through a long period of development to store reserve materials in the form of yolk.

Diakinesis. The distinction between diakinesis and diplonema is not a sharp one although diakinesis is characterized by a more contracted state of the chromosomes, by the disappearance or detachment of the nucleolus from its associated chromosomes, and by the even distribution of the bivalents throughout the nucleus. The chromosomes continue to shorten by coiling more tightly. The bivalents consequently assume a more rounded shape, with the homologues joined to each other largely at their terminal ends. This union comes about by the terminalization of chiasmata as the chromosomes shorten. If the chromosomes are small they may assume a spherical shape with the terminal unions representing the vestiges of whatever chiasmata had formed earlier. In larger chromosomes with several chiasmata terminalization is never as complete, so that a particular bivalent may exhibit various shapes which are dependent upon the number and the position of chiasmata present, and on the location of the centromere.

Metaphase. Metaphase is characterized by the complete disappearance of the nuclear membrane and the formation of the spindle. The latter forms as it does in mitosis. Similarly, as in mitosis, the bivalents congress onto the metaphase plate where they subsequently become properly oriented. Some authors have described a prometaphase stage which includes the period between dissolution of the nuclear membrane and the full appearance of the spindle. In some insects, as in the mantids, this is a conspicuous part of the meiotic cycle, for the chromosomes undergo a stretching process that lengthens them considerably.

A difference between the mitotic and meiotic chromosomes should be noted. In mitosis, the metaphase chromosome possesses a functionally undivided centromere, which, together with the centromeres of the other chromosomes, lies on the metaphase plate. In meiosis, the bivalent has two functionally undivided centromeres, which instead of lying on the plate are simply oriented in the long axis of the spindle, the distance between them being regulated by the proximal position of the chiasmata. At this time, and prior to the separation of the chromosomes, an active repulsion appears to exist between homologous centromeres; for if the

chiasmata are adjacent to the centromeres, thus bringing them close together, the regions of the chromosome between the centromere and the
first proximal chiasmata are obviously under tension, being stretched until
the diameter of the region is often a good deal less than that of the remainder of the chromosome.

Anaphase. The movement of chromosomes from the metaphase plate
to the poles constitutes anaphase. Unlike mitosis, in which the centromere
divides and sister chromatids pass to the opposite poles, the centromeres
of each bivalent in meiosis are undivided as they move poleward with the
result that whole chromosomes instead of chromatids segregate. Each
anaphase group, therefore, is made up of a haploid number of chromosomes instead of a diploid number of chromatids. In this manner a reduction in chromosome number results from the first meiotic division.

As the chromosomes begin their poleward movement, the chiasmata—
which have been, for the most part, the retaining mechanism for the ad-
herence of homologous chromosomes in pairs as bivalents—lose their
retentive influence and free the separating chromosomes. This takes place
by the chromatids simply falling apart, and, as movement occurs, the two
chromatids often flare apart widely, being bound together only at the undivided centromere.

Telophase. Telophase and interphase are not necessarily component
stages in the full meiotic cycle. In most organisms a nuclear membrane is
formed in telophase, and a regrouping of the chromosomes occurs with a
relaxing of the coiled structure of the chromosome. Grasshoppers, maize,
and Tradescantia follow this procedure, with a delay of varying duration
existing between the first and second meiotic divisions. In Trillium, however, the anaphase chromosomes of the first division in the pollen mother
cells orient themselves at the pole following the disappearance of the
spindle, and pass directly to metaphase of the second division. The coiling of the chromosomes is retained, and persists in fact through to the interphase which terminates the meiotic divisions.

Second meiotic division. The meiotic process is completed when each
of the two haploid nuclei divide by a process that is essentially mitotic.
It is, in fact, often referred to as a *meiotic mitosis,* and four haploid nuclei
result. Whether the usual mitotic prophase is present depends upon
whether or not there was an interphase period.

In any event, three differences serve to distinguish the second meiotic
division from a mitotic division. First, the chromosomes are present in a
haploid number; second, the chromatids in general are widely separated
from each other and exhibit no relational coiling; and third, each chromatid might be quite different genetically from its condition at the initiation
of the meiotic process. This will of course depend upon the number of
times each chromatid was involved in chiasma formation, and since
chiasma formation is generally the cytological expression of genetical

crossing over, the genes along the chromosome length may exist in quite different allelic combinations.

Because the reduction in chromosome number occurs at the first meiotic division, this has been designated the *reductional division,* in contrast to the *equational,* or second meiotic, division, which is essentially mitotic and which brings about separation of sister chromatids. The terms *meiosis I* and *meiosis II* are also used to designate the two divisions.

The end result of the meiotic process is the production of four haploid nuclei or cells from an original diploid cell. These will become modified according to the reproductive mechanism of the organism in question.

Cytokinesis in meiotic cells. Segmentation of the original meiotic cell by walls or membranes may or may not take place. The process has considerable variability from species to species.

In the higher plants, the meiotic cells, or microsporocytes, of the anther usually develop a cross wall at the end of the first meiotic division and in a plane at right angles to the axis of division. A second wall at right angles to the first divides the cells at the end of the second meiotic division. Each of the four cells, or *microspores,* has its own wall, and as they enlarge they burst through, freeing themselves from the original wall of the meiotic cell. In some species, such as those of the genus Erica, the four spores may remain together to be shed as a tetrad of spores.

In Paeonia, wall formation differs to the extent that no walls are formed until after the second meiotic division, when the two walls, at right angles to each other, form simultaneously. In the lower plants the formation of walls around the spores varies widely, and the student is referred to Sharp (1934) for the particular details.

The spermatocytes of animals behave like the microsporocytes of the higher plants in that four cells are formed from a single meiotic cell. Cytokinesis, however, is by a proces of furrowing, as it is in somatic cell division of animals.

The end product of meiosis in the ovaries of animals results in but a single functional cell, the egg. In plants the process and the end products vary from one group to another. Their mode of formation can be more profitably considered in the following section on reproduction.

REPRODUCTION

The introduction of meiosis into the life history of organisms is correlated with the introduction of another mechanism of opposite consequences: that of *syngamy,* the fusion of cells or nuclei. Where meiosis reduces chromosome number from a diploid to a haploid condition, syngamy restores diploidy by the fusion of haploid cells, called gametes. When one of the processes is absent or modified, the other must compensate for it to insure the successful continuance of the species (see Chapter 17). The variety of such mechanisms is bewildering, with many species approaching the bizarre in reproduction to compensate for modifications that have become established within races and species of particular groups.

Space prohibits an extensive description of the reproductive cycles characterizing the various groups of plants and animals. The plants, in particular, exhibit a confusing array of reproductive cycles, made difficult because of the structural modifications of the sex organs and the varying complexity, size, and relative independence of the gametophyte and sporophyte generations. Consequently, and in addition to the animal reproductive cycle which can be reduced for descriptive purposes to a representative type, only the angiosperm reproductive history will be considered. The student is referred to the standard botany texts for other life histories.

Reproduction in animals. The life cycle in multicellular animals, where sexual reproduction is obligatory, follows a regular chain of events. The fertilized diploid ovum divides and differentiates to form the animal body, a portion of which becomes the germ line. In the ovaries or testes production of gametes through meiosis brings about the reduced chromosome number which is restored when syngamy occurs in the matured ovum. The germ line is usually determined in early embryonic stages, and in the undivided eggs of some insects may even be recognized as an altered portion of the cytoplasm.

In mammals, the eggs are relatively few as compared to the vast numbers produced by some fish and invertebrates. The sperm cells are generally numerous in most of the animal phyla. Whatever the number, however, both eggs and sperm arise from cells that multiply within the sex organs. These proliferating cells are the *oögonia* and the *spermatogonia,* which will mature, respectively, into the *oöcytes* and *spermatocytes,* preparatory to the initiation of the reduction divisions.

Oögenesis in animals. The eggs of animals contain, in general, a large amount of reserve food materials stored for the nutrition of the embryo following fertilization. The presence of this reserve food probably has much to do with the fact that but a single functional egg matures from the original meiotic cell, instead of the usual four cells (Fig. 3–17).

Oögenesis is initiated in the oögonial cells of the ovary, these enlarging to form the *primary oöcytes.* Meiosis occurs in these cells where it follows the usual course except that during cellular enlargement, prophase is often interrupted and long delayed in the pachytene or diplotene stage if the egg is to contain large amounts of yolk material. The chromosomes, as in the amphibian egg, may reach a phenomenal length during this period, assuming a fuzzy appearance as the result of lateral outgrowths which arise along their length. These have become known as "lamp-brush" chromosomes because of their obvious resemblance to a tubular brush.

With the return of the chromosomes to conventional length, meiosis proceeds again, taking place close to the egg membrane and opposite the stored food reserves. The spindle in most oöcytes is generally quite small.

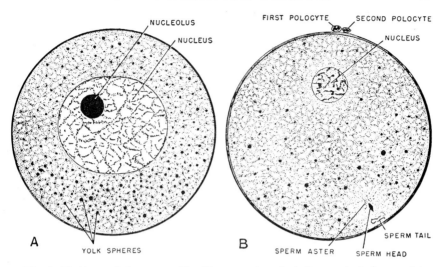

Fig. 3–17. Eggs of the sea urchin, Toxopneustes; A, before meiosis is complete, and B, after meiosis and the entrance of the sperm from Huettner, *Fundamentals of comparative embryology of the vertebrates,* copyright 1949, and used with the permission of The Macmillan Co.

The completion of the first meiotic division results in the budding off of a small nucleated cell, the first *polar body*. The second division produces a similar cell, the second polar body. The remaining haploid nucleus sinks back into the egg where it will ultimately unite with the nucleus of the entering sperm. During this time the first polar body may have divided, and these two plus the second polar body result in three small cells clustered together on the surface of the egg where they disintegrate.

The polar bodies, or *polocytes,* usually behave as described above, but certain modifications are known. In eggs with a mass of yolk, such as those of insects and crustacea, the polar bodies do not actually form as such but remain as unextruded polar nuclei embedded in the periphery of the egg cytoplasm. In other insects of the coccid group, a single polar body may be formed, but it later sinks back into the egg to fuse with the egg nucleus, thereby effecting an unusual form of fertilization. Other polar bodies in the same group become infected by a fungus to form an organ called a *mycetosome* whose function is not known. The polar bodies may also undergo abnormal enlargement and division, and they have been occasionally seen to be penetrated by spermatozoa. It seems clear that they must be regarded as vestigial sexual cells which have lost in most instances the power of further development.

Spermatogenesis in animals. The potential germ cells of the animal testes are spermagonia which, by repeated division, form the *primary spermatocytes* in which meiosis occurs. The end products of this process are four haploid *spermatids,* which, by a complicated process of differentiation called *spermiogenesis,* eventually are transformed into motile spermatozoa (Fig. 3–18).

The mature spermatozoan consists largely of a *head* and a *tail.* The former portion contains the highly compacted nucleus and the *acrosome*

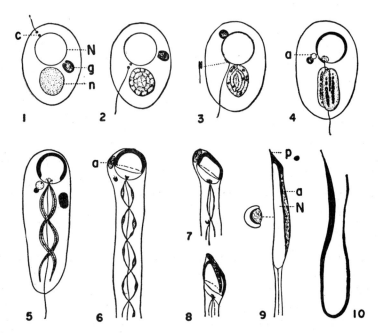

Fig. 3–18. Diagrammatic representation of animal spermiogenesis: a, acrosome derived from the Golgi material; c, centrioles from which the flagellum develops; N, nucleus; n, nebenkern or mitochondrial mass which forms a 2-stranded helix extending into the tail; p, the pointed tip of the sperm head (by permission from *Introduction to Cytology* by L. W. Sharp, 1934. McGraw-Hill Book Co., Inc.).

which caps the nucleus and which is believed to be derived from the Golgi materials. The acrosome may possess a pointed tip which apparently functions as a device for the penetration of the egg membrane at fertilization. The tail is usually subdivided into the *axial filament* and the *filament sheath.* The filament is formed through the elongation of a part of one of the two centrioles present in each spermatid; the remainder of this centriole, together with the second centriole, is transformed into various structures at the base of the nucleus, these joining the head and the axial filament. At the base of the filament, in the vicinity of the head, is a spiral or compacted mass of modified chondriosomal material. The filament sheath is of cytoplasmic origin.

Fertilization. Fertilization involves the penetration of the spermatozoan into the egg, and the subsequent union of the paternal and maternal nuclei. In addition, the sperm, which contributes its nucleus and centriole, generally serves to activate the egg, thus initiating the processes of cleavage. To be sure, functionally parthenogenetic eggs require no activation to begin development processes, but wherever syngamy is a normal event in the life cycle of an organism it appears that the entrance of the sperm nucleus into the cytoplasm of the egg sets off a trigger mechanism that brings about the physiological changes necessary for the conversion of a dormant egg to one actively undergoing cleavage. The nature of the physiological transformation is poorly understood, but it is known that various physical and chemical factors can be substituted for the usual sperm as a means of activation.

The sperm of some animals penetrate before meiosis, or the *maturation process* as it is sometimes called, has been completed in the egg. Indeed, in certain forms of insects, annelids, the frog, and the mouse, penetration of the sperm is necessary for the completion of meiosis, the process being stopped at various stages if fertilization fails to occur. In the sea-urchin, however, meiosis is completed before the sperm enters.

The sperm nucleus is the essential genetic contribution of the male in fertilization, but it is not the only contribution. In the sea-urchin Echinus and in Ascaris, the penetrating sperm head carries into the cytoplasm of the egg the sperm centriole, which is instrumental in forming the first cleavage spindle. There is also evidence suggesting that mitochondria and Golgi materials are brought in by the sperm, as for example in the mouse, but whether they add to the cytoplasmic components of the fertilized egg, or simply disintegrate, is not known.

After penetration by the sperm has been accomplished, and the maturation process has been completed, the two nuclei fuse. This may occur before the prophase of the first cleavage is initiated, or it may not occur until metaphase, as in Ascaris, at which time the male and female chromosome mingle on the metaphase plate. In Cyclops, a copepod, the maternal and paternal groups of chromosomes divide synchronously, but remain visibly distinct through the early cleavage stages, and may even form double nuclei. Fusion, however, takes place eventually to produce a diploid somatic nucleus.

Reproduction in plants. The life cycle of the higher plants, the only group considered here, is a complex affair involving an *alternation of generations* (Maheshwari 1950).

The *sporophyte* of the angiosperms, be it tree, shrub, or herb, makes up the dominant portion of our vegetation. Within the ovaries or stamens of the sporophyte occurs meiosis, which gives rise to asexual spores. Each of these, in turn, develops into a *gametophyte,* a parasitic structure in angiosperms which produces the sexual gametes. The fused gametes, after pollination, again lead to the sporophytic generation. Since the products of meiosis in the angiosperm are spores of two sizes, the processes have been termed *megasporogenesis* (Fig. 3–19) and *microsporogenesis* (Fig.

3–20). The former takes place in the ovary and the latter in the stamens.

Megasporogenesis in angiosperms. The *megagametophyte* of the higher plants is a reduced and parasitic generation surrounded by, and nutritionally dependent upon, the sporophytic tissues. Its evolution can be traced, in its broad aspects at least, to the free-living gametophytes of the more primitive land plants. Reduction has reached almost the ultimate limit in the angiosperms, for the gametophyte is retained within the wall of an original cell, the *megaspore,* or in some instances the *megasporocyte,* although within these confines it may assume a multicellular or multinucleate condition.

The megaspore is formed within the ovule of a closed ovary. A single cell, the megasporocyte, situated just beneath the outer layer of cells of the *nucellus,* enlarges and undergoes meiosis. From here on the process varies from species to species, and only two representative processes will be described.

In maize (Fig. 3–19) the products of meiosis are four megaspores arranged in a linear order. Three ultimately degenerate while the fourth enlarges to form the *embryo sac,* which initially possesses a single haploid nucleus, and which is the *megagametophyte.* Before fertilization this nucelus undergoes three mitotic divisions to give eight haploid nuclei lying free in the cytoplasm of the embryo sac. Three of these come to lie against the wall of the embryo sac opposite the *micropyle,* the latter being the opening between the *integuments* through which the pollen tube will enter. These three nuclei, which develop cell walls around them, are the *antipodals.* In most plants these degenerate following fertilization, but in maize the antipodals divide to form a mass of tissue which functions in a nutritive manner.

At the opposite end of the embryo sac cell walls separate three of the remaining nuclei. The central one becomes the *egg cell,* the other two, which serve no apparent function, being the *synergids.* The remaining two nuclei of the original eight come together in the center of the embryo sac and either fuse to form a *diploid fusion nucleus,* or, as in maize, simply remain adjacent to each other. This is the condition of the embryo sac at the time of fertilization.

In the lily, a linear tetrad of haploid cells is not formed as a result of meiosis. Instead, the megasporocyte is transformed by meiosis directly into the megagametophyte. One of the four haploid nuclei, which are still within the wall of the original megasporocyte, remains at the micropylar end, while the other three approach the opposite, or *chalazal,* end where they fuse to form a triploid nucleus, i.e., the nucleus now contains three sets of chromosomes. Both the haploid and the triploid nucleus undergo two mitotic divisions, yielding four haploid nuclei at the micropylar end of the embryo sac, and four triploid ones at the chalazal end. Three of the triploid nuclei come to lie against the wall of the embryo sac to serve as

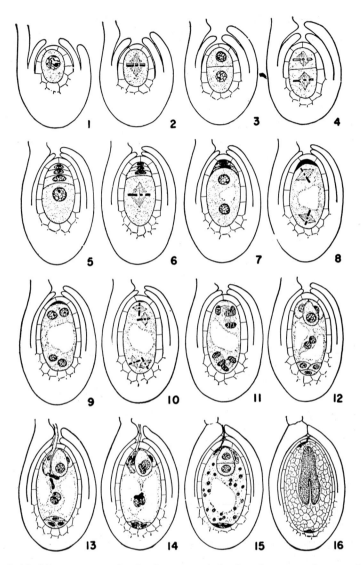

Fig. 3–19. Megasporogenesis, development of the female gametophyte, and early embryogeny in an angiosperm, of which maize is an example. 1–5, meiotic divisions leading to the formation of a linear tetrad of megaspores; 6–12, development of the embryo sac by three successive mitoses in the innermost megaspore; 12, egg and two synergids at the top, two polar nuclei in the center, and three antipodals at the bottom; 13, discharge of two sperm cells into the embryo sac from the penetrating pollentube; 14, double fertilization, with one sperm cell fusing with the egg nucleus and the other with the fused polar nuclei, to give, respectively, a diploid zygote and a triploid endosperm nucleus; 15, 2-celled embryo and the endosperm in a free nuclear state; 16, embryo with two colyledons and a cellular endosperm (by permission from *Introduction to Cytology* by L. W. Sharp, 1934. McGraw-Hill Book, Co., Inc.).

antipodals, while three of the haploid nuclei form the egg and the two synergids. The remaining two nuclei, one haploid and the other triploid, unite in the center of the embryo sac to form a fusion nucleus containing four haploid sets of chromosomes. It is therefore tetraploid, as contrasted to the diploid condition of the maize fusion nucleus.

Microsporogenesis in angiosperms. Meiosis in the anthers occurs before the flowers open (Fig. 3–20). Each *microsporocyte,* of which there are many in each anther, enlarges, goes through meiosis, and eventually produces a tetrad of four cells, the *microspores.* These generally separate from each other and develop into *microgametophytes.* In each, the single nucleus divides to form a *generative nucleus* and a *tube nucleus.* These are frequently referred to as "cells," but as a rule no distinct walls are formed around them.

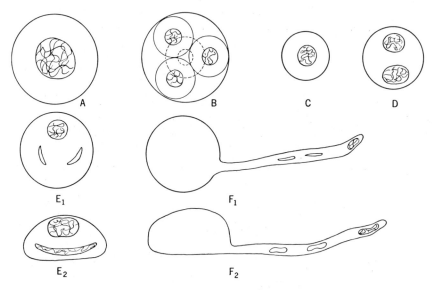

Fig. 3–20. Microsporogenesis and the development of the male gametophyte. A, microsporocyte; B, quartet of microspores resulting from the two meiotic divisions; C, microspore prior to the first microspore division; D, microspore after the first microspore division with tube (top) and generative (bottom) nuclei; E_1, mature pollen grain as in maize with two sperm cells resulting from the division of the generative nucleus; E_2, mature pollen grain as in Tradescantia with elongated generative nucleus; F_1, germinating pollen grain with tube nucleus at the tip of the pollen tube; F_2, germinating pollen grain after second microspore division has taken place in the pollen tube.

The generative nucleus is generally densely compacted, somewhat elongated, and stains darkly, while the tube nucleus is rounded and takes a lighter stain. The generative nucleus later divides to form the two *male gametes* or sperm. The time of this division varies. In maize, it takes place before the pollen is shed; hence at anthesis, i.e., the opening of the anthers to liberate the pollen grains, the mature pollen grain contains three nuclei —the tube nucleus, and the two sperm nuclei (which have walls around them and consequently can be considered as sperm cells). In the lily, however, the division takes place in the pollen tube as it passes down the style on its way to the micropylar opening of the ovule.

Fertilization. The pollen grain, landing on the stigma through the agency of wind, water, or insects, germinates to form a tube which passes down the style and eventually reaches the micropyle of the ovule to discharge its contents into the embryo sac. The tube nucleus usually enters the pollen tube first, and it is generally to be found at the tip of the tube where it is said to govern pollen tube growth. It is followed by the sperm cells or the generative nuclei; if the latter, then division of the generative nucleus takes place in the tube.

When the pollen tube reaches the micropyle, it is probably digestion of tissues that permits its entrance into the embryo sac. The two sperm pass in, one fusing with the egg to form the *zygote,* the other with the fusion nucleus to form the *endosperm nucleus.* In maize, the endosperm nucleus will be triploid; in the lily, it will be pentaploid. The zygote in both instances will be diploid. Since both sperm have been utilized in the process, the term *double fertilization* has been used.

Following fertilization, the zygote will develop into the embryo seed plant while the endosperm nucleus forms a mass of nutritive tissue upon which the developing embryo will subsist. The endosperm, which precedes the embryo in cell division, may form cell walls at the onset, or it may exist in what has been called a "free nuclear" state, the nuclei lying in a mass of cytoplasm against the wall of embryo sac. Cell walls may or may not form later, depending upon the species. Failure of the endosperm to develop results in abortive seed production.

The angiosperm seed is consequently a "genetic mosaic" consisting of maternal, zygotic, and endospermal tissue, each having its own chromosomal and genetic constitution. At maturity, however, the endosperm may or may not be present as a definitive tissue. In maize, for example, it forms the bulk of the seed, and supplies the developing embryo with its initial nutrients. A wide variety of genetic factors affect the composition and color of the endosperm in maize, and effective use has been made of them in cytogenetic studies. The garden-bean seed, however, possesses no endosperm at maturity. While originally present, it has been digested by the developing embryo, and stored in the cotyledons as reserve foods to be utilized during germination and early growth.

CHAPTER 4

The Function of the Chromosome

Cytogenetics is based upon the assumption that the chromosome is the principal vehicle of hereditary transmission. The facts of mitosis and meiosis can be integrated with genetical data only if this be true.

Acceptance of this now rather obvious fact was long delayed, for until unequivocal proof was obtained, many biologists were loath to consider that the chromosome occupied so eminent a role in the hereditary determination of the characteristics of individuals and species. These doubts, however, have been replaced by the generally accepted belief that the answers to the problems of growth and differentiation, which in the final analysis delineate the individuality of an organism, are to be sought through further knowledge of the molecular nature of the chromosome and its chemical relationships with the surrounding cellular environment. This belief has not been shaken by the recognition that the cytoplasm contains particulate structures of a self-duplicating nature which may exhibit varying degrees of autonomy.

The discoveries of the early cytologists, from 1875 to 1900, clearly indicated the importance of the chromosomes in cell lineage and in species continuity. The Chromosome Theory of Inheritance had not been formally stated, however, because of the lack of confirmatory genetic evidence, and it was not until the parallelisms of genetic transmission and of meiotic behavior of the chromosomes were recognized that the central role of the chromosomes came to be realized in its full significance.

THE PHYSICAL BASIS OF MENDELIAN GENETICS

Mendel's first law of inheritance. The Mendelian laws of genetics form the basis of classical genetics. Published in 1865, but recognized for their intrinsic worth only some 35 years later when they were rediscovered, these laws placed heredity upon a quantitative basis, and made it an exact science that permitted the prediction of traits among offspring according to the laws of chance.

Mendel's first law, which deals with the segregation of genetic determinants, stated that within sexual organisms there are *pairs of factors* (later called genes by Johannsen) *which segregate from each other in the parent,* but which reunite in the offspring. Thus in a cross involving dwarf and tall peas (the parental, or P, generation) Mendel demonstrated that the off-spring of the F_1 generation were all tall, but that when two tall F_1 plants were crossed, the F_2 generation would consist of tall and dwarf plants in a ratio of three tall to one dwarf. The dwarf character did not appear in the F_1 generation, but its reappearance in the F_2 offspring was proof that the "factor" governing it was not lost or modified. It was simply not expressed. Hence tall was considered to be *dominant* to dwarf which was *recessive*.

By assuming that the tall plant had a genic composition of *AA* and the dwarf plant a composition of *aa,* then, if segregation and subsequent union occurred, the F_1 would be *Aa,* a genotype that would be expressed as tall because *A* was dominant to the recessive *a.* Segregation of the *Aa* geno-type in the F_1 would consequently give factors *A* and *a* in the haploid gametes, factors which according to the laws of probability and random union, would give in the F_2 $1AA:2Aa:1aa$ (Fig. 4–1). Since the hetero-zygous *Aa* would show the same phenotypic expression as the homozy-

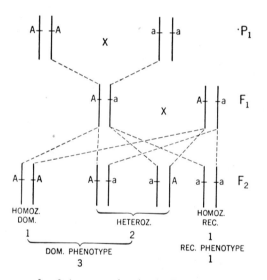

Fig. 4–1. Diagram of a 3:1 segregation in the F_2 generation. Should the hetero-zygous *(Aa)* F_1 or F_2 individuals be distinguishable from the homozygous dominant *(AA)* types, the F_2 ratio would be 1:2:1.

gous *AA,* the phenotypic ratio of 3:1 would be expressed. If, however, incomplete dominance of *A* over *a* were the rule, thus permitting recog-nition of the heterozygotes, the ratio would follow the genotypic consti-tution of $1AA:2Aa:1aa$. A crucial test of the assumption involved can be made by crossing the heterozygous F_1 plants to the homozygous recessive type. A 1:1 ratio of dominants to recessive should be obtained. Mendel made this backcross, and full confirmation was evident when equal numbers of the two kinds of offspring were obtained. Extensive experiments with many genes in a variety of organisms has demonstrated the wide applicability of this law in the organic world.

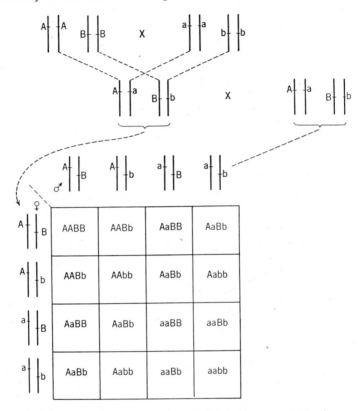

Fig. 4–2. Diagrammatic representation of di-hybrid cross which gives a 9:3:3:1 ratio in the F₂ generation. Depending upon the interaction which might take place between the two genes, modified ratios of 9:3:4, 9:6:1, 9:7 or 15:1 are also possible.

Mendel's second law of inheritance. When two pairs of contrasting factors were studied together, Mendel found that they segregated independently of each other. A two-factor, or a dihybrid, ratio was obtained in the F₂ generation, with all combinations of *alleles,* as the factors may now be called, being realized in those proportions expected on the basis of random assortment (Fig. 4–2). Backcrosses of the heterozygous F₁ plants to the homozygous double recessive verified the correctness of Mendel's assumption. Mendel consequently formulated his second law of inheritance, the *law of independent assortment,* which states that pairs of factors segregate from each other in an independent fashion.

CYTOLOGICAL BASIS OF MENDELIAN INHERITANCE

Mendel was quite unaware of the details of fertilization and meiosis as they are known today, a fact that only serves to emphasize the remarkable ingenuity he displayed in analyzing the problem of character inheritance. It remained to give the abstract factor, or gene, some tangible form. This was done by Sutton, Boveri, and de Vries in the period 1902–04, shortly after Mendel's laws had been rediscovered. The following facts indicate that the behavior of the Mendelian genes in inheritance is mirrored in the behavior of the chromosomes in fertilization and meiosis:

1. Fertilization in both plants and animals involves the union within the egg of maternal and paternal nuclei (O. Hertwig, Strasburger), providing a means for the union of parental characteristics in the offspring. Since the contribution of the sperm consists primarily of nuclear materials, the nucleus is the source of all paternal genetic contributions.

2. Meiosis, insofar as it relates to nuclear behavior, provides for a reduction in the number of chromosomes in the egg and sperm, with fertilization restoring the somatic number in the zygote (Van Beneden, Boveri, Montgomery). The somatic, or diploid, chromosome number is therefore made up of two equivalent haploid sets of chromosomes, one of maternal and the other of paternal derivation. Every chromosome has a mate with which it is linearly homologous (Sutton).

3. A mechanism for the segregation of the maternal and paternal derivatives of every chromosome pair is provided through the process of synapsis. The two members of every pair synapse in meiotic prophase, separate from each other and pass to opposite poles at anaphase, and thus are incorporated into the nuclei of different gametes (Winiwarter, Montgomery).

Drawing on these facts, Sutton and Boveri showed clearly that the chromosomes exhibited a behavior that paralleled exactly the behavior of the abstract factor in segregation and recombination. The Sutton-Boveri chromosomal theory of inheritance has since been amply demonstrated in a wide variety of ways. The first critical demonstration of the relationship of a particular character to a particular chromosome was that involving sex determination.

Although chromosomes now known to be sex- or X-chromosomes were first found in an insect by Henking in 1891, it was not until 1901–02 that McClung inferred that a chromosome behaving somewhat abnormally in certain insect spermatocytes was actually a sex-determining chromosome. He arrived at this hypothesis from a consideration of the fact that there are two types of sperm produced in equal numbers by an XO male (one

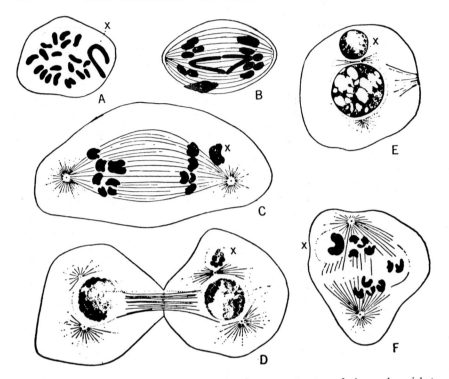

Fig. 4–3. Behavior of the X-chromosome in spermatocytes of the male cricket Gryllus (n 11). A, spermatogonial metaphase with single large X-chromosome; B, spermatogonial anaphase; C, anaphase I with the X-chromosome passing to one pole in advance of the other chromosomes; D, interphase with the X-chromosome in a separate vescicle; E, later stage of D showing the two separate nuclei; F, late prophase II with the spindle beginning to form and the X-chromosome already at one pole (Wilson 1925 after Brunelli).

X-chromosome as opposed to two in an XX female), and that there are two sexes produced in equal numbers. Since the two types of sperm differ only in that one type has an X-chromosome while the other lacks one (Fig. 4–3), the X-chromosome must be influential in determining the sex of the offspring. Proof was provided by Boveri and Gulick in 1909, and by Merrill in 1910. That two types of sperm are produced is seen in the spermatid nuclei of the hemipteran insect Protentor, where the X-chromosome can be seen as a darkly stained body (Fig. 4–4). The egg receives a single X-chromosome as the result of chromosome segregation; whether the resulting zygote will be male or female is determined by the type of sperm that effects fertilization.

Proof that the random assortment of two pairs of contrasting alleles (Mendel's second law) is paralleled by the random assortment of paired chromosomes was provided by Carothers in 1913. Sutton had previously postulated that a random distribution of chromosomes occurred in meiosis

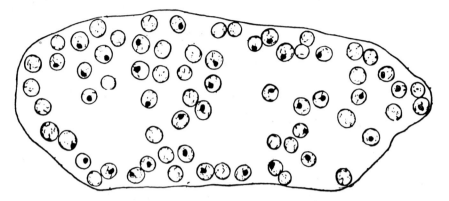

Fig. 4–4. Spermatid nuclei of the hemipter Protentor, with 36 of the X-class show-ing the heteropycnotic X-chromosome, and 33 of the no-X-class (from Wilson's *The Cell in Development and Heredity,* copyright 1925, and used with the permission of The Macmillan Co.

such that the resultant haploid gametes received all possible combinations of paternal and maternal chromosomes. The conclusive proof lacking was supplied by Carothers from a study of the distribution of the members of a *heteromorphic* pair of chromosomes in the male orthopteran Brachystola.

The members of this pair of chromosomes, which regularly synapsed and segregated from each other, differed visibly in size. Using the X-chromo-some of the XO male as a basis for comparison, the distribution of the heteromorphic homologues could be shown to be completely random, pro-ducing four classes of sperm in equal numbers (Fig. 4–5). In two other orthopterans, Trimerotropis and Circotettix, the number of heteromorphic pairs in various individual males varied from one to eight. By comparing the distribution of two or more heteromorphic pairs with each other, or with the X-chromosome, Carothers (1917, 1921) again demonstrated that the Mendelian expectancy of random assortment was always achieved. There remained little room for doubt that the behavior of the genes is mirrored in the behavior of the chromosomes insofar as segregation and independent assortment are concerned.

Additional assumptions and proofs. Acceptance of the above relation-ships between gene and chromosome required that two additional con-ditions be fulfilled. The first was that there must be a chromosomal continuity from cell to cell from the fertilized egg through to gamete production (to account for the genetic continuity demanded by Mendelian inheritance). Also the chromosomes of the haploid egg or sperm must be qualitatively different from each other insofar as their genetic effect is concerned (to account for the allelic differences known to determine de-velopment). That these conditions are cytologically fulfilled was proven through the brilliant researches of Boveri.

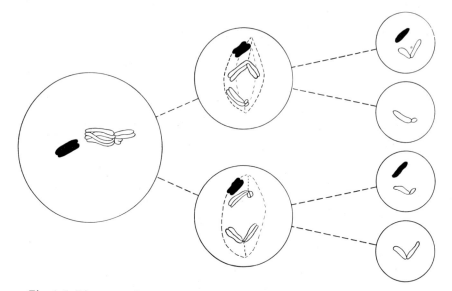

Fig. 4–5. Diagrammatic representation of the origin of four kinds of sperm nuclei resulting from the random segregation of the X-chromosome with the two members of a heteromorphic bivalent. X-chromosome black, heteromorphic homologues white.

Demonstration of the continuity of the chromosomes from one cell generation to the next, with a retention of their morphological individuality, presents a rather stiff challenge because the chromosomes are generally lost to view during interphase. To follow a single chromosome from egg to adult through successive cell divisions is, of course, an impossibility. Boveri was able to show, however, that in the early blastomere nuclei of *Ascaris megalocephala* the chromosomes in prophase appeared in essentially the same relative positions they had occupied in the preceding telophase, and that the size and shape of the chromosomes remained unchanged. This study was made possible by the fact that the nuclei become lobed by the failure of the free ends of the large V-shape chromosomes to be drawn up into the body of the nucleus in telophase reorganization (Fig. 4–6). In the succeeding prophase the free ends are to be found in these lobed areas, with sister nuclei being more or less mirror images of each other.

The behavior of the X-chromosome of many insects provides additional proof of genetic continuity since it remains pycnotic and clearly visible at all stages of division. More recently, Ris and Mirsky (1949) have shown the chromosomes of an optically homogeneous living cell in interphase to be invisible only because of the dispersed state of their structure; changes in salt concentration bring the chromosomes clearly into view. Claude and Potter (1943), as well as later investigators, have also demonstrated that chromatin threads can be isolated from interphase nuclei by rupturing followed by centrifugation.

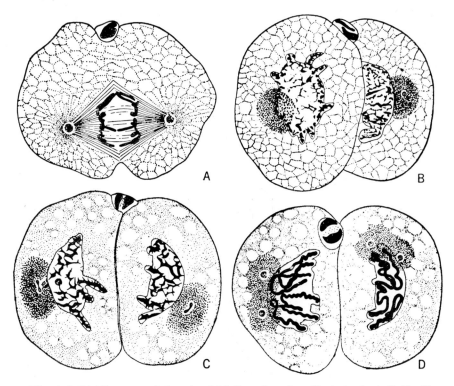

Fig. 4–6. Dividing eggs of Ascaris which Boveri used to illustrate the individuality of the chromosomes. A, anaphase of first cleavage; B, two-cell stage with lobes in the nucleus formed by the projecting ends of chromosomes; C and D, early and late prophases showing chromosomes in the same position as they occupied in the preceding telophase (Wilson 1925 after Boveri).

That the chromosomes of the haploid complement are qualitatively different from each other in a genetic sense was determined by Boveri through a study of the developmental behavior of dispermic eggs of the sea urchin. These are eggs that have been fertilized by two spermatozoa. Since each sperm introduces a centrosome into the egg, and each centrosome divides in anticipation of the first cleavage division, the initial metaphases and anaphases are often characterized by a *tetraster,* i.e., a spindle with four poles. Tripolar cleavages may also be formed in dispermic eggs. Since the dividing nucleus is triploid (one egg plus two sperm nuclei), the distribution of the chromosomes to three or four poles in anaphase must inevitably be irregular. Boveri isolated many of the first-division blastomeres from these dispermic eggs, and demonstrated that most were abnormal in development, but that all were not alike in their abnormalities. Boveri had previously known that haploid, triploid, or tetraploid individuals could develop normally; he therefore concluded that abnormal development resulted from the irregular distribution of chromosomes brought on by the first multipolar division (later divisions are regular). Each chromosome must consequently have possessed a certain individual quality which expressed itself in development. The qualitative differences between chromosomes are now known to reside in the qualitatively different genes that make up the chromosomes.

SEX LINKAGE

The parallelisms between genic and chromosomal behavior discussed above did not provide more than strong circumstantial evidence that the genes are carried on, or are a part of, the chromosomes. It remained for Bridges (1916) to demonstrate, in a classical series of studies, that a particular gene was to be found in a particular chromosome.

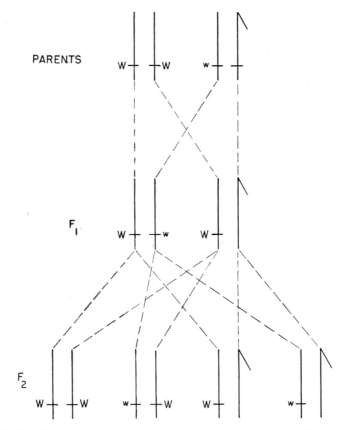

Fig. 4–7. The F_1 and F_2 results of crossing a wild type red-eyed (W) female to a white-eyed (w) male in D. *melanogaster*.

T. H. Morgan had shown that the transmission of *white*, a recessive eye color gene in *Drosophila melanogaster*, depends upon which sex carries the gene initially. For example, if a white-eyed male is crossed to a red-eyed female, the F_1 flies of both sexes are red-eyed, while the F_2 females are all red-eyed, the F_2 males red- and white-eyed in equal numbers (Fig. 4–7). With the sexes being produced in equal numbers, this gives a normal 3:1 ratio with the exception that the recessive white-eyed flies are always male. When the reciprocal cross is made, using a white-eyed female and a red-eyed male, the F_1 males are white-eyed and the F_1 females red-eyed. In the F_2 generation, one-half of the males and females are white-eyed and the other half red-eyed.

This type of inheritance paralleled the transmission of the X-chromosome, as diagrammed in Figure 4–8. Bridges (1916), however, showed conclusively that the gene *white* was located on the X-chromosome. When

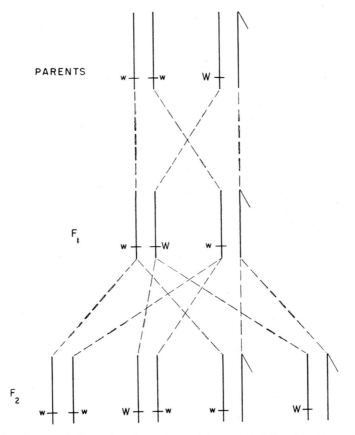

Fig. 4–8. The F_1 and F_2 results of crossing a white-eyed (*w*) female with a red-eyed (*W*) male in *D. melanogaster*.

making a cross between a white-eyed female and a red-eyed male, he noted the appearance of exceptional individuals whose genotype was such as to suggest a failure of the usual criss-cross type of inheritance of the X-chromosomes. Thus, in an F_1 population that should have contained only red-eyed females and white-eyed males, there appeared white-eyed females and red-eyed males, with the exceptional females occurring with a frequency of one in 2500. The frequency of exceptional males was about one in 1200.

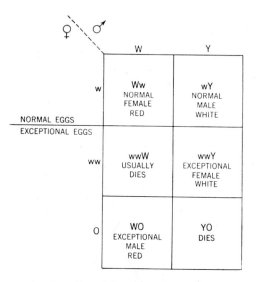

Fig. 4–9. Diagram showing the origin of exceptional individuals in *D. melanogaster* when non-disjunction of the X-chromosome gives rise to 2X and no-X eggs (after Bridges 1916).

Bridges' explanation of the phenomenon, known as *primary non-disjunction,* is diagrammed in Figure 4–9. The exceptional females result from the fact that in the meiotic divisions of the egg both X-chromosomes are included in the egg nucleus, to be fertilized later by a Y-bearing sperm. That all white-eyed exceptional daughters were XXY instead of XX was verified cytologically. The exceptional red-eyed sons resulted from the fertilization of a no-X egg by an X-bearing sperm.

The XO males are sterile due to the absence of the Y-chromosome. Their higher frequency suggests that no-X eggs are more numerous than XX eggs, and this can be explained by assuming that no-X eggs are produced both by primary non-disjunction (at a rate of 1 in 2500) and by the failure of one of the X-chromosomes to be included in the egg nucleus, possibly through anaphase lagging. Bridges also found that the process of primary non-disjunction could be demonstrated for a variety of other genes known to be on the X-chromosome, as well as for those found on the tiny IV-chromosome which can occur in a haploid, diploid, or triploid condition. In each instance, the correlation between genetical and cytological inheritance was exact. There could no longer be any doubt that the qualitative differences between chromosomes, in Boveri's sense, was the result of the qualitatively different genes found associated with particular chromosomes.

L. V. Morgan (1922) later discovered a strain of *Drosophila melanogaster* that gave 100 percent non-disjunction. As in the case of Bridges' exceptional individuals, the daughters appeared to receive both X-chromosomes from their mother, and the sons their single X-chromosome from their father. Cytological examination of the chromosomes of the female, which were XXY, showed the two X-chromosomes attached to each other in the neighborhood of their centromeres, with the result that they always passed to the same pole. The inheritance of *attached-X flies,* as these have become known, is outlined in Figure 4–10.

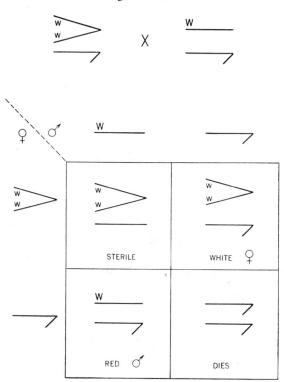

Fig. 4–10. Attached X-chromosome inheritance in *D. melanogaster* showing transmission of *red (W)* and *white (w)* eye color.

LINKAGE AND CROSSING OVER

The number of haploid chromosomes of an organism is limited; in *Drosophila melanogaster* the number is four. With the discovery of an increasing number of mutant genes came recognition of the fact that some of these genes must occupy positions on the same chromosome. Each of these genes individually yielded F_2 ratios that were in conformity with Mendelian expectations, but when studied in pairs or in groups of three or more, they yielded F_2 ratios that frequently departed from the normal segregations expected on the basis of random assortment. These discrepant ratios, first found in 1905 by Bateson in the sweet pea, were at first thought to be exceptional cases, but when confirmed in other organisms the data to many biologists seemed to invalidate Mendelian law. A general acceptance of the Chromosome Theory of Inheritance was, in fact, delayed by such findings until the elucidation of *linkage* and *crossing over* by the Drosophila geneticists under Morgan (1910–15) made it quite clear that the Mendelian law of random assortment, while not invalid, was not as universally applicable as it was once believed. Where the number of known genes exceeds the haploid number of chromosomes, some of the genes must inevitably show linkage, i.e., they tend to be inherited as a group rather than individually.

Linkage groups have been established in a number of plants and animals. Those worked out in *Drosophila melanogaster, Zea mays* (maize), and Neurospora (a fungus) are by far the most complete, but other less extensive groupings have been established in tomato, wheat, several of the fowl and rodent genera, and in man.

Complete linkage. Purple (*pr*) and vestigial (*vg*) are two autosomal recessive genes found on Chromosome II of *D. melanogaster*. Their linkage relationships have been studied by Bridges, and the following data were obtained when a wild-type female $\dfrac{+\ +}{+\ +}$ was crossed to a male $\dfrac{pr\ vg}{pr\ vg}$ bearing both mutant genes in a homozygous condition (taken from Sturtevant and Beadle, 1939):

$$\text{Parents}\quad \frac{+\ +}{+\ +}\ \female\ \times\ \frac{pr\ vg}{pr\ vg}\ \male$$

$$F_1\quad \frac{+\ +}{pr\ vg}\ \female\female\ \text{and}\ \male\male$$

$$\text{Testcross} - \frac{pr\ vg}{pr\ vg}\ \female\ \times\ F_1\ \male$$

	wild-type (+ +)	519
	purple vestigial (pr vg)	552
Testcross	vestigial (+ vg)	0
progeny	purple (pr +)	0
		1071

(Note: the double male or female sign, e.g., $\female\female$, is a plural sign. The testcross involves a cross of the organism tested, in this case the $F_1\ \male$, to the homozygous recessive form of the other sex. Such a test determines the types of gametes produced by the heterozygous individual. The horizontal line drawn between the two pairs of alleles indicates that those above the line are on one chromosome, those below on the other homologue.)

Of the 1071 flies examined, only those having the original parental combinations of genes were found, i.e., the $+$ $+$ and pr vg combinations remained intact and showed no segregation. Linkage in this instance is complete.

Incomplete linkage. Actually, the linkage data described above are exceptional in that Drosophila is one of a group of organisms whose genes show complete linkage in the male gametes. If the identical cross is made again, but in this instance the F_1 females are testcrossed to homozygous recessive males, the following data are obtained (taken from Sturtevant and Beadle 1939):

$$P \qquad \frac{+\ +}{+\ +}\ ♀ \times \frac{pr\ vg}{pr\ vg}\ ♂$$

$$F_1 \qquad \frac{+\ +}{pr\ vg}\ ♀\,♀\ \text{and}\ ♂\,♂$$

$$\text{Testcross} \qquad \frac{+\ +}{pr\ vg}\ ♀ \times \frac{pr\ vg}{pr\ vg}\ ♂$$

Testcross progeny		
	$+$ $+$	1339
	pr vg	1195
	$+$ vg	151
	pr $+$	154
		2839

All four possible phenotypes are recovered in the testcross progeny, but it will be noticed that the parental types, $++$ and pr vg, are more numerous than the new recombinations, $+$ vg and pr $+$. The departure from random assortment is obvious. The percentage of recombination is found by adding the new types and dividing by the total number of flies $\frac{151\ +\ 154}{2839}$, and this figure, 10.7, provides a measure of the genetic distance separating the two genes on the chromosome. The same percentage, within the range of experimental error, would be obtained if the original parental stocks had been $\frac{+\ vg}{+\ vg}$ and $\frac{pr\ +}{pr\ +}$, indicating that the frequency of recombination is not conditioned by the particular parental combination, but by the spatial relationships of the genes on the chromosome. Thus, a similar cross, using the genes brown (bw) and speck (sp) on the same chromosome, would yield a recombination percentage of 2.5. In a genetic sense, these two genes are consequently considered closer to each other than pr is to vg.

CYTOLOGICAL BASIS OF CROSSING OVER

The process that leads to incomplete linkage is known as *crossing over*. The parental gene combinations represent *non-crossover* types, the new recombinations *crossover* types.

A study of the events occurring in meiosis provides a clue as to the physical basis of the phenomenon. It will be recalled that in meiotic prophase the homologous chromosomes synapse with each other in such a manner that by pachytene they are paired along their entire length. In diplotene, which follows immediately, the homologues separate from each other, being held together only at certain points along their length. These points of union are the chiasmata, and it is generally agreed that they represent the points of genetical crossing over. Crossing over, in other words, must therefore represent an actual exchange of chromatic material between homologous chromosomes. The homologues in diplonema are also longitudinally split into two chromatids, and in clear preparations of meiotic cells it can be seen that a chiasma involves only two of the four chromatids of any bivalent. Crossing over takes place between chromatids, therefore, not between whole chromosomes.

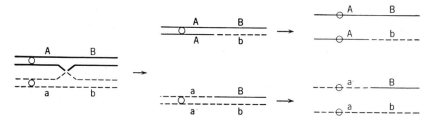

Fig. 4–11. Crossing over between linked genes A and B. Two of the four chromatids exchange segments at every point of crossing over, and the crossover would be recognized cytologically as a chiasma.

Figure 4–11 presents in diagrammatic fashion the cytological interpretation of crossing over. On various grounds, it can be shown that chiasmata represent crossovers that have taken place between non-sister chromatids; those that might occur between sister chromatids would not be recognized as chiasmata. The sister chromatids remain associated on either side of the chiasma until anaphase when the paired chromosomes are separated. The unchanged chromatids will give rise to *non-crossover* offspring, the changed chromatids to the *crossover* types.

When more than one chiasma occurs between any two homologous chromosomes, the opportunities for rearrangement within linkage groups are increased, but it is obvious that a chiasma must occur between two genes in order for crossing over to be detected. The number of chiasmata between a pair of homologues does not vary greatly from cell to cell (e.g., the X-chromosome of *D. melanogaster* has 0 to 3 chiasmata per cell), and is generally dependent upon the length of the chromosomes. The position of the chiasmata may vary widely in some species, however, while being rather constant in others.

A certain relationship exists therefore between the cytologically visible chiasmata and the occurrence of crossing over. A single chiasma between a pair of homologous chromosomes leads to the eventual formation, when meiosis is completed, of two non-crossover chromatids and two crossover chromatids. To state it otherwise, if, in 25 meiotic cells, a single chiasma always occurred at a particular region lying between two genes, and if all of the 100 chromatids were recovered from these cells, 50 would be non-crossovers, the other 50 crossovers. Consequently 100 percent chiasma frequency leads to 50 percent crossing over, the maximum crossing over that can be attained between two genes under the circumstances described. In the *pr vg* linkage relationships discussed above, the 10.7 percent crossing over would result from a chiasma frequency of 21.4 percent.

As the linear distance between two genes increases, the possibility that two chiasmata may occur in the intervening region also increases. The occurrence of multiple chiasmata between two genes does not, however, alter the fact that the maximum detectable amount of crossing over between two genes, regardless of their distance apart, is still 50 percent. The cytological basis for this reasoning, which has been experimentally verified, is illustrated in Figure 4–12. Here the crossover at the right (Region I) is assumed to be constant in position, while those at the left

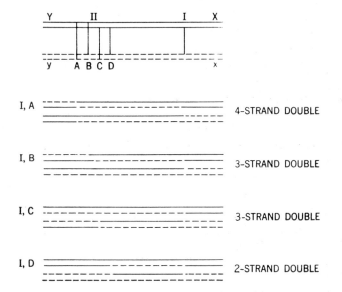

Fig. 4–12. Double crossing over between genes X and Y, and the resultant chromatids. Crossing over in region I is indicated as fixed, that in region II as random, with A to D indicating the four possible types. With respect to the genes involved, the ratio of crossover to non-crossover chromatids would be 4 non-crossovers: 8 single crossovers: 4 double crossovers.

(Region II), designated A, B, C, and D, represent the four possible types that can occur with reference to the right crossover. These types involving the four possible combinations of two non-sister chromatids, occur at random, and the recovered chromatids are indicated at the right of the figure. When the chromatids of the various types are totaled, i.e., the non-crossovers, the single crossovers in Region I, the single crossovers in Region II, and the double crossovers (Regions I and II), it is found that each is represented four times. The crossover chromatids are three times as frequent as the non-crossover chromatids. Insofar as detectable crossing over in a genetical sense is concerned, however, it will be noticed that linkage of the two genes, X and Y, is still intact in all double crossover chromatids. Phenotypically these would be indistinguishable from the non-crossover types, and crossing over would consequently remain at a maximum level of 50 percent.

In an actual experiment, it would be virtually impossible to recover the four chromatids from any single meiotic cell, except in some lower plants such as Neurospora. In the eggs of higher plants and animals only one remains. In animals, the others pass into the polar bodies and are lost; in plants, they are variously distributed depending upon the type of embryo sac formation. In male meiotic cells, each chromatid enters a sperm or a pollen grain, but no existing method permits the certain recovery of any particular chromatid. The frequency of crossing over, as a consequence, must be determined by statistical means; experience has shown, however, that these procedures are reliable and reproducible when environmental conditions are held constant.

In some fungi, such as the ascomycete Neurospora, all the chromatid products of a single meiotic cell can be recovered by isolating in serial order the ascospores from the ascus. The hypotheses developed from genetic studies in other organisms can be directly tested in this manner, and with minor exceptions (to be discussed later) verification has been provided.

GENETIC MAPS

Further study of crossing over in *Drosophila melanogaster* by Morgan, Sturtevant, Muller, and Bridges (1915), presented initially in comprehensive form in their classic volume, *The Mechanism of Mendelian Heredity,* led to an important series of hypotheses that firmly established the parallelisms between the abstract genes on the one hand and the material chromosomes on the other. These hypotheses have since been fully confirmed in other organisms.

Limitation of linkage groups. Sutton (1902, 1903) had hypothesized, on the basis of his own studies as well as those of Van Beneden, Boveri, and Montgomery, that the somatic or diploid chromosome number was made up of two groups of chromosomes, each of which constituted a haploid group. One was of maternal, the other of paternal origin. Boveri had also shown that each chromosome of the haploid group was qualitatively different from the others in its developmental influence. With the knowledge that different alleles of the same gene had to be on homologous chromosomes in order to conform with Mendelian expectations of segregations, it could be assumed that the linked genes would fall into groups, the number of which would not exceed the haploid number of chromosomes. This principle is known as the *limitation of linkage groups.* The hundred or more genes known in *D. melanogaster* in 1915 fell into four groups, and no more, and the haploid number of chromosomes was also four. Although many additional genes have since been discovered in this species of Drosophila, all have been located in the same four linkage groups.

In maize the number of linkage groups is ten; in the garden pea it is seven. In these two plants, the haploid number of chromosomes is ten and seven, respectively. The same holds true for other genetically well-known plants and animals. In no case have the linkage groups exceeded the haploid number of chromosomes. It is true that certain genetic effects seem not to be associated with known chromosomes (as discussed in Chapter 2), but these are single effects, not grouped phenomena inherited in linked fashion.

Linear order of the genes and map distances. Morgan postulated from a study of genes in the X-chromosome that the genes were arranged in a linear order, each gene having its apportioned place along the length of the chromonema. Its allele occupied a corresponding position in an homologous chromosome. Such a postulate arose as a natural corollary out of the observations that (1) the many genes in *D. melanogaster* could be divided into four linkage groups corresponding to the four haploid chromosomes, and (2) the evidence that linkage, when incomplete, was incomplete at a certain constant ratio that could be interpreted as a function of the constant spatial relationship between linked genes. Roux, in 1883, and Correns and de Vries later, had discussed the possibility of such an arrangement of hereditary units, but correlative genetic evidence was necessary to formalize the hypothesis, and to predict the location of genetic loci. Sturtevant (1915) devised a test whereby the position and linear order of a third gene could be determined with reference to two other genes on the same chromosome. Since three genes are used simultaneously, the test has become known as a *three-point cross.*

If it is assumed that the correct serial order of three hypothetical genes is *abc,* and that the distances between the genes are reflected in the frequencies with which crossing over takes place between them, then a testcross of the heterozygote $\dfrac{+\ +\ +}{a\ \ b\ \ c}$ to the triple recessive $\dfrac{abc}{abc}$ can yield the following possible phenotypes, the complementary types being grouped:

$$\text{non-crossovers} \quad \left\{ \begin{array}{ccc} + & + & + \\ a & b & c \end{array} \right.$$

$$\begin{array}{c} \text{single crossovers} \\ \text{Type I} \end{array} \quad \left\{ \begin{array}{ccc} + & b & c \\ a & + & + \end{array} \right.$$

$$\begin{array}{c} \text{single crossovers} \\ \text{Type II} \end{array} \quad \left\{ \begin{array}{ccc} + & + & c \\ a & b & + \end{array} \right.$$

$$\text{double crossovers} \quad \left\{ \begin{array}{ccc} + & b & + \\ a & + & c \end{array} \right.$$

On the basis of the mechanism of crossing over presented above, the non-crossover group would be the largest in number. The Type I single crossovers would arise from a chromatid interchange in the region between genes a and b; Type II singles from an interchange in the region between genes b and c.

The frequencies of the two types of single crossovers will, in general, depend upon the linear distance between a and b, and b and c. The double crossover group will contain the smallest number of individuals. This results from the fact that the occurrence of a crossover between any two genes is a statistical function of distance; the simultaneous occurrence of crossovers in two adjacent regions would be the product of the individual single crossover probabilities, and would therefore be less than either alone.

An experiment carried out in maize will illustrate use of the three-point cross. The genes brown midrib (bm), red aleurone (pr), and virescent seedling (v) are located in Chromosome 5, and the data obtained from linkage studies are as follows (Emerson, Beadle, and Fraser 1935):

$$\text{Parents} \quad \frac{+ \ + \ +}{+ \ + \ +} \times \frac{bm \ pr \ v}{bm \ pr \ v}$$

$$F_1 \quad \frac{+ \ + \ +}{bm \ pr \ v}$$

$$\text{Testcross } F_1 \times \frac{bm \ pr \ v}{bm \ pr \ v}$$

Testcross progeny:

$$\begin{array}{lll} + \ + \ + & 232 \\ bm \ pr \ v & 235 \end{array} \right\} \text{non-crossovers} = 42.1\%$$

$$\begin{array}{lll} + \ pr \ v & 84 \\ bm \ + \ + & 77 \end{array} \right\} \begin{array}{l} \text{single crossovers between} \\ bm \text{ and } pr = 14.5\% \end{array}$$

$$\begin{array}{lll} + \ + \ v & 201 \\ bm \ pr \ + & 194 \end{array} \right\} \begin{array}{l} \text{single crossovers between} \\ pr \text{ and } v = 35.6\% \end{array}$$

$$
\begin{array}{lr}
+ \ pr \ + & 40 \\
bm \ + \ v & 46 \\
\hline
\text{Total} & 1109
\end{array}
\left.\begin{array}{l} \\ \\ \end{array}\right\}
\begin{array}{l}
\text{double crossovers between} \\
bm \text{ and } pr, \text{ and } pr \text{ and } v \ = 7.8\%
\end{array}
$$

From the above groupings, each composed of complementary types, certain facts are readily deduced. The non-crossover types, of course, are those that preserve the original parental gene groupings; the double crossover types are recognizable because they form the group with the lowest frequency. The latter group also provides information as to the linear order of the genes. With respect to *bm* and *v*, the gene *pr* has shifted positions with its dominant allele as Figure 4–13 shows.

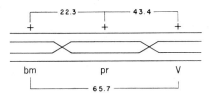

Fig. 4–13. Linkage map of the *bm-pr-v* region of Chromosome 5 of maize showing the order of the genes and the total map distance between the genes.

The order of the three genes is therefore *bm pr v*. The two remaining classes constitute the single crossover types, one class representing the interchanges taking place between *bm* and *pr*, and the other those between *pr* and *v*.

In calculating the genetic distance between two genes, all interchanges that have occurred in a particular region must be taken into consideration. The distance between *bm* and *pr* is not 14.5, but 14.5 *plus* 7.8, or 22.3. In other words, the single crossover frequency for the *bm-pr* region does not represent the total frequency of interchanges; to it must be added the double crossover frequency, which also represents interchanges in the *bm-pr* region. Similarly, the total crossover frequency for the *pr-v* region is 35.6 + 7.8, or 43.4. Figure 4–13 gives a genetic map constructed from these data. The total distance from *bm* to *v* would be 65.7, since units of the map can be successively added to indicate genetic distance.

A further word of explanation may be added concerning this map. The gene *bm* lies 22.3 map units from *pr*. (A map unit has been arbitrarily defined as that linear distance on the chromosome within which there will occur, on an average, one crossover per 100 gametes.) In the maize experiment described above, 22.3 out of every 100 gametes showed a crossover in the *bm-pr* interval. Crossover frequencies and map units are therefore synonymous and interchangeable, provided that double crossovers are taken into account. At the cytological level, the crossover frequency, interpreted in terms of chiasma frequency, means that in every 100 meiotic cells there were 44.6 that showed a chiasma between the two homologous Chromosome 5's in the *bm-pr* interval.

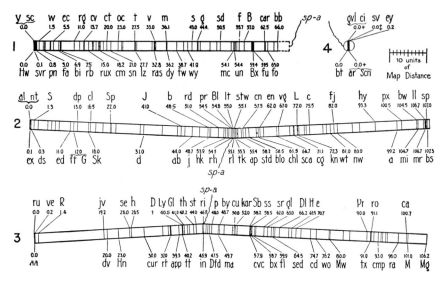

Fig. 4–14. Linkage maps of the 4 haploid chromosomes of *D. melanogaster*. The figures refer to map distances from the left end of each chromosome and as calculated from the percentage of recombination (by permission from *Principles of Genetics*, by Sinnott, Dunn and Dobzhansky, copyright 1950, McGraw-Hill Book Co., Inc.).

Through the accumulation of genetic data on the frequencies of crossing over it has been possible to construct genetic, or chromosome, maps in which the serial order of the genes and their genetic spacing have been accurately determined. The genetic maps of *D. melanogaster* and maize are illustrated in Figures 4–14 and 4–15, respectively. In addition to a mutant name and an abbreviated symbol, each gene, or *locus,* is designated by a number, which is obtained by summing up the crossover values for all known intervals to the left. Thus the gene *facet* (fa) on the X-chromosome of *D. melanogaster* is located at position 3.0. Since *yellow* (y) is at the extreme left end of the X-chromosome it is given a zero (0.0) designation. *Yellow* and *white* (w) show a crossover frequency of 1.5; *white* and *facet* show a similar frequency. *Facet* therefore lies 3 map units from the left end of the X-chromosome.

Of course, only those regions of the chromosomes that possess detectable mutant genes can be mapped. It has also been found that the shorter the map distance between two genes, the more accurately they can be located. The reason for this lies in the fact that when two genes are more than 10 to 20 map units apart, double crossovers can occur, which will give a spurious crossover frequency if they are not taken into account. A more

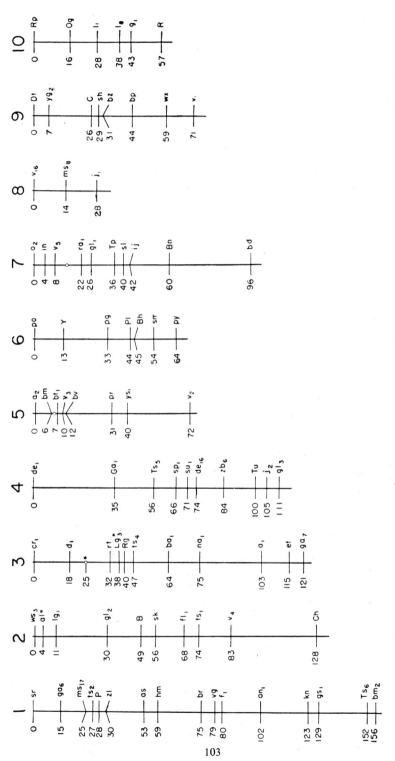

Fig. 4–15. Linkage maps of the 10 haploid chromosomes of maize. Centromeres are indicated by circles only when known with certainty; genes marked with asterisks are located approximately (Rhoades 1950).

103

accurate map of a chromosome can be made, therefore, by the addition of successive short intervals than by utilizing intervals between genes that are widely separated on the chromosome. In this respect it is of interest to compare the 1915 genetic map of *D. melanogaster* with the present-day map. Because mutant genes are more readily discovered in the X-chromosome than in the autosomes, the maximum genetic length of the X-chromosome was soon determined. An increase of only 0.5 units have been added since 1915 (65.5 then as opposed to 66.0 now). Chromosome II, however, has increased in map length from 91.9 to 107.0, and many genes such as *black, purple, vermilion,* and *curved* have been assigned new numerical values as additional genes have been discovered and added to that linkage group.

Interference. If, in a chromosome, genes *a, b,* and *c* are linked in the order given, theoretically it should be possible to predict the frequency of double crossing over when the map length of the *a-b* and *b-c* intervals are known. If it is assumed that the *a-b* interval is 10 map units long, and the *b-c* interval is 15 map units, then the frequency of double crossing over would amount to the probability of the two single crossovers occurring simultaneously. This would be 10 percent of 15 percent, or 1.5 percent, *provided the two single crossovers are without influence on each other's occurrence,* i.e., if they occur independently of each other.

Crossover studies, however, have revealed that adjacent crossovers do not occur independently, and that a crossover occurring in, for example, the *a-b* interval would tend to suppress those crossovers occurring in the *b-c* interval. The effect, therefore, would be to reduce the frequency of double crossing over. Muller, who first discovered the phenomenon, termed it *interference.* Interference may be defined as the tendency of one crossover to interfere with the occurrence of another crossover in its vicinity. Interference is more pronounced as the distance between successive genes becomes shorter; it decreases with increasing distance. Two examples will serve to illustrate its effect.

The genes *yellow, white,* and *bifid* on the X-chromosome of *D. melanogaster* are located at 0.0, 1.5, and 6.9. The *y-w* interval is therefore 1.5 units, the *w-bi* interval 5.4 units. When these three genes are studied by means of the three-point cross, it is found that there are no double crossover individuals among the progeny of the testcross. Only single crossovers in the *y-w* or the *w-bi* intervals are recovered. It is true, of course, that the frequency of double crossovers would be extremely low when such short intervals are being considered, but they should, nevertheless, be detectable when large populations are raised. The fact that none are recovered means that interference is complete. Experience has shown that, in *D. melanogaster,* interference within a chromosome arm is complete within map intervals of 10 units or less, and non-operative when distances of 40 units or more are involved. There is no interference across the centromere, the two arms of a chromosome being independent of each other insofar as this phenomena is concerned.

The crossover data in maize discussed earlier illustrates partial interference. The map distances for the *bm-pr* and *pr-v* intervals are 22.3 and 43.4 respectively. The expected frequency of double crossing over, based on independent occurrence, would be 9.7 percent, i.e., 22.3 percent of 43.4 percent. Only 7.8 percent double crossovers were recovered among the testcross progeny. To express the degree of interference, Muller has coined the term *coincidence,* which is an inverse measure of interference. The *coefficient of coincidence,* which is equal to one minus interference when the latter is given in terms of a decimal fraction, is calculated by dividing the expected number of double crossovers into the observed number. In the above experiment this would be $\dfrac{7.8}{9.7} = 0.804 =$ coefficient of coincidence.

Therefore, only 80.4 percent of the expected double crossovers were recovered, indicating a partial interference of 19.6 percent.

CYTOLOGICAL PROOFS OF CROSSING OVER

Since the genes are located in the chromosome, the various aspects of gene arrangement and crossing over must be physically mirrored in the chromosomes' structure and behavior. Some of these will be considered in detail in later chapters; others that are fundamental to an understanding of the chromosomal basis of inheritance will be taken up in this section.

To enumerate, the facts that have been established through genetical reasoning and that can be related more or less specifically to the chromosomes are: (1) the linear order of the genes, (2) complete linkage in such forms as the males of Drosophila species, (3) partial linkage, or crossing over, between homologous chromosomes, (4) limitation of crossing over to 50 percent between two genes, and (5) interference.

Linear differentiation of the chromosome. The fact that genetical evidence shows the genes to be serially arranged in the chromosome does not necessarily imply that the chromosome will exhibit a similar linear differentiation of a morphologically visible nature. The genes are submicroscopic in dimensions and there is no certainty that they will ever be recognized as morphologically defined entities even with the great resolving powers of the electron miscroscope.

Chromosomes do, however, possess morphological differences that have a constancy of position and size. These serve as landmarks by which sections of individual chromosomes may be identified with certainty. Although this topic will be discussed at length later, the linear arrangement of distinctive regions can best be seen in the type of banding exhibited by the giant salivary gland chromosomes of certain dipteran species, including those in the genus Drosophila (see Chapter 5). It has also been shown by appropriate means (see page 159) that certain genes are associated with certain clearly recognized bands. From this it can be judged that the genetical concept of a constant arrangement of genes in a serial order is supported by the morphological characteristics of the chromosomes.

Cytological basis of complete linkage. The male Drosophila and the female silkworm, *Bombyx mori,* are examples of organisms in which crossing over does not occur in the meiotic cells. Both are heterogametic in that each produces two kinds of gametes, X- and Y-bearing sperm in the case of the male Drosophila, and X- and Y-bearing eggs in the female silkworm (the X- and Y-chromosomes of those species in which the female is heterogametic are often referred to respectively as the Z- and W-chromosomes).

The lack of crossing over between the X- and Y-chromosomes could be readily accounted for, since in Drosophila these are only partially homologous, thus providing little or no opportunity for the homologous pairing that precedes crossing over. But the lack of crossing over between autosomes, which are homologous, must be accounted for on a different basis, and the usual explanation is that no chiasmata are formed between homologous pairs of chromosomes in the spermatocytes. Cytological studies of *D. melanogaster* spermatocytes, on the other hand, have indicated that the autosomes at metaphase are held together by chiasmata (Cooper 1949), which means either that not all chiasmata are related to crossing over, or that other pairing conditions can give rise to chromosomal configurations that simulate chiasmata. This important topic, which has immediate bearing on the mechanism of crossing over, will be discussed more fully in Chapter 8.

Cytological basis of crossing over. Earlier in this chapter the cytological basis of crossing over was discussed, and it was pointed out that the chiasmat a, visible initially in early diplonema, provided an appropriate mechanism for the transfer of genes from one homologous chromosome to another. Through an exchange of chromatin material, all genes distal to the chiasma would be reciprocally transferred to non-sister chromatids, and crossing over consequently appears to involve not single genes but blocks of genes. The correctness of this genetical hypothesis was ascertained through the use of heteromorphic homologues which permitted the correlation of chromosome behavior with the disruption of linkage through crossing over. Stern (1931), working with *D. melanogaster,* and Creighton and McClintock (1931), with maize, provided the experimental evidence.

Stern's experiment is diagrammed in Figure 4–16. The male parent in the experimental cross possessed a normal chromosomal complex, with an X-chromosome marked by the recessive eye-color gene *carnation (car)* and the normal allele $(+^B)$ of the dominant gene *Bar (B),* which narrows the eye. The female parent was derived from a cross between two races, one of which had a large portion of the Y-chromosome attached (translocated)

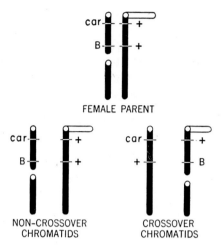

FEMALE PARENT

NON-CROSSOVER
CHROMATIDS

CROSSOVER
CHROMATIDS

Fig. 4–16. Diagram of the model used by Stern (1931) to show that crossing over involved an exchange of chromatin between homologous chromosomes. In the female parent, one X-chromosome is represented as broken into two pieces; the top portion possesses its own centromere (open circle), the bottom piece has a centromere derived from the IV chromosome through translocation. The other X-chromosome in the female parent is further distinguishable by the fact that it possesses an arm derived from the Y-chromosome (shown in outline). The crossover and non-crossover chromatids are indicated below, and their respective genetic constitutions are shown.

to the end of the X-chromosomes; this altered X-chromosome carried the normal alleles of carnation ($+^{car}$) and Bar ($+^{B}$). In the other race, the X-chromosome had been broken into two separate parts; the piece bearing the centromere carried the genes *car* and *B,* while the other fragment was translocated to the tiny IV chromosome. Both of these races were viable, and when crossed gave females that were heterozygous for the two genes in question. They also possessed two kinds of X-chromosomes which could be morphologically distinguished from each other as well as from the normal X-chromosome, which, in the F_1 females, was derived from the father.

The parental heterozygous female can give crossover and non-crossover eggs, which, when fertilized by an X-bearing sperm containing the two recessive genes *car* and $+^{B}$, will give four types of female offspring (the males were disregarded). The two non-crossover types will be phenotypically *carnation-Bar* and wild type, respectively. The former should, on cytological analysis, possess the two X-chromosome fragments, while the latter should possess the X-chromosome bearing the piece of the Y-chromosome. Both will, of course, have a normal X-chromosome in addition. The two crossover types will be *carnation* with normal shaped eyes, or *Bar* with red (wild type) eyes. The former should have two normal X-chromosomes, while the latter should possess a normal X-chromosome plus the two X-chromosome fragments, one of which will bear a portion of the Y-chromosome. Stern made a cytological study of 364 cross-over and non-crossover F_1 females, and in all but five (unaccounted for) there was perfect agreement between genetical and cytological facts.

On this basis, crossing over is accompanied by an exchange of chromatic material. Are all chiasmata, however, to be considered cytological manifestations of crossing over? The affirmative is suggested by cytological studies of Chromosome 9 in maize (Beadle 1932), in which a particular region known to show 12 percent crossing over was found to exhibit a chiasma frequency of 20 percent. This is in good agreement with the expected figure of 24 percent, calculated on the basis that 100 percent chiasma frequency equals 50 percent crossing over. These data have been widely cited as critical evidence to support the thesis that all chiasmata represent points of crossing over, but because of the uncertainty of the location of chiasmata in maize with respect to sharply defined regions, and the findings in male Drosophila as regards chiasma formation without crossing over (Cooper 1949), the problem cannot be considered satisfactorily solved. However, the extensive study of Brown and Zohary (1955) in *Lilium formosanum* supports the concept of a 1:1 ratio between chiasmata and crossing over even when environmental and cytological conditions are varied widely.

Proof that crossing over occurs between two of the four chromatids. That crossing over involves only two of the four chromatids at any one locus is suggested by the observations that the frequency of crossing over between two genes rarely exceeds 50 percent, regardless of their distance apart (exceptional cases of greater than 50 percent crossing over will be discussed in Chapter 8). Proof of this was provided by Anderson (1925) through use of the attached-X stock of Drosophila. The females have an $\widehat{XX}$ Y composition, as illustrated in Figure 4–10. Through appropriate means, individuals can be obtained that are heterozygous for certain X-chromosome genes. When these are bred to any male, it will be found that a certain percentage of the offspring are homozygous recessive, the frequency being a function of the position of the gene on the chromosome. (Fig. 4–17). From an $\widehat{XX}$ female, heterozygous for the gene *yellow*, for example, approximately 20 percent of the offspring will be homozygous recessive. Eighty percent will appear wild type, but through further breeding it can be shown that one quarter of them (20 percent of the total) will be homozygous wild type, the remainder being heterozygous for yellow. It would be difficult to interpret these results on any other basis than that crossing over occurs in the *four-strand* stage, and between two of the four chromatids. Such a conclusion is also supported by cytological observations revealing that a chiasma involves only two of the four chromatids in early diplotene.

Chiasmata and interference. Interference indicates that there is a certain minimal length of chromatin within which double crossing over does

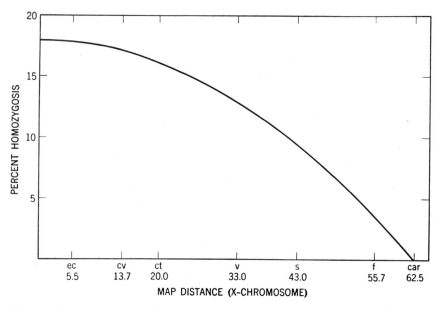

Fig. 4–17. Percent homozygosis of recessive alleles in offspring of attached-X mothers whose genes were heterozygous (Beadle and Emerson 1935).

not take place. In the X-chromosome of *D. melanogaster* this distance involves approximately 10 map units; interference disappears completely if the distance exceeds 45 map units. It appears that an average length of chromatin separates two crossovers; a similar picture is obtained when the distribution of chiasmata between homologous chromosomes is studied. The chiasmata, when there are more than one per bivalent, are spaced along the length of the bivalent, and in no instance do they appear to be crowded. The cytological data are consistent, therefore, in this respect with the genetical concept of interference.

CHAPTER 5

Chromosome Structure

The importance of the chromosome in heredity has made inevitable a search for detailed information regarding its structure and behavior, but quite apart from any genetical considerations the visible form and intricate maneuvers of the chromosome in cell division have presented many fascinating problems of intrinsic interest. As a result, the chromosome has unquestionably become the most thoroughly investigated structural feature of the cell. But despite the attention thus focussed on the chromosome, many questions still remain unanswered. Among these are questions of structure, physiology, and mechanics that must be answered if the functioning of the chromosome in the metabolism of the cell, as well as in its own hereditary role, is to be understood in its full significance.

It is noteworthy, therefore, that in recent years the chemist and the physicist have become intensely interested in cytological problems, and if the results already obtained represent what may be achieved through biochemical and biophysical means, it may be confidently predicted that the future stands to reveal much of importance, and perhaps, as Schrader (1948) has stated, to usher in a new era in biological thought.

The cell and the chromosome are assumed to be systems governed by the laws of physics and chemistry, and the microscopically visible structures and movements of the cellular components to be but higher-level manifestations of molecular configurations, forces, and reactions. But such considerations in nowise minimize the importance of morphological studies, for these provide the basis to which the submicroscopic details of structure and function must be referred.

In discussing the morphology of the chromosome, reference will be made principally to those findings obtained through the use of the light microscope, which, in the hands of the cytologist, is essentially a descriptive tool. Chemical structure will be discussed in a later chapter.

GENERAL MORPHOLOGY OF THE CHROMOSOME

Chromosome shape. It is usual to compare the shapes of chromosomes by their morphology as seen in somatic metaphase or anaphase. In these two stages the chromosomes have reached their maximum contraction, attaining a length that under ordinary environmental conditions remains

110

remarkably constant from cell to cell. Shape characteristics are equally
constant, and use has been made of them in identifying the various chromosomes within and between species.

The shape of a chromosome is largely determined by the type and position of its centromere. The centromere is generally not visible at somatic
metaphase as a definable entity, but its structure creates a constriction in
the chromosome. This constriction may be located at a terminal, sub-
terminal, or median position, causing the chromosome, as it proceeds poleward in anaphase, to assume, respectively, a rod, J, or V shape (Fig. 5–1).
Ring chromosomes are known in Drosophila and maize, but they constitute
an abnormal type, and presumably do not survive indefinitely in nature
because of the changes they undergo as a consequence of irregular duplication. Reasonably stable stocks of *D. melanogaster* possessing a ring X-chromosome have been maintained in the laboratory; but in maize, where the
behavior of ring chromosomes has been thoroughly studied (McClintock
1932, 1938; Schwartz 1953), the rings change size in both somatic and
germinal tissue, and also are frequently lost. When these chromosomes
carry marker genes whose loss leads to an altered phenotype, their behavior can be followed by genetic as well as by cytological means.

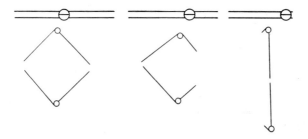

Fig. 5–1. Diagrammatic representation of V-, J-, and rod-shaped chromosomes as
they would appear in metaphase and anaphase of mitosis.

Although it is customary to consider rod-shaped chromosomes, such as
those found in some species of grasshoppers, as possessing a terminal
centromere, there is good reason for believing that most normal rod-shaped
chromosomes are two-armed, with the short arm being exceedingly minute.
This is known to be true of the X-chromosome of *D. melanogaster,* which
was long thought to be *telocentric,* i.e., possessing a terminal centromere.
Telocentric chromosomes, arising through a transverse fracturing of the
centromere, are believed to be unstable owing to the centromere's irregular
manner of division. Darlington (1939, 1940) has termed this a *misdivision*
of the centromere, a process which leads to the formation of *isochromosomes,* i.e., those in which the two arms are of equal length and genetically
homologous with each other. A case of this kind has been extensively
studied in maize (Rhoades 1936, 1940), the telocentric Chromosome 5

being present as an extra member of the regular complement. This chromosome, consisting only of the short arm, undergoes structural change and loss in somatic tissue. In germinal tissue some of the aberrant chromosomes may be recognized as isochromosomes by virtue of the fact that the arms synapse with each other. Under natural circumstances such chromosomes would tend to be eliminated because of their irregular somatic and meiotic behavior.

Cleveland (1949) has clearly shown, however, that telocentric chromosomes exist normally in certain species of holomastigote protozoa (Figs. 3–3 and 3–4). It is possible that their undoubted stability may result from an almost continuous contact with the centrioles. If these chromosomes duplicate when in contact with the centrioles, a condition not present in other organisms in which the chromosomes contact the spindle only at metaphase and anaphase, a mechanism is available that can prevent misdivision of the centromeres; for the plane of division of the centromeres would invariably follow the plane of division of the elongated centrioles.

Very small chromosomes, of the order of 1–2 microns or less in length, may appear elongated in somatic metaphases, with distinct centric constrictions, but in meiotic cells as spherical dots. It can be assumed that the contraction of such chromosomes has been so great as to cause the centromere to disappear in the body of the chromosome, thus obscuring details that would be visible in larger ones.

Not all centromeres are pin-point structures sharply localized on the chromosomes. This will be discussed in greater detail later, but in connection with chromosome shape it should be pointed out that the so-called *diffuse centromere* imposes certain characteristics on the chromosome. In insects of the order Hemiptera (Schrader 1953; Hughes-Schrader 1948; Hughes and Ris 1941), and in the plant Luzula (Malheiros, de Castro and Camara 1947; Östergren 1949; Brown 1954), the chromosomes, instead of engaging the spindle at a specific point as is usual, do so along their entire length. Each chromosome thus has a rod shape, but, rather than proceeding to the pole with its long axis oriented parallel to the long axis of the spindle, it moves in such a manner as to keep the daughter chromatids parallel with each other (Fig. 5–2). The centromeric activity, therefore, is spread over the surface of the chromosome, and does not serve to divide the chromosome into two distinguishable arms.

The localized centromere produces the *primary constriction*. In addition, *secondary constrictions* in certain chromosomes provide constant and characteristic landmarks. When occurring in the distal portion of an arm, they pinch off a portion of the end which remains attached to the main body by a tenuous thread of chromatin (Fig. 5–3). These terminal bodies have been termed *trabants* or *satellites,* and such chromosomes bearing them are often referred to as SAT-chromosomes. It should be pointed out that the apparent relationship between SAT- and satellite, while convenient, is quite for-

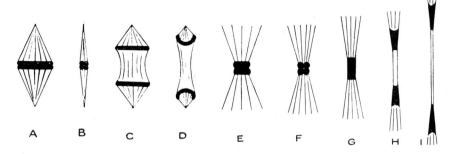

Fig. 5–2. Diagram of the coccid type of mitosis and meiosis showing the behavior of a chromosome possessing a diffuse centromere. A, somatic metaphase chromosome in lateral view with spindle fibers arising from the entire surface; B, same in end view; C, somatic anaphase showing parallel disjunction; D, later view of C; E, single meiotic metaphase chromosome that will divide equationally, lateral view; F, same in end view; G, formation of sheath which encloses and obscures chromosome and spindle fibers; H and I, early and late meiotic anaphases. It will be noticed that the sheath very greatly compresses the chromosome, making the meiotic spindle considerably narrower than the mitotic spindle. (Hughes-Schrader 1948, with the permission of the Academic Press, Inc.).

tuitous. The descriptive term was coined by Heitz because the constriction area setting the satellite off from the remainder of the chromosome was found to be without thymonucleic acid *(sine acido thymonucleinico)*. As will be discussed later, the secondary constrictions are often associated with the formation of nucleoli.

Chromosome size. The size of chromosomes, as determined from metaphase configurations, is a relatively constant feature within a species, although some size variation may be detected in the chromosomes of different

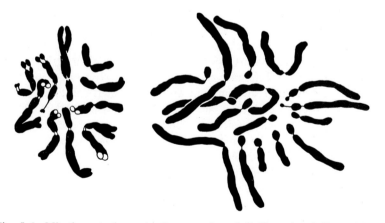

Fig. 5–3. Mitotic metaphases in the root tips of *Pollia subumbellata* (left) and *Campelia zanonia* showing a pair of satellited chromosomes in each (Darlington 1937b).

tissues even within a single organism. The diameter and length of a chromosome covary inversely, the chromosome becoming thicker the more it is contracted.

One might suspect that the length of a chromosome is principally a function of the number of genes it contains. As a first approximation, this would be a reasonable assumption, for genetic evidence from *D. melanogaster* indicates that the number of genes in each of the three major chromosomes—the X, II, and III—is roughly proportional to length. On the other hand, the Y-chromosome, which in somatic cells is larger than the X, is practically devoid of genes in the usual sense. In this particular instance it is known that the Y-chromosome is almost totally made up of a kind of chromatin (heterochromatin) that generally lacks genes, so that size does not provide a reliable guide to genic content. The X-chromosomes and the two autosomes also possess heterochromatin in the vicinity of their centromeres; but their bulk is largely made up of euchromatin, which contains the types of genes that are most readily detected and studied.

Another illustration of the fact that chromosome size is no indication of gene content is provided by comparisons that can be made between closely related genera, or even within species. In the plant family Droceraceae a size ratio of 1000:1 can be found by comparing the total volume of the chromosomes in various species complements (Behre 1929), while differences in other families of 30 or 40 to one are not uncommon, as in the monocot family Commelinaceae (Fig. 5–4) (Darlington 1929, 1937; Anderson and Sax 1936). Within the graminaceous species, *Lolium perenne,* individual plants show marked size variations (Fig. 9–6), leaving little doubt that a genetic control of chromosome size is being exercised (Thomas 1936). The differences very probably relate to the amount of non-genic material contained in the chromosome, and to the degree to which the chromosome is contracted.

Variations in size of chromosomes within a species can be readily induced by a number of environmental agents. Cells dividing at low temperatures have, in general, shorter, more compact chromosomes than at higher temperatures. Whether this difference can be related entirely to a greater degree of contraction, or to a greater amount of chromosomal substance formed, is a moot question. Colchicine, an alkaloid drug which interferes with spindle formation and cell division, also tends to shorten the chromosomes, although in this instance the greater degree of contraction apparently results from a more protracted prophase period during which contraction continues beyond the usual state reached by metaphase. Walker (1938) has shown in Tradescantia that, when colchicine prevents cell division by an inhibition of the spindle without reducing the rate of chromosome division, the chromosomes become smaller and smaller as the polyploidy of the cells increases. A depletion of available materials for the synthesis of chromatin can probably account for the reduction in size. This phenomenon is paralleled by the rather common observation that cells that regularly go through

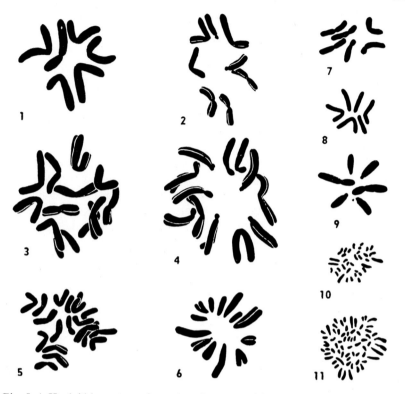

Fig. 5–4. Haploid karyotypes from the microspores of members of the family Com-melinaceae. 1, *Tradescantia humilis;* 2, *Tradescantia sp.;* 3, *T. canaliculata;* 4, *T. rosea (Cuthbertia graminea);* 5, *Setcreasea brevifolia;* 6, *T. micrantha;* 7, *Rhoeo discolor;* 8, *Spironema fragrans;* 9, *Callisia repens;* 10, *T. geniculata;* and 11, *Tradescantia sp.* (Anderson and Sax 1936).

successively rapid divisions, as, for example, those in the early blastula stage of marine invertebrates, tend to possess smaller chromosomes than cells that have long interphase periods between divisions. It would appear that the rate of cell division proceeds more rapidly than the formation of a normal amount of chromatin material by the cells' synthetic processes.

The interesting observations of Pierce (1937) on Viola may have a bear-ing on this problem. In this plant the amount of phosphate in the nutrient medium has a marked effect on the size of the chromosomes, high con-centrations giving plants with larger chromosomes than those in plants growing in low concentrations or in tap water. Since phosphate is an integral part of the nucleic acid molecule, it would seem that the amount of nucleic acid in the chromosome can be varied to give alterations in size without impairment of function, but this possibility appears less likely when it is considered that the amount of chromosomal nucleic acid is quite constant from cell to cell (see Chapter 11).

The size of chromosomes varies within wide limits (Warmke 1941).

The fungi, in general, possess minute mitotic chromosomes, the entire nucleus in the mycelial strands being seen only with difficulty. On the other hand, the meiotic chromosomes of some ascomycetous fungi such as Neurospora are of sufficient length to be usable in cytogenetic studies (Mc-Clintock 1945; Singleton 1953). Among the higher plants, the monocots generally possess larger chromosomes than the dicots, although the genus Paeonia in the Ranunculaceae provides a striking exception of large dicot chromosomes. Of the monocots, Trillium has somatic metaphase chromosomes as long as 30 microns, while those of Lilium, Allium, Tradescantia, and the whole group of spring-flowering bulbs range from 10 to 20 microns in length. In the animal kingdom, only the Orthoptera and the amphibians are characterized by their large chromosomes. Those of the human are about 4 to 6 microns in length, an average size. The mitotic chromosomes of the two most thoroughly studied organisms, Drosophila and maize, average 3.5 and 8–10 microns respectively at metaphase, but they have not been employed in cytogenetic investigations to any considerable extent, the salivary gland chromosomes of the former and the pachytene chromosomes of the latter being of more adequate size and of more clearly defined morphology.

Whether chromosomes normally exist that are too small to be visible in the light microscope must remain a moot question. Kodani and Stern (1946) have induced an "invisible" chromosome in Drosophila by x-rays. Composed of a small number of bands as seen in salivary gland nuclei (Fig. 5–5), it is completely invisible in mitotic cells. The work of Lederberg

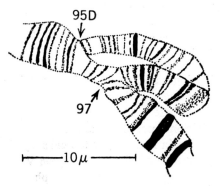

Fig. 5–5. A minute chromosome in D. *melanogaster*, which has been derived from a section of chromosome 3 including 95 D/E to 97 C1, and possessing a centromere of unknown origin. It is shown above (as the looped portion above and to the right) synapsing with the deficient chromosome 3 from which it was derived, but in mitotic cells it is invisible (Kodani and Stern 1946).

(1948, 1955) and others suggests the existence of one or more linkage groups in the colon bacterium, *E. coli,* but the chromosome situation in this organism remains to be clarified. Delbrück and Bailey (1946) and Hershey

(1946) have similarly demonstrated recombination of characters in the bacterial viruses, suggesting, by analogy with higher organisms, the presence of chromosomes or chromosome-like materials, but electron microscopy has not yet revealed whether the linked genes are carried in a submicroscopic chromosome.

Within any particular species, the size range of the chromosomes of a haploid group is not great, the smallest usually being no more than ⅓ to ½ that of the largest. There are, however, numerous exceptions to this rule. For example, Chromosome IV of *D. melonogaster,* which is many times smaller than the others, while in the plant Yucca the haploid complement consists of five large and 25 quite small chromosomes (Fig. 13–7). There is, theoretically, no minimum limit to the size a chromosome may have, provided it possesses the essential structures for reproduction and anaphase movement. There is, on the other hand, an upper limit, and this is determined by the maximum distance from the pole of a spindle to the metaphase plate. Chromosomes longer than this would suffer loss of their terminal regions by the action of the cell plate or furrow as it divides the cell into halves.

Chromosome number. The number of chromosomes in the somatic cells of a higher organism can be expressed as the *zygotic, diploid,* or *somatic number,* while those in the reduced egg or sperm are the *gametic* or *haploid number.* These have been characteristically labelled *2x* and *x* numbers, respectively. The recognition, however, of the existence of polyploid series of chromosome numbers in whole, or in parts of, organisms necessitates the establishment of a primitive, or original, number from which the polyploid cells or individuals arise. The chromosomes of this original number make up the *base number,* called *n.* Thus in the wheats is found a series of species having 14, 28, or 42 chromosomes as their somatic *(2x)* number, or 7, 14, or 21 as their gametic *(x)* number. The base number *(n)* of the entire series is 7, since the 28- and 42-chromosome wheats, which are tetraploids and hexaploids, respectively, are types derived from 7-chromosome ancestors.

Chromosome number varies widely in both plants and animals, being as low as three for a haploid number in *Crepis capillaris,* as well as in a number of Crocus species, and ranging to over several hundred in other organisms. Belar (1926) has, in fact, recorded that Aulacantha, a radiolarian, has as a diploid number approximately 1600 chromosomes. *Ascaris megalocephala* var. *univalens* exhibits a single pair of chromosomes in the cells of the germ line, but, since in the diploid soma the two chromosomes fragment into numerous small chromosomes, the single haploid chromosome has to be considered an aggregate chromosome which for reasons unknown maintains its unity under the conditions imposed by the cells of the germ line.

For rather obvious reasons, the study of chromosomal organization has been conducted on plants and animals possessing a few large chromosomes. The greater portion of the present-day information has been derived from the plants Trillium ($n = 5$) and Tradescantia ($n = 6$), together with data from a variety of liliaceous and graminaceous plants, the Orthoptera, the Amphibia (both somatic and oöcyte chromosomes), and from various members of the Diptera with their giant salivary gland chromosomes.

Individuality of the chromosomes. Boveri's classic study of the dispermic eggs of the sea urchin provided evidence that the chromosomes in a haploid complement are qualitatively different from each other insofar as their effect on development is concerned. Linkage studies of gene relationships in Drosophila and maize established this principle with certainty. The cytologist, however, in working with organisms about which little is known genetically, must depend upon morphological criteria for purposes of identification. The shape and size of chromosomes are his guideposts, and their constancy has enabled him to determine for purposes of comparison the *karyotypes* or *idiograms* (haploid complements) of many plants and animals. Such studies, in lieu of genetic data, are necessary if comparative relationships within and between species are to be made. This has been done most successfully in Drosophila and in Crepis (Compositae), but other organisms readily yield such data. Several karyotypes are illustrated in Figure 5–4, while Figure 5–6 illustrates that of the mouse. From this it is obvious that chromosome number, metaphase length, position of primary and secondary constrictions, and presence (or absence) and size of satellites provide the usual criteria for identification. The constant chromomere pattern of the pachytene chromosomes can be used for similar purposes.

DETAILED MORPHOLOGY OF THE CHROMOSOME

A precise description of the structure of the chromosome, with its topographical features changing during the course of cell division, will ultimately be given in chemical terms. A great deal has already been learned of the grosser chemical composition of the chromosome, and this knowledge will eventually be integrated with the considerable amount of morphological data accumulated over the past half-century. Not all of the topography of the chromosome is known to the extent that a complete morphological description can be given, but the salient features have been studied in sufficient detail to yield a picture of reasonable clarity.

The chromonemata. The chromosome can be visualized as being composed of a number of longitudinal subdivisions called *chromonemata* (singular *chromonema*). It is these that form the gene-bearing portion of the chromosome, although each chromonema may contain non-genic materials that serve to maintain its integrity.

One of the problems of cytology has been the determination of the degree to which the chromosome is subdivided during its various stages of mitosis and meiosis. This problem is of lesser concern to the geneticist, for to him

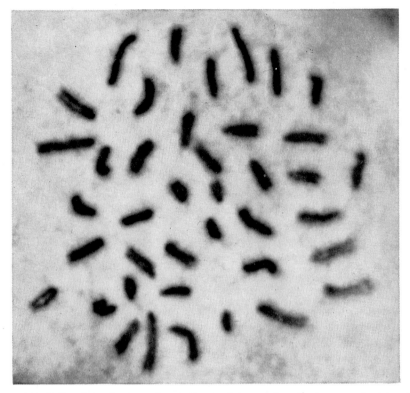

Fig. 5–6. Polar view of a metaphase plate in the somatic cell of a mouse grown in tissue culture (courtesy of Dr. T. C. Hsu).

the chromatid is the functional unit of the chromosome in cell division, in gene segregation, and in crossing over. It is quite clear, however, that the chromatids, which are readily seen in mitotic prophase chromosomes, are still further subdivided. To what degree subdivision of the chromosome extends beyond this is a matter of controversy.

A variety of techniques, including pretreatment of chromosomes before fixation with weak acids and alkalies, have been employed in an attack on this problem, and Figure 5–7 illustrates the most generally accepted view of the minimal number of strands in the anaphase chromosome of mitotic cells. The bipartite chromosome of prophase and metaphase demanded by Mendelian genetics is, therefore, still further subdivided (Huskins 1947; Kaufmann 1948). Nebel (1939, 1941) and Kuwada (1939) have considered that the anaphase chromosome is again split to give a quadripartite structure, with the prophase chromosome being octipartite. These observations are based on the unravelled free ends of treated chromosomes, and the argument has been advanced that the method of treatment is responsible for the optical images observed. An occasional quartenary split is seen in

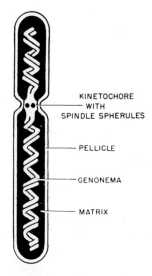

KINETOCHORE
WITH
SPINDLE SPHERULES

PELLICLE

GENONEMA

MATRIX

Fig. 5–7. Diagram of the morphology of an anaphase chromosome in mitosis with the minimal number of strands indicated. The coiling structure as indicated would lead to a relational coil between chromatids in the succeeding division. Taken from Schrader (1953, used with the permission of the Columbia University Press) the diagram was used to illustrate a metaphase chromosome, but it is believed to be more applicable to that of a chromosome in anaphase. The centromere (kinetochore with spindle spherules) may or may not be divided in anaphase. The terminology is that employed by Schrader.

coccid chromosomes at the first meiotic metaphase (Hughes-Schrader 1940). These observations seem irrefutable, since each subdivision of the chromosome forms its own separate spindle. Manton's (1945) use of ultra-violet photography supports this view, for four distinct chromonemata are revealed in the anaphase chromosomes of the fern Todea.

It should be recognized that microscopical observations often do not reveal the entire story. The lampbrush chromosomes in the diplotene stage of the frog oöcyte appear optically single, and chromatids can be demonstrated only with difficulty; yet the existence of chiasmata between the homologues is reasonable evidence of their inherent duality at a previous stage in the same division cycle (Duryee 1941, 1950). The observations of Berger (1938) and Grell (1946) are also of interest in this connection. In early prophase, the chromosomes of the epithelial cells of the hind gut of the mosquito, *Culex pipiens,* may appear single; later in the same prophase, each chromosome may be resolved into as many as 16 or 32 separate chromonemata.

Use has been made of various radiations to explore chromosome structure, the rationale being that breaks in the chromosome would reveal more clearly the number of subdivisions. Nebel (1936, 1937) has used ionizing radiations to demonstrate the multiple-stranded condition of the prophase chromosomes in the microsporocytes of Tradescantia, and both ionizing and photochemical radiations show the prophase chromosomes in pollen tubes of the same plant to be at least quadripartite (Swanson 1947). La Cour and Rutishauser (1954), Crouse (1954), and Sax and King (1955) have supported these observations, while Östergen and Wakonig (1954) have opposed this interpretation. Yet it is common knowledge that the interphase chromosomes in the microspores usually respond to x-rays as though they were undivided, while prophase chromosomes generally behave as though they were simply bipartite (Sax 1941).

To what extent these changing pictures and responses may be due to reversible chemical changes in the chromosome is at the present time difficult to say. It seems quite clear, however, that the number of subdivisions in the chromosome is no longer as important a problem from a cytogenetical point of view as it was once supposed; for, considering a microscopically visible chromosome in terms of its possible molecular framework, the subdivisions of nucleic acid or nucleoprotein chains may number in the hundreds, being expressed in visible form only when a sufficiently large number of them become visibly aggregated to produce what is called a chromonema. It is not surprising, then, that the variable conditions of treatment and fixation of chromosomes yield different pictures of internal structure. As Huskins (1947) has made clear, the question becomes one not merely of the number of chromonemata in a chromosome, but rather one of why a polytene (many-stranded) chromosome behaves as if it were double-stranded, since in cell division, crossing over, and coiling, it is the chromatid—not some smaller subdivision—that is the functional unit. Gene and chromosome reproduction may well be a more or less continuous process dependent upon available building materials within the cell, while at the same time providing a minimum number of functional chromonemata for the purposes and maneuvers of the chromosome in mitosis and meiosis.

The singleness or doubleness of the leptotene and zygotene chromosome takes on an added significance, however, since a number of theories dealing with meiotic phenomena take the singleness of the leptotene chromosome as an initial and basic premise. Darlington's (1937) *Precocity Theory of Meiosis* and White's (1954) *Theory of Crossing Over* are based on this assumption. These theories will be discussed in detail in a later chapter; but, suffice it to say, both have been weakened by a wealth of contradictory evidence. There appears to be no logical support for the suggestion that meiotic and mitotic prophase chromosomes differ in the number of chromonemata, although Smith (1942) has contended that the chromosomes of the sawfly, although at least double in all other anaphases, are single in pre-meiotic anaphase and telophase, and the synapsis begins at this early stage rather than at the following zygonema.

The matrix. The chromonemata are supposed by most cytologists to lie embedded in a mass of achromatic material called the *matrix* which is bounded at its outer limits by a *sheath* or *pellicle* (Fig. 5–7). Presumably the matrix and the sheath are composed of non-genic materials. Although the existence of such structures is vigorously denied by some (Darlington 1937; Ris 1945), reasonable photographic evidence has been obtained in such plants as maize (McClintock 1934), Trillium (Iwata 1940) and Tradescantia (Swanson 1942, 1943), and in the grasshopper Podisma (Makino 1936). Hirschler (1942) has described a technique that differentially blackens the sheath of the chromosomes of the beetle Palomena. Painter (1941) clearly indicates the presence of a matrix and a sheath in his drawings of the development of the chromosomes in the cells of the salivary glands of Drosophila. Apart from these more positive pieces of evidence, the presence of a matrix may also be inferred from the fact that the end view of a chromosome presents a hollow rather than a solid appearance, and the coils of a metaphase chromosome do not form a solid rod, as can be readily demonstrated by treating the chromosomes with dilute acids or alkalies to relax the coiled structures (Kaufmann 1948). The presence of a sheath is similarly inferred from the fact that the stained metaphase chromosome presents a smooth rather than a corrugated outline. The latter configuration would be expected if the coiled structure of the chromosomes lay bare in the nuclear medium.

The term "matrix" has been employed in a different sense by the cytochemists who have been interested in resolving the chemical composition of chromosomes (Mazia and Jaeger 1939; Ris 1942; Serra 1947). Schrader (1953), agreeing with these investigators, defines the matrix as the main mass of the chromosome, and that part that characteristically is Feulgen-positive. It can be removed by chemical or enzymatic means, leaving a Feulgen-negative strand which has been termed the "residual chromosome." This interpretation, disregarding previous usage of the term, also disregards the evidence obtained from Drosophila salivary chromosomes where the so-called matrix stains with fast green, as does the nucleolus, indicating the absence of Feulgen-positive chromatin. The confusion is further heightened by the observations in maize (McClintock 1934), which indicate that the substance of the Feulgen-negative nucleolus passes into the chromosome to surround the chromonemata at metaphase, at which stage it is Feulgen-positive.

The function and structure of the matrix is not known. Presumably it aids in keeping the chromonemata within bounds so that the maneuvers of the chromosome during cell division can take place unhindered, but whether it actually functions in contraction of the chromonemata, as Kuwada (1939) has stated, is problematical. The possibility exists that it may also serve as an insulating sheath for the genes during cell division.

The only experimental data concerned with the relationships of the matrix with other nuclear components are those of McClintock (1934) in maize microsporocytes and microspores. It is known that the nucleolus diminishes in size during prophase, and reappears in telophase. This nucleolar cycle is correlated with the behavior of the matrices of the chromosomes. McClintock suggests that in late prophase the nucleolus contributes materially to the formation of the visible matrix, while in telophase the nucleolus is formed from matrical substance under the influence of a particular chromosome region, the nucleolar-organizer. When this element is missing, the expanded matrical substance remains with the individual chromosomes, to coalesce eventually into nucleolar-like droplets at telophase. In the succeeding prophase, the droplets gradually disappear as the chromosomes become more stainable.

The structure and function of the nucleolus is still somewhat obscure (Vincent 1955). It appears to have a relatively high density, with protein forming up to 90 percent of the dry weight. Ribose nucleic acid is present in amounts up to 3.5 percent of the dry weight, and what desoxyribose nucleic acid is found in nucleoli is probably of chromosomal origin rather than being an integral part of the nucleolar structure. Electron microscopy shows that the nucleolus may possess an internal fibrous structure (Fig. 1–2), or be without structural detail. These observations, however, shed no light on its mode of formation or on the meaning of its internal organization.

Difficulty is also encountered when an assessment of nucleolar function is made. Vincent lists a number of possible functions, the most plausible of which are as follows: 1) the site of transfer of chromosomal influences to the cytoplasm, 2) the site for a limiting rate synthetic reaction necessary for the maintenance of cytoplasm synthesis, 3) a reservoir of materials produced by the chromosomes, 4) a reservoir of unused chromosomal or intranuclear products, and 5) a reservoir of energy source for nuclear activities. It has not yet been possible to make an experimental distinction between these hypotheses, but it seems likely that if the nucleolus plays any role at all in the nucleus it is probably of a non-genetic nature.

The chromomeres. Genetics informs us that the chromosome is linearly differentiated into a variety of genes qualitatively different from one another insofar as they affect developmental processes. Long before this principle was established, however, it was demonstrated that the chromosomes, particularly in the attenuated state of early meiotic prophase, were similarly differentiated into morphologically distinct regions which were *constant in size and position*. These regions, called *chromomeres,* were first described by Balbiani in 1876, and by Pfitzner in 1881. Since then they have been described in practically all organisms that have clearly differentiated zygotene or pachytene stages. Figures 3–13 and 3–14 show the chromomeric structure in the chromosomes of Trillium and maize.

The term "chromomere" covers a wide variety of morphologically recognizable structures even though there is every likelihood that they are structurally quite dissimilar. It includes a diversity of structures such as (1) the dark staining bands in the giant salivary gland chromosomes, (2) the *chromioles* and larger chromomeres of the tremendously long lampbrush chromosomes in the amphibian oöcyte, (3) the *telochromomeres* such as seen in the meiotic chromosomes of the tomato (Brown 1949), as well as (4) the usual type found, for example, in *Lilium*. The large knobs found in the pachytene chromosomes of maize are not chromomeres in the usual sense, since they are heterochromatic rather than euchromatic. Used in this varied sense, the term "chromomere" is a descriptive one, and it implies, without further qualification, the existence of reproducible structures, constant in position, that differ in size and staining capacity from other portions of the chromonemata.

Attempts to define the chromomere in structural terms have met with difficulty, and two hypotheses have been advanced. One, the "chromomere hypothesis," considers the chromomere to be structurally different from the remainder of the chromonema because of "a distinct reactivity of its own in nucleic acid synthesis" (Pontecorvo 1944). In other words, the chromomere is of greater size than adjacent portions of the chromonema because of its ability to synthesize, or accumulate on itself, greater amounts of stainable nucleic acid or nucleoprotein. This point of view has been upheld most recently by Kaufmann (1948), but it was first given its most tangible support and expression by Belling (1928), who erroneously described the ultimate chromomeres of liliaceous plants as the sites of the genes.

The other hypothesis describes the chromonema as a microscopically uniform thread, with the chromomeres being constant expressions of the coiling system (Ris 1945). This view gains its support from a number of studies which have shown that, in a variety of plants and animals having a number of types of chromomeric expression, the chromomeres can be resolved into coils, leaving only a chromonema of uniform staining capacity. Thus, stretching of the chromonema by microdissection methods transforms it from a structurally differentiated thread into one of uniform appearance, while in organisms such as Tradescantia (Swanson 1943; Taylor 1949), Allium and Aloe (Kosky 1934, 1937), Hyacinthus (Naithani 1937), Trillium (Keeffe 1948), and grasshopper (Ris 1945), the leptotene chromomeres (coils) progressively increase in size and decrease in number until they become the distinctly visible coils of later prophase.

The chromomeric structure of the salivary gland and lampbrush chromosomes, which are considerably longer than ordinary meiotic prophase chromosomes, may or may not be open to the same interpretation. Although Ris (1945; Ris and Crouse 1946) believes the heavy bands of the salivary gland chromosomes to be coiled structures, there is observational evidence for the contention that stretching of the chromosomes does not disrupt the chromomeric pattern as would be expected if they represented coils (Hinton 1946; D'Angelo 1946, 1950). The same holds true for the chromomeres in the lampbrush chromosomes of the frog oöcyte according to Duryee (1941, 1950). Since these chromosomes are fully extended, although still retaining considerable elasticity, it would appear that their chromomeres are not comparable to those of ordinary meiotic chromosomes which, regardless of size, seem to be structural features reflecting a differential pattern of coiling along the chromonemata. The more recent data of Gall (1956) suggest, however, that Ris' interpretation may be applied to lampbrush chromomeres as well as to those of other meiotic types.

There is little support for the belief, put forth by Belling (1928), that the meiotic chromomeres are genic loci. For one thing, they are much too large, and for another, it has been shown that genes may be located in the lightly staining spaces between chromomeres (McClintock 1944). It will be demonstrated later, however, that the chromomeres (bands) of the salivary chromosomes are associated with certain genes, although it is obviously difficult to determine with certainty that the genes lie in the band or the inter-band regions.

The centromere. The centromere, forming the primary constriction of metaphase chromosomes, is an indispensable portion of the chromosome. Chromosomes lacking a centromere fail to orient themselves properly on the metaphase plate, lag at anaphase, and eventually are eliminated. Occupying a constant position relative to the ends of chromosomes, the centromeres are responsible for the shapes of chromosomes as they move poleward in anaphase. Their function in terms of movement is therefore definite, and in addition they also appear to be at least partially responsible for the formation of the chromosomal fibers in the spindle. Carlson's (1938) demonstration of the poleward movement of acentric (lacking a centromere) fragments in orthopteran neuroblast cells does not invalidate this hypothesis, for such movement can be accounted for on the basis of flow currents in the cytoplasm moving from the equatorial regions to the poles.

The centromere may, under certain conditions, relinquish its role to secondary centers of movement. But these are exceptional cases. In maize, the phenomenon is governed by the presence of an abnormal Chromosome 10 which has an extra piece of chromatin attached to the distal end of the long arm (Rhoades and Vilkomerson 1942; Rhoades 1942, 1952). Occurring only in meiotic cells, and more frequently when the abnormal Chromosome 10 is in a homozygous condition, anaphase movement takes place somewhat prematurely, as judged from the degree of chromosome contraction, with the distal ends of the chromosomes moving poleward instead of the centric regions (Fig. 5–8). A similar case has been reported in inbred strains of Secale (Fig. 5–9), where these new centers of movement are clearly connected to the poles by spindle fibers (Praaken and Muntzing 1942; Östergren and Praaken 1946). It would appear that the shifting of function takes place by a flow of material to new centers of movement, although this remains to be proved.

Fig. 5–8. Metaphase in a microsporocyte of maize showing the precocious anaphase movement of secondary centric (neo-centric) regions. The undivided normal centromeres, represented as open-circles in some chromosomes, still remain at the equatorial plate (Rhoades and Vilkomerson 1952).

The centromere is believed to become functionally divided in the logitudinal axis of the chromosome at the beginning of anaphase, and its movement poleward is governed by its attachment to the spindle. Division may also occur, infrequently, at right angles to the longitudinal axis, giving two fragment centromeres to which are attached the two chromatids of each arm (Fig. 5–10). This structure, being composed of two arms of like genetic nature, has been termed an *isochromosome* by Darlington (1939). McClintock (1932) has experimentally demonstrated that such breakage may be induced by x-rays, with each fragment portion of the centromere remaining functional. These data suggest that the centromere is a compound structure whose parts ordinarily are coordinated in division and movement.

The centromere does not usually occupy a terminal position. It was formerly thought that some orthopteran chromosomes were truly telocentric, but it has been shown by White (1935) that a very short arm is invariably present in such chromosomes. Even the tiny IV chromosome of *D. melanogaster* is now known to be two-armed (Panshin and Khvostova 1938; Griffen and Stone 1940). The belief has, therefore, been expressed by many that telocentric chromosomes are unstable, as Rhoades (1940) has found in maize, but an apparently unequivocal case of telocentric chromosomes has been found in certain species of Protozoa that inhabit the digestive tract of wood-eating temites (Cleveland 1949). These may represent special cases, however, for the centromeres are in almost constant association with the long centrioles. As pointed out earlier, this feature may serve to impose upon the centromeres a regularity of division which, determined or guided by the division of the centriole, would permit its survival.

The structure of the centromere is difficult to demonstrate, and various interpretations have been made (Fig. 5–11). In somatic chromosomes it appears simply as a non-staining constriction with no morphological evidence of structure. In the pachytene chromosomes of maize it takes the form of a distinct ovoid body, non-stainable and structureless, and somewhat larger in diameter than the remainder of the chromosome (McClintock 1933). In plants with large chromosomes such as Tradescantia the

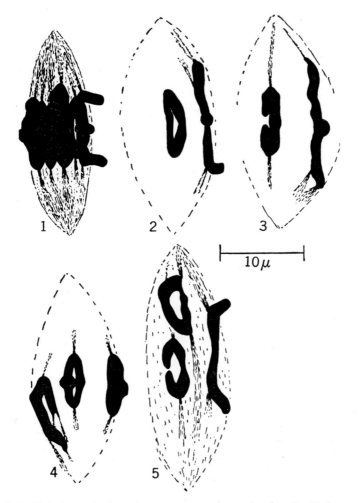

Fig. 5–9. Metaphases in the microsporocytes of rye showing the T-chromosomes which produce spindle fibers from the ends of the chromosomes. The centromeres are medianly located (Östergren and Prakken 1946).

centromere may be seen at meiotic metaphase or early anaphase as a tiny, stainable granule connected to the remainder of the chromosome by thinly stretched threads, the stretching due possibly to the resistance of the body of the chromosome to the pull of the centromere. The granule is Feulgen-positive, and it appears not to be surrounded by a *commisural cup* such as Schrader (1936, 1939) has described in the amphibian Amphiuma. The granule, when visible, is less than 0.5 microns in diameter, and it is this that appears to contact the spindle elements to function as an organ of movement.

Centromeres in the pachytene chromosomes of Secale and Agapanthus

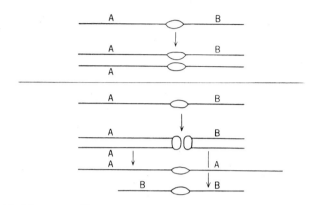

Fig. 5–10. Diagram to illustrate misdivision of the centromere and the origin of isochromosomes. Above, normal plane of division in the longitudinal axis of the chromosome; below, transverse division of the centromere, giving rise to isochromosomes AA and BB (after Darlington 1939).

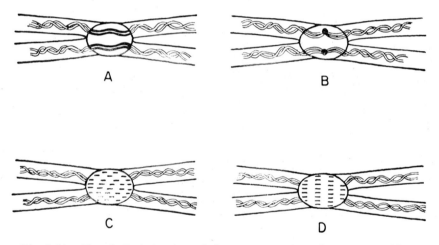

Fig. 5–11. Hypothetical structure of the centromere in a chromosome with two pairs of chromonemata. The centromere is pictured as an ellipsoidal structure with the essential organ of movement in the form of A, a regionally modified portion of the chromonemata; B, a spindle spherule connected to the chromonemata; C, a number of oriented micelles; and D, a number of oriented micelles arranged in such a way as to facilitate misdivision in a transverse instead of a longitudinal plane (Schrader 1953, after various authors and used with the permission of the Columbia University Press).

show three distinct zones of differentiation (Fig. 5–12) (Lima-de-Faria 1949a, b, 1954). On either side of the central region are slender fibrillae which appear to be similar to those separating ordinary chromomeres. Two or three pairs of granules make up a chromomeric zone within the centromere, and these are separated from each other by other fibrillae which makes up the third distinct region. The paired granules, called a "reverse repeat" by Lima-de-Faria, indicate a compound structure in the centromere, a conclusion supported by the fact that the centromere can be fractured transversely, yet with each half retaining the capacity for initiating anaphase movement. The granules, which may vary in size, appear to the observer to be no different from other chromomeres, but their unique properties indicate that they must possess a different chemical constitution. Other centromeres, such as that found in Tradescantia, seem to reveal but a single granule (Fig. 5–12).

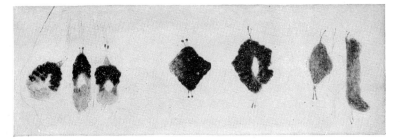

Fig. 5–12. Chromosomes showing the structure of the centromere. Above, chromosomes of *Agapanthus umbellatus* at pachynema, midprophase II and late prophase of mitosis (in descending order). The centrally located centromere at pachynema shows two granules with fine fibrils between them and extending on either side to the remainder of the chromonemata; chromomere size shows a gradient in size from centromere to end. Below, metaphase I bivalents of Tradescantia showing the spindle spherule extending beyond the body of the chromosomes (Agapanthus from Lima-de-Faria 1954; Tradescantia from Schrader 1939).

It is of some interest that the centromere has been considered to be homologous with the centriole on structural as well as on theoretical grounds (Schrader 1936; Darlington 1936). This relationship, originally postulated on the similarities of staining and behavior during the mitotic cycle, has been greatly strengthened by observations of the Pollisters (Pollister 1939; Pollister and Pollister 1943). A study of meiosis in the oligopyrene sperm (abnormally low in chromatin content) of *Vivipara malleatus,* a prosobranchiate snail, reveals that the low chromatin content results from the disintegration of a large number of the chromosomes. The centromeres of these chromosomes persist, however, and finally pass into the cytoplasm where they behave as extra centrioles, each functioning as a blepharoplast to produce a single axial filament.

In addition to the sharply localized type of centromere described above, there exists a type, characteristic of the hemipteran and heteropteran insects, described by Schrader (1935, 1953) as a diffuse centromere. Although its structural nature is unknown, anaphase movement is such as to imply that the entire poleward surface of the chromosome possesses a centromeric function, causing the chromosomes to move poleward in parallel fashion (Fig. 5–2). The structure of such a centromere is difficult to imagine; the correctness of the diffuse interpretation, however, is indicated not only by the multiplicity of chromosomal fibers which connect each chromosome to the poles but by the fact that when the chromosomes are fragmented by x-rays, each fragment, regardless of size, divides and passes to the poles at anaphase with regularity, and through many cell cycles (Hughes-Schrader and Ris 1941; Ris 1942; Hughes-Schrader 1948).

A somewhat similar centromeric behavior has been described in the scorpion, *Tityus bahiensis,* by Piza (1939), who has considered each chromosome to have a terminal centromere at both ends. There is reason for believing, in this organism, that a polycentric rather than a dicentric or diffuse condition is present, because related species have many small chromosomes rather than a few large ones. Also, breakage of the chromosomes by x-rays produces fragments that are but smaller editions of the larger ones, whereas rod-shaped fragments would be found if two terminal centromeres were present (Rhoades and Kerr 1949). The chromosomes of Tityus are, therefore, more comparable to the polycentric type found in the germ line of *Ascaris megalocephala* than they are to the diffuse hemipteran centromere.

Non-localized centromeres have also been found in the wood rush *Luzula purpurea,* a member of the family Juncaceae (Malheiros, de Castro, and Camara 1947; Östergren 1949; Brown 1954), and in certain fungi, algae, and mosses (Vaarama 1954). There is no certainty as to the type of centromere, whether polycentric or diffuse, but a polycentric type is considered most likely to be the case by Rhoades and Kerr. Östergren, however, in a theoretical discussion of diffuse centromeres in general, visualizes such a centromere as a strip of material, possessing motile properties, and running lengthwise of the chromosome. Even when in a coiled condition, as metaphase chromosomes undoubtedly are, this motile strip always faces the poles and gives rise to, or connects with, the chromosomal fibers. A mechanism or a structure that would permit such maneuvering is difficult to imagine.

Vaarama has considered that the diffuse centromere represents a primitive type from which the localized form arose. On the basis of simple mechanics such a postulate is perhaps logical, since it represents an example of cellular economy in that a specialized function is performed by a specialized structure. However, the sporadic occurrence of diffuse centromeres in widely separated species types, and the further fact that hemipteran insects and such forms as Luzula obviously stem from more primitive forms with localized centromeres, suggests that we are dealing with a derived rather than a primitive structure. This concept is further supported by the observation that in such species as maize and rye other regions of the chromosomes—notably the knobs in maize and the ends of rye chromosomes—may secondarily acquire the property of a typical centromere, thus suggesting that other regions are capable of evolving in this direction. If such a property were acquired by all chromomeres, a diffuse centromere could come into existence. Schrader (1947) postulates that there may be transition types that bridge the gap between the diffuse and the localized centromere; but these, if they exist, have not been identified with certainty, unless the situation in maize and rye represents such a condition.

The polycentric type of chromosome found in *Ascaris megalocephala* is unique in that it is restricted to those cells that ultimately form the germ line. In variety *univalens*, the two large chromosomes were shown by Boveri to undergo diminution in the somatic cells, the heavily staining ends being lost. Accompanying chromatin diminution is the fragmentation of the central portion of the two large chromosomes into many smaller chromosomes which retain their individuality throughout the remainder of the somatic divisions. Retention of the polycentric chromosomes in the germ line must obviously be determined by the cytoplasmic environment in which they lie. It would appear that the *Tityus bahiensis* chromosomes, if correctly interpreted as polycentric, are stabilized in both germinal and somatic tissues.

Secondary constrictions. The secondary constrictions seen in somatic metaphase chromosomes generally arise as the result of nucleolar formation (Heitz 1931). The nucleolus diminishes in volume during prophase, finally to be detached from the chromosome and disappear in the cytoplasm. Its location on the chromosome is marked by the space it formerly occupied remaining in an uncondensed or lightly staining state, the satellite being merely that portion of the chromosome distal to the constriction. The nucleolus will again form at the identical area during the telophase reorganization of the nucleus. The constrictions, or the adjacent parts, are therefore special regions which have assumed a particular function.

The structure of this region apparently differs from one organism to another. Best seen in pachytene stages, when the nucleolus is large, the nucleolar-organizing regions of maize (Fig. 3–14), *Medeola virginiana* (Stewart and Bamford 1942), and tomato (Fig. 5–13) are each associated with a large heteropycnotic region. The same chromosomes at somatic metaphase would show only a constriction, the nucleolar organizer being merged indistinguishably with the remainder of the chromosome. In Polygonatum (Therman-Suomaleinen 1949), as well as in a num-

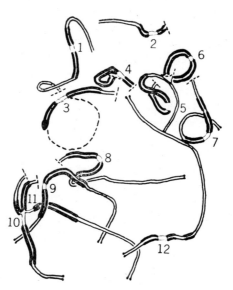

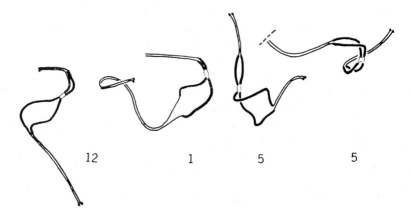

Fig. 5–13. Meiotic prophase chromosomes of the tomato. Above, a pachytene nucleus showing the differentiation of the chromosomes into heavily and lightly stained regions. Terminal chromomeres are evident in some of the chromosomes; the dotted line terminating some of the chromosomes indicates that the particular one could not be followed throughout its entire length. The nucleolus is associated with the short arm of chromosome 3, but it is uncertain what part of the short arm is the nucleolar organizer. Below, four meiotic chromosome pairs in late zygonema showing that the centromeres and lightly staining regions pair first, with the heavily staining regions becoming paired by pachynema, as seen above (Brown 1949).

ber of other organisms (Kaufmann 1948), no such deeply staining knobs are present, and it is uncertain whether the nucleoli are formed by the chromonematic region within the constriction, or by adjacent parts.

In maize, McClintock has definitely shown that the heteropycnotic knob is the nucleolar organizer. When the knob was broken into two unequal halves by x-rays, both portions were shown to be capable of forming nuclei, the smaller portion forming the larger of the nucleoli. However, when a microspore nucleus contained but one of the fragmented portions, a full-sized nucleolus developed, indicating that, while one organizer was able to assemble all of the nucleolar material into a single structure, two organizers within the same nucleus competed for the available material. The different sizes of the nucleoli revealed that the intact organizer was a compound structure whose parts had differential rates of organizing reaction. When no organizer was present, each chromosome appeared to form nucleolar-like droplets from the matrical substance.

That there is a competition by nucleolar organizers for available materials has been beautifully demonstrated by Navashin (1934). When certain species of Crepis are crossed with each other, the satellites of one of the parents frequently disappear in the F_1 hybrid. The competitive activity of the nucleolar organizers of the various species apparently differs in strength, with the stronger organizer taking over the entire nucleolar activity of the cell. The chromosome containing the non-functional element consequently develops no constriction in the absence of a nucleolus, and its metaphase morphology is changed. *C. capillaris,* for example, possesses a strong organizer, and in F_1 species hybrids it suppresses the activity of the organizers of *alpina, neglecta, tectorum,* and *dioscorides.* The *capillaris* organizer, in turn, is suppressed by that of *parviflora,* but, having an organizer of the same strength as that of *setosa,* both form nucleoli of reduced size when both are in the same cell. It is possible by this method to show a nicely graded series of organizer strengths, and also that the activity of a non-functional organizer can be restored by transferring it to a more compatible environment.

The constricted area has been frequently depicted as traversed by a thin chromatin thread. It now appears from the studies of Stewart and Bamford (1943) that the so-called "constriction" is an illusion, at least in some organisms, this region having a diameter as great as the remainder of the chromosome. Similar observations have been made in Polygonatum (Therman-Suomaleinen 1949). It is also quite clear that these are areas of weakness wherever they occur. Considerable bending and some breakage has been found at the secondary constrictions in Polygonatum, together with a wide variance in the length of the area. Because of these characteristics, it has been assumed by Therman-Suomaleinen, as well as by Resende (1940), that the constrictions possess a spiral structure similar to that of the remainder of the chromosome, but that the chromatin contained therein exhibits a negative heteropycnosis.

In addition to those constrictions associated with the formation of nucleoli, others that have been observed in a variety of plants and animals represent regions of differential spiralization, nucleic acid content, or weakness (Kaufmann 1948). The one found in the left arm of Chromosome 2 of *D. melanogaster* has been extensively studied (Kaufmann 1934; Hinton 1942), and it appears to be an area bridged by a very thin and stretchable chromatin strand. At prophase, the two parts of the chromosome may be separated by the entire width of the nucleus; yet at metaphase the gap is relatively short. Whether the shortening of the attenuated thread takes place through spiralization, or by some other method of contraction, is not known.

Other secondary constrictions can be induced by low temperatures. Darlington and La Cour (1938, 1940), who first demonstrated the phenomenon in Trillium, postulated that these regions were sites of heterochromatin, which under these conditions could not synthesize nucleic acid as efficiently as could adjacent euchromatin. The differential segments consequently would appear negatively heteropycnotic, i.e., lightly staining regions, and create gaps that appear as constrictions. This topic will be discussed more fully in a later section of this chapter.

The telomere. The chromosome terminates at either end in a structure called the *telomere,* a term coined by Muller (1938) to indicate the uniqueness of this portion of the chromosome. This uniqueness does not lie in any particular visibly evident morphological characteristic, because the ends of chromosomes vary widely in appearance. The meiotic chromosomes of the tomato (Fig. 5–13), for example, are all terminated by a distinct telomere [*telochromomere* according to Brown's (1949) terminology], whereas those of rye, Agapanthus, or sorghum trail off into ghostlike ends (Fig. 5–12). The somatic chromosomes of all four species terminate similarly in that they do not exhibit any special structural features.

The uniqueness of the telomere lies, rather, in its characteristic behavior. The intact end of a chromosome does not enter into permanent association with other parts of the chromosome, and the loss of the telomere imparts an instability to the chromosome to which it was once attached. This instability results from the fact that the freshly broken end of a chromosome is in an unsaturated state, i.e., it will unite with other similarly broken ends of other chromosomes, or, if the chromosome is longitudinally double, the two broken ends of the chromosomes will unite with each other. Broken ends of chromosomes can sometimes "heal" to assume the behavior and structure of a telomere, but all experimental evidence on broken chromosomes indicates that this phenomenon is relatively rare.

Other types of behavior also characterize the telomeres. Through their attraction to the nuclear membrane in the vicinity of the centrosome, they lead to a pronounced polarization of chromosomes (bouquet stage) in meiotic prophase (Hughes-Schrader 1943). During the same division stage in the fly Habropogon, there appears to be an attraction between the centromeres and the telomeres (Ribbands 1941). In Secale, the telomeres seem to be able to take over the function of centromeres. Telomeres have also been observed to exhibit both homologous and non-homologous pairing. The "touch-and-go" pairing described by Schrader (1940) is of a homologous type, while the terminal adhesion of the telomeres of Drosophila salivary gland chromosomes is apparently of a non-homologous type although at the same time non-random (Hinton 1946; Warters and Griffen 1950). What these various observations mean in terms of specificities and homologies of structures is difficult to say; it only serves to emphasize the uniqueness of the telomere as a structural portion of the chromosome.

The point has been made that telomeres do not unite permanently with other telomeres, or with other parts of the chromosome. One exception, if it be that, exists. In the germ line of the roundworm Ascaris, the compound chromosomes are made up of many smaller chromosomes united end to end (telomere to telomere?). Only in the somatic cells do these compound structures break up into their component parts.

EUCHROMATIN AND HETEROCHROMATIN

Frequent mention has been made of the fact that chromosomes are made up of two kinds of chromatin: *euchromatin* and *heterochromatin* (Figs. 2–14, 5–13). The former contains the type of gene that mendelizes, while the latter is generally considered to be devoid of genes in the usual sense.

The distinction between the two kinds of chromatin was first made on a cytological basis. In interphase or prophase nuclei, certain chromosomes, or parts of chromosomes, stain darkly while other chromosomes in the same cell stain lightly or not at all. Heitz (1928, 1929) first described this prococious chromatin in the liverworts and coined the word *heterochromatin* to replace the earlier term *prochromosome*. When only a portion of the chromosome is differentially condensed, the involved portions are usually located distally or immediately adjacent to the centromere. In Drosera chromosomes, the tips are heterochromatic, while in Drosophila, *Vicia faba,* Oenothera, and tomato it is the centric regions. When entire chromosomes are heterochromatic, these are usually those relating to sex, such as the X-chromosomes of many insects and the Y-chromosomes of such forms as *D. melanogaster,* a fact that led early investigators to the belief that heterochromatin was concerned with sex (Heitz 1928). At metaphase such chromosomes, or chromosome parts, are generally indistinguishable from euchromatin, although in some organisms, such as the grasshopper Mecostethus, the X-chromosome may exhibit a negative heteropycnosis, being more lightly stained than the autosomes (White 1936). Chemically, the difference between euchromatin and heterochromatin appears to be quantitative rather than qualitative, the latter being more or less continuously and heavily "coated" with nucleic acid while the former varies with the cell cycle. Coleman (1943) has demonstrated that, insofar as the orthopteran X-chromosome is concerned, the differential condensation results from a tightly coiled state of the chromonemata at a time when the autosomes are in a relatively uncoiled condition. Ris (1945) has accepted and extended this concept to include all differentially stained chromatin segments. The difference, therefore, between the two types can be attributed to a differential coiling reaction rather than to differential amounts of nucleic acid.

The earlier concept of heterochromatin being genetically inert has been shown to be an over-simplification of the problem. Certainly the X-chromosome of the orthopteran cannot be considered to be devoid of genetic influence, and even the Y-chromosome of *D. melanogaster,* although genetically inert except for some allele of the gene *bobbed* which it carries, is required by the male for fertility while in females it tends to stabilize certain mutable genes (Schultz 1947). The concept of inertness has been gradually replaced by others that consider the heterochromatin to be involved either in chromosome metabolism, in the modification of processes governed by euchromatic genes (Mather 1944; Pontecorvo 1944), in nucleic acid synthesis, or in the transfer of energy or substances at the nucleolar or nuclear membranes (Vanderlyn 1949; Hannah 1951). Since this problem is intimately involved in the relationships between the gene and the chromosome, further discussion will be deferred to a later chapter.

Morphologically, heterochromatin can be shown to differ from euchromatin under a variety of natural and experimental conditions. Somatic interphase nuclei display the *alpha* heterochromatin of Heitz. In the somatic metaphase chromosomes of *D. melanogaster* no ready distinction is possible, but in the salivary gland nuclei, the proximal third of the X, the entire Y, and the centric regions of the II and III chromosomes, as judged by somatic lengths, are reduced to an amalgamated mass, the *chromocenter,* which can be resolved in a comparatively few, faintly staining bands (the *beta* heterochromatin of Heitz). A third type of heterochromatin is that supposedly found in the euchromatin of *D. melanogaster* chromosomes, where it exists as single bands or as blocks of material. It is not cytologically distinguishable from euchromatin, but its presence is inferred from the fact that it behaves like *beta* heterochromatin in showing a high breakability when exposed to x-rays, a stickiness with known heterochromatic regions, and a capacity to impart a variability of phenotypic expression to euchromatic genes (Hannah 1951).

The variability of heterochromatin stainability in the salivary gland chromosomes has been shown to be a function of its position in the chromosome as well as of the general nuclear environment (Schultz 1941). In *D. palidipennis,* some of the bands in the salivary gland chromosomes appear euchromatic in some cells, heterochromatic in others (Dobzhansky 1944). Geitler (1939), too, has shown that the X-chromosome of the water strider, Gerris, may be either euchromatic or heterochromatic in somatic cells. A similar situation has been found for entire haploid sets of chromosomes (Schrader 1929; Hughes-Schrader 1935).

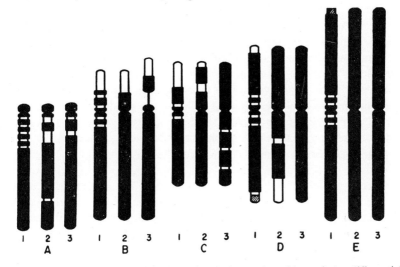

Fig. 5–14. Schematic representation of the size and position of the differentially staining regions (heterochromatin) in the five haploid somatic chromosomes of Trillium when cell division takes place at low temperatures. 1, *T. erectum;* 2, *T. grandiflorum;* 3, *T. undulatum.* Letters indicate the different chromosomes of the haploid set. Cross-hatched regions appear only rarely even under conditions of low temperature (Wilson and Boothroyd 1941).

It would appear, therefore, that heterochromatin is considerably more variable in its cytological expression than is euchromatin. This is borne out by experimental studies. Prolonged cold treatments (0° C.) of somatic cells have revealed in Trillium heterochromatic segments that normally could not be detected (Fig. 5–14) (Darlington and La Cour 1938, 1940; Callan 1942; Wilson and Boothroyd 1941, 1944). Darlington and La Cour have explained this phenomenon by assuming that at low temperatures the amount of nucleic acid synthesized is at a minimum and that, in competing for it, euchromatin is more successful, leaving the heterochromatin undercharged. Wilson and Boothroyd, however, have considered that the differential expression, which is not constant from cell to cell, is a function of the degree of coiling, the heterochromatin existing in a somewhat less contracted state than the euchromatin. Whether the differential contraction is related to a change in nucleic acid relationships cannot readily be determined, but Levan (1946) has shown that the heterochromatin in the metaphase and anaphase chromosomes of Allium can be detected by differential staining, the technique employing prefixation treatments of root tips with 0.005 mercuric nitrate. This suggests a differential chemical makeup between heterochromatin and euchromatin.

SPECIAL TYPES OF CHROMOSOMES

With but few exceptions, the preceding discussion has been concerned with the morphology of the type of chromosome usually seen in mitotic or meiotic cells. There exist, however, other forms of these same chromosomes as well as supplementary chromosomes of unknown origin. Of these, the compound chromosomes found in the germ line of Ascaris have already been mentioned, and no further discussion is warranted until the subject of chromatin elimination is taken up in a later chapter. The lampbrush chromosomes of the vertebrate oöcyte, the giant chromosomes of the salivary gland cells of the Diptera, and the accessory chromosomes found in both the plant and animal kingdom merit detailed examination.

Lampbrush chromosomes. Throughout the vertebrate group of animals, the somatic chromosomes present the usual cytological picture when dividing cells are examined [see Matthey (1950) for an extensive review]. But within the developing oöcytes of those vertebrates that possess a yolky egg, and during the diplotene stage of meiosis, the same chromosomes undergo a remarkable change characterized by an enormous increase in length and the appearance of radiating hairs or side loops which appear to originate from the chromomeres (Figs. 5–15 and 5–16). Chromosomes of a similar nature may be found in the spermatocytes of some invertebrates (Ris 1945), but they have been best studied in the shark Pristiurus, in the birds, and in amphibians (Duryee 1941, 1950; Gall 1952, 1954, 1956; Alfert 1954). In the frog *Rana temporaria,* for example, and at a stage in enlargement when the egg is approximately half-size, the 13 pairs of chromosomes may be individually identified, each pair exhibiting a relatively constant number of chiasmata, a chromomeric pattern that is characteristic but not necessarily constant, and a more or less constant length. In this particular species, the chromosome pairs may remain in synaptic union for a period of a year or more, attaining at the time of greatest extension the enormous length of 800 to 1000 microns per chromosome. In the newt, *Triturus viridescens,* the 11 chromosome pairs range from 350 to 800 μ in length, with a total length of 5900 μ at the period of greatest extension (Gall 1954). They become, therefore, nearly three times longer than the longest dipteran salivary gland chromosomes.

According to Duryee, each chromosome resembles a single plastic cylinder in which, at specific loci, are embedded chromatic granules. In a bivalent these granules, some 150 to 200 in number, are generally paired, although not invariably so. Two sizes of granules are found: smaller "chromioles," and larger "chromomeres," and these latter are often ellipsoidal in appearance as though squeezed inside a matrix. It is from the latter that the lateral loops arise to give the characteristic lampbrush appearance.

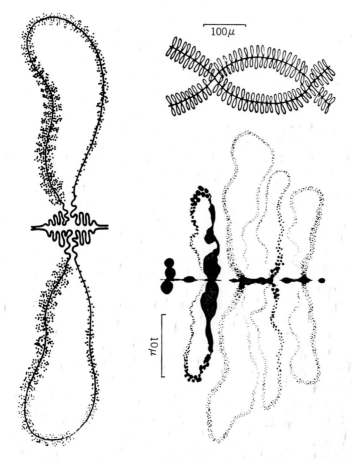

Fig. 5–15. Diagrammatic representation of the lampbrush chromosomes of the newt, *Triturus viridescens*. Top right, a bivalent with homologous chromosomes joined by two chiasmata, and showing the paired arrangement of loops. Bottom right, semi-diagrammatic view of a section of a single chromosome showing the variation which exists in loop and chromomere morphology. It will be noticed that the loop is always heavier in structure one side than on the other. Left, postulated structure of a chromomere and its attached loops (Gall 1956).

A study of the developing oöcyte indicates that the loops grow in number and size up to a maximum in diplotene, and then decrease and disappear as meiosis proceeds toward metaphase. One to nine loops may arise from a single chromomere, and, although the length varies among the loops, those of the frog average 9.5 microns while those of the newt are longer, some being 200 μ long. A decrease in number of loops occurs by disintegration rather than by reabsorption back into the chromomere. On this basis, the loops are considered to be chromatin material synthesized by the chromomeres for eventual utilization by the developing oöcyte, and

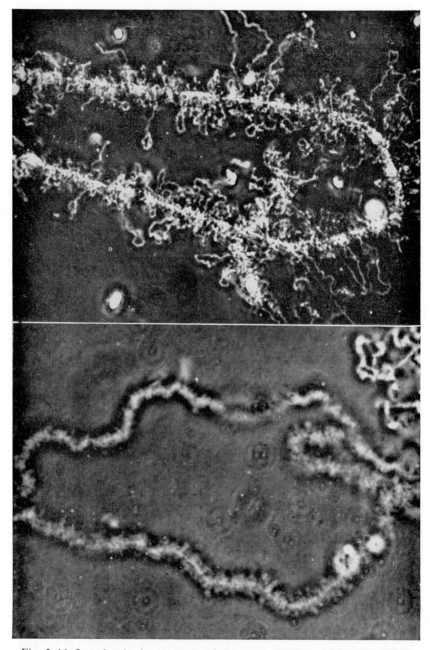

Fig. 5–16. Lampbrush chromosomes of the newt, *Triturus viridescens*. Top left, phase contrast photograph of a portion (ca. 110 microns) of a single bivalent showing the multiplicity of loops and a chiasma located at the right center of the lower strand; bottom left, phase contrast photograph of a single pair of giant loops, each about 70 microns long and extending from the main axis of the chromosome (one

not an integral portion of the chromonemata extended in the form of a major coil as proposed by Ris (1945). Duryee's hypothesis of lateral synthesis is supported by the fact that stretching of the chromosomes by micromanipulation, or contraction by calcium ions, does not cause the loops to disappear or to be displaced, and that dissolution of the loops by a variety of substances into chromatic granules does not affect the integrity of the chromonemata. Gall (1956), however, shows quite conclusively through electron microscopy that the loops are a part of the chromonemata, and that their apparent disappearance is due to the fact that prior to contraction they shed their coating of nucleic acid. The length of a single chromosome, counting the loops, must consequently be of the order of millimeters rather than of microns.

The lampbrush chromosomes of amphibian oöcytes appear each to consist of but a single chromonema, although a basic duality of structure is suggested by the fact that chiasmata are present. Gall (1954), however, suggests a system whereby chiasmata could arise between unsplit homologues, and thus be in keeping with the observational evidence, but his electron studies clearly indicate that the chromosomes are split (Gall 1956).

The chromosomes possess a remarkable elasticity. In the living state they may be stretched by microneedles to many times their original length before breaking; on release from stretching, they once again assume their normal size without apparent distortion. In one instance a single chromo-

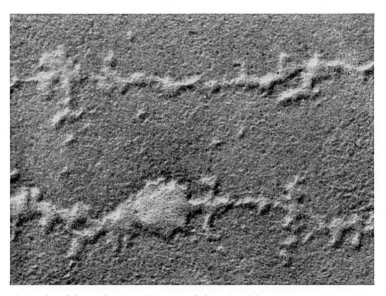

loop is to the right and somewhat out of focus); right, electron micrograph of a portion of a loop after digestion with pepsin and shadowed with chromium (1 cm ca. 0.3 microns) (Gall 1956).

some was stretched 125 times to over 100 percent of its relaxed length without breakage or alteration of structure. The chromosomes may also be contracted to one-fifth their normal length by chemical means, yet no visible coils are to be observed to account for their extensibility or contractility. During these manipulations the chiasmata do not shift their position along the chromosomes nor do the chromomeres lose their identity, although they may merge on contraction. The elastic or contractile property appears, therefore, to reside in the inter-chromomeric portions of the chromosome, a feature also found in the salivary gland chromosomes.

The lateral loops extending from the chromomeres are more fragile, breaking when stretched more than 50 percent of their length. Under certain conditions, however, the chromomeres open up, revealing that the loops are an integral part of the chromonemata (Gall 1956). Figure 5–15 gives Gall's interpretation of chromomeric structure in the newt.

Nucleoli formation in lampbrush chromosomes follows an unusual pattern. As many as a thousand nucleoli may be found floating free in the nucleoplasm. As in most organisms, the nucleoli appear to arise from specific loci, but unlike the usual chromosome, or chromosome pair, which produces a single nucleolus during its mitotic or meiotic cycle, the amphibian nucleolar chromosome gives rise to a succession of nucleoli which, acording to Duryee, become detached, migrate to the nuclear membrane, and finally at the time of ovulation pass into the cytoplasm. Others have questioned the passage of these bodies through the nuclear membrane. The significance of this phenomenon is not understood, and the homology of these nucleoli with the ordinary somatic or meiotic type is not clear; but, since the nucleoli are rich in proteins and ribose nucleic acid, their addition to the cytoplasm during oögenesis could provide a source of available synthetic materials for growth.

Salivary gland chromosomes. Balbiani is generally credited with the discovery, in 1881, of the giant chromosomes in the salivary gland cells of dipteran species. Their cytogenetic importance, however, was not realized until many years later when Kostoff (1930) pointed out the similarities between their banded structure and the linearly arranged genes on the chromosome, and Painter (1933, 1934) and Heitz and Bauer (1933) established the fact that each of the visible chromosomes actually consisted of a pair of homologous chromosomes intimately synapsed. Since then the use of these giant chromosomes has enabled Drosophila cytogeneticists to approach a degree of precision scarcely considered possible when only the usual mitotic and meiotic chromosomes were available for study.

The salivary gland chromosomes are the largest chromosomes known that are readily available for cytogenetical study. In *D. melanogaster* they are, in the late larval (3d instar) stages, approximately 100 times the length of the somatic metaphase chromosomes, which total about 7.5

microns (Fig. 5–17). When prepared for study and stretched by the smear technique commonly used, these chromosomes in aggregate reach a length of 1180 microns (Bridges 1938). Subsequent revisions place the total length closer to 2000 microns (Bridges 1942). In Chironomus, another dipteran genus, a pair of synapsed chromosomes is 20 microns in diameter and 270 microns in length (Beermann 1952). Those of a related genus, Rhyncosciara, are even larger (Pavan and Breuer 1952).

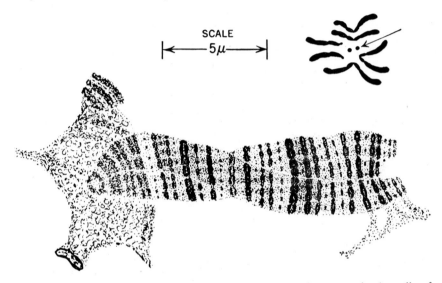

Fig. 5–17. The IV chromosome of *D. melanogaster*, as it appears in the cells of the salivary gland and in gonial cells (upper right, and indicated by arrow). The mass of material at the left end of the IV chromosome is the chromocenter to which the other chromosomes are also attached. The comparison of gonial and salivary gland chromosomes gives an indication of the wealth of detail which can be obtained from these giant structures (Bridges 1935).

More important than size, however, are two other characteristics these giant chromosomes invariably demonstrate. In the first place the homologous chromosomes show a type of synapsis at least as intimate as that characteristic of meiotic chromosomes in pachytene. Secondly, the chromosomes reveal a distinctive pattern of transverse banding which consists of alternating chromatic and achromatic areas. These bands differ in thickness and in other structural features in a manner so specific that it permits the accurate mapping of each chromosome throughout its euchromatic length. The significance of the synaptic behavior and the band specificity was fully recognized when it was realized that the synapsis was a band-to-band phenomenon, thus permitting the identification of many small irregularities that might arise in the internal structure of chromosomes, and that would pass unrecognized in smaller chromosomes. With the full realization later that certain gene loci could be identified with certain bands, the opportunity for a closer investigation of the relationship between the gene and the chromosome was presented.

In *D. melanogaster* the nucleus of the salivary gland cell shows one short and five long strands radiating out from a single more or less amorphous mass, the *chromocenter* (Fig. 5–18). These strands have been

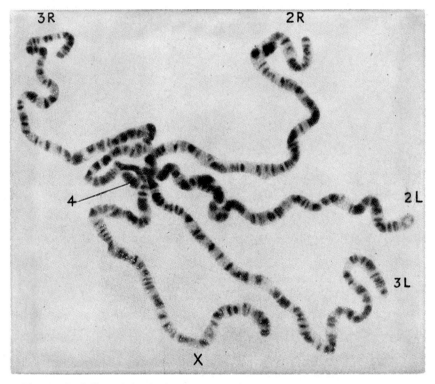

Fig. 5–18. Salivary gland chromosomes of a *Drosophila melanogaster* female showing the X-chromosome, the arms of the two autosomes (2L, 2R, 3L, and 3R), and the small 4 chromosome. The diploid number of chromosomes is present, but the homologues are in intimate synapsis (courtesy of Dr. B. P. Kaufmann).

identified as follows: the short strand, consisting of but a few bands, constitutes the tiny IV chromosome; one of the long strands is the X-chromosome; the remaining four strands are the arms of the long II and III chromosomes. All are united in the chromocenter by their centromeric regions. Failure at first to locate the Y-chromosome from male larval smears results from the fact that this chromosome, despite its rather large somatic size, is represented in these cells only by a few lightly staining bands submerged in the chromocenter (Prokofieva-Belgowskaya 1937). It has since been shown that the chromocenter represents a fusion of all, or most, of the heterochromatic regions of all of the chromosomes. Since the Y-chromosome is entirely heterochromatic, and since the other four possess heterochromatic portions adjacent to their centromeres, their union gives the characteristic grouping seen in the cells of the salivary glands. Chironomus, Camptomya (Fig. 5–19) and Sciara, genera related to Drosophila, do not exhibit a similar clumping of the chromosomes even though these organisms also possess heterochromatic regions.

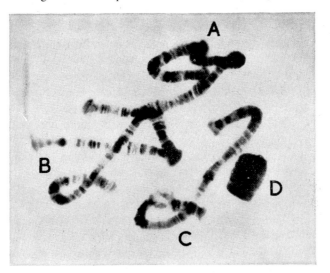

Fig. 5–19. Salivary gland chromosomes of the dipteran *Camptomya sp.* The chromosomes are arbitrarily lettered, with C being the nucleolar chromosome (the nucleolus would be located at the puff) and D the so-called wide chromosome which is much shorter, wider and more deeply staining than the other three (White 1951).

Structurally, the salivary gland chromosomes present an enigma (Alfert 1954). The enormous length cannot readily be accounted for by a simple straightening out of coiled somatic chromosomes; there appears to be, in addition to the straightening-out process, an actual increase in overall length. Whether the molecular structure of the chromosomes unfolds to give added length is not known. Their development from somatic chromosomes of typical appearance can be traced (Buck 1937; Cooper 1938; Painter 1941; Metz 1941; Kodani 1942; Melland 1942), and up to a certain point there is good agreement as to the events taking place. The chromosomes prior to synapsis consist of four clearly defined strands chromomeric in appearance. As synapsis proceeds the chromosomes grow in diameter and in length while at the same time they become relationally coiled about their pairing homologue. Agreement as to structural interpretations ceases at this point, and a number of hypotheses have been advanced to explain the morphology of the fully extended chromosomes.

Painter (1941) believes that the increase in diameter is due to an enlargement and (probably) a continuing duplication of the individual chromomeres, but without a visible separation of individual chromonemata. Thus, in the course of development, each original chromomere becomes resolved, by separation through stretching, into a number of smaller chromomeres; the enlargement, duplication, and aggregation of homologous chromomeres produce the appearance of transverse chromatic bands. The chromosome, therefore, becomes multi-stranded, or *polytene*, but the individual chromonemata, which according to Painter may be as many as 1024, remain invisible. Beermann (1952) estimates the degree of polyteny to be as high as 16,000, while chemical studies place the figure at 500 (Kurnick and Herskowitz 1952) or 1024 (Swift and Rasch 1954).

The concept of polyteny is supported by the observation that as many as 16 bodies can be counted in a single transverse band, but the band appearance is often deceptive in an incompletely stretched chromosome. White (1954) states that the bands correspond to the chromomeres seen in the mitotic and meiotic chromosomes, but there are obviously many more bands than there are identifiable chromomeres in the salivary gland chromosomes prior to enlargement. Over 1000 bands have been identified in the X-chromosome of *D. melanogaster* (Bridges 1935, 1938). The larger, thicker bands, on stretching, are in some instances found to be made up of several thinner bands, while others are clearly non-divisible. The thinner bands present a granular appearance, and the granules have been interpreted by Painter as the individual chromomeres. Support for this contention, as well as for the polytene hypothesis, has been provided by D'Angelo (1946, 1950), who has shown, through the use of microdissection methods, that linear strands of the chromosome lifted free of the main bulk retain the chromomeric pattern of banding. It is not certain, however, that these fibrils represent chromonemata. It has not been possible to shred the chromosome lengthwise to ascertain the exact number of chromonemata present, although the frayed ends of occasional chromosomes suggest such a polytene structure. This is also indicated in the structure known as "Balbiani's ring" (Fig. 5–20). Additional studies by D'Angelo (1950), which support the polytene concept, reveal that when a band is laterally stretched it resolves itself into a beaded structure, an observation suggesting that the chromomeres are being separated from each other. No chromonemata separation was detectable, however, by this method.

Metz (1941), like Painter, supports the polytene nature of the salivary gland chromosomes. His interpretation, called the "alveolar hypothesis," differs as to the nature of the transverse banding. Metz considers the bands, although highly specific as to appearance and position, to be simply accumulations of chromatic material at the junctions of alveoli, or vesicles, between the invisible chromonemata; he considers the chromonemata sometimes observed by Painter to be nothing but striations, or lines of stress, in the body of the chromosome.

A quite different interpretation has been placed upon the structure of these chromosomes by Kodani (1942). Disagreeing with the polytene con-

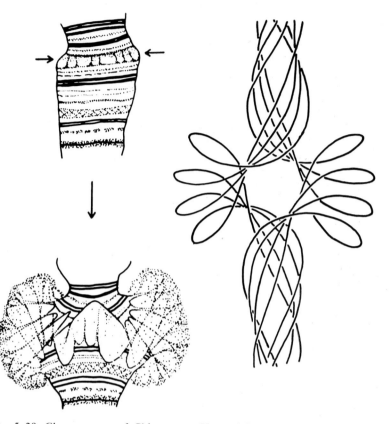

Fig. 5–20. Chromosomes of Chironomus. Upper left, the normal banded appearance of a portion of a salivary gland chromosome which will expand locally (indicated by arrows) into a Balbiani ring (lower left). Right, Beermann's interpretation of the chromonematal structure of the Balbiani ring, but with only a few of the many strands indicated (Gall 1956).

cept, he believes the paired homologues to consist of but four chromonemata, swollen by lateral enlargement of the inter-band regions, but not further subdivided. The bands are believed to be coiled structures, their darkly stained appearance being due to the radial arrangement of hairs encrusted with chromatin. Alkali treatments are believed to uncoil the bands, loosen the hairs, and convert the structure into a lampbrush type of chromosome similar in all respects to those found in vertebrate oöcytes. A somewhat similar, but less involved, hypothesis has been advanced by Ris and Crouse (1945), and for this reason it would appear inadvisable to adopt wholeheartedly the term "polytene chromosome" for structures which, in terms of number of chromonemata, may be no more subdivided than ordinary mitotic or meiotic chromosomes.

Whatever the correct interpretation, it is certain that the salivary gland chromosomes present a constant pattern of linear differentiation that has been of immeasurable aid in detecting chromosomal alterations that would escape the attention of the cytologist in the smaller, more closely packed, somatic and meiotic chromosomes.

No existing data permit an accurate comparison of the synaptic behavior of homologous chromosomes in meiotic and in salivary gland nuclei. Very likely, the extended period during which synapsis takes place in the gland cells permits a more intimate pairing than that found in meiotic cells, and the greater length of the chromosomes provides a greater pairing surface compared to that of the less subdivided but relatively more compact zygotene chromosomes. Undoubtedly the two forms of synapsis have a common basis, since both are governed by homologies, but one clear-cut distinction exists. In meiotic zygotene stages of plants, a two-by-two association of homologues at any single point along their length is characteristic even for triploids or tetraploids; in the salivary gland nuclei of a triploid Drosophila the three homologues are synapsed along their entire length. The meaning of the difference is not clear, although the suggestion has been made that the zygotene attraction of homologues may be governed by bilateral symmetries whereas in the salivary gland chromosome, where the possibility of multiple strands exists, a radial symmetry with multiple pairing faces is possible (Cooper 1938).

These chromosomes, while customarily studied in the salivary gland nuclei, are not peculiar to this tissue. They have been found as well in the

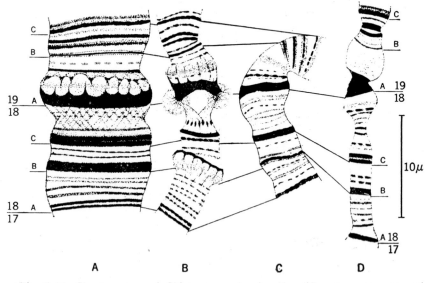

Fig. 5–21. Chromosomes of Chironomus, showing the different appearance and size in different tissues. A, salivary gland; B, Malpighian tubules; C, rectum; and D, midgut (Beermann 1952).

cells of Malpighian tubules, fat bodies, ovarian nurse cells, and gut epithelia (Makino 1938; Cooper 1938; Beermann 1952; Stalker 1954; Breuer and Pavan 1955), but they are not as accessible for study, nor do they reach the maximum size found in the nuclei of the salivary glands. Of considerable interest is the observation that the banded structure and size of polytene chromosomes may differ during larval development and in different tissues of the same organism (Pavan and Breuer 1952; Breuer and Pavan 1955; Beermann 1952). There is an essential similarity in the banding pattern (Figs. 5–21 and 5–22), but differences in the degree of development of individual bands lead to a differential appearance and stainability. This suggests that the changing appearance of the bands is a reflection of functional activities of the parts of the chromosome in the metabolism and differentiation of the cell, and that these activities differ in time and in different types of cells.

Supernumerary chromosomes. The complements of some plant and animal nuclei contain, in addition to the normal chromosomes, one or more *accessory* or *supernumerary* chromosomes. Wilson first discovered these in 1905 in the hemipteran insect Metapodius; since then they have been found in a variety of insects and in a great many higher plants (Darlington 1937, Table 16; Hakansson 1945; Fernandes 1946; Östergren 1947; Melander 1950). In some instances their nature and origin can be assumed with some certainty; for example, those in Metapodius apparently are derived from the Y-chromosome. More commonly their ancestry is entirely unknown.

Generally of smaller size than other members of the chromosome complement, although the reverse is true for the so-called "limited" chromosomes of Sciara, the supernumeraries appear to be genetically inert. Whether almost absent, or present in large numbers, they produce little detectable phenotypic expression in the organism in which they are found. This suggests that structurally they are largely heterochromatic, a hypothesis supported by the fact that they may also exhibit the differential staining characteristics of heterochromatin. Not all are heterochromatic, however; those in Tradescantia species appear entirely euchromatic, while the B-chromosomes in maize are partly heterochromatic, partly euchromatic.

It is, of course, possible that supernumeraries' continued presence in certain populations indicates that they perform some as yet undetermined function that guarantees their survival but that is too subtle to detect genetically. In certain plants, however, their perpetuation is assured by their manner of division. In Secale and *Anthoxanthum aristatum,* the supernumeraries regularly undergo non-disjunction in the first microspore division, both halves being included in the generative nucleus (Muntzing 1945, 1946; Östergren 1947). They behave similarly in the embryo sac of Secale, but not in Anthoxanthum. The B-chromosomes of maize exhibit a comparable behavior except that non-disjunction occurs at the second

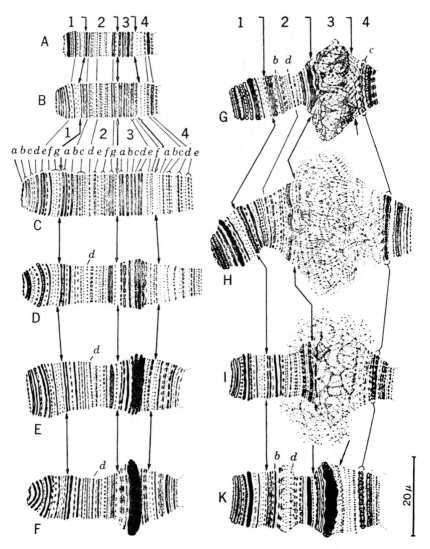

Fig. 5–22. The distal end of a salivary gland chromosome of *Rhynchosciara angelae,* showing the varied appearance at different stages of larval development. C, from a full grown larva; C to K, successive days of larval development, with K being the youngest of the group; A, 16 days younger than stages H and I; B, eight days older than A. Arrows connect corresponding bands (Breuer and Pavan 1955).

microspore division (Roman 1947). The failure to segregate properly has been traced to the centromeres, which fail to divide properly at anaphase. In maize, non-disjunction of the supernumeraries approaches a frequency of 100 percent. Preservation in the germ track is thus assured, while their transference to the next generation is fostered by the fact that sperm-bearing B-chromosomes preferentially fertilize the egg nucleus.

This phenomenon is strikingly demonstrated in *Sorghum purpureo-sericeum* (Darlington and Thomas 1941) and in some types of *Poa alpina* (Muntzing 1946) where the supernumeraries are eliminated by lagging from the somatic tissues, as judged by roottip examination, yet maintained in those cells that become the germ track. A similar case has also been reported in Xanthisma (Berger, McMahon, and Witkus 1955).

The most extensively studied of these types is the B-chromosome of maize, first described by Randolph (1928) and found in widely distributed strains of Indian maize (Longley 1938). As many as 25 to 30 may become accumulated in a single plant; but, even though devoid of known genes, some reduction in vigor and fertility results when too many are present in the same nucleus (Randolph 1941). They cannot, therefore, be considered genetically inert as had been previously supposed. McClintock (1933) has described the morphology of the B-chromosome in some detail (Fig. 5–23), and from pairing behavior as well as from morphological considerations it appears to possess no portion homologous with any region of the other ten haploid chromosomes.

Fig. 5–23. Diagram of the B-chromosome of maize in the pachytene stage of meiosis. The centromere is represented as terminal although it may be slightly subterminal; the segment to the left with the six small chromomeres is euchromatic, the remainder largely heterochromatic (redrawn from Rhoades 1955).

Supernumerary chromosomes, as a group, are relatively unstable members of a chromosome complement. In addition to their peculiarities of segregation in the microspores of plants, they segregate irregularly at meiosis, undergo somatic non-disjunction and elimination, and frequently change in morphology through fragmentation. Randolph (1941) has described a number of different forms of the B-chromosome, as has Muntzing (1945, 1946, 1950) in Secale. Their essential features have been discussed in detail by Hakansson (1945), while Fernandes (1946) has considered the possible causes of size alteration.

Melander (1950), in a study of accessory chromosomes in the freshwater turbellaria *Polycelis tenuis,* has suggested that the basic cause of their differential behavior is a change in strength and rhythm of division of the centromere. In Polycelis, the accessories are eliminated in somatic tissues but retained in ovarial cells. Presumably they serve a function since they tend to be preserved, but under certain environmental conditions they are definitely detrimental, causing a delay in growth and sexual maturity to such an extent that individuals possessing accessories fail to breed with the normal population. The accessories, therefore, bring about a reproductive isolation, yet they persist since individuals possessing them interbreed successfully.

In plants, the supernumerary chromosomes are of unknown origin, although Swanson (1943) and Lewis (1951) have discussed possible sources. Those in certain animals, however, appear to have arisen from members of the sex-chromosome complement, as for example those described by Wilson in *Metapodius terminalis*. These could easily have arisen by deletion from the heterochromatic Y-chromosome; any fragment would be preserved since the chromosomes of Metapodius have a diffuse centromere. Slack (1939) reports that only two of the three to 15 "fragment" chromosomes of the bedbug *Cimex lectularis* have a sex-determining influence, the remainder being accessory. Darlington (1940), however, considers that all of the extra chromosomes are X's, that since they are preserved in natural populations they have a selective value, but that since they can be reduplicated indefinitely they are relatively dosage-indifferent. A related species, *C. columbarius,* appears to be without the extra chromosomes, and interspecific crosses between it and *C. lectularis* indicate that the extra chromosomes are transmitted through the female only. In the male they are eliminated at meiosis by lagging.

CHAPTER 6

Variations in Chromosome Structure and Number

We noted in the preceding chapter that the karyotypes of different species are often sufficiently characteristic to provide the cytologist with morphological criteria that can be used for purposes of identification much in the manner that the taxonomist may employ the floral structures of plants or the genitalia of insects as guideposts to systematic relationships. The constancy of the karyotype, and hence its usefulness in comparative studies, stems from the fact that, at a given stage of cell division and in a given tissue, each cell of an organism has a constant number of chromosomes of reasonably definite volume, length, and shape, except where chromosomal aberrations or polyploidy intervene. These chromosomal constants are determined in turn by a fixed number of genes per chromosome, arranged in a definite serial order, with a centromere occupying a fixed position. Chromosomes with diffuse centromeres would of course provide exceptions. Secondary constrictions, trabants, and heterochromatic bodies of varying size and number may also contribute characteristic features to certain chromosomes or chromosome sets.

The constancy of the karyotype from one cell to another, and from one generation to the next, lies in its capacity to duplicate itself exactly at each cell division. As a result of duplication the number of genes, and their lineal relationship to one another, are preserved in the newly formed daughter cells. However, in different tissues of the same individual the chromosomes may exhibit a wide variation in form and sometimes in number. Differences in nutrition, temperature, physiological function of the various cells, and genotype exert an influence on chromosome form, while variations in number may arise through accidents in chromosome segregation and cell division or as a result of the consequences of the regular developmental processes of maturation. A comparison of the chromosomes in the gonial and salivary gland cells of Drosophila provides an example of the variations in form that chromosomes can assume in different tissues, while increased chromosome numbers are sometimes exhibited in certain mature tissues of plants and animals whose cells no longer undergo division as a regular process. A shuffling of the genes through a rearrangement of the chromatin of a complement can also occur without a change in chromosome number, and this may bring about striking changes in the form of the chromosome.

The karyotype constants therefore possess only a relative stability, and this must be taken into account when comparative chromosome studies are being made. The chromosomes undergo change as a natural event even as genes mutate, and the newly constructed karyotypes, like their original counterparts, are duplicated exactly at each cell division thereafter. Should the structural and numerical changes persist, new karyotypes become established either as chromosomal races within a species, or, if the change is accompanied by many gene mutations, even as new species.

The types of karyotype change can be classified as either structural or numerical. In the former, the gene number is left unchanged, or varied slightly by small gains or losses, while new gene arrangements are created; in the latter, gene position remains stable, while gene number is varied either by the gain or loss of whole chromosomes, or of whole complements of chromosomes. Both types of change occur spontaneously, but at a relatively low frequency, the rate varying apparently according to the species, and by means not now fully understood. Experimental means have now been found, however, that permit a rather easy manipulation of chromosome structure and number to provide a wealth of new types. Structural changes are readily produced by the ionizing radiations such as x-rays, and by chemical agents such as mustard gas or its derivatives. Numerical changes have been most successfully induced by the alkaloid drug, colchicine, although many other drugs have a similar action.

In this chapter the structural and numerical changes will be examined only from the cytological point of view of structure and behavior; their evolutionary importance will be taken up in a later chapter.

STRUCTURAL CHANGES

Chromosomal aberrations leading to rearrangements in the linear order of genes may be grouped into four classes: (1) deletions or deficiencies, (2) duplications, (3) inversions, and (4) translocations. The first three, as a general rule, affect only single chromosomes, while translocations may involve one, two, or more chromosomes. Their detection can be made both cytologically and genetically in favorable material; in less favorable material, certain aberrations can be inferred from the chromosomal configurations found at metaphase and anaphase of meiosis I.

Deficiencies. A deficiency involves the detachment and loss of a portion of an arm from the remainder of the chromosome. The deleted portion will not survive if it lacks a centromere since it will have no power of movement in anaphase. Such a loss, of course, could occur only with chromosomes having localized contromere, since fragmentation of a chromosome having a diffuse centromere would lead to an increase in chromosome number, but no loss, each fragment possessing the power of movement. The portion of the chromosome carrying the centromere functions as a deficient chromosome, its movement being relatively unimpaired.

Deficiencies can be either terminal or interstitial. The former can arise by a single break in a chromosome followed by a healing of the broken end; the latter results from two breaks followed by the reunion of broken ends, as indicated in Figure 6–1. Each type, if large enough, can be

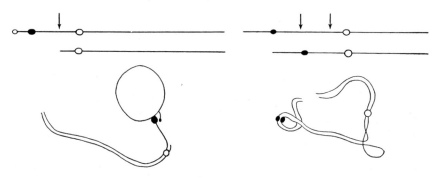

Fig. 6–1. Diagram to illustrate the origin of terminal (left) and interstitial (right) deletions, and to illustrate their appearance in pachynema when paired in the heterozygous state. Arrows indicate position of breaks, and the deleted chromosome is represented below its normal homologue. The paired pachytene chromosomes have been observed in maize (redrawn from McClintock 1932).

recognized in pachytene or salivary gland chromosomes by the manner in which pairing takes place with a normal homologue. The location of deficiencies can be determined with considerable exactitude in the salivary gland chromosomes of Drosophila by comparing the band structures of the deficient and normal chromosomes (Fig. 6–2), but such a procedure is not always possible in plants or in animals lacking giant chromosomes. In maize, for example, the phenomenon of non-homologous pairing leads to considerable difficulty in exact determination of the deficient region, for the unpaired loop may shift along the length of the pachytene chromosome (McClintock 1933). When a study of deletions in plants is contemplated, therefore, chromosomes well marked with specific genes, and, if possible, with cytologically recognizable chromomeres or knobs, become a virtual necessity.

There is some question about the nature of terminal deficiencies. Their formation requires the loss of the normal telomere and the transformation of a bipolar segment of the chromosome into a unipolar structure; i.e., the broken end must heal into a stable condition in order to prevent elimination or further change resulting from the fusion of chromatid ends when

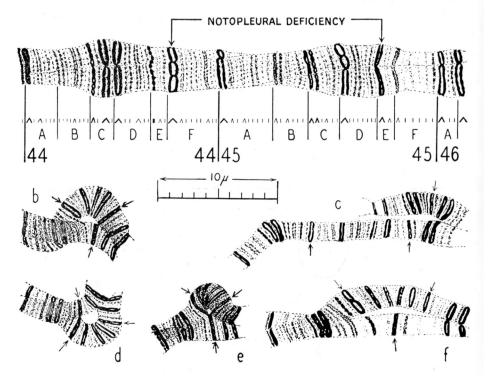

Fig. 6–2. Salivary gland chromosomes of *D. melanogaster* showing the *Noto-pleural* deficiency in the right arm of chromosome 2. Above, normal chromosome indicating the limits of the deficiency; b–f, *Notopleural* heterozygotes. b, synapsed at the right limit of the deficiency; c and f, non-synapsed strands; d, synapsed at the left limit; e, synapsed at both limits (Bridges, Skoog and Li 1936).

the chromosome divides, an event that McClintock (1941b) has shown to occur. This healing can occur in plants, particularly if the deficiencies are caused by ultraviolet radiation, but terminal deficiencies seem to be extremely rare in Drosophila regardless of the manner of origin.

Demerec and Hoover (1936), however, have described several in *D. melanogaster* that involve the loss of the tip of the left end of the X-chromosome, including apparently the telomere and a number of known genic loci (Fig. 6–3). One involves the loss of 10 or 11 bands, includes the *y, ac,* and *sc* loci, and when in a hemizygous condition is lethal to individual cells and to the whole organism; another involves the loss of eight bands, includes *y* and *ac,* and in a homozygous condition is lethal to the whole organism but not to individual cells; a third consists of a four-band loss, does not include any known loci, and is viable in a homozygous or hemizygous state.

Sutton (1943a), on the other hand, has described a deficiency that involved the two terminal bands A 1–2, and that in a homozygous or

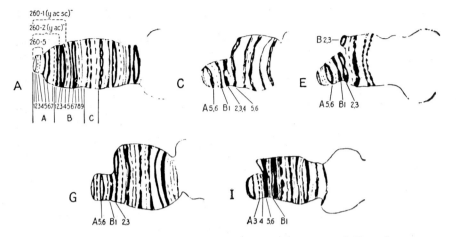

Fig. 6–3. Three deficiencies at the tip of the X-chromosome of *D. melanogaster.* A, normal tip; C, deficiency of 10 or 11 bands (260–1) which includes the genes *y*, *ac* and *sc*, and which is cell and organism lethal when homozygous; E and G, two drawings of the same 8-band deficiency (260–2) which includes *y* and *ac*, and which is organism but not cell lethal when homozygous; I, deficiency of 4 bands (260–5) which does not include these three genes, is not cell or organism lethal, and only reduces fertility in homozygous females (Demerec and Hoover 1936).

hemizygous state behaved as a yellow mutant, suggesting that the locus for *y* is more distal than previously realized. Muller (1935) has also shown that the interstitial loss of *y* and *ac* is viable in a homozygous state, while Gershensen (1933) has demonstrated that portions of heterochromatin in the X-chromosome can be lost without causing lethality when homozygous.

It is difficult to prove with certainty, however, that the actual end of the chromosome is missing, and in view of the rarity of terminal deletions in this organism, it may well be that a truly terminal deficiency cannot persist. This hypothesis could be tested, it would seem, by studying the adhesion of terminal ends in the salivary chromosomes as described by Hinton and Atwood (1941), with loss of the terminal chromomere being reflected in a loss of terminal adhesive capacity. Kikkawa (1938), on the other hand, showed that different strains of *D. ananassae* exhibit varying degrees of deficiencies at the ends of certain chromosomes. Similar changes have also been reported in Chironomus (Goldschmidt 1942), and it may well be that some organisms can withstand loss far better than others, or that the process of healing of broken ends takes place more readily in some species than in others. Kodani's (1947) study of the terminal structure of *D. melanogaster* salivary chromosomes injects a note of caution into any speculations based on purely cytological observations since he has shown that in the same organism the tip of the X-chromosome exhibits a varying picture from cell to cell; some of the cells could be judged to possess deficiencies were it not known for certain that the chromosomes are normal.

Interstitial deficiencies occur spontaneously, or they can be readily induced by radiation. Slizynski (1942) has described a number of these in Drosophila that are associated with a recessive lethal condition, the spontaneous ones being indistinguishable from those arising as the result of exposure to x-rays or to ultraviolet radiation. In maize, ultraviolet appears to give rise chiefly to terminal deficiencies, x-rays to only interstitial deficiencies (Stadler 1941; Stadler and Roman 1948). On the other hand, Barton (1954) has shown that ultraviolet radiation can induce interstitial losses in tomato chromosomes, thus raising the question whether there exists a species specificity as to the type of aberration that will arise following exposure to various types of radiation.

Since a deficiency involves the loss of genic material, it would be expected that deficiencies would have deleterious effects on an organism, the effect depending upon the amount of genic material and its quality. Homozygous viable deficiencies would be expected to be rare. Creighton (1934) has described one such deficiency in maize that survived in the haploid state, i.e., passed through the male gametophyte, but the great majority act as gametophyte lethals in that they cause pollen abortion. In Drosophila, homozygous losses involving the tip of the X-chromosome are viable provided they are very minute. Apparently loss of the genes *yellow, achaete,* and *scute* can be withstood in either a hemizygous or a homozygous condition, but these genes constitute a very small portion of the entire chromosome. Even deficiencies existing in a heterozygous condition have their size limits. Maize, Datura, and other plants can withstand the loss of a whole chromosome to give $2n - 1$ sectional chimeras or even entire plants, but in *D. melanogaster* a loss of more than 50 bands is generally considered to be lethal even when the homologous chromosome is intact. When one considers that the X-chromosome alone possesses approximately 1000 bands, it must mean that genetic balance can readily be upset, and that elimination under natural conditions would soon take place for large deficiencies. Deficient gametes, however, can survive to take part in fertilization in animals (Muller and Settle 1927), but the haploid generation in plants serves as a very effective screen for the removal of such gametes. Deficient chromosomes can survive more readily through the female side in plants, but on the male side, if they are not entirely eliminated by the formation of unviable pollen grains, the pollen grains that contain them cannot successfully compete with normal grains.

Since a deficiency results in a loss of genes, it is not surprising that they give rise to certain genetic effects. Many deletions act as recessive lethals, but in addition, they frequently produce detectable morphological changes that are inherited as dominant characters. The following Drosophila characters are all associated with deficiencies, and all are dominants: *Blond, Pale, Beaded, Carved, Snipped,* and *Plexate.* In addition, many of the *Notch* and *Minute* mutations are known to be deficiencies; on the other hand, some do not appear to involve a loss of chromatin.

Deficiencies have been employed to locate genes on the salivary chromosomes of Drosophila (Mackensen 1935; Slizynska 1938). A thorough study of this sort has been made on the left end of the X-chromosome as indicated in Figure 6–4. Of particular interest are those deletions labelled

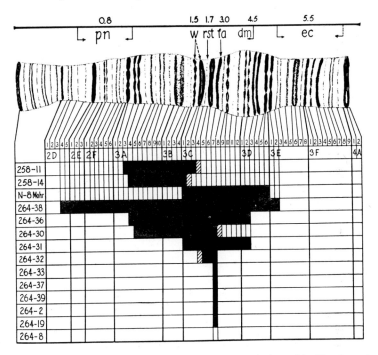

Fig. 6–4. Genetic and salivary chromosome maps of the *white-Notch* region of the X-chromosome of *D. melanogaster,* together with a diagram indicating the extent of fourteen deficiencies, all of which produce the *white-Notch* phenotype. Black areas represent certain deficient regions, shaded areas uncertain deficiencies (Slizynska 1938).

258–14, 264–31, and N–8 Mohr. They have, in common, the loss of a single band $3C_2$, and coincidently, the loss of the *white* locus. It appears reasonably certain therefore that this locus is located in or near the $3C_2$ band, although it is now recognized that the *white* locus consists of at least two separate genes associated with the doublet band $3C_{2-3}$ of which $3C_2$ is a part (Lewis 1952). In the same study Slizynska showed that the genes *roughest* and *facet* can be as sharply identified with other bands, while *pn, dm,* and *ec* are identified only within certain groups of bands. The dominant genes *Carved, Snipped,* and *Depillate* are all related to deficiencies that involve the *vestigial* locus, the different effects being related to differences in the number of bands lost. The *Notch* effect occurs, however, whenever a loss of the *facet* locus ($3C_7$) occurs. The number of bands involved appears not to be related to the morphological effect produced, and as stated earlier, *Notch* may appear even with no loss detectable. The *Minute* effect may or may not be related to a deficiency of chromatin, but it differs from the *Notch* effect in that *Minute* "genes" are located in many different regions of the chromosome complement.

Some deficiencies in Drosophila are known that involve the loss of but a single band. In plants or in animals that do not possess giant chromosomes such minute deficiencies would escape cytological detection altogether, and the use of genetical methods permits only a detection of their presence, but not necessarily the accurate delineation of their size.

A most elegant and painstaking study has been made of three deficiencies of the A locus in maize (Stadler and Roman 1948). Induced by x-rays, these deficiencies behaved phenotypically as though there had been mutation of the A locus to a recessive allelic form, while a cytological study of the pachytene chromosomes showed no detectable loss of chromatin. A critical study of these changes revealed there was a reduced, or a lack of, transmission through the male gametophyte, that these deficiencies could not be obtained in a homozygous condition, and that there was an associated loss or reduction of anthocyanin and chlorophyll content and cell viability. Two of the three deficiencies produced a marked effect on crossing over in their neighborhood. The demonstrable loss of several separable genetic effects provides reasonable evidence of a deficiency in contrast to a mutation.

McClintock (1938, 1941a, b, 1944) has provided evidence that viable mutations in maize can be produced by homozygous minute deficiencies. In Chromosome 5, the method of producing deficiencies was through the use of small ring chromosomes that included a functional centromere plus the proximal chromomeres of the short arm. The aberrant behavior of the ring chromosomes led to progressive losses of chromatin (see p. 356), and it could be demonstrated that simple mutants resulted from a particular minute segment of chromatin while compound mutants involved larger pieces of the ring. Since these ring chromosomes were always used in association with a deficient rod chromosome from which the ring was derived, loss of chromatin from the ring would lead to the total absence of that chromatin segment, and the mutant phenotype, which in some instances duplicated the appearance of known mutant genes, would be expressed. A similar study of Chromosome 9 led to similar conclusions, namely, that loss of chromatin produced mutant phenotypes when in a homozygous condition. In this instance the terminal chromomeres were involved, and their progressive loss was brought about by the breakage of the chromatin bridge produced by crossing over in meiosis (see p. 357). The progressive loss is indicated in Figure 6–5, showing the phenotypes produced when homozygous and when in combination with each other.

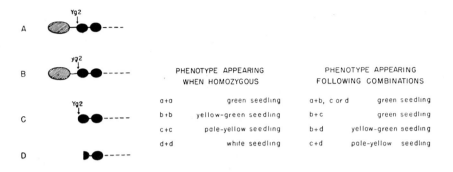

	PHENOTYPE APPEARING WHEN HOMOZYGOUS	PHENOTYPE APPEARING FOLLOWING COMBINATIONS
a+a	green seedling	a+b, c or d green seedling
b+b	yellow-green seedling	b+c green seedling
c+c	pale-yellow seedling	b+d yellow-green seedling
d+d	white seedling	c+d pale-yellow seedling

Fig. 6–5. Schematic representation of the chromomeres at the end of the short arm of chromosome 9 of maize, together with the progressive deficiencies which have been detected. These give the equivalent of a pseudoallelic series, and the phenotypes of homozygous and heterozygous combinations are indicated (McClintock 1944).

Duplications. An extra piece of a chromosome, whether attached in some manner to one of the members of the regular complement, or existing as a fragment chromosome, is known as a *duplication*. When attached to a chromosome in the form of an added section, the duplication may be in tandem, in reverse tandem, or as a displaced piece. Thus if the duplicated piece is represented by the letters *def,* a tandem duplication would be *abcdefdefghi;* a reverse tandem as *abcdeffedghi;* and *rstdefuvw* or *rstfeduvw* as a displaced duplication.

Figures 6–6 and 6–7 represent a variety of duplications involving portions of the X-chromosome of *D. melanogaster.* In Figure 6–6 Nos. 112, 101, 134, and 102 are fragment chromosomes in which both ends of the chromosome are preserved, but from each of which large interstitial portions of varying size and genic content have been removed. Since each fragment possesses a centromere (SF), passage through cell division in a regular manner is assured. T-3 and T-7 show the left end of the X-chromosome displaced, respectively, to the ends of the III and II chromosomes, while 126 involves the insertion of an interstitial portion of the X-chromosome into the centric heterochromatin of the III chromosome. These three are essentially translocations and can be considered duplications only when the entire X-chromosome is intact in the same cell. Nos. 138 and 105 illustrate additional duplications in which different portions of the X have been added to the right end beyond the centromere, thus converting the X into a distinctly two-armed chromosome.

Figure 6–7 illustrates the tandem duplication associated with the well-known *Bar* phenotype. Seven bands in the 16A region are involved, and the salivary gland picture shows that the normal males have the 16A region represented once, *Bar* males twice, and *Bar-double* males three times. As shown by Sturtevant (1925), the frequency of reversions to normal and to *Bar-double* are similar, and their occurrence, which takes

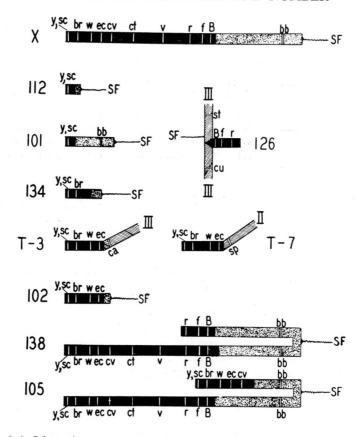

Fig. 6–6. Schematic representation of various duplications of the X-chromosome of *D. melanogaster*, with the normal X-chromosome diagrammed at the top. See text for explanation (Dobzhansky 1934).

place only in females, can be accounted for through the phenomenon of unequal crossing over. The manner by which this takes place is indicated at the bottom of Figure 6–7. Through the same process, the number of 16A regions in a single X-chromosome can be increased beyond three, and Rapaport (1940) has been able to obtain individuals with as many as eight regions in tandem sequence. Sutton (1943b) has localized the *Bar* "locus" in the 16A$_{1-2}$ bands. A somewhat similar tandem duplication has been described by Demerec and Hoover (1939). Giving rise to a dominant character known as *Hairy wing (Hw)*, only a single band is thought to be duplicated, and as yet no unequal crossing over has been detected although this may be due to the fact that crossing over is normally low in the *Hw* region.

As might be expected, duplications are more frequent and less lethal to the individual than are deficiencies. Duplications can be more readily de-

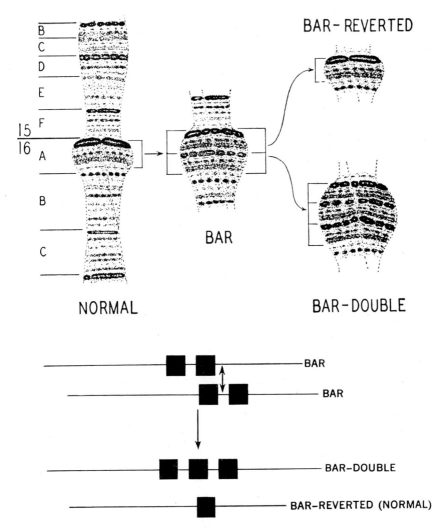

Fig. 6–7. *Bar*-locus in the salivary gland X-chromosome of *D. melanogaster,* indicating that duplication of the 16A region is responsible for the *Bar* phenotype while triplication gives the *Bar-double* phenotype. Below, diagram to indicate the manner by which unequal crossing over causes *Bar* to give rise to normal (*Bar-reverted*) and *Bar-double* chromosomes (Morgan, Bridges and Schultz 1936).

tected in species such as Drosophila because of the detailed structure of salivary chromosomes, but even in plants a study of meiotic pairing in haploid individuals reveals some apparently homologous synapsis, which would presumably point to the presence of duplications (Ivanov 1938). In Drosophila (Bridges 1935; Slizynski 1945) and Sciara (Metz and Lawrence 1938), the "repeats," as these duplications are called, are recognized by their mutual attraction and similarity of band pattern. Slizynski has termed this "ectoptic pairing," but in this instance it may be more a reflection of the non-homologous pairing of heterochromatin than of the homologous pairing of euchromatin. Bridges, for example, points out that in the left arm of Chromosome II section 32F to 33C is, band for band, strikingly similar to section 34F to 35C. And section 37E to 38A has a morphology identical to that found in 39CDE. Other areas scattered throughout the chromosomes appear to be reverse repeats. The "turnback" in region 36, the "shield" in 30A, and the "weak spots" at 3C and 11A, all suggest duplications. In addition, Bridges suggests that the doublets, or thick-walled capsules, such as that at 21E, may be single band repeats, as indeed Lewis (1952) has shown to be true for the *white-apricot* region at $3C_{2-3}$, leading to the possibility that the total gene content of an organism may be increased in this manner. The work of Lewis (1945, 1951, 1955), Green and Green (1949) and Green (1953, 1954, 1955a, b) on similar, but distinguishable, loci repeated in very close sequence supports such an hypothesis, but since this topic has a most important bearing on the nature of the gene, discussion will be deferred until a later chapter.

Just as deficiencies can be recognized by a loss of a dominant effect when altered sperm are used to fertilize females of a recessive phenotype, so duplications can be recognized by the loss of recessive characters. Fertilization of a recessive female of an $X\bar{X}$ stock by treated sperm from a dominant male will yield occasional females normal in all respects except that certain dominant phenotypic expressions are present. The duplicated section covering the recessive genes can then be located by cytological examination of the salivary chromosomes.

Inversions. The structural aberration most frequently encountered in wild populations, and probably the one most useful to the geneticist in a wide variety of experimental designs, is the *inversion*. Since first detected in Drosophila through the altered order of genes in linkage groups (Sturtevant 1921), inversions have been found in a wide variety of species; and in such plant genera as Tradescantia and Paris, few individuals seem to be free of them. Many species of Drosophila, and in particular *D. willistoni* and *D. pseudoobscura,* show a wealth of inversions which can be studied in precise detail in the salivary chromosomes. Some groups of animals, on the other hand, seem to be relatively free of inversions (White 1951). *D. meridiana* falls into this group along with the anopheline mosquitoes, the urodele Amphibia, and many species of grasshoppers.

An inverted chromosome is one in which a portion of the gene sequence has been rearranged in a reverse order. If confined to a single arm of the chromosome, such a rearrangement is a *paracentric* inversion; if it includes the centromere a *pericentric* inversion results. Since the consequences of crossing over within the two types are quite different, the initial discussion will deal with the paracentric form, which is more commonly encountered.

If, for example, the sequence of arrangement of a normal chromosome is represented as ABCDEFGH, an inverted homologue might be ABFEDCGH, with the CDEF section being shifted in its relation to neighboring loci. If the CDEF region contained known genes whose linkage to other genes outside of the inversion were altered, such an alteration could be detected, in inversion homozygotes, by genetic tests. The process is laborious, however, and would be employed today only when other simpler means would not suffice. In pachytene and salivary chromosomes, an inversion in a heterozygous condition can be recognized by the inversion "loop" which is formed when all portions of the two chromosomes synapse in an homologous fashion (Fig. 6–8). In anaphase of meiosis, the commonly observed inversion bridge, with its accompanying acentric fragment, results when a single crossover takes place within the inverted section. The frequency with which such inversion crossing over takes place depends upon the length of the inverted segment, its location in the chromosome, and the crossover characteristics of the individual, and it is quite evident that the chromatids involved will be abnormal as the result of duplication and deficiency. The acentric fragment will be lost having no capacity for movement at anaphase, and the bridge will be broken either by the strain of anaphase movement, or by the cell wall which will cut across it. Occasionally neither event will happen, and the dicentric bridge will be simply suspended between the two polar groups of chromosomes, to be eventually lost by failure to enter the telophase nuclei.

It would be expected that breakage of the dicentric bridge and loss of the acentric fragment would lead to inviability in the haploid cells arising from the reduction division. The expectation is, without doubt, realized whenever the four products of a single meiotic cell persist as functional gametes (as in male animals) or as asexual spores (as in most higher plants), and it may account for the relative absence of inversions in those species of animals having chiasmata in both sexes (White 1951). In Drosophila, however, no reduction in gamete viability is encountered as the result of inversion heterozygosity, although zygotic lethality results from deficient sperm.

The situation in males is readily explicable since no crossing over occurs, but in females it must be assumed that the failure of inversions to reduce egg viability results either from a lack of crossing over within an inversion or from the exclusion of the dicentric bridge from the egg nucleus. On genetic grounds, and from an exhaustive study of crossing over in a number of X-chromosome inversions in Drosophila, Sturtevant and Beadle (1936) have shown that the latter hypothesis is correct. Carson (1946) has provided cytological confirmation in Sciara. The dicentric chromatid, resulting from a single crossover within an inversion, always passes into the polar bodies, and the innermost chromatid which is not involved in crossing over remains to be included in the functional egg nucleus.

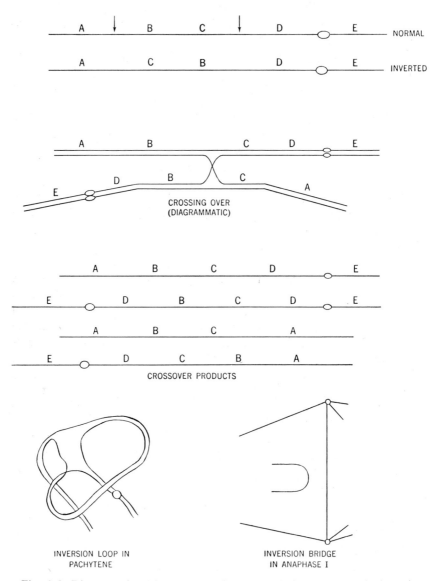

Fig. 6–8. Diagram of pairing and crossing over within a paracentric inversion, with the crossover products and the anaphase I bridge formation indicated. Pachytene configuration (lower left) in maize.

Three- and four-strand inversion crossovers would of course contribute to a reduced viability of eggs, but their relative infrequency is such as to reduce the offspring but slightly in numbers. Novitski (1952), however, has demonstrated that the selective orientation mechanism in Drosophila operates only with such telocentric chromosomes as the X; when four-strand double crossovers occur in chromosomes having two arms, the egg nucleus receives a deficient chromosome, and egg viability is reduced.

Whether a similar situation holds in the embryo sacs of the higher plants is know only for certain in maize, but the conditions of survival would depend upon the mode of embryo sac formation. In maize, where the basal megaspore develops into the embryo sac, the conditions are such as to suggest the inclusion of the non-crossover chromatid into the basal cell, but since the inversion bridge is always broken at anaphase I, the deficient chromosome can be included into the basal megaspore and thus contribute to zygotic inviability (Rhoades and Dempsey 1953). In the lily, where all four haploid nuclei become part of the embryo sac apparatus, the circumstances are more complicated, and at least partial seed sterility is to be expected as the result of inversion crossing over.

Inversions can be long or short. Probably the shortest inversion detectable cytologically is that described by Painter (1939) in Drosophila. It involves only bands IE1–3 in the X-chromosome, and appears in a species-hybrid obtained by crossing D. *melanogaster* with D. *simulans*. Horton (1939), in a study of the same hybrid, has also found inversions that appear to involve one or two bands, and he further suggests, on the basis of a failure of synapsis in regions where band similarity is apparently undisturbed, that smaller rearrangements below the limits of detectability may exist. Whether there are inversions at submicroscopic levels remains to be determined. The longer inversions have been studied most intensively, however, and as length increases the possibilities of multiple crossing over similarly increase.

When two crossovers are formed within an inverted segment, the results will depend upon the number of chromatids involved. From the diagrams in Figures 6–9 and 6–10, it can be seen that two-strand double crossing over will yield four normal chromatids, two of which are non-crossovers and the other two crossovers. The presence of alleles in heterozygous form lying both within and without the regions of crossing over would be necessary to detect such an event. Three-strand crossing over yields one non-crossover chromatid, one crossover chromatid, and a dicentric bridge with its acentric fragment; four-strand crossing over would yield two dicentric chromatids and two acentric fragments, and duplication and deficiency would presumably lead to death of the four products of meiosis.

Clearly, therefore, inversions seriously interfere with the recovery of chromatids that have been involved in crossing over, and since multiple crossing occurs infrequently under such circumstances of structural heterozygosity, the geneticist has made use of inversions whenever experimental design demands freedom from crossing over in a particular region of a chromosome. The use of multiple inversions reinforces the situation, of course, and an absolute block of crossing over in a particular chromosome

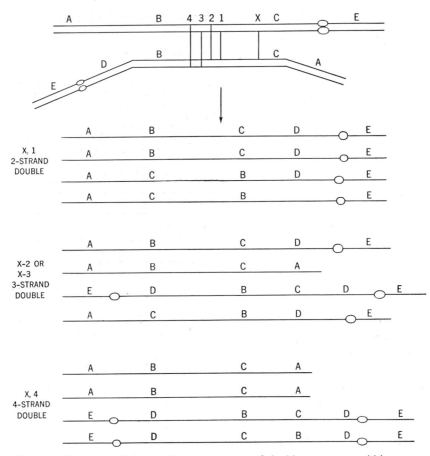

Fig. 6–9. Diagram to illustrate the consequences of double crossovers within a paracentric inversion.

can be readily achieved. The further incorporation of a lethal gene within the limits of an inversion also serves as a means for indefinitely preserving structural heterozygosity. The now famous *ClB* stock of *D. melanogaster* developed by Muller for his early radiation studies owes its usefulness to the *C* component which, in the form of an inversion, acts as a crossover suppressor, and to the *l* component, a recessive lethal, which prevents homozygosity for the ClB chromosome. Other balanced lethal stocks make use of a similar system of inversions and lethal genes.

In Drosophila, the limits of an inversion can be readily determined by a comparison of band sequence. Such cytological accuracy is not possible with other animal or plant chromosomes; however, the length of the acentric fragment provides a means of determining the approximate limits of any particular inversion. The length of the fragment will be twice that of the uninverted region from the distal break to the end of the chromosome

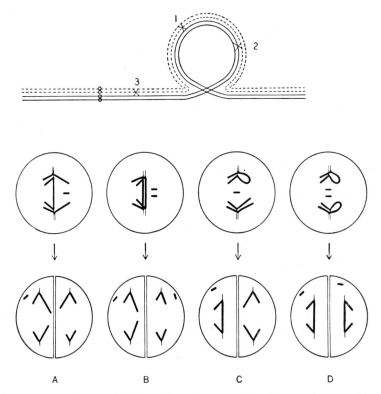

Fig. 6–10. Anaphase I and II configurations resulting from various combinations of crossovers within a paracentric inversion. A, from single crossovers at positions 1 or 2 within the inversion; B, from 4-strand double crossing over at positions 1 and 2; C, from two crossovers within and outside of the inversion at positions 2 and 3; D, from a triple crossover at positions 1, 2 and 3 (McClintock 1938).

plus the inverted region represented singly. The same sized fragment may therefore result from two inversions having quite different distal and proximal break points. Pachytene configurations must then be utilized, but these are difficult to observe clearly in most organisms except maize.

More than a single inversion is sometimes found within an arm of a chromosome, and when two, for example, are present they may exist as *adjacent, included,* or *overlapping* with respect to each other. Their pairing configurations and modes of origin are illustrated in Figure 6–11. Many of these have been found in the salivary chromosomes of wild populations of Drosophila, and Dobshansky (1951) in particular has made use of overlapping inversions to trace the gene sequence history of the third chromosome of *D. pseudoobscura* (see Chapter 15).

The inversions that have been described are those confined to a single arm of a chromosome. These, known as *paracentric* inversions, are by far the more common type. Another type, known as *pericentric* inversions,

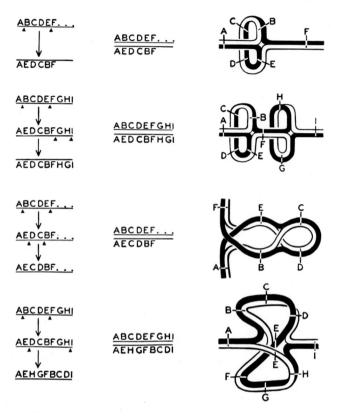

Fig. 6–11. Diagrams of chromosome pairing in salivary gland chromosomes of *D. pseudoobscura,* which are heterozygous for various types of inversions. Top, single inversion; 2nd from top, two independent inversions; 3rd from top, two inversions with one included within the other; bottom, two overlapping inversions. The configurations at the left indicate the origin of the inversions, with the black triangles indicating the break points (Dobzhansky 1951).

involve both arms, and include the centromere as well. Clearly, if the two breaks involved in formation of the inversion were equidistant from the centromere, the chromosome would appear unchanged. Should they occur at different distances from the centromere, a shift in the centromere would obviously take place. To what extent this type of aberration has altered the shapes of chromosomes in natural populations cannot be estimated at present, although in certain species of Drosophila and in members of the Orthoptera, where centromeric shifts occur, there is a strong suggestion that pericentric inversions have been influential in producing new karyotypes.

The pericentric inversion is of interest however as regards the chromatid products of crossing over. As Figure 6–12 indicates, a single crossover within the inversion loop does not give rise to a dicentric chromatid and

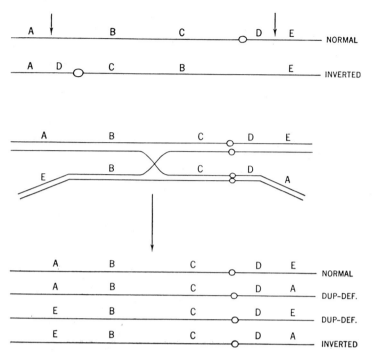

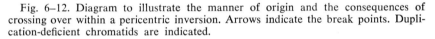

Fig. 6–12. Diagram to illustrate the manner of origin and the consequences of crossing over within a pericentric inversion. Arrows indicate the break points. Duplication-deficient chromatids are indicated.

an acentric fragment, but instead produces two new chromatids each of whose ends are identical in genic content. Duplication and deficiency obviously result, and sterility would ensue, but the inversion could be cytologically detected only in the pachytene stage of meiosis, or by the production of chromosomes with identical ends on the two arms.

Translocations. Fragmentation of two chromosomes and the mutual exchange through reunion of the fragments is known as a *reciprocal translocation* (Fig. 6–13). The two new chromosomes will function normally if each possesses a single centromere; should the reunion be such as to produce chromosomes with two centromeres or with no centromeres, these will be eliminated, since during cell division they would fail to segregate properly.

Other types of translocations are also known. *Simple translocations,* which involve the transfer of the end of one chromosome to the end of another, occur rarely, if at all. The telomeres of unfragmented chromosomes apparently prevent the terminal addition of extraneous pieces of chromatin distal to them. A *shift* is a translocation in which an interstitial piece is removed from the arm of one chromosome, and either reinserted into the same arm but at a different location, or shifted to an interstitial position

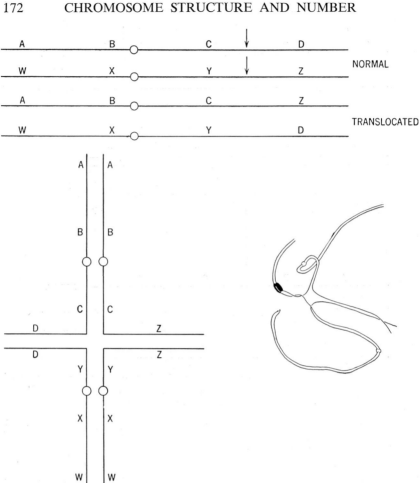

Fig. 6–13. Diagram to illustrate the manner of origin and the pattern of pachytene pairing in a translocation heterozygote. The lower right figure is of a heterozygous translocation in the pachytene stage of maize, with the two pairs of centromeres being represented as open circles, and a knob on the long arm of chromosome 2 as a dark body (McClintock 1932).

in the other arm or in a non-homologous chromosome. Such a displacement could of course take place only if three breaks were available at the same time. Translocations more complicated than those described are possible, [Kaufmann (1943), for example, has described an aberration involving 32 breaks], but the most commonly found are the reciprocal type and the shift.

Translocations, like inversions, may exist in either a homozygous or a heterozygous state, provided the aberration in question does not have associated with it, as is true in Drosophila, a lethal condition. Homozygous translocations behave as do the normal chromosomes from which they arose, except that new linkage groups become established. If they persist in the state of nature such rearrangements can give rise to a new chromosomal race. These are relatively rare in animals, but common to some genera of plants such as Oenothera and Datura. *Translocation heterozygotes* are readily recognized by the characteristic pairing configurations formed during prophase and metaphase of the first meiotic division. This is illustrated in Figure 6–14. Since homologies determine synapsis, complete

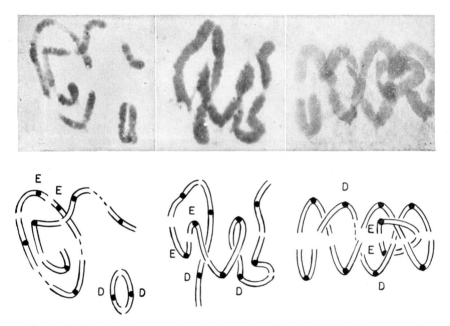

Fig. 6–14. Translocation complexes in *Paeonia californica*. Bottom figures are diagrammatic representations of the photographs above. Left, two rings of 4 plus 1 bivalent, with one of the rings showing as an open chain; middle, ring of 10, shown here as an open chain due to the failure of a chiasma to form which would close the ring; right, ring of 8 plus 1 bivalent. The D and E chromosomes are ones which can be readily identified (Walters 1942).

pairing requires that the chromosomes form the cross-like figure at pachytene, with the pairing partners being changed at the point of the translocation break. This relationship permits a determination of the position of the translocation break, provided the synaptic behavior is exact. Non-homologous pairing such as that encountered in maize would make this less exact, however. If chiasmata are formed in each of the paired arms, a ring of four chromosomes would result; should one arm fail to form a chiasma, as might happen if the translocation involved only a small fraction of the chromosome length, the result would be a chain of four. The degree of terminalization of chiasmata would determine the appearance of the ring or chain at diakinesis of metaphase. Figure 6–15 illustrates translocations

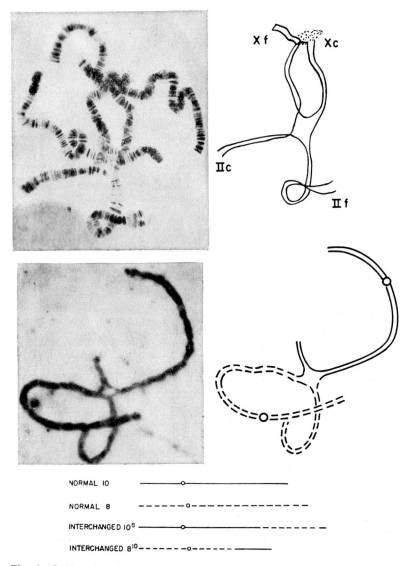

Fig. 6–15. Translocations in Sciara and maize. Above, an X-II translocation as seen in the salivary gland chromosomes of *Sciara coprophila*. In the diagram, c represents the centromeric ends of the two chromosomes, f the free ends. Below, an 8–10 translocation as seen in the pachytene nucleus of a microsporocyte of maize (left), with a diagram (right) to indicate the identity of the chromosomes in the complex. The normal and the translocated chromosomes are diagrammed at the bottom (Sciara figures courtesy of Dr. Helen V. Crouse; others from Rhoades 1955).

as seen in Sciara and in maize. In dipteran salivary gland chromosomes, these are easily recognized, and the banded structure permits the exact points of breakage to be determined with certainty. If known genes are located adjacent to the translocation breaks, it can be determined by linkage tests whether they have remained as before, or whether they have passed on with the displaced piece.

When a translocation ring of four chromosomes reaches the metaphase plate, several arrangements are possible, and each, since the arrangements determine anaphase disjunction, has its own genetic consequences. The three possible arrangements, with their anaphase results, are illustrated in Figure 6–16. In adjacent-1 and adjacent-2 types, the rings are so oriented

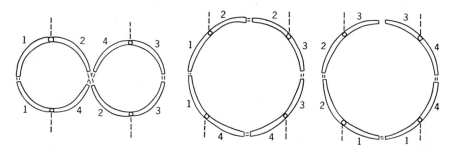

Fig. 6–16. Diagram of alternate (left), adjacent-1 (middle), and adjacent-2 (right) arrangement of a translocation ring of 4 chromosomes. Segregation from these positions should lead to viable gametes from the alternate position; duplication and deficiency from adjacent-1, with homologous centromeres going to the same pole; and duplication and deficiency from adjacent-2, with non-homologous centromeres going to the same pole.

that adjacent chromosomes go to the same anaphase pole, and the gametes formed, while different from each other, are both deficient and duplicated for certain regions of the chromosomes. The remaining arrangement differs in that alternate chromosomes go to the same pole, and the gametes formed are of two kinds, one having a normal set of chromosomes, the other the translocated set. Neither gamete is deficient or duplicated in any way, each having a full complement of the genes represented by the two chromosomes.

If the three types of orientation occurred at random it would be expected that a translocation would lead to inviability in approximately two-thirds of the gametes. In plants, however, and particularly in maize (Burnham 1934) where the phenomenon has been studied extensively, sterility, as determined by the frequency of inviable seeds or defective pollen, is nearer to 50 percent. This can only mean that in maize the zigzag metaphase arrangement, leading to movement of alternate chromosomes to the same pole, occurs with a frequency approaching 50 percent. In Drosophila, it has been shown that there is a definite correlation between the type of disjunction and the amount of crossing over taking place in the translocated segments (Brown 1949; Pipkin 1940). Glass (1935) has also found that the segregation of translocation heterozygotes in Drosophila is not at random, being skewed decidedly in the direction of viable combinations, but this he has attributed to the establishment of a single predetermined axis for segregation. The determination of the axis he feels is not affected by crossing over, contrary to the opinions of Brown and Pipkin.

Probably several factors govern orientation of a ring of four on the metaphase plate, these being (1) length of the chromosomes involved, (2) position of the breaks, (3) number and position of chiasmata, and (4) degree of terminalization of chiasmata. Presumably, the more flexible the ring, the greater would be the opportunities for maneuvering the chromosomes to give the alternate disjunction, but the importance of the problem of preferential segregation, known to exist in the well-established translocation complexes such as found in Oenothera, will be discussed more fully in a later chapter.

Although the duplication-deficiency gametes are inviable in plants because of the inability of the gametophyte to survive such genic changes, they can survive in animals. Genic loss or gain apparently does not affect the viability of eggs or sperm of Drosophila while they are in the haploid state, as Bridges (1916) demonstrated in his non-disjunction studies, and as is demonstrated by the fact that Y-bearing sperm, which lack most of the X-chromosome genes, function as well as do X-bearing sperm. This holds for the other chromosomes as well, as illustrated by the fact that studies of the offspring of two translocation heterozygotes involving Chromosomes II and III reveal that viable individuals are obtained from the union of two duplication-deficiency gametes, provided that they are complementary types. What is absent or duplicated in one gamete is compensated for in the other, to give a full diploid set of genes.

The translocations discussed have involved only two non-homologous chromosomes. Should, however, the arm of one of the translocated chromosomes be involved in a second interchange with a third non-homologous chromosome, a ring or chain of six would form at metaphase. A third interchange would give a ring of ⑧. The process can go on until the entire complement of chromosomes is involved to produce what is known as a *translocation complex*. This situation is met with in *Rhoeo discolor,* a monotypic genus in the family Commelinaceae, and in which a ring of twelve chromosomes can be formed. Surprisingly enough, the plant is highly fertile. Oenothera and Paeonia represent the various stages that may be found. In *Paeonia californica* (Walters 1942), which has 5 pairs of chromosomes, plants have been found with a ring of four (④) and 3 bivalents (3_{II}), a ⑥ and 2_{II}, a ⑥ and a ④, a ⑧ and 1_{II}, and a ⑩ (Fig. 6–14). Oenothera, the genus worked on by de Vries, and from the study of which he formulated his theory of mutation, exhibits a similar tendency which varies with the species. *O. hookeri* has seven normal bivalents, while other species may have up to all 14 chromosomes linked in a ring at meiosis.

VARIATIONS IN CHROMOSOME NUMBER

If the chromosome numbers of a group of random individuals of a particular species were determined, in all likelihood they would be similar. This situation would be expected, for species are reasonably constant biological entities, and it is not difficult to appreciate that this stability is determined by a constancy in the numbers and kinds of genes and chromosomes. Even as the genes mutate, or change in number through loss or addition, so obviously must the chromosomes. The process is slow, for cell and chromosome divisions are remarkably regular phenomena, but variations do occur, and they are sometimes perpetuated to give rise to new chromosomal races.

Variation in chromosome number produces two types of individuals: (1) those whose somatic complements are exact multiples of the basic number characteristic for that species, and (2) those whose somatic complements are irregular multiples of the basic complement. Individuals of the first type are *euploid,* and the individual organism may be haploid (monoploid), diploid, triploid, tetraploid, and so on, with the higher multiple members above the diploid state being collectively referred to as polyploids. Consequently, a tetraploid individual, for example, would produce diploid gametes and gametophytes much as a diploid organism produces haploid gametes and gametophytes. Individuals having irregular chromosome numbers are called *aneuploids,* and an organism that has gained an extra chromosome can be designated as $2n + 1$; a loss of one would be indicated as $2n - 1$. The terms *hyperploid* and *hypoploid* have also been used, but less frequently. A combination of polyploidy and aneuploidy can produce variable numbers of chromosomes in any single individual, race, or species.

Euploidy. A haploid organism contains but a single genome, or set of chromosomes. It is consequently homozygous, or more properly *hemizygous,* for the genes represented in the genome. A diploid organism, however, may have its two genomes similar or dissimilar. Members of a pure diploid species would have similar genomes; an organism resulting from a cross between two diploid species would have dissimilar genomes, and is generally referred to as a *diploid hybrid.* Where more than two genomes are involved, however, the terminology becomes increasingly complex as the number of genomes increases, so that polyploid organisms possessing similar genomes are known as *autopolyploids,* those with dissimilar genomes as *allopolyploids.* The latter must obviously arise through hybridization. By definition, therefore, a clear-cut distinction can be made between auto- and allo-polyploidy; in practice, however, the distinction breaks down, as may be seen from the diagram in Figure 6–17. Reference will be made to this figure as the various kinds of euploidy are discussed.

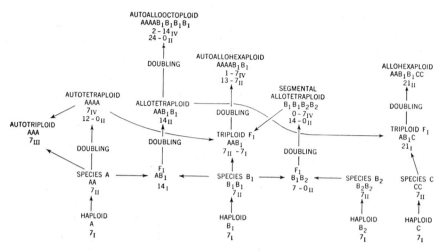

Fig. 6–17. Diagram showing the interrelationships, genome constitution, and mode of origin of typical autopolyploids, allopolyploids, segmental allopolyploids and autoallopolypoids (modified from Stebbins 1950).

Haploidy.—Haploidy may be a normal or an abnormal state. The gametophytic stages of lower plants, and the males of certain insects, such as the bees, wasps, and other hymenopteran forms, are regularly haploid, and the production of gametes proceeds in normal fashion since these organisms are adjusted, evolutionarily speaking, to this mode of existence.

The meiotic divisions vary among different species. In the meiotic cells of the male honeybee, for example, synapsis cannot occur between the dissimilar chromosomes, but this is overcome by the virtual elimination of the first meiotic division (Fig. 6–18). All of the chromosomes pass into one cell, none into a cytoplasmic bud which is pinched off. The second meiotic division, which is equational, is quite regular except that the cytoplasmic division is uneven, producing daughter cells of different size; only the larger is transformed into a functional sperm. There is consequently no reduction in the number of chromosomes during meiosis, and meiosis, in comparison to that of diploid organisms, is anomalous. In other hymenopteran insects the first division of meiosis is missing entirely, and only a single mitotic division, yielding two sperm cells per spermatocyte, remains to constitute the maturation process.

Haploid organisms that are normally diploid cannot adjust their mode of meiotic behavior to the number of chromosomes present, and meiosis as a consequence is highly irregular. The chromosomes, which have no homologues with which to pair, pass as univalents onto the metaphase plate, where they segregate at random (some may divide equationally at times). Since this leads to deficient gametes or spores, the sterility of such haploids is very high. Occasionally, however, haploids produce functional gametes, as would be expected on a random basis of segregation. Thus if

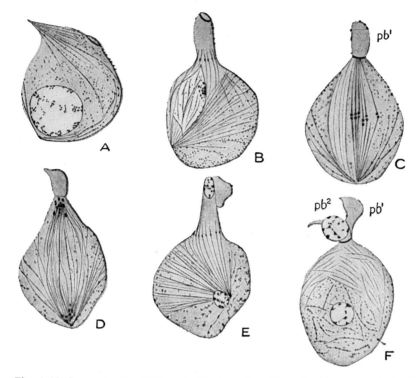

Fig. 6–18. Spermatocyte divisions in the honeybee. Two divisions occur, but only the second one is functional and it is equational as well. The first polar body (pb₁) formed contains no chromosomes, but the second one (pb₂) does (Wilson 1925 after Meves).

the possibilities of any particular chromosome passing into a certain anaphase nucleus is ½, then the probability of obtaining a functional famete is $\frac{1}{2}n,$ where *n* equals the number of chromosomes in the haploid genome. Clearly, the higher the haploid number, the less likely will be the possibilities of viable gametes.

In plants, where haploidy has been more commonly observed as an abnormality than in animals, the haploid individuals can generally be characterized as being smaller than their diploid progenitors. This is not an absolute criterion, for Christensen and Bamford (1943) state that haploids of the pepper are similar in size to the diploid forms. High sterility would provide the first criterion of recognition, followed by an examination of the size of stomatal cells, and then by a direct determination of chromosome numbers. Such positive identifications of haploids have been made in maize, rye, Nicotiana, Datura, and other plant species, and in two species of the newt (Ivanov 1938; Fankhauser 1937; Fankhauser and Griffiths 1939). These animals were small, morphologically and physiologically abnormal, and failed to reach maturity before death.

Haploids can be produced in a variety of ways. In plants, an unfertilized egg can be stimulated to develop by pollen which takes no further part in the developmental processes, or by some kind of environmental shock. Most haploids have been discovered fortuitously, and their method of origin was undetermined, but Chase (1949) indicates that in maize the type of pollen parent is influential in determining the incidence of haploidy. Kostoff (1929) has produced a haploid Nicotiana with paternal characteristics, which suggests that the male sperm penetrated the embryo sac and then developed spontaneously when the egg nucleus failed to function. Fankhauser (1937) induced haploidy in the newt by cutting an egg in two after the entrance of the sperm, but before union of the two nuclei had taken place.

Haploids are of intrinsic interest for two reasons. Having been obtained in plants, the chromosome number can be doubled by colchicine, or they may produce seed by self-fertilization. Such offspring would be completely homozygous for all genes, and would achieve in one step a condition that would require many generations to approach through close inbreeding. The importance of this in plant breeding, where isogenicity is a factor in experimental design, can readily be appreciated (Chase 1949). In the second place, a study of haploid meiosis provides a clue as to the nature of the basic chromosome complement. In haploids of Sorghum, for example, which has ten instead of the usual 20 chromosomes, most cells have ten univalents (Brown 1943). Some, however, have an occasional bivalent suggesting either that ten is not the basic number, or that duplications are present. A similar situation has been found in the pepper ($n = 12$) and as many as 6_{II} have been found, leading to the suggestion that the supposed diploid is really a polyploid in which many, if not all, of the genes are duplicated (Christensen and Bamford 1943). In economic plants this becomes a factor of importance when the genetics of a particular character are being determined.

Autopolyploidy.—If, as indicated in Figure 6–17, a diploid species has its two similar genomes designed AA, then an autotriploid becomes AAA, and an autotetraploid AAAA. The latter would have its origin directly from the diploid by doubling of its chromosomal number either by somatic doubling or by the union of two diploid (unreduced) gametes, while the former could arise as an offspring of a tetraploid and a diploid parent, or from diploid parents by the union of an unreduced and a reduced gamete. Once thought to be quite common in plant species (Muntzing 1936), autopolyploids are now believed to be relatively rare in nature (Clausen, Keck, and Hiesey 1945; Stebbins 1950). Through the use of colchicine, autotetraploids are relatively easy to produce artificially, and a comparison with their diploid progenitors can be made.

Autopolyploids are, in many respects, larger than their related diploids as a result of an increase in cell size (Fig. 6–19). This criterion cannot be used indiscriminately, however, for the increase in size depends upon

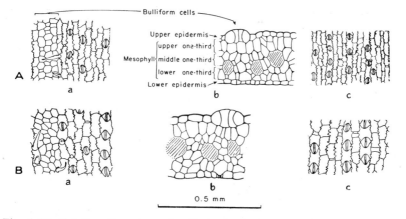

Fig. 6–19. Relative dimensions of cells in the leaf epidermis and mesophyll of diploid (A) and tetraploid (B) maize. a, upper epidermis, b, cross section, and c, lower epidermis (Randolph 1941).

the genotype of the diploids from which the autopolyploids arose. In the grass *Stipa lipida* (Stebbins 1941), autotetraploids derived from different sister diploids had leaves both broader and narrower than the ancestral diploid. In general, however, there is an increase in size of various plant parts, a delay in growth and in flowering, and often an increase in the darkness of the foliage as one goes from haploid, to diploid, to tetraploid plants of the same genetic stock. This is a visible manifestation which can often be checked by determining the size of stomatal cells or pollen grains. As one goes beyond the tetraploid level, however, increases in chromosome number often result in abnormalities such as dwarfing, wrinkled foliage, and weak plants (Stebbins 1950). Presumably this results from the genetic consequences of high polyploidy, and the degree of polyploidy at which unbalance sets in will depend upon the species, or even the individual, in question.

Cytologically, autopolyploids are characterized and identified by the presence of multivalents formed at metaphase of meiosis I. In autotriploids, the three homologous chromosomes pair with each other to give trivalents; in autotetraploids, quadrivalents would result. The number is not constant for each cell, and will depend, of course, on the degree of synapsis and chiasma formation taking place in meiotic prophase. Figures 6–20 and 6–21 illustrate several types of multivalent formation in autopolyploids.

As might be expected, autotriploids are highly sterile because of the random segregation of the three chromosomes of each trivalent. In the triploid *Tradescantia bracteata* ($n = 6$), for example, the pollen grains can receive anywhere from six to 12 chromosomes, with nine being an average number (King 1933). Only those few cells receiving a complete haploid set, or two haploid sets, of chromosomes are likely to survive,

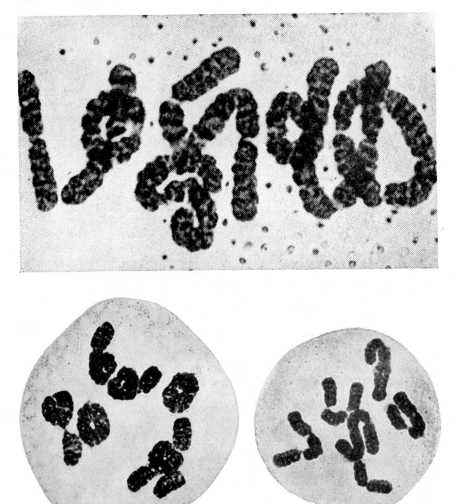

Fig. 6–20. First meiotic metaphases in tetraploid and triploid Tradescantia. Above, tetraploid cell showing quadrivalents and bivalents (Anderson and Sax 1936); below, trivalents in *T. bracteata* (King 1933).

the remaining pollen grains with unbalanced numbers aborting. Autotetraploids also have some pollen sterility as the result of unbalanced chromosome numbers arising out of irregular segregation of quadrivalents or by the lagging of univalents.

The varying degrees of sterility in autotetraploids, however, suggest that disharmonies of a genetic nature are more probably the basis of sterility than is irregular segregation, for segregation may be reasonably regular yet high sterility is encountered. Stebbins (1949) has shown that colchicine-

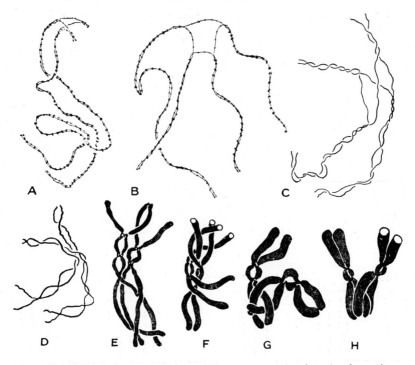

Fig. 6–21. Meiosis in a tetraploid, *Allium porrum,* showing the formation and appearance of quadrivalents. a, b, pachynema; c, d, diplonema; e-g, diakinesis; h, metaphase (Levan 1940).

produced autotetraploids of the grass Ehrharta have a 75–80 percent fertility, and autotetraploid maize sets a very high proportion of its seeds (Randolph 1941). Yet autotetraploids of the cultivated lettuce (Einset 1947) and of *Gossypium herbaceum* (Beasley 1940), which are similar as regards chromosome relationships to the fertile types mentioned above, are highly sterile. In some instances, as in the autotetraploid snapdragon (Sparrow, Ruttle, and Nebel 1942), sterility may be partially correlated with disturbances in the later stages of meiosis, but the fact that autotetraploids from different diploid varieties behave differently points to a genetic basis of undetermined nature.

Only a single clear-cut case of autotetraploidy in nature, that of *Galax aphylla,* a monotypic genus of eastern North America (Baldwin 1941), is known for certain, although there remain other suspected forms (Stebbins 1950). The phenomenon, it would appear, has been of little evolutionary consequence (see Chapter 16 for further discussion), but horticulturally the induction of larger, hardier, and longer flowering autotetraploids is of some importance, particularly if the form, when once induced, can be perpetuated and increased through vegetative means.

Since in an autotetraploid each gene is represented four times, inheritance in such plants can be expected to be more complicated than in normal diploids. As regards a single locus, five stages are possible in terms of dominant and recessive genes (Sansome and Philp 1939): quadruplex *SSSS,* triplex *SSSs,* duplex *SSss,* simplex *Ssss,* and nulliplex *ssss.* Expected ratios can be predicted on the basis of random pairing of chromosomes in two-by-two association at any one level, and of regular disjunction of two chromosomes to each pole. This has been done in a theoretical manner by Muller (1914) who early considered the problem on the assumption of random chromosome segregation, and by Haldane (1930) who considered segregation on a chromatid basis. Their predictions are given in Table 6–1.

TABLE 6–1

Theoretical expectations of segregation in autotetraploids of a single locus when selfed and when testcrossed to the quadruple recessive.

Genotype	Muller Random chromosome segregation		Haldane Random chromatid segregation	
	Selfed	Testcross	Selfed	Testcross
SSSS	1 : 0	1 : 0	1 : 0	1 : 0
SSSs	1 : 0	1 : 0	783 : 1	27 : 1
SSss	35 : 1	5 : 1	21 : 1	3.7 : 1
Ssss	3 : 1	1 : 1	2.48 : 1	13 : 15
ssss	0 : 1	0 : 1	0 : 1	0 : 1

Muller's predictions would clearly hold only for genes that lie between the centromere and the first chiasma, assuming that reductional rather than equational division is the rule for this region, while Haldane's prediction would be valid only for genes that lie distal to the first chiasma. The fact that recessive types can be recovered from a triplex *(SSSs)* plant by selfing or testcrossing is sufficient proof of the fact that in an autotetraploid, as in a diploid, the chromatid and not the chromosome is the unit of segregation. As Sansome and Philp (1939) indicate, actual experimental data agree rather closely with Haldane's predictions. Little (1945) has extensively reviewed the whole subject, but except for the inheritance in a small number of autotetraploid plants of economic interest, the concepts involved only provide confirmation of what has long been known in diploids.

Allopolyploidy.—Considering for the moment only allotetraploids, the genome constitution would be represented as AAB_1B_1 (Fig. 6–17), with the tetraploid having arisen by a doubling of the chromosome number of an F_1 hybrid between Species A and Species B_1. If the genomes are sufficiently dissimilar to preclude any synapsis in the F_1 hybrid (A B_1), it is clear that the hybrid will be highly sterile because of irregular chromosome distribution during the reduction divisions. Doubling of the chromosome number to give the allotetraploid AAB_1B_1 will however provide the opportunity for complete synapsis and regular segregation. Genome A will pair with genome A, genome B_1 with genome B_1. The gametes will be AB_1, and if sterility in the F_1 hybrid is due only to irregular chromosome distribution, then the allotetraploid can be expected to have a high degree of fertility. Such pairing where A pairs with A, and B_1 with B_1, is known as *autosyndesis;* should there by any pairing of A with B_1, *allosyndesis* is said to have taken place, and some irregularities of meiosis might result from quadrivalent formation.

The classical intergeneric cross between Raphanus (radish) and Brassica (cabbage) illustrates the point just made (Karpechenko 1928). The nine haploid Raphanus chromosomes are distinctly different from the nine haploid Brassica chromosomes. No pairing occurs in the F_1 hybrid, and a high degree of sterility ensues. A number of unreduced gametes are formed, however, and in the F_2 population Karpechenko recovered a number of tetraploids. If R and B represent the Raphanus and Brassica genomes respectively, the allotetrpaloid is then RRBB. Meiosis is normal, and the gametes produced are RB only. The allotetraploid, therefore, behaves in all respects very similar to a normal diploid, and had the origin been unknown it might well have been considered a distinct species.

The diploid behavior of the Raphanobrassica tetraploid also holds for certain heterozygous genes known to have been present in the diploid parents. These genes show normal segregating properties according to diploid expectations. Were the segregating genes in both the R and B genomes concerned with similar characters, however, a duplicate ratio might have been encountered as in tetraploid wheats, or the genes from one genome may have obscured the expression of the genes from the other genome. Such a behavior has been found in an allotetraploid Rubus (Sansome and Philp 1939). The two original parents differed in types of prickles on the stem. In the allotetraploid, one type bred true, the other was never recovered. Such a phenomenon was known formerly as *shift,* and is an indication of heterozygosity that can persist in allotetraploids, and that may account in part for their greater vigor as compared to the diploid parents.

Allopolyploids of a more complex nature than that represented by the allotetraploids can arise, and probably have arisen many times in the evolution of plant species (Stebbins 1950). A possible method of origin for an allohexaploid is given in Figure 6–17. In this particular case, the fusion of an AB_1 gamete from the allotetraploid AAB_1B_1 with a C gamete from species C, will give an F_1 triploid AB_1C which has three genomes from three different species. If there is no or very little synapsis among the 21 chromosomes, high sterility is to be expected. Doubling of the chromosome number, however, would lead to an allohexaploid (AAB_1B_1CC) characterized by high fertility, with each gamete possessing A, B_1, and C genomes. Any allosyndesis present in either the F_1 triploid or its doubled offspring would alter the sterility aspects to a certain degree, raising it in the former and lowering it in the latter (assuming that the basis of sterility in both instances is wholly chromosomal rather than genic).

The doubling of an allotetraploid to give an octoploid individual would lead to a complex polyploid type having the characteristics of both auto- and allo-polyploidy. Stebbins has referred to such an individual as an auto-allooctoploid, with a representative karyotype being $AAAAB_1B_1B_1B_1$. Such a genotype could also arise through the hybridization of two auto-tetraploids, AAAA and $B_1B_1B_1B_1$, followed by doubling. Most auto-allopolyploids, however, appear to be hexaploids having a general formula of AAAABB. The two species *Phleum pratense* and *Solanum negrine* are thought to be of this nature on the basis of the chromosomal behavior of haploids derived from them. A haploid of *P. pratense* shows 7_{II} and 7_I at meiosis, leading to the belief that its genome can be represented as AAB (Nordenskiöld 1941, 1945; Stebbins 1950), while that of *S. negrine* shows 12_{II} and 12_I (Jorgenson 1928). The origin of such autoallohexaploids is probably through the union of an unreduced AA gamete with a B gamete, followed by doubling, rather than through the crossing of an autotetraploid AAAA with species B, followed by doubling.

Segmental allopolyploids.—The allopolyploids discussed above are those in which the chromosomes of genome A have few or no homologies with those of B or C, and only autosyndesis characterizes the meiotic behavior. Not all hybrids between diploid species, however, show a complete absence of meiotic pairing, and some indeed may have a reasonable degree of fertility. When doubled, these form mostly bivalents but the formation of some quadrivalents, plus the meiotic pairing of the diploid hybrids, indicates that some chromosomal segments are homologous in the two sets. Stebbins (1947, 1950) has referred to these as segmental polyploids, and it is believed that they are more common in nature than are the true allopolyploids. As might be expected, the segmental allotetraploid shows meiotic irregularities as the result of some quadrivalent formation, and some sterility ensues. Typical examples of this form of polyploidy at the tetraploid level are *Delphinium gyposophilum* [derived from *D. hesperium* × *D. recurvatum* (Lewis and Epling 1946, Epling 1947)], *Tradescantia canaliculata-humilis* (Skirm 1942), and *Primula kewensis* known to be derived from *P. floribunda* × *verticillata* (Newton and Pellew 1929). Higher levels of such polyploidy can also exist as Stebbins has pointed out.

Clearly, therefore, allopolyploidy and autopolyploidy, in a sharply de-fined cytological sense, are only the extremes of a spectrum of meiotic homologies ranging from complete homology between genomes (auto-tetraploidy) to a complete lack of homology (allotetraploidy). The seg-mental polyploids represent the intermediate types having some degree of homology, with the basis of decision resting upon the degree of meiotic pairing.

Polyploidy in animals. The relative scarcity of polyploidy among animals presents a sharp contrast to its widespread prevalence among plants, particularly in the angiospermous groups. This problem was early considered by Muller (1925), who came to the conclusion that polyploidy would be quite limited among animals because the sharp separation of the two sexes rests upon a chromosomal mechanism that does not permit a juggling of the chromosome numbers to the same extent that is possible in hermaphroditic plants. The evidence bears out this hypothesis. Where polyploidy is known with certainty in the form of established races, it is usually intimately bound up with a parthenogenetic mode of development.

Some polyploidy, however, is present among certain animal groups, although the type of polyploidy in most instances remains to be established. White (1954) has published a number of histograms of chromosome numbers based on the tabulations of Harvey (1917, 1920) (see also Makino 1951) in which it seems quite clear that polyploidy of some sort has functioned to produce the variations in chromosome numbers that have been found. Thus, in the oligochaete worms, which are hermaphroditic, haploid numbers of 16 and 32 are most commonly encountered. In the Hirudinea, the numbers 8 and 16 have been found together with others in between. The genus Mesotoma of the Rhabdocoela contains one species with a haploid number of 2, six species with 4, one with 5, and one with 8. This would strongly suggest that the 4- and 8-chromosome species are tetraploid and octoploid, but as White (1954) points out, such an assumption would require exact knowledge of the basic chromosome number for the genus, and in many groups this determination becomes a virtual impossibility. White is thus reluctant to accept the views of Slack (1938), Gates (1942), and Vandel (1938) that polyploidy has played a major role in animal evolution.

Smith's (1941, 1942) study of the sawflies has revealed an authentic case of polyploidy unassociated with parthenogenesis. Most of the species of Neodiprion and Diprion have seven chromosomes in the males and 14 in the females, the males developing parthenogenetically as in other hymenoptera. *D. simile,* however, has 28 in the female, 14 in the male. Meiosis in the males is similar to that found in hymenopteran males in that the first division is missing, and the second is equational, while in the females bivalents but not quadrivalents are formed. On this basis Smith has considered *D. simile* to be an allotetraploid, but it may be, as White suggests, that the small size of the chromosomes, and their low chiasma frequency, precludes quadrivalent formation, thus obscuring what may well be a good case of autotetraploidy.

Although no known polyploid race, with the likely exception of the golden hamster (White 1954), has become established in the vertebrate group, triploids and tetraploids are by no means uncommon as individuals in natural populations of urodeles (Fankhauser 1938, 1939, 1945; Böök

1940). Fankhauser and Humphrey (1950) have also bred a tetraploid female axolotl to a diploid male. Ninety-eight of 102 eggs were fertile, but only two out of 19 larvae studied had a $3n$ number of 42 chromosomes, the remainder ranging from 32 to 44. The tetraploid female clearly produced many aneuploid but functional eggs. Circulatory abnormalities and extreme edema were encountered in the offspring, perhaps because of chromosome unbalance, and none survived to a breeding age.

Aneuploidy. In general, the two members of a pair of homologous chromosomes regularly segregate during meiosis in a normal diploid to give a haploid set of chromosomes in each gamete or spore, or to give, in mitosis, two cells of like chromosomal constitution. Exceptions in the form of accidents occur, however, to give products deficient or duplicated for a particular chromosome. Bridges (1916) recognized the phenomenon, and utilized it in his classical study of exceptional individuals in Drosophila (see Chapter 4). He referred to the process as one of non-disjunction, i.e., the members of a pair apparently failed to disjoin, both passing into the same anaphase nucleus. It is now recognized that the occurrence of aneuploid gametes or spores results rather from a failure to pair initially, and with a random passage to one or the other of the two poles, both chromosomes will occasionally pass into the same nucleus. The two complementary gametes, one $n + 1$ and the other $n - 1$, will, on union with a normal gamete, give individuals which are $2n + 1$ or $2n - 1$. Such individuals are commonly referred to as *trisomics* and *monosomics* respectively; the particular chromosome in question is represented in triplicate or singly instead of in the usual disomic condition.

Trisomic types. $2n + 1$ types occasionally are found among the offspring of diploid organisms, as described above, but they can more readily be obtained by selfing a triploid (in plants), or by crossing a diploid with a triploid. The irregular distribution of chromosomes in a triploid is such that unbalanced gametes are frequently formed, and if in plants the female is a triploid the possibilities are somewhat greater for producing unbalanced offspring since the egg can survive unbalance to a greater extent than can the pollen grain.

Trisomics have been studied most extensively in Datura, maize, tomato (Rick and Barton, 1954), Nicotiana (Smith 1943), and Drosophila. In the latter organism, the small fourth chromosome is the only autosome that can exist in a trisomic state to give a functional breeding fly, and the genetic ratios obtained are in agreement with what would be expected on the basis of chromosome segregation, and of non-elimination of unbalanced gametes [however, see Sturtevant (1936) for exceptions in regular segregation]. Thus if an $+ + ey$ trisomic female (usually called triple-IV) is crossed to an *ey ey* male, a $5+ : 1$ *ey* ratio is obtained. This results from the segregation of the three IV chromosomes to give a ratio of $2+ : 2+$ *ey* : $1++ : 1$ *ey* gametes. In plants, however, the unbalanced pollen grains either fail to take part in fertilization, or they compete only with difficulty with normal pollen grains. In maize, between 1 and 2 percent transmission of $n + 1$ pollen grains occurs, while in the eggs, the transmission is from 25 to 50 percent in a $2n + 1$ individual (Einset 1943), with longer chromosomes being transmitted in higher frequencies than short ones. Einset suggests that elimination of the extra chromosome is due to failure of synapsis and subsequent failure at telophase to be included in either nucleus, thus increasing the number of n gametes at the expense of the $n + 1$ type.

The study of trisomics made in Datura has been particularly elucidating (Blakeslee 1930). Datura has a haploid number of 12 chromosomes, with the consequence that 12 different trisomics are possible. All have been identified, and each produces certain characteristic phenotypic aspects that distinguish it from the others. Figure 6–22 illustrates the 12 possible types as they affect the morphology of the seed pod.

Each of the 12 normal chromosomes is designated by labelling their ends. Thus the chromosomes become 1·2, 3·4, 5·6, ..., 23·24. The trisomic *Rolled,* for example, has the 1·2 chromosome in triplicate, and in meiosis the trivalent formed would take one of the forms illustrated in Figure 6–23. Such trisomics in which an unmodified chromosome is present in triplicate are referred to as *primary trisomics.*

Secondary trisomics arise from primary trisomics, and in addition to producing an altered phenotype that is characteristic, they can be recognized by the fact that a closed ring of three chromosomes is possible (Fig. 6–23), a condition not possible with a primary trisomic. On the basis of like ends of chromosomes pairing with like ends, a secondary trisomic consists of three chromosomes, two of which are normal, while the extra chromosome has two similar ends. Thus, if the two normal chromosomes are 1·2, the extra one must be 1·1 or 2·2. In other words, for every primary trisomic there are two secondaries, and in the case of the 1·2 chromosomes mentioned, the primary trisomic *Rolled* has the 1·2 chromosome in triplicate, while the secondary trisomics *Sugarloaf* and *Polycarpic* have chromosomes 1·1 and 2·2, respectively, as the extra member. Of the 24 secondary trisomics possible in Datura more than half have been identified. This type of aneuploidy has also been found in maize (Rhoades 1938) and Matthiola (Philp and Huskins 1931).

The extra chromosome of a secondary trisomic may or may not be an isochromosome. If it is, it has resulted from a misdivision of the centromere, and both arms are identical throughout their entire length. Secondary trisomics can also arise by crossing over within a pericentric inversion, but in this event only their ends are identical. The former hypothesis seems most likely since primary trisomics give rise to secondaries in most instances, probably as the result of chromosomal or genetic unbalance.

Tertiary trisomics have an extra chromosome which is made up of parts of two non-homologus chromosomes. For example, the extra chromosome that gives the phenotype *Hedge* is 1·9, produced by a translocation between

NORMAL

ROLLED   GLOSSY   BUCKLING   ELONGATE

ECHINUS   COCKLEBUR   MICROCARPIC   REDUCED

POINSETTIA   SPINACH   GLOBE   ILEX

Fig. 6–22. Seed Capsules of normal and primary trisomic types of the Jimson weed, *Datura stramonium*. In "rolled," the extra chromosome is 1·2, in "glossy" 3·4, and so on to "ilex" with 23·24 (Sharp 1943, after Blakeslee).

chromosomes 1·2 and 9·10. In meiosis such a trisomic could be recognized by the characteristic configurations that are produced by the conjugation of the five chromosomes (Fig. 6–23).

Monosomics. The loss of a chromosome is a far more deleterious change than the addition of one. In fact, monosomic organisms that are basically diploid are relatively rare. This is undersandable since, as pointed out earlier in the chapter, deletions of more than 50 bands (as defined in salivary gland chromosomes) are lethal in the heterozygous state in Drosophila.

Probably the best known monosomic type is the haplo-IV Drosophila.

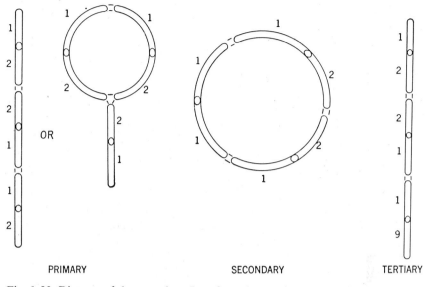

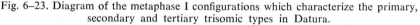

Fig. 6–23. Diagram of the metaphase I configurations which characterize the primary, secondary and tertiary trisomic types in Datura.

Drosophila males can lose a Y-chromosome to become haplo-X and still survive, and the males of many insect groups are normally so, but this represents a special type of genic balance to which the organisms have become adjusted. The haplo-IV flies are recognizable by certain body characteristics, but they are of interest only insofar as studies on gene dosage are involved.

Where $2n - 1$ plants are found to exist there is good reason for believing that the plants are polyploid rather than diploid. Their constitution is therefore not $2n - 1$, but $3n - 1$, $4n - 1$, and so on. McClintock (1929) has described a $2n - 1$ chimera in maize, with the odd chromosome behaving in meiosis as a univalent, but since maize is presumably a diploid, such an individual would be incapable of giving rise to similar $2n - 1$ offspring; the deficient gametes would fail to function. Conger (1940) has described a deficient microspore in Tradescantia with only five chromosomes $(n - 6)$, but it is unlikely that the spore would develop into a functional pollen grain.

In polyploids, the unbalance created by chromosome loss can be more easily withstood. This problem has been extensively studied by Clausen (1941) in the amphidiploid *Nicotiana tabacum* and by Sears (1944, 1954) in the 42-chromosome, or hexaploid wheats, *Triticum vulgare (aestivum)*. Twenty of the 24 possible monosomics have been identified in *N. tabacum*, while all of the possible 21 have been studied in *T. vulgare*. In the latter species, the monosomics do not have a phenotypic expression appreciably different from the normal, as one might expect on the basis of the polyploid nature of the species. One exception, however, is monosomic IX (Sears' designation) or C [Huskin's (1946) designation], which gives rise to the speltoid phenotype, so-called because of the resemblance of such individuals to *T. spelta*.

Selfing of monosomics leads to the production of *nullisomics,* which are characterized by the loss of a single pair of homologous chromosomes. Found among selfed progeny in frequencies ranging from 0.9 to 10.3 percent, their phenotypes depart from normal in varying degrees and particularly in vigor, while a similar variability occurs in both male and female fertility. Transmission of deficient ($n - 1$) gametes by monosomics through the female side is greater than 50 percent, at the same time that it is very appreciably lowered through the male side. Elimination of deficient pollen grains in the gametophyte generation accounts for the lowered male transmissibility, but the excess of $n - 1$ eggs can be accounted for on the basis of lagging chromosomes.

Nullisomic individuals have proven useful in a variety of ways. Certain genetic factors have been located because of the aberrant ratios issuing from the disturbed chromosomal segregations and transmissions. The frequency of monosomics in normal populations can also be determined by crossing nullisomics by normals. From these studies Sears has been able to show that certain chromosomes, notably IV and XV, are more frequently involved in the formation of monosomics than are the other members of the complement. These same chromosomes are known to have a lower chiasma frequency than the other 19 members, and presumably a lack of pairing and the lagging of unpaired chromosomes leads to the production of the deficient gametes.

The univalents encountered in monosomics often give rise to telocentric chromosomes and isochromosomes. From monosomic-VI, five plants were obtained, two having univalents that were telocentric and three that were isochromosomic. The same arm of Chromosome VI was involved in each case so that it can be assumed that the univalency of the chromosome provides the cause for its instability in division, although the underlying mechanism remains obscure.

Trisomes ($6n + 1$) and tetrasomes ($6n + 2$) have also been found by Sears in *T. vulgare*. These have a lesser effect on fertility and viability than do the corresponding monosomics and nullisomics, but from the standpoint of polyploidy, and considering the presence of partially duplicated genomes, it is of interest to note that tetrasomic II compensates almost completely for nullisomic XX, even to the extent of preventing the elimination of the tetra-II, nulli-XX pollen through competition with normal pollen grains. From this it may be concluded that Chromosomes II and XX are reasonably homologous, although not to the extent of permitting pairing in a normal hexaploid individual. A similar compensating nullisometetrasome combination involves nulli-XVI and an unidentified tetrasome. Such substitution studies, together with the possibilities opened up by the nullisomic technique, permit both the establishment of linkage groups in the three genomes that go to form *T. vulgare,* and the determination of similarities existing in the several genomes.

CHAPTER 7

Chromosome Movement

Time-exposure films of living cells in division reveal the intricate and exacting maneuvers performed by the chromosomes as they pass through the successive stages of mitosis and meiosis. Such motion pictures belie the static conception ordinarily derived from a study of stained preparations, and emphasize forcibly that the cell in division presents a picture of constantly changing activity, an activity arising from an interplay of forces that have their origin in the cytoplasm and within the chromosomes. These forces, as yet but dimly apprehended and not fully understood, undoubtedly have their origin in the biochemical systems that function within the confines of the intact cell.

Many hypotheses have been advanced to explain the various aspects of chromosome and cell dynamics, but until the systems themselves are understood in a physical and chemical sense the causal mechanisms involved can only be guessed at. This situation should evoke no discouragement. The descriptive phenomena are known with some measure of certainty, and, in most fields of science, description precedes causal analysis. Indeed, the present rapid progress in cytological research at the physical and chemical levels suggests that cytology will soon witness the solution of many of the problems that, at the moment, appear incomprehensible.

The microscopically visible activities occurring within the cell during division are directed toward the achievement of a single goal, that, namely, of providing additional cells of essentially similar genetic constitution. Whether the process of cell division results simply in an increase in cell number as one phase of an organism's growth, in an increase in organism number as in the bacteria or Protozoa, or in the formation of sexual cells or asexual spores, the various changes the chromosomes and the cytoplasm undergo appear to be similar in detail, and, probably, in origin.

Meiosis differs from mitosis in that the events that take place are more complex, and the products that result are more diverse, but these differences can be considered adaptive modifications that have become established in the course of the evolution of sexual mechanisms. Judging from the differences exhibited by various types of cells, mitosis, too, must have had a diversified evolution of its own, although the almost universal occurrence of a regular and well-integrated mitosis in organisms precludes any reconstruction of mitotic evolution that would be at all elucidating.

In the following discussion of chromosome and cytoplasmic dynamics, it should be borne in mind that these are adaptive phenomena enabling the cell to perform better the function of perpetuating its kind. To view them in any other light is meaningless. For convenience, an arbitrary separation may be made between those activities that prepare the chromosome for division, and those that provide the mechanism of division. The former are essentially chromosomal in origin, the latter cytoplasmic.

The phenomenon of chiasma formation (genetical crossing over) should logically be considered as an integral portion of meiotic prophase activity; but, because of its cytogenetic importance, it will be taken up separately in the next chapter.

CHROMOSOME REPRODUCTION

It is not possible, with our present knowledge, to state definitely the manner by which chromosomes reproduce themselves. The problem is intrinsically biochemical, for presumably the chromosome, by an autocatalytic process, fashions a replica of itself out of the materials available in its immediate neighborhood.

The usual analogy that has been drawn, in the absence of positive information, is that chromosome reproduction is similar to that found in the crystalline viruses. Presumably the original virus particle, in an active metabolic state, can act as a template or model for the replication process. The viruses, when introduced into a cell, rapidly multiply by converting the protein and nucleic acid of the cell, or their precursors, into virus nucleoprotein. As the number of virus particles increases, the protein of the cell diminishes in quantity (Frey-Wyssling 1948). It is assumed that the cell proteins, when in contact with, or acted upon by, the virus protein are transformed into units of chemical structure identical with that of the infecting particle. A trypsin molecule apparently has the same properties, converting any protrypsin in its vicinity into active trypsin.

The analogy of virus reproduction with that of the chromosome gains support by virtue of the fact that both are nucleoproteins, and it is becoming apparent that the nucleoproteins exert their profound effects, directly or indirectly, through enzymatic action. To progress beyond this point with the analogy, however, is to enter the realm of speculation, for a more intelligent interpretation must obviously be based upon a more detailed knowledge of the molecular structure of the chromosome, as well as of its energetics. Delbrück (1941) has presented an ingenious, if theoretical, hypothesis about the autocatalytic synthesis of polypeptides and its relationship to chromosome reproduction, synapsis, and repulsion; but its validity must obviously await further experimentation.

One thing is certain. With rare exceptions, the genes and the chromosomes reproduce themselves exactly. The evidence for such duplication is seen in every cell division when each chromosome resolves itself into two chromatids. It has been thought by many that the duplication occurs once for every gene in every cycle of the cell (cf. Delbrück 1941), but this is by no means a certainty even in rapidly dividing cells. Huskins (1947) has stated that for a cell to remain diploid it must regularly pass through a division cycle; where delays occur, as, for example, in the cells of the midgut of the mosquito which show multiple-chromosome complexes (Berger 1938; Grell 1946), or where division has ceased without cessation of the activity of the cell, as in the salivary gland cells of the Diptera, the chromosomes continue to divide to give polytene structures or polyploid cells (White 1946b). Duplication of the chromosome must consequently occur during the resting state, and not during the active stages of division. Duplication appears also to be a continuing process, independent of cell or nuclear division, although coordinated with them in embryonic or meristematic tissues. Frequent reference has been made in cytological literature to the "time of chromosome splitting," but often the interpretations are without general significance, since different agents show different times of effective splitting. Interpretations of chromosome structure have, therefore, often been made without reference to the process of duplication, although the two are patently related. Since this topic clearly relates to the chemical structure of the chromosome, further discussion will be deferred until this topic is taken up (Chapter 11).

CHROMOSOME CONTRACTION

A feature characteristic of chromosomes during cell division is the considerable contraction they progressively undergo as they pass from early prophase stages to metaphase. This process is clearly an adaptive mechanism that allows an elongated chromosome to complete its division within relatively narrow confines, a shorter chromosome being mechanically more maneuverable on the spindle than a lengthy and tenuous one. Preparations of metaphase cells of Trillium or Tradescantia, pretreated with ammonia vapors or with a dilute solution of KCN before fixation and staining, reveal the large chromosomes to be made up of a series of coils closely packed together in the manner of a wire spring (Fig. 7–1). In overstained preparations the coils produce the corrugated appearance commonly observed in metaphase and anaphase chromosomes. Their frequency is a function of temperature (Fig. 7–2), genotype, and probably nutrition. Where the chromatids are clearly separated from each other, each can be observed to be independently coiled, and it is generally assumed that the chromatid is the unit of coiling. In some instances, as in the meiotic chromosomes of the insect Puto (Hughes-Schrader 1944), the half-chromatids have been demonstrated to contract, and to separate, independently; but this has not been observed in somatic cells. In most organisms the half-chromatids ordinarily would be indistinguishable.

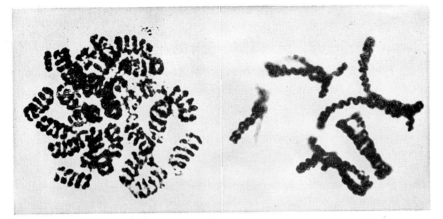

Fig. 7–1. Major coils as seen in the meiotic metaphase chromosomes of Tradescantia (left) and Trillium (right) (Swanson 1943; Huskins 1937).

There can be little doubt that the prophase contraction of mitotic and meiotic chromosomes is largely a consequence of the coiling mechanism. On the other hand, the elongation and contraction of chromosomes unre-

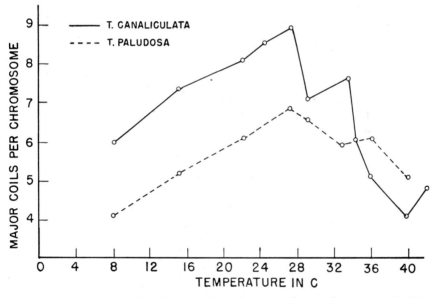

Fig. 7–2. The relationship of the number of major coils per chromosome to temperature in two species of Tradescantia (Swanson 1942).

lated to any visible structural changes complicates any consideration of the mechanism involved. Once considered to be a relatively simple process, the contraction of chromosomes has been shown to be deceptively complex; and, despite the results of several decades of rather intensive research, no

general agreement has been reached as to either the nature of the coils or
their ontogenetic development.

Much of the disagreement revolves around interpretations of structures
that lie at the limits of resolution, and for this reason further progress is
likely to be slow. The use of different organisms for the clarification of
controversial points, and the possibility of a variety of coiling mechanisms
that give rise to similar structural appearances, preclude any generalization
that covers all contraction phenomena.

The electron microscope has, to date, been of little use in furthering
an understanding of the problem. It has consequently been stated, somewhat facetiously but with a good deal of truth, that in the study of chromosome contraction one can see what one wishes to see, and nothing more.

In considering contraction of the chromosome a distinction must be
made *between chromosome length* and *chromonema length*. The former
designates the over-all length of the chromosome from one end to the other
without reference to the degree to which the chromonemata within it are
coiled. In another sense, "chromosome length" is also matrix length.
Chromonema length is that of the chromonema proper, regardless of its
state of coiling. In an uncoiled chromosome, chromonema length can be
determined by direct measurements; the length of a coiled thread, however, can only be ascertained by knowing the length of the chromosome,
and the number, diameter, and pitch of the coils. The necessity for maintaining a distinction between the two types of measurement becomes obvious, since it has been shown that (1) a shortening of the chromosome
length is readily achieved by the development of a coiled system within a
chromonema of unchanging length (a wire door spring provides an excellent analogy), (2) chromonema length can vary widely without a corresponding change in chromosome length (Huskins 1941), and (3) chromonema length can increase or decrease without visible manifestation of any
structural change related to a coiling system. Duryee (1941) has demonstrated this last point in the oöcyte chromosomes of Amphibia, while
D'Angelo (1946), through micrurgical studies, has similarly demonstrated
it in the salivary gland chromosomes of Chironomus.

Changes in chromosome and chromonema lengths. Metaphase and anaphase chromosomes are more easily studied because they represent a state
of greater contraction than that found in earlier stages, and the degree of
contraction may be readily determined from cells prepared with the smear
techniques. The contraction is greater in meiotic cells, and it is not necessarily identical for all types of somatic cells (Table 7–1). In meiotic cells,
such measurements are generally made at pachynema as a stage representative of prophase, but it is generally agreed that leptotene chromosomes are
longer than those found in pachynema. The chromosomes at pachynema, according to Sax and Sax (1935), are seven to 11 times longer than they are
at meiotic metaphase, this representing a considerably greater reduction

TABLE 7–1

Average chromosome lengths in microns at prophase (P) and metaphase (M)
of mitotic and meiotic divisons (Sax and Sax 1935).

| Species | Mitotic | | | | Meiotic | |
| | Roottip | | Microspore | | | |
	P	M	P	M	P	M
Vicia faba	48	13	36	11	98	9
Tradescantia sp.	56	21	61	12	81	9
Lilium regale	35	22	—	15	83	12
Secale cereale	37	14	—	—	61	8

in length than that characteristic of mitosis where a contraction ratio of 2:1 to 4:1 is more commonly found. Manton (1939, 1950), in a study of the royal fern, *Osmunda regalis*, has shown that the leptotene chromosomes are fully 50 percent longer than those in pachynema. Consequently, over-all contraction of meiotic chromosomes is even greater than that estimated from pachytene stages. Manton has also indicated that the length of the pachytene chromosome is roughly comparable in length to that in the earliest measurable mitotic prophase. The leptotene chromosome thus possesses a far greater length than the same chromosome in mitosis. By calculating the chromonema length during the various stages of mitosis and meiosis, Manton has found that in mitosis no length changes were evident, while in meiosis the length was 33 to 50 percent shorter than that of somatic chromosomes, a shortening that has been attributed to a super-contraction of the fibrils of the chromonemata, much as keratin or myosin may be contracted by a folding of the protein molecules. Chromosome length was progressively reduced during both mitosis and meiosis.

The data derived from a detailed study of Trillium chromosomes do not agree in general with those cited above (Huskins 1941). Considering the five haploid chromosomes as a unit, Huskins and his co-workers have found that chromosome length in meiosis increases from 86 to 125 microns during diakinesis, then decreases to approximately 100 microns by metaphase I. This length remains unchanged to anaphase II, when it is decreased to about 80 microns, a length comparable to that found at metaphase and anaphase of the first microspore division. Chromonema length, however, fluctuated markedly. A process of elongation changes the leptotene length of 920 microns to 1040 by zygonema. Though pachynema, diplonema, and early diakinesis a contraction reduces the length to 100 microns. By the end of diakinesis, a second elongation phase increases the length to 200, by metaphase I to 300, and by anaphase I to 350 microns. The latter length is maintained until anaphase II. In the succeeding microspore division, the prophase chromonema is again approximately 1000 microns long, decreases to 650 microns at metaphase, and then elongates to 1000 microns by anaphase.

Since it is apparent that chromosome lengths at metaphase and anaphase of the microspore division are comparable while chromonema lengths differ appreciably, it must mean that the chromonema is more tightly packed in the anaphase than in the metaphase chromosome (Sparrow 1942). It is also apparent from a comparison of chromosome and chromonema lengths from diakinesis to metaphase I that a contraction of the former may be accompanied by an increase in the latter. No similarly exacting studies have been made on other organisms; it is, therefore, uncertain how universally applicable these findings may be.

The coiling of chromosomes. It will be necessary to preface the discussion of chromosome coiling with a consideration of the terminology to be employed. The literature on the subject is confusing to an extreme, with the definitions of many of the terms overlapping. The terms used here have been arbitrarily selected, although wherever possible they conform with general usage.

Large somatic chromosomes ordinarily present a solid appearance when prepared by the usual techniques of fixation and staining. By special pretreatments with hot water, KCN, or ammonia fumes, it is possible to show that each chromosome at metaphase is a coiled structure, the coiling being similar in a sense to that of an elongated wire spring (Fig. 7–3). The

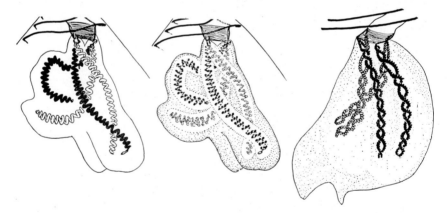

Fig. 7–3. Prophase chromosomes in the protozoan, *Holomastigotoides tusitala,* showing the major coils (left) and minor coils (middle) in the separated chromatids. The right figure indicates the relational coiling that can sometimes be shown to exist between half-chromatids. The spindle is rectangular in shape and is stretched between the long slender centrioles (Cleveland 1949).

individual turnings, or *gyres,* make up the *somatic,* or *standard, coil* which is renewed at each division prophase. Within a single organism, and even between organisms of the same species, the number and diameter of gyres is reasonably constant. The free separation of the chromatids at anaphase, without entanglement, reveals that the chromatid is the unit of coiling. As the coiled chromosomes pass into interphase, and reappear in the next prophase, the somatic coils will have been largely lost, the only vestige of a coiled structure being the loose spirals which soon straighten out, and are eliminated, as the chromosomes undergo a new somatic coiling cycle. These loose spirals are the *relic coils* (Fig. 7–3).

In prophase of a somatic division, the relatively long chromosomes clearly consist of two chromatids. These are loosely wound around each other in the manner of a two-stranded electric cord (Fig. 7–3). As prophase proceeds, and the chromosomes shorten, the chromatids disengage themselves, and eventually come to lie side by side, a process apparently accompanied by a rotation of the ends of the chromatids, with the functionally undivided centromere being the single fixed point of the chromosome. The loose wrapping of one chromatid about another constitutes the *relational* coils.

Like the relic coils, the relational coils' origin traces back to the previous somatic coils of anaphase. Two interpretations of their origin are possible. If, as Darlington (1937a) has maintained, the anaphase chromosome is a single-stranded structure, then its longitudinal cleavage or replication at the beginning of prophase, together with its subsequent straightening, will leave the two chromatids entangled. Such a phenomenon may readily be demonstrated by cutting a coiled strip of paper along its longitudinal plane without allowing the ends to rotate. Stretching of the strip to its full length will reveal the longitudinal halves coiled around each other in a long loose spiral.

The other interpretation is based on the generally accepted hypothesis that the anaphase chromosome is already subdivided, having been so at the time that, as a chromatid, it was undergoing coiling in prophase. Since the chromatid in prophase is the unit of coiling, then relaxation of the standard coils into relic coils at the next prophase will leave the new chromatids (the half-chromatids of the previous division) relationally coiled. There are not as many relational coils in early prophase as there were somatic coils in the preceding anaphase, but the discrepancy in agreement probably relates to the fact that rotation of the chromatid ends, as shortening occurs, induces a progressive loss until at metaphase none, or very few, are present.

Two additional terms will serve to elucidate somatic coiling relationships. Two chromatids, as in prophase, relationally coiled about each other, are said to possess a *plectonemic coil* (Fig. 7–4); i.e., the chromatids cannot separate laterally along their entire length without a revolution of the chromatid ends. On the other hand, if two chromatids, coiling together, are free to separate laterally without entanglement, their coiling relationships are said to be *paranemic*. The latter type of coiling is best illustrated by the independent contraction of chromatids in meiosis which permits their free lateral separation at anaphase I.

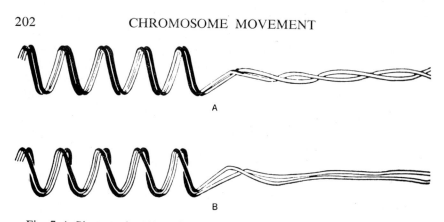

Fig. 7–4. Plectonemic (A) and paranemic (B) coiling. Straightening out of the former leads to a relational coiling of chromatids; the latter, when similarly straightened out, leaves the chromatids free (Sparrow, Huskins and Wilson 1941).

For demonstration purposes, the two types of coils, plectonemic and paranemic, can be constructed from two wire strands. If the strands are wrapped around a stick with the strands running parallel at all times, and the intact coil is then slipped from the stick and stretched, the two wires will be coiled relationally, or plectonemically. The same wires will form a paranemic coil if, for each turn of the wires about the stick, a half-twist in the wires is made in the opposite direction. Such a demonstration in no way implies, however, that chromosomes coil by this method.

In meiosis, the coiling picture is comparable to, but more complicated than, that found in mitosis, owing to the occurrence of synapsis and chiasma formation, and to the greater degree of contraction attained by the chromosomes. Metaphase bivalents in such organisms as Trillium and Tradescantia (Fig. 7–1) are characterized by their conspicuous coils which are larger in diameter, but fewer in number, than the same chromosomes at somatic metaphase. These are the *major coils;* although differing in name, they are homologous with the somatic coils.

Chromatid separation within the coiled chromosomes is not evident at metaphase, but their free anaphase separation indicates their paranemic nature. In addition, there can be distinguished, in clear preparations of Tradescantia, a small-gyred *minor* coil which runs the length of, and at right angles to, the major coil. Discovered in Tradescantia by Fujii in 1926, its existence in other organisms has been disputed. While there appears to be little doubt that the large chromosomes of Tradescantia are doubly coiled, Huskins (1941) has stated that the minor coil in Trillium is nothing more than a mere waviness of the chromonema. Coleman and Hillary (1941) and Keeffe (1948), on the other hand, have presented reasonable photographic evidence of minor coiling in the same organism. It is quite likely that the time period of coiling may have some effect on the development of the minor coils, thus allowing different interpretations even in identical species.

As in mitosis, relic and relational coils may be present in meiosis, the former most certainly, the latter provisionally. If it is considered that the leptotene chromosome is longitudinally subdivided, then it must also be relationally coiled, as in somatic prophase. This, however, is a conclusion the acceptance of which depends upon the initial premise from which the investigator proceeds, and agreement is not general.

The ultimate fate of the meiotic coils varies among different organisms. The two most thoroughly studied plants, Tradescantia and Trillium, differ. The former, which is more nearly representative of both plants and animals, loses its major coils in meiotic interphase, and it is believed that the minor coils enlarge to become the conspicuous coils of metaphase II. The vestiges of the metaphase II coils appear in the first post-meiotic (microspore) prophase as relic and relational coils. In Trillium an interphase stage is lacking, and the major coils persist through both meiotic divisions (anaphase I passes directly to metaphase II without any intervening stages) to be lost finally as the relic coils of the microspore prophases. The difference between the two genera is, however, not one of kind but simply one of degree.

It should also be noted that, in the clearest preparations of large chromosomes at metaphase I and anaphase I, the chromatids are subdivided at least once more into half-chromatids. These are always plectonemically coiled, except possibly in some heat-treated materials where the coiling has been undone owing to excessive contraction (Swanson 1943c; Kaufmann 1948). It is these half-chromatids that will become the chromatids of the first microspore division, where a plectonemic relationship is known to exist (Sparrow 1942). Mickey (1946) has shown that a similar condition holds for the grasshopper, Romalea. Figure 7–5 presents in diagrammatic fashion the entire coiling cycle from meiotic prophase I to the first microspore division.

No unanimity of opinion exists concerning the origin of the coils and their subsequent behavior during cell division. This lack of agreement stems largely from the difficulties in determining the dynamics of a process by observing static preserved material, and from differences in interpreting certain structural features of the chromonemata that affect, or result from, the coiling process. There are, however, several features that are known with reasonable certainty, and that must be explained by a comprehensive mechanism of coiling.

Thus it is known that (1) ring chromosomes in Drosophila and maize can contract and effect an anaphase separation without entanglement of their chromatids (those in maize may, or may not, entangle depending upon their size and the extent to which sister-strand crossing over occurs); (2) the direction of coiling, i.e., either right- or left-handed, is at random on either side of the centromere; and (3) reversals of the direction of coiling may occur in an arm of chromosome. Such reversals have been

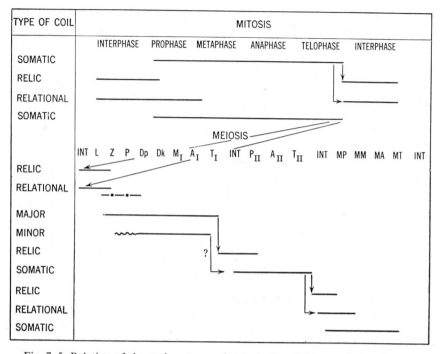

Fig. 7–5. Relation of the various types of coils to the division cycle in mitosis and meiosis. Vertical arrows connect related coiling systems, e.g., undoing of the somatic coil in mitosis gives rise to the relic and relational coils of the next division. The long diagonal arrows connect the last pre-meiotic somatic with the relic and relational coils of meiotic prophase. The dot-dash line in meiosis represents the relational coil between homologues, and is to be distinguished from the relational coils between sister chromatids (this assumes that the leptotene chromosomes are longitudinally double). The wavy portion of the minor is to indicate uncertainty as to the time of its origin, while the question mark beside the arrow connecting the minor coil of meiosis I with the somatic coil of meiosis II indicates an uncertain relation.

shown to be independent of chiasma formation in meiotic chromosomes (Huskins and Wilson 1938), while in Spirotrychonympha, a protozoan, the two sister chromatids of a somatic chromosome have been found to vary both in direction of coiling as well as in location of the points of direction reversals (Cleveland 1938, 1949).

The manner of coiling is inextricably bound up with the mechanism that determines the phenomenon. While the descriptive interpretations of coiling have been numerous, a mechanical or chemical explanation has so far eluded cytologists, and will continue to do so until the physical and chemical structure properties of the chromosome are more thoroughly understood. Darlington (1935) has postulated that a molecular coil sets up an internal pace that determines the microscopically visible pattern of behavior. This hypothesis leads to the assumption that the tightly coiled metaphase chromosome is under a state of tension, an assumption that is supported by observations that under certain conditions of treatment such as heat, ammonia vapors, or a solution of KCN, the coils often relax to the extent that they are lost. The logical extension of this molecular theory is to consider that the configurations of the nucleic acids and proteins in the chromosome framework govern the coiling of chromosomes, and from studies of the nucleic acid and protein structures it appears that the natural state of these molecules is in the form of helices.

The matrix of the chromosome has figured prominently in interpretations regarding the origin of coils. Sax and Humphrey (1934) have postulated that the major coil in Tradescantia results from the contraction of the matrix which forces the straight chromonemata into a helical arrangement. Huskins and his co-workers (Huskins 1941) have concluded that the elongation of the chromonemata within a matrix of unchanging length accomplishes the same thing in Trillium. Coleman and Hillary (1941) agree in general with his interpretation, except that they have considered the apparent elongation of the chromonemata to be only an opening out of a minor coil already present in diplonema. The reversal of the direction of coiling suggests that the initiation of the coils may occur at any region of the chromosome in an independent fashion. The role of the matrix in coiling is also accepted by Kuwada (1939) and Nebel (1939), but not by Darlington (1937a).

The progressive development of the coils, regardless of the mechanism involved, is from many gyres of small diameter in early prophase to few gyres of large diameter (Table 7–2). Temperature and, very likely, genetic factors govern the degree of coiling found in any individual plant or animal (Fig. 7–3). This is true for mitosis (Koller 1938, golden hamster; Sparrow 1942, Trillium) and meiosis (Swanson 1943b, c; Tradescantia; Ris 1945, grasshopper; Keefe 1948, Trillium; Manton 1950, Osmunda). From such diverse materials, the agreement has been good.

In meiosis, the leptotene chromosomes show a relic coiling which persists as a remnant of the preceding somatic coil. The chromonemata appear to be longitudinally double, but the uncertainties of observation make it difficult to determine whether a relational coiling of chromatids exists. Theoretically it should if the chromosomes are double in structure. The leptotene chromosomes also show a beaded structure, the so-called "chromomeres" described by many authors. In Tradescantia microsporocytes and grasshopper spermatocytes, these "chromomeres" are resolvable into tiny gyres which represent the beginnings of the coiling system. Since the gyres are initiated in leptonema, or even earlier in the premeiotic interphase or telophase (Ris 1945), they are somewhat irregular in size and number, but as prophase progresses and as the chromosomes shorten the gyres assume a more regular outline.

A decrease in gyre number is accompanied by an increase in gyre diameter. Consequently, the development of the coiled structure up to

metaphase and anaphase can be considered as a process of *despiralization,*
or gyre elimination, with the period of gyre initiation in leptonema, or
earlier, being the period of *spiralization.* Despiralization is not complete
until the relic coils are lost in the following prophase. As Koller (1938)
and Sparrow (1942) have demonstrated, a like interpretation applies to
somatic chromosomes (Table 7–2).

TABLE 7–2

**Chromatid length in microns and gyre number in the haploid set of five
chromosomes at various stages of cell divison in the microspores of
Trillium grandiflorum (Sparrow 1942).**

Stage of division	Chromatid length	Gyre number
Early prophase	346	554
Mid prophase	203	259
Late prophase	156	169
Metaphase	90	120
Anaphase	95	130

The acceptance of the above explanation necessitates the additional
acceptance of several corollaries. It means that the synaptic attraction of
chromosomes during zygonema and pachynema takes place when the chromosomes are in a coiled condition, not when they are completely stretched
out into an uncoiled state as has been previously thought by the majority of
cytologists. It means, too, that the chromonema, the basic unit of the
chromosome, is a microscopically uniform thread, not linearly differentiated
into bead-like structures of any sort. Thus, as Ris (1945) has stated, "the
differentiation of the mitotic (and meiotic) chromosomes, primary and
secondary constrictions, satellites, and heterochromatic regions are expressions of the differential coiling of the chromonemata." Ris extends this
hypothesis to include chromomeres of the amphibian lampbrush chromosomes and the bands of salivary gland chromosomes, but the manipulation
and stretching of these chromosomes with microneedles with no loss of
chromomeric structure suggests that all chromomeres are not necessarily
resolvable in terms of a coiling system (Duryee 1941; D'Angelo 1950).
Gall (1956), on the other hand, has interpreted the chromomeric structure
of lampbrush chromosomes in terms of a coiled system (Fig. 5–15), agreeing thus with Ris.

It is certain, however, that heteropycnotic structures, such as the X-chromosome of male grasshoppers, are tightly coiled while the autosomes are
in a relatively uncondensed state (Coleman 1943; White 1954). It is
possible therefore to have different chromosomes, or parts of chromosomes,
exhibit varying degrees of coiling within the same cell. This is indicated by
Brown's (1949) study of contraction in the tomato (Fig. 7–6). It would
be of much importance to know with certainty the structure of the knobs
and chromomeres of maize as regards their coiled or uncoiled state.

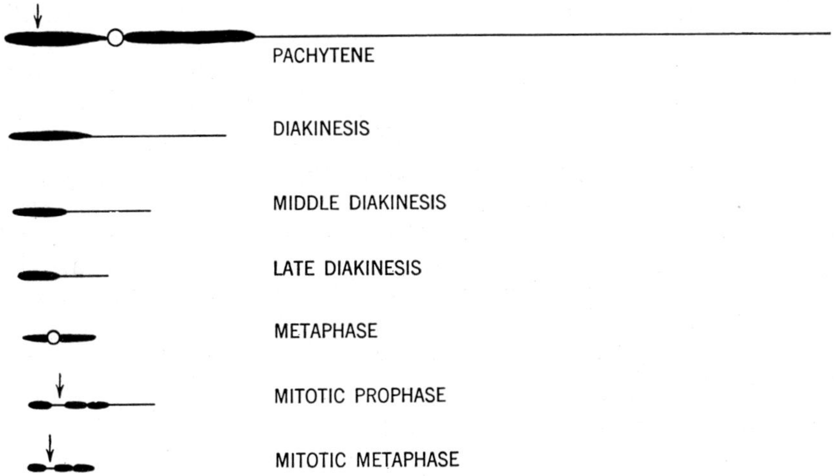

Fig. 7–6. Diagram to illustrate the changes in length of the chromatic (heavy portion) and achromatic (thin line) portions of the nucleolar chromosome in the tomato as a function of stage of meiotic and mitotic division. Arrows indicate nucleolar region, centromere as an open circle or a constriction (Brown 1949).

While no experimental data exist on the relationship between chromosome coiling and crossing over, it is of some interest to note that the chromatid is the basic unit of both processes. Furthermore, Darlington (1937a) has considered that the undoing of the relational coil between homologous chromosomes leads to crossing over, while Sparrow (1942) has demonstrated that the despiralization of chromatids eliminates the relational coils. The temporal coincidence during meiosis of coiling and crossing over suggests that the two are more closely related than has heretofore been apparent.

SYNAPSIS

In the conventionally studied cytological materials of plant and animal origin, such as members of the Orthoptera and the grass and lily families, synapsis, or the pairing of homologous chromosomes, is a characteristic feature of meiosis. In these organisms, the process begins by definition in zygonema, the active stage of pairing, and reaches its full expression at pachynema, the stable stage of pairing. It is then lost by diplonema when an open bivalent structure becomes visible. It is, in general, a process governed by chromosome homologies; and the associations in meiosis, at least, are two-by-two even in those cells where three or more homologous chromosomes exist simultaneously.

Synapsis is not without its variations, however. In maize, a two-by-two association is attempted even though its fulfilment may necessitate the pairing of non-homologous parts (Rhoades and McClintock, 1935). Thus, in a trisomic maize plant, one of the three homologues may, through competition in pairing, find itself without a pairing partner. If so, and in order to satisfy a necessary two-by-two association, it will double back and pair with itself. This applies particularly to the B-chromosomes in maize, suggesting that heterochromatin may determine to a certain extent such an anomalous non-specific pairing relationship. Usually, non-homologous synapsis does not lead to crossing over, but that crossing over may follow such union and lead to chromosomal rearrangements has been suggested (Stadler 1936).

The time of synapsis and the degree to which the chromosomes are condensed when synapsis begins appear to vary within wide limits. Most cytologists accept the hypothesis that synapsis begins in zygonema, but Smith (1941, 1942a, b) has presented evidence that the process may be initiated as early as late telophase of the preceding mitosis. If this is a general phenomenon, a longer period of time is available for synapsis than has previously been realized, assuring in this manner the complete synapsis that is characteristically found in meiotic cells (barring, of course, structural differences that alter synaptic relationships). This point of view contradicts Darlington's (1940c) hypothesis that one of the principal factors governing synapsis is the time element, a variable which he states is responsible for the degree of synapsis and the extent of chiasma localization. A reduced synaptic period would leave certain segments of the chromosomes unpaired, and these segments would not form chiasmata. Since pairing generally starts in the centric regions, or at the ends of chromosomes, and proceeds in zipper-like fashion along the arms of the chromosomes, a logical extension of the hypothesis would mean (1) that long chromosomes in the same nucleus with smaller ones would exhibit a less complete degree of synapsis, and (2) that, if localization of chiasmata occurred, it would have to be in the neighborhood of the centromere or the ends. A survey of the literature shows that neither assumption is borne out.

Several different types of chromosome associations are found in certain insects of the Hemiptera-Homoptera group. In *Rhytidolomia senilis,* the X- and Y-chromosomes form a terminal union of euchromatic ends in diakinesis when the chromosomes are highly condensed (Fig. 7–7). This union is of brief duration and does not involve any crossing over, but it bespeaks a definite force of attraction no less specific than that operating in the more commonly observed zygotene-pachytene type of synapsis. Wilson (1925) had earlier termed this "touch-and-go" pairing. In *Edessa irrorata,* the touch-and-go pairing does not occur between the X and Y until the second spermatocyte division (Schrader 1941a). The same insect exhibits a non-homologous association of heterochromatic segments which persists until late diakinesis, but this phenomenon is probably related to the non-specificity and stickiness of heterochromatin rather than to any peculiarity of synaptic forces.

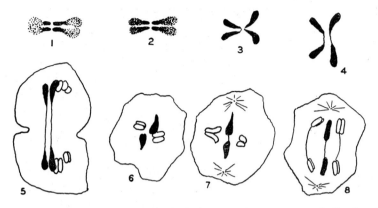

Fig. 7–7. Pairing and segregation of the sex chromosomes of the hemipter, *Rhytidolomia senilis*. 1 and 2, diakinesis; the chromosomes pair terminally (touch-and-go) at the euchromatic ends with the heterochromatic ends not yet fully condensed. The X is at the right, the Y at the left. 3 to 5, poleward movement of the chromosomes with the heterochromatic ends leading. 6, X and Y chromosomes coming together for second division orientation. 7 and 8, movement poleward of X and Y; note that the heterochromatic ends are now terminally joined and that the euchromatic ends lead to the pole. Autosomes are indicated in outline (Schrader 1940).

A third variation of synaptic behavior is described by Hughes-Schrader (1940, 1942) in *Llaveiella taenechina*. The two chromatids of the X-chromosome, which are wholly separate from each other in the first meiotic division, reassociate in interphase, and function as a unit in the second division (Fig. 7–8). The cases described are anomalous types when viewed

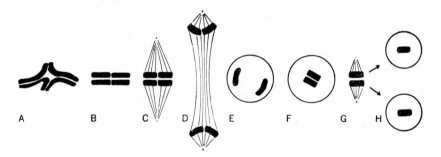

Fig. 7–8. Coccid type of meiosis. A and B, bivalent in diakinesis, with chromatids entirely separate from each although the homologous chromosomes are paired end-to-end; C, metaphase I with independent orientation of each chromosome prior to equational separation; D, anaphase I; E, separate chromatids in interphase; F, secondary, parallel pairing of chromatids formerly disjoined; G, metaphase II; H, end of second division (Hughes-Schrader 1948, and used with permission of the Academic Press, Inc.).

in the light of what is generally known about synapsis, but they are presented because the behavior exhibited undoubtedly depends upon the functioning of some force of attraction. Whether this force can be homologized with that operating at zygonema is at present uncertain.

Although synapsis is considered to be a meiotic process, it is present in other types of cells. Somatic synapsis is a rule in Drosophila species (Metz 1916). The homologous chromosomes often are closely coiled around each other, and may even exhibit chiasma-like structures (Cooper 1949). This, of course, provides a ready explanation for the somatic crossing over that has been found to occur in this organism.

Somatic synapsis reaches its ultimate expression in the intimate pairing relationships exhibited by the salivary gland chromosomes. Homologous band is paired with homologous band, which emphasizes the fact that synapsis is not a phenomenon governing the pairing of whole chromosomes as entities, but rather that it is a process bringing together homologous units. In the salivary gland chromosomes, this unit appears to be no larger than a single band. The size of the pairing blocks in a meiotic chromosome is not known, and it is not yet justifiable to state with conviction that synapsis is gene for gene. The study of chromosomes heterozygous for structural abnormalities has made certain, however, that the pairing units are portions of chromosomes and not whole chromosomes.

The exactness of synapsis points to the existence of attraction forces of extraordinary specificity. With the exception of the non-specific pairing characteristic of heterochromatin, e.g., the chromocenter of Drosophila, this exactness is clearly evident from meiotic and somatic pairing, salivary gland chromosome synapsis, and the touch-and-go behavior of certain insect chromosomes.

In considering any hypothesis bearing on the physico-chemical basis of synapsis, it will be well to bear in mind definite observational data for which an accounting must be made. Fabergé (1942) has presented these in the following manner: (1) the homologues, which may be far apart in the nucleus, eventually come to lie side-by-side (or end-to-end, as in Rhytidolomia); (2) this union may be two-by-two, as is the case for pachytene chromosomes, or three-by-three, as in the salivary gland cells of triploid Drosophila; (3) it may be extraordinarily specific as in the band-for-band pairing of salivary gland chromosomes, and as in the chromomere-for-chromomere pairing of chromosomes in maize spermatocytes or frog oöcytes, or non-specific as in heterochromatin of Drosophila or in unpaired chromosomes of maize; (4) synapsis is, in meiotic cells, begun at zygonema, completed by pachynema, and dissolved by diplonema, but it may take place in diakinesis or interphase.

Is there but a single mechanism that would explain all of the above facts—i.e., a mechanism that functions differently under different circumstances—or are several different mechanisms operative? No ready answer can be given at present, although certain inferences as to governing factors may be drawn.

If, for the moment, it is considered that touch-and-go pairing is a type of synapsis peculiar unto itself in that it involves the union of condensed chromosomes, it is then clear that the process is favored by elongation of the chromosomes. Zygotene length is greater than mitotic prophase length (Manton 1939), and in the salivary gland cells synapsis takes place after an initial elongation of the chromosomes has begun. That extreme elongation does not provide an absolute clue, however, is made evident by the somatic pairing of chromosomes in Drosophila; these chromosomes appear to be no more elongated than those of other somatic cells of other organisms where somatic pairing is not known.

Factors other than elongation that may play governing roles are the initial spatial separation of chromosomes, time interval of pairing, and size of the pairing unit. The distance travelled by two homologues in uniting is difficult to determine in the living cell, but it must be of the order of microns rather than of submicroscopic units. This presents no insuperable difficulties, for it may be that chance meeting of homologues provides the initial contact point, with synapsis operating in zipper-like fashion in both directions. Close proximity of homologous centromeres through telophase orientation, or of terminal ends through polarization, could easily provide the necessary contact surfaces.

Darlington (1940) and Frankel, Darlington, and La Cour (1940) have considered time of pairing to be an important factor in synapsis; but since their conclusions are derived from the distribution of chiasmata at metaphase rather than from synaptic configurations, and since complete synapsis, except in structural hybrids, is a rule, time is of questionable significance as a limiting factor in determining the degree of synapsis.

Estimation of the size of the pairing units, or blocks, presents its difficulties. It may well be that the chromomere, the band, or the gene is the pairing unit; but, as Fabergé has emphasized, it should be recognized that *active* zygonema may be governed by units, or forces, of a different order of magnitude than those determining the *stable* pairing of pachynema. Studies of structural hybrids, however, suggest that the pairing units are small, although possibly of larger size than the gene.

Several hypotheses have been proposed to explain synapsis as a cellular phenomenon. Darlington (1937) has assumed that the chromosomes exist in a paired state at all times except from anaphase to the next prophase. In mitosis, this condition is met in that the chromosomes entering prophase are already double. In meiosis, however, the chromosomes are presumed to be single. Consequently they are in an unsatisfied, or unsaturated, state electrostatically; to become saturated they must pair homologously. When the chromosomes become double in late pachynema, the satisfied state is between sister chromatids instead of homologous chromosomes; the paired homologues consequently fall apart and diplonema is initiated.

These assumptions form the basis of Darlington's *Precocity Theory of*

Meiosis; i.e., the chromosomes enter prophase precociously in that they are not yet replicated. Logically beautiful in superficially explaining the genetical implications of meiosis, it is inconsistent with cytological facts relating to the structure of the chromosomes, i.e., the doubleness of the chromosomes in leptonema prior to synapsis. As Huskins (1937) has stated, physiological and morphological unity are not necessarily identical, and the subdivisions of the chromosome, which could conceivably run into hundreds of fibrils each having all the genetic potentialities of the entire chromosome, may have little to do with either synapsis or the time of visible doubleness.

Sax and Sax (1935) and Beasley (1938) have considered meiosis and synaptic behavior from the point of view that a retardation of cellular activity is involved. To phrase it otherwise, meiosis is a more leisurely process than mitosis, providing in this manner an opportunity for the chromosomes to lose their relic coils before the assumption of new meiotic coils. Sax and Sax have hypothesized that homologous chromosomes exhibit an attraction for each other at all times, an attraction which, in mitosis, is prevented by the coiled condition of the homologues from earliest prophase. The completely uncoiled state of the leptotene chromosomes provides a maximum of pairing surface, and synapsis becomes possible. Other studies in Tradescantia and the grasshopper indicate that a coiled condition of the chromonemata is no deterrent to synapsis. Beasley, accepting the hypothesis that homologous chromosomes attract at all times, has postulated that the great enlargement of meiotic nuclei, the decreased viscosity of the nuclear fluid, and the relatively long time span during which prophase goes on, exert determining roles in synapsis. Neither hypothesis attempts an explanation of the physical basis of attraction of homologous parts.

Fabergé (1942) has considered the problem of synaptic attraction from a theoretical point of view, and has drawn the conclusion, as had Lamb (1907) earlier, that it is explicable in terms of known physical laws. Electrostatic charges are ruled out on the basis that, in triploids and tetraploids, any two of the three or more homologues are capable of contact pairing, thus eliminating the possibility of "plus" and "minus" charged chromosomes being attracted to each other. As earlier stated, a differentiation can be made between zygotene pairing, which is unsaturated, and pachytene pairing, which is saturated. Thus, if two or more homologues are present, Fabergé considers that all can come together in zygonema; in pachynema, however, only a two-by-two pairing is evident, even though the cell may be polyploid. Consequently, the forces necessary to bring the chromosomes together in zygonema must be long-range forces operating over a distance of several microns, while those necessary to effect the saturated condition of pachynema need operate only at small distances. Once contact has been made initially, entire alignment of the chromosomes is readily accomplished by a zipper action. Also, since a two-by-two association brings about saturation, a three-by-three, or higher, association is not possible even in polyploid cells.

The phenomena postulated by Fabergé and Lamb to bring about initial contact is a hydrodynamic principle known as the Guyot-Bjerknes effect. It involves long-range forces, and is based upon the following considerations. All molecular systems are in a state of motion, each system having its own characteristic frequency of vibration. If vibrations of the same frequency are exhibited by two or more systems in the same liquid medium, and they are in phase, they will be attracted to each other. The force of attraction developed between the systems will be inversely proportional to the square of the distance between them. If the vibrations are out of phase, the systems will repel. Systems having different vibrational frequencies will be without effect on each other. While these principles of hydrodynamics have a sound basis on a gross scale, their applicability to the pairing units of the chromosome is problematical. The pairing units, whatever their dimensions might be, are undoubtedly molecular systems, and while vibrational frequencies provide a speculative means for initial contact—a contact that could easily be brought about by chance contact— the question of why pachytene chromosomes provide a saturated pairing condition remains unanswered.

Two additional hypotheses have been proposed. Delbrück (1941), who has considered long-range forces physically impossible in synapsis, has sought an explanation in the processes involved in chromosome reproduction. Briefly, Delbrück's hopothesis states that "pairing is an association of self-reproducing entities within the chromosome coupled with the chemical reduction of each paired pair of peptid bonds, so that between each pair the resonance bond can be formed." The resonance bond is postulated as an intermediate for the synthesis of new peptid bonds in polypeptide synthesis. The pairing force would be specific locally, and permit union of units in pairs. With a change in the redox situation in the nucleus, the pairing would cease at the same time that synthesis of the new homologue (chromatid) was completed. This would lead to repulsion, as evidenced by diplotene configurations. Chemically, the hypothesis is difficult of proof as it relates to the chromosomes; cytologically, it is inconsistent with the idea that the leptotene chromosome is already divided.

On the basis of antigen-antibody reactions through molecular films of known thickness, the existence of long-range forces that could be operative in chromosome pairing has been postulated. Hinton (1945) has utilized the argument to explain somatic pairing in Drosophila, but Cooper (1948) has given evidence that places Hinton's data in doubt. Superficially, chromosome pairing is similar to an antigen-antibody reaction; chemically, however, an antigen and its specific antibody are structurally different, while homologous chromosomes, insofar as is known, are identical, although a "front-to-back" pairing relationship is possible.

It is patently obvious that the problem of synapsis is an enigma still awaiting satisfactory solution, and that the "force of attraction" that brings together homologous chromosomes is hypothetical indeed, and at present experimentally unapproachable.

CHIASMA TERMINALIZATION

Chiasmata, first visible in early diplonema when the homologous chromosomes separate from each other, do not always remain constant in position as meiotic prophase progresses. This movement, which varies in degree in different organisms, has been called *terminalization* by Darlington.

Depending upon the amount of terminalization occurring between diplonema and metaphase, a shift in position of the chiasmata may or may

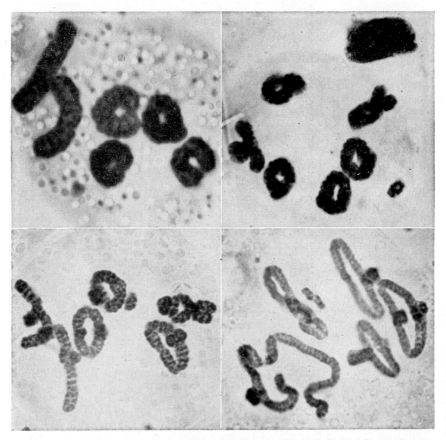

Fig. 7–9. Microsporocytes of *Tradescantia canaliculata,* showing different degrees of coiling and chiasma terminalization. Top left, from a field grown plant; top right, at 27° C; bottom left, at 33° C; bottom right, at 40° C. At 40° C, the coiling system is very variable, and either very short or very long chromosomes are found (see Table 7–3), but in general the more numerous the coils the less complete is terminalization (bottom right figure from Swanson 1942).

not be accompanied by a change in the frequency of chiasmata per cell or per bivalent (Fig. 7–9). In *Campanula persicifolia* complete terminalization is achieved by metaphase (Fig. 3–16); all of the chiasmata initially formed at interstitial loci come to lie at the terminal ends of the chromosomes (Gairdner and Darlington 1931). A decrease in the frequency of chiasmata also occurs. In *Anemone* as well, excessive terminalization not only moves all of the chiasmata to terminal loci, but also reduces their number (Moffett 1932). Organisms having large chromosomes, such as *Fritillaria imperialis* (lily) or *Stenobothrus parallelus* (grasshopper), show little if any movement of chiasmata.

An analysis of the process has made it clear that terminalization is in a distal direction, that is, toward the ends of the chromosome arms and away from the centromere. It is also greater per unit of chromosome length in small bivalents than in large ones. There may be some movement initially toward the centromere, a movement that would not only be difficult to detect but would in all probability soon cease before any piling up of chiasmata in the centric region could occur. The degree of movement can be conveniently calculated by determining the *terminalization coefficient,* which is defined as the proportion of total chiasmata terminal at any given stage or time.

A consideration of bivalent shapes demands an interpretation of the mechanics of the process in terms of forces acting on the homologous chromosomes from within themselves. The fact that the adjacent loops formed by successive chiasmata lie at right angles to each other, and that a stretching of chromosomes occurs at the centric region, is evidence of torsions operative during terminalization. Three mechanisms have been advanced to account for the process of terminalization: (1) electrostatic forces (Darlington and Dark 1932), (2) tensions developed through the coiling of chromosomes (Swanson 1942b), and (3) elastic chromosome repulsions (Östergren 1943).

According to Darlington's electrostatic hypothesis, two forces govern the movement of chiasmata distally. The first and more effective of the two forces is a repulsion localized in the centromere; the second is a generalized repulsion distributed evenly over the surface of the chromosome. The resultant movement of chiasmata is in a distal direction because of the greater repulsion existing between the centromeres, allowing the adjacent chiasmata to gain at the expense of the more distal ones until an equilibrium is reached between successive loops, or until the chiasmata have been completely terminalized. The degree of terminalization is thus conceived to be a visible expression of the effectiveness of these forces acting on the chromosomes throughout the duration of prophase following chiasma formation. The two forces, together with the number of chiasmata and the degree of chromosome contraction, also determine the shapes of the bivalents during prophase and metaphase.

The hypothetical existence of these forces rests upon a number of observations and considerations. The stretching exhibited by the portion of
bivalents between the centromere and the first proximal chiasmata at
metaphase implies the existence of strong repelling force operating between
the centromeres, a force that, according to Darlington, reflects the similar
electrical charge carried by each centromere. Since charges of like sign
repel, so do the centromeres.

Such reasoning by analogy is not without its pitfalls, and some criticism
can be offered. Although terminalization occurs between diplonema and
metaphase, the stretching of the centric regions occurs in most organisms
only during metaphase and early anaphase, and only when the bivalents
are in contact with the spindle. Thus the existence of forces residing in the
centromeres may be questioned, and the stretching may simply reflect a
connection between the centromeres and the polar regions which depends
upon some spindle element functioning as an agent of movement. On the
other hand, it appears that in the males of certain mantids (White 1941;
Hughes-Schrader 1943a) and in the dipteran male Melophagus (Cooper
1941) a certain autonomy of centromeric repulsion exists, but in neither
case are chiasmata formed; so the effect of a localized repulsion on terminalization remains a moot question.

The circular form attained by the loops between adjacent chiasmata,
the fact that terminalization is more effective in bivalents with closed loops
than in those having but a single chiasma in one arm only, and the assumed
presence of a surface charge on the chromosome such as that characteristic
of ampholytes (of which nucleoprotein is an example), are cited as supporting evidence for the existence of a generalized repulsion distributed over
the body of the chromosome. Evidence from a study of meiosis in male
mantids seriously questions the existence of such a force. Hughes-Schrader
(1943a) has shown that, even though no chiasmata are formed between
homologues, they remain paired in a parallel fashion with no semblance of
a repulsion acting between the chromosome arms.

Despite these objections to the electrostatic hypothesis, it has been
widely used by cytologists to explain many meiotic phenomena because
the postulated charges can be conveniently increased or decreased as the
immediate situation warrants. As more cytological information is gathered,
it is becoming apparent that no general theory of electrostatic forces governing meiotic behavior can be applied in the manner in which it was first
conceived.

The "coiling" hypothesis is an attempt to relate terminalization to
mechanical tensions developed within the chromosome without assigning
hypothetical forces to the chromosome or its parts. As indicated above,
the meiotic coiling cycle is a continuous and progressive phenomenon. The
incipient coils are small and numerous, and as prophase proceeds the decrease in the number of coils is accompanied by an increase in the diameter

of the individual gyres. The progression, therefore, is from a long, laxly coiled thread to one that becomes relatively shorter and, presumably, more rigid. The development of the minor as well as the major coils accentuates the shortness and the rigidity of the chromosomes. Under such circumstances of increasing rigidity, the homologous chromosomes, bound to each other by chiasmata, will tend to seek a spatial disposition that will most effectively distribute the force developed by the rigidity over the greatest possible area. The regions between adjacent chiasmata will bow out into loops which will come to lie at right angles to each other. The tension induced by the development of the coils will eventually become greater than the force binding the chromosomes at the point of chromatid exchange, and the chiasma will slide along the chromosomes. The rigidity of the coiled system will be lessened as the diameter of the loops between adjacent chiasmata increases; but as coiling is a progressive and a continuous process, terminalization when once initiated will continue. The direction of movement must be distal, since movement in a proximal direction would increase rather than decrease the tension.

Unlike the electrostatic hypothesis of terminalization, the coiling hypothesis can be put to test by varying the degree of coiling. This can be done by temperature. When inflorescences of *Tradescantia paludosa* are subjected to temperatures of 40° C for 24 hours, the degree of coiling is variable (Fig. 7–2) (Table 7–3), and the metaphase chromosomes in different cells from the same bud may be long and lax with many coils (l-chromosomes), or short and rigid with few coils (s-chromosomes). As the chromosomes shorten, more and more of the interstitial chiasmata are terminalized, with a possible loss of some of them.

TABLE 7–3

Chiasma frequencies at 40° C (Swanson, 1942a).

	Interstitial chiasmata per cell	Terminal chiasmata per cell	Total chiasmata
Controls (22° C)	4.14	7.37	11.51
40° C (24 hours)			
Bud #1			
l-chr.	8.45	3.21	11.66
s-chr.	1.96	7.92	9.88
Bud #2			
l-chr.	9.70	2.90	12.60
s-chr.	1.35	8.67	10.02

Additional support for the hypothesis is gained from two mutant chromosome types. Lesley and Frost (1927) have described a long-chromosome mutant in the plant *Matthiola incana* in which the meiotic chromosomes fail to attain their normal state of contraction, and the chiasmata remain at interstitial loci, in contrast to the normal type where the chromosomes are short and the chiasmata terminal. Upcott's (1937) description of a male-sterile plant of the sweet pea, *Lathyrus odoratus,* revealed exactly the opposite type of mutant (Fig. 7–10). The normal plant had long chromosomes and interstitial chiasmata, the mutant type short chromosomes and terminal chiasmata. In each case the mutations, which were recessive in character, affect the coiling process, which in turn determines the degree of terminalization.

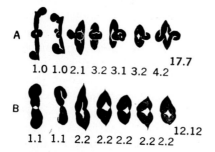

Fig. 7–10. Degree of terminalization in normal (A) and pollen sterile (B) plants of *Lathyrus odoratus.* Figures below each bivalent represent total number of chiasmata per bivalent to number terminalized (Darlington 1937 after Upcott).

Many organisms, however, exhibit a distinct contraction of the chromosomes but little or no terminalization of chiasmata. It must be assumed that terminalization will not occur until a certain degree of rigidity and tension is attained in the paired chromosomes. A certain threshold of force is, therefore, necessary for chiasma movement, and it is significant to point out that in those organisms having large, not too greatly contracted chromosomes such as are found in Lilium, Tulipa, and Fritillaria, no terminalization occurs, while in plants such as Campanula, *Primula sineneis,* and normal *Mathhiola incana* the chromosomes are short and compact, and terminalization is complete.

Östergren (1943) has approached the problem of chiasma terminalization from the point of view of *elastic chromosome repulsions.* By this he means that all bodies possessing a definite shape (such as paired homologues bound together by chiasmata) resist any change that tends to alter their shapes. A chiasma, therefore, forces the chromosomes out of shape by its binding force, and a resistance or repulsion is established at the point of exchange. This repulsion, if strong enough, will tend to force the chiasmata distally, since this is the only direction in which relief from tension can be achieved. Östergren suggests, but does not state specifically, that the spiralization of chromosomes is a factor in determining the degree of resistance at the points of chiasma formation.

OTHER PRE-ANAPHASE MOVEMENTS

In addition to the chromosomal movements just described, a variety of other maneuvers occur within the cell which contribute to an orderly development of the metaphase plate, the latter being a necessary prerequisite for an equally orderly anaphase progression.

Schrader (1947a, 1953), in summarizing and synthesizing the pertinent data, has stated that an analysis of *metaphase mechanics* must take into account the operation of two centers of force. One of these, localized at the poles or centers, becomes increasingly more influential as cell division proceeds from interphase to metaphase. The other, residing in the chromosomes, becomes increasingly more responsive to influences emanating from the poles during the same prophase period. The chromosomal force may, under certain conditions, be sharply localized in the centromeres; under other circumstances, it may clearly involve only the ends of the chromosomes or even the chromosome, or chromosomes, as a whole.

Obviously, an analysis of this kind can be done only on organisms whose cells possess well-defined centers and spindles. The visual absence of a morphologically defined center in the higher plants precludes a critical study such as is possible in many of the animal species, but since the essential features of mitosis and meiosis are so similar throughout the plant and animal world it is not unreasonable to assume that the basic mechanisms are equally similar even though certain structures may escape microscopic detection or be absent from the cells.

Polar and chromosomal forces reveal themselves through the responses exhibited by three structures: the nucleus, the chromosomes, and the spindle. In most organisms the orderliness of cell division is such that many of the factors governing the cellular maneuvers are hard to detect. Attention, therefore, will be given to those seemingly aberrant forms in which an exaggeration of some component of cell division permits an investigation of its role in the workings of the normal cell.

The reaction of the nucleus to the polar forces is first evidenced in diakinesis when the chromosomes have reached almost full contraction. In Brachystethus, a pentatomid insect, the nucleus is initially displaced from a central position in the cell to a point close to one of the centrioles that lies rather at the periphery of the cell than close to the nuclear membrane. Immediately, a marked elongation of the nucleus takes place. When the polarity of the nucleus is thus established, and the now pointed tips make contact with the centers, the nuclear membrane breaks down, and spindle formation is initiated. The cell at this time may be distinctly flattened in the polar region, indicating that the centers have become rather firmly fixed to the cell membrane once they have reached their final position.

That the reaction with polar forces involves only the nuclear membrane is demonstrated by the fact that during this time the chromosomes exhibit no special displacement. Also, in *Loxa picticornis,* a related insect, the interaction is sufficiently strong to pull the nuclear membrane out into a sharp point (Fig. 7–11). Later, however, the nucleus-centriole contact is broken, the nucleus rounds up, and finally the centrioles leave their peripheral position and once more establish nuclear contact just prior to spindle formation.

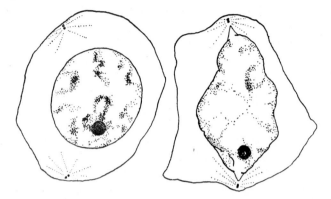

Fig. 7–11. Spermatocytes of the hemipter, *Loxa picticornis,* illustrating the prophase stages prior to, and after, the attraction of the nuclear membrane to the centrosome (Schrader 1947).

The size of the nucleus has a direct bearing on the size of the spindle. In general, it may be stated that the size of the nucleus is a function of the number of chromosomes contained within it, with the amount of extra-chromosomal material varying proportionately, i.e., a tetraploid nucleus has twice the volume of a similar diploid nucleus. This is an equivocal generalization, however, for in the bug Arvelius, Schrader has shown that the cells found in the different lobes of the testis, while having the same size and number of chromosomes and producing the same size sperm, may show an enormous range in size of nucleus and spindle. The size differences are observable by diakinesis, and are related to factors as yet undetermined.

Although structurally the nuclear membrane appears to be little more than an envelope separating the cytoplasm from the nuclear sap, neither its effect on the chromosomes, nor its relationship to the centers, is by any means passive. Many species exhibit a characteristic spacing of bivalents at diakinesis in that they lie evenly distributed on the nuclear membrane. Mutual repulsion between chromosomes has been generally advanced as the reason for the observed distribution. In the dermopteran insect Anisolabis, however, dissolution of the nuclear membrane causes the chromosome to clump suddenly in the center of the cell, from which position they take their metaphase orientation. If mutual repulsions were involved, maneuvers of this sort would be most unlikely. Schrader has proposed that surface-tension forces may operate to produce both the diakinetic distribution and the pre-metaphase clumping; these would be difficult to detect experimentally, but they may prove to be the determinants for many cellular phenomena that have not yet yielded to analysis, such as *synizesis* when the prophase chromosomes clump into a dense knot, or the *confused stage* (in diplonema) of many insects when the chromosomes are diffuse and impossible to analyze in detail.

A feature characteristic of the spermatocytes of many animal species and, to judge from published accounts, characteristic to a lesser degree of plant species, is the definite orientation of the chromosomes prior to synapsis. In earliest prophase a *Rabl* orientation is most commonly found, i.e., there is a close approximation of the centromeres to the centrioles. The fact that this orientation, which was established in the preceding anaphase and telophase when the chromosomes were moved to and grouped at the poles, is maintained until prophase is evidence that no new cellular or

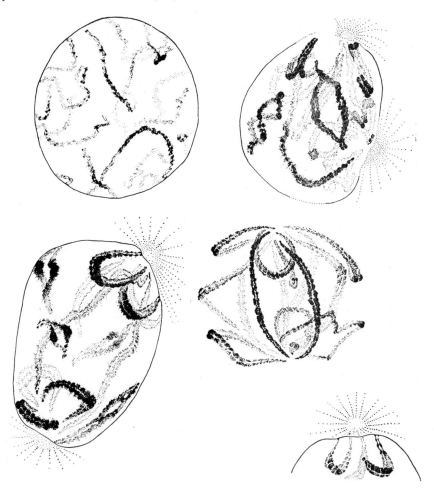

Fig. 7–12. Spermatocytes of the mantid, *Stagmomantis carolina*, showing polarization of the bivalents to active centers. Top left, non-polarized chromosomes in early pachynema; top right, beginning of polarization in pachynema with the ends of the chromosomes oriented to the centers as these migrate along the nuclear membrane; bottom left, somewhat later stage in pachynema; middle, full polarization, with some bivalents stretched from pole to pole, others with both ends attracted to the same center; bottom right, detail of the preceding figure (Hughes-Schrader 1943).

chromosomal activity has upset the arrangement during the pre-meiotic interphase.

With the onset of leptonema, a new orientation manifests itself (Fig. 7–12). It involves a movement of the chromosomes such that the ends of the chromosomes rather than the centromeres are now attracted to the centers, with the remainder of the chromosome bodies projecting into the nuclear sap. This polarization forms what has been called the "bouquet" stage, which may persist for some time but which rarely extends beyond pachytene. In certain mantids the first polarization is followed by another which results in a similar regrouping of chromosomes in mid-pachynema (Hughes-Schrader 1943). As in the earlier bouquet stage, the regrouping is clearly the result of an interaction between the ends of the chromosomes and the centers.

Polarization, however, is not restricted to the attenuated chromosomes of leptonema and pachynema. It may occur when the chromosomes are very nearly in a fully condensed state. In Anisolabis, the diakinetic chromosomes gather against the nuclear membrane and in close proximity to the divided but still unseparated centrioles. As the centrioles migrate to the poles, each is followed by a group of chromosomes, providing a striking illustration of some strong attraction between chromosomes and centers (Schrader 1941b). It was not possible in this case to determine whether the interaction was between centromeres, ends, or the chromosomes as a whole. There is a possibility that it may be related to heteropycnosis (Vanderlyn 1949), for the X-chromosome of many Orthopteran forms always lies against the nuclear membrane when it is present.

Of interest from the point of view of the mechanics involved are the observations of Marengo (1949) on polarization. In the fern Onoclea sensibilis, not only are the chromosome ends polarized inside the nuclear membrane and in proximity to the centrioles, but so are the mitochondria outside the membrane (see also Wilson 1925). Later they become oriented in the form of a ring around the equatorial plate (the chromosomes of many species are similarly distributed to form a hollow spindle). Having no centromeres, the mitochondria do not move during anaphase, but their movement is a clear demonstration of a definite orientation resulting from forces residing in the centers. Since the mitochondria are the metabolic centers of the cell, their clustering may also be related to some transfer of energy necessary for spindle formation and chromosome movement. This remains to be proved.

An additional pre-metaphase interaction between centers and centromeres is seen in the so-called "stretch" stage of meiosis described by Hughes-Schrader (1943b, 1947a) in the mantids and phasmids. As dissolution of the nuclear membrane is occurring, but before a definitely established spindle or metaphase plate is in evidence, the paired centromeres of the bivalents suddenly orient themselves so forcibly toward the opposite poles that the arms of the chromosomes are visibly stretched (Fig. 7–13). Faint fibers connect the centers with the centromeres. Elongation of the developing spindle assists in reinforcing the stretch phenomenon; but even

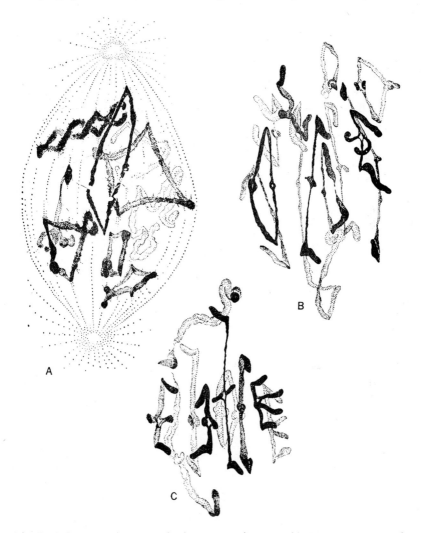

Fig. 7–13. Pre-metaphase stretch phenomenon in a mantid, *Stagmomantis carolina*. A, early stage, with some bivalents responding, others unoriented; B, mid-stretch period; C, metaphase orientation partially completed, but with the sex trivalent (at the top) as yet unoriented (Hughes-Schrader 1947).

though its meaning is obscure it is essentially an expression of centromeric repulsion independent of the interaction of centers and centromeres, since it occurs even though the bivalents are quite irregularly displaced in the cell. The stretched condition of the chromosomes does not persist, for the centromeres soon approach each other again, and contraction of the chromosomes is resumed until full metaphase is established.

Formation of a metaphase plate is completed when the chromosomes lie oriented within or on the spindle and equidistant from the two poles. The chromosomes must move from their positions in the nucleus and orient themselves on the plate. Darlington (1937) has referred to these movements as *congression* and *orientation,* and has attributed the movements to repulsions between the centromeres and centrioles. The data derived from a study of the spermatocytes of the testis of the lobster Homarus are particularly instructive as regards this point (Fig. 7–14). As the nuclear

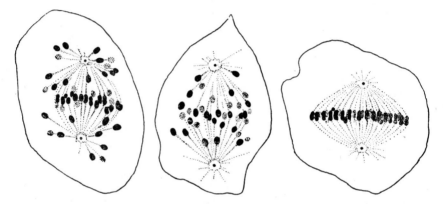

Fig. 7–14. Spermatocytes of the lobster, *Homarus americanus,* illustrating prometaphase (left and middle) with the chromosomes well scattered and connected by a spindle fiber to only one pole, and metaphase (right) with the chromosomes oriented on the metaphase plate with connections to both poles (Schrader 1947).

membrane breaks down, fibers form almost at once from the centers to the centromeres of the chromosomes. The fibers are formed first from the nearest pole to the centromeres, but soon connecting fibers from the other pole arise and the chromosomes are drawn onto the metaphase plate by the two half-spindle fibers (Schrader 1947a). For those chromosomes that are not centrally placed, this means that some fibers must contract while others elongate without disruption of their structure. Analysis of the stretch phenomenon supports this hypothesis, which has an important bearing on an understanding of chromosomal movement, for it suggests that, since the two half-spindle fibers connecting a chromosome or bivalent to the two poles are similar, their traction forces are at an equilibrium when the chromosomes are on the metaphase plate. The simplest explanation of the fibers' structure is that they are protein chains capable of folding and unfolding. Repulsion forces do not appear to be involved.

Arrangement of the chromosomes on the spindle is a function of the chromosomes themselves. It may be orderly or at random, and may fluctuate in the same individual. Thus in the hemipteran insect Gelastocoris, the male shows no regular arrangement of chromosomes in the first meiotic division, but in the second division a regular ring of autosomes forms around the centrally placed sex chromosomes. The female shows no regularity whatsoever, and the suggestion is that heteropycnosis and heterogamy are involved (Troedsson 1944; Schrader 1947a). Where both large and small chromosomes are found in the same cell, the smaller lie in the center of the spindle with the larger on the periphery, as in the plant Yucca (O'Mara 1932) and the reptile Tupenambis (Matthey 1933).

Östergren (1945) has hypothesized that the structure of the spindle is such that a *transverse equilibrium* is set up within it. If it is considered that the spindle is constructed of long molecules or micelles having a definite spatial arrangement that provides for equilibrium, then the insertion of bodies into the spindle would upset the equilibrium and increase the potential energy of the system. Foreign bodies would tend to be ejected. That chromosomes can be pushed to the side of the spindle despite the force of the fibers which tends to keep them on the metaphase plate has been shown in the insects Brachystethus and Mecistorhinus (Fig. 7–15). A transverse

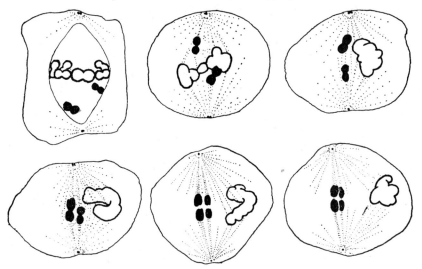

Fig. 7–15. Spermatocytes in the hargequin lobes of the hemipter, *Brachystethus rubromaculatus*, showing the differential behavior of the sex chromosomes (black) and the autosomes (in outline) on the metaphase plate. The former undergo regular orientation while the latter are pushed to the side of the cell by what appears to be an elongation of the spindle fibers (Schrader 1947).

equilibrium is in effect, therefore, when the chromosomes maintain their normal metaphase orientation.

It is possible to conceive of differences in degree of upset of the equilibrium that would account for the variations in chromosomal arrangements that have been observed; but it is clear from the spermatocytes of Mecistorhinus and Brachystethus, where the sex chromosomes and autosomes behave differently, that the chromosomes are not entirely inert bodies being shunted from the spindle, but that they individually determine the maintenance of the transverse equilibrium. A longitudinal equilibrium must also be in operation to prevent the chromosomes from slipping toward the poles before anaphase movement has commenced. It would be logical to assume that this is one of the functions of the half-spindle fibers.

A natural proof of the effect of the spindle on the chromosomes is provided in a study of the behavior of the X-chromosome of an XO male of a mantid (Hughes-Schrader 1948a). It would be expected that if a single X-chromosome in a spermatocyte were subjected to an ejection force by the spindle it would easily be shunted out, since only a single spindle fiber anchors it to one pole. In most XO organisms, this is avoided by a precocious passage of the X-chromosome to one of the poles before general anaphase movement is accomplished, although a slight expulsion is characteristic of many species. In the mantid Humbertiella, the centromere of the X-chromosome is delayed in its interaction with the pole, and its spindle fiber does not form until after the autosomes have established polar connections. The X-chromosome is passively shunted out of the spindle, and only after it is in the cytoplasm does it become attached to the nearest pole by a spindle fiber (Fig. 7–16). The passage of the X-chromosome to the pole is likewise delayed, although it eventually undergoes typical anaphase movement. Finally, it should be pointed out that occasionally an X-chromosome functions as do the autosomes: spindle fibers from both poles connect with the centromeres, the division is equational at anaphase I, and anaphase movement is regular. Under these circumstances, the X-chromosome is not expelled from the spindle.

Probably the most striking evidence of polar activity is the role of the centers in the formation of the spindle. By necessity, the information bearing on the problem must be obtained from those organisms, mostly animal, that have structurally visible centers. The mode of formation of the spindle in the higher plants must, therefore, remain in doubt because of their lack of visible centers. Even in animals the problem is one of exceeding complexity, since the spindle apparently can arise in a variety of ways, with the centers, the nucleus, and the chromosomes exerting varying degrees of influence on the ultimate determination of spindle structure.

One fact stands out, however. To insure the establishement of a true functional biacuminate spindle, i.e., one pointed at both ends, two centers and a nucleus are necessary (Schrader 1947a). Where the nucleus is lacking, as in enucleated eggs, the centers can form astral rays, but it is only by chance that these may overlap to simulate a true spindle (Harvey 1936). Lams (1910) has shown that in the egg of the mollusk Arion the centers form a spindle through union of the overlapping astral rays before the nuclear membrane has broken down, but this spindle must incorporate

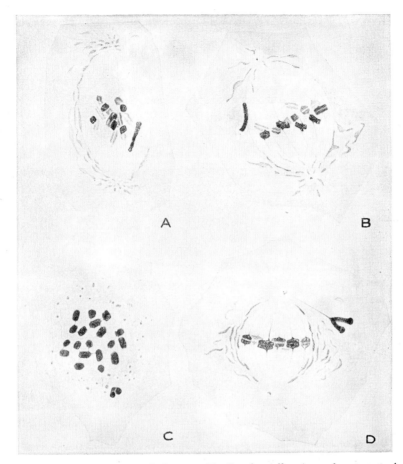

Fig. 7–16. Spermatocytes of the mantid, *Humbertiella*. A, early prometaphase with the spindle beginning to form, and the X-chromosome unoriented; B, late prometaphase, with the X-chromosome still unoriented but also ejected from the spindle; C, metaphase I, polar view, with the X-chromosome outside of the spindle area; D, same as in C but from a lateral view and showing the X-chromosome outside of the spindle proper, but with a single spindle fiber attaching it to the nearest pole. The mitochondrial mantle about the spindle is quite evident in *Humbertiella* (Hughes-Schrader 1948).

nuclear material into itself before it becomes functional. This definitely suggests that the karyolymph is an essential portion of the spindle even though no information is available to provide a clue as to the manner by which the karyolymph is transformed into spindle substance. Mazia (1955), in fact, believes that the nuclear contribution to the spindle cannot be great, and that the bulk of the spindle proteins are of cytoplasmic origin. It appears that polar activity, at the time of the dissolution of the nuclear membrane, induces a longitudinal orientation of the molecules of the cytoplasm and the karyolymph which imparts to the spindle its peculiar properties. Whether this activity is the result of physical or chemical reactions is not yet known.

A word of caution is needed at this point. It has been suggested that the materials of the spindle are of both nuclear and cytoplasmic origin, but this is based on observational rather than analytical evidence. In addition, little is known of the chemical nature of karyolymph. The technique of Mazia and Dan (1952; Mazia 1954, 1955) offers a means of solving this problem, for they have succeeded in isolating the spindles of sea-urchin eggs in mass (Fig. 7–17). The spindle is largely proteinaceous, sulphur

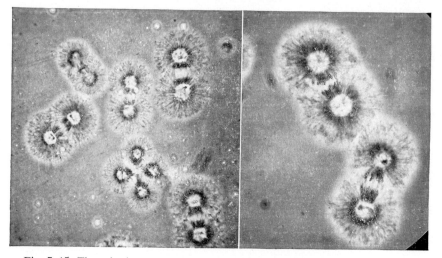

Fig. 7–17. The mitotic apparatus as isolated from sea urchin eggs, and consisting of asters, spindles, and chromosomes. Most of the figures are of anaphase stages, with a single metaphase in the illustration to the left. This plate also contains a tetrapolar figure (courtesy of Dr. D. Mazia).

linkages are important in maintaining its stability, the protein fibers exhibit a strong birefringence in polarized light, as Inoue (1952, 1953) has shown, and it accounts for about 12–15 percent of all of the protein of the egg. Further experimentation should throw light on the origin of this spindle protein, and on the biochemical reactions leading to its aggregation into the form of a functional spindle.

By way of illustration, two extreme types of spindle formation can be cited. One is the remarkably clear development of the spindle components in a protozoan, Barbulanympha (Cleveland 1938). In this organism, the centriole is a long slender structure 15–30 microns in length, attached anteriorly to the flagellar apparatus and terminated posteriorly by a spherical centrosome (Fig. 3–6). The spindle is entirely composed of astral rays which overlap and fuse. These arise from the free end of the centriole, the diffuse centrosome merely governing the direction the astral rays will take, and hence indirectly determining the shape of the spindle. Thus some protozoan species having a flat centrosome will form a thin spindle, while others possessing a spherical one will form a fuller, rounder spindle. In addition, in Barbulanympha, other astral rays form the *extranuclear chromosomal fibers* which become attached to the intact nuclear membrane, joining there with the *intranuclear chromosomal fibers* which extend from the centromeres to the inner surface of the nuclear membrane. Only the extranuclear chromosomal fibers appear to function in the movement of chromosomes. Division in this species is intranuclear, the membrane never undergoing dissolution. It is uncertain, therefore, whether the karyolymph actually forms a part of the spindle, although without the nucleus the chromosomal fibers would remain simply functionless astral rays.

The formation of the first meiotic spindle in the egg of the insect Acroschismus is direct, the spindle being entirely intranuclear in origin (Hughes-Schrader 1924). A similar situation holds for many of the coccid insects as well (Fig. 7–18), (Hughes-Schrader 1948b). In Protortonia and Llaveia,

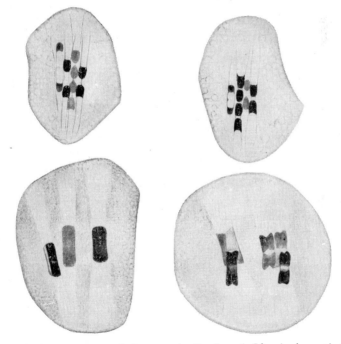

Fig. 7–18. Spermatocytes of *Protortonia* (top) and *Llaveia bouvari* (bottom) showing the separate chromosomal spindle elements grouped into a more or less single functional structure (Schrader 1931 and Hughes-Schrader 1931).

each chromosome forms its own group of chromosomal fibers from the diffuse centromere, and these are without orientation to the prospective polar regions. It is only when the polar forces come into play in late prophase that the chromosomes, with their fibers, exhibit an arrangement that leads to a metaphase plate formation. Such a spindle obviously is made up of separate parts corresponding in number to the chromosome pairs. The nuclear membrane breaks down shortly before metaphase, but long after the chromosomal fibers have made their appearance. No continuous fibers appear to be present.

Other species exhibit modes of spindle formation that lie somewhere between these extremes. It would appear that chromosomal fibers can be initiated by the centromere alone without reference to the centers, or by an interaction of the centers with the centromeres. It is not known for certain whether there exist forms of spindles that are made up of continuous fibers only, although this is thought to be the case in the butterfly Orgyia (Cretschmar 1928).

The state of condensation of the chromosomes is not without influence on spindle formation and action. In the spermatocytes of the coccid Gossyparia one set of chromosomes is condensed before the other, and this heteropycnotic set becomes attached to a monopolar spindle, moves to the pole, and is cast off before the other set is ready for metaphase orientation.

The various ways in which spindles are formed would lead us to infer that they can be of diverse structure. A variety of techniques have indicated that the spindle is of a homogeneous nature, although opposed to this are several observations of spindle fibers in the living cell (Cleveland 1934; Cooper 1941; Inoue 1952, 1953). In stained preparations, the spindle reveals a striated structure; but it remains problematical as to how much of the striated appearance is due to shrinkage, since fixation methods known to cause shrinkage are those characteristically used to bring out the fibrous elements of the spindle. For example, it is a rather common observation that, in tissues, the spindles of well-fixed cells at the surface are generally homogeneous, whereas spindles in cells in the interior of a block of tissue, which often undergo a shrinkage as the result of improper or slow fixation, exhibit spindle fibers quite distinctly.

Bĕlăr's observations form the original basis for much of the later studies on spindle structure. His evidence supporting the hypothesis that there is a longitudinal orientation of spindle elements has been summarized by Schrader (1953) as follows: (1) in hypertonic solutions, shrinkage of the spindle is greater transversely than it is longitudinally; (2) in bent spindles, the fibers are closer to each other in the neighborhood of the bend; (3) Brownian movement of particles that happen to become incorporated within the spindle is greater longitudinally than it is transversely; (4) a split in the spindle induced by pressure or shrinkage is always longitudinal. It is now generally believed that the spindle must be some sort of liquid crystal or a tactoid, these being structures possessing a definite molecular orientation or lattice-work. The fact that, in polarized light, the living spindle in Chaetopterus eggs exhibits birefringence supports the conclusion that there are fibrous components oriented in the long axis (Fig. 7–19)

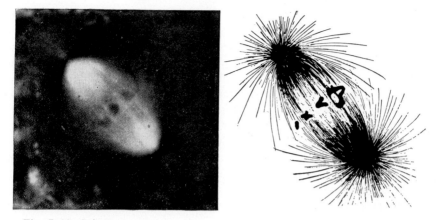

Fig. 7–19. Spindle in the egg of the marine worm, *Chaetopterus* (left) taken in polarized light. Right, a rendering of the same figure in more detail than can be demonstrated in the photograph (Inoue 1953).

(Inoue 1952, 1953). These need not be visible, however, except where distortion tends to accentuate them, or polarized light reveals their orientation. Inoue's studies indicate that birefringent fibrils extend from pole to pole, and from pole to centromere, but Swann (1951) has not been able to confirm the fibrillar structure of the spindle even though a birefringence of the spindle as a whole is quite evident.

The question arises, therefore, as to whether the spindle is a composite structure composed of fibrils in a basic ground substance, or whether only ground substance, strongly oriented, is present. The fibrils need not be chemically different from the ground substance, but only more definitely oriented by the interaction between poles, or between pole and centromere. Several lines of evidence support the idea that the spindle is of a composite nature, and that it is made up of a basic ground substance through which the fibers not only pass, but also freely contract and elongate. This is suggested by the manner in which chromosomes are expelled from the nucleus (Hughes-Schrader 1948a; Schrader 1947a), and it is implicit in Östergren's (1945) hypothesis of spindle equilibria which pictures the chromosomes as being drawn into the ground substance by the fibers. Inoue has also shown that colchicine destroys the birefringence of the ground substance of the spindle and asters first, while the chromosomal fibers lose their birefringence more slowly.

ANAPHASE MOVEMENT

The movement of chromosomes from the metaphase plate to the polar regions has been one of the most intensively studied of cell processes, owing to the readiness with which cells in the living state can be examined. Precise measurements of movements can be made, enabling the investigator to obtain quantitative descriptive data which can then be correlated with structural changes occurring simultaneously.

Schrader (1953) has extensively reviewed the many hypotheses advanced to explain anaphase movement, and it is obvious in most instances than an interpretation of the mechanism involved depends upon the initial beliefs held by the investigator regarding structure of the spindle. Thus, Darlington (1937a), who has long held that the spindle fibers are fixation artifacts, has hypothesized that all movements of the chromosomes in the nucleus and on the spindle can be related to repulsions or attractions of an electrostatic nature. This idea, an elaboration of an hypothesis put forth by Lillie in 1909, is embodied in his "Balance Theory of Mitotis," according to which anaphase movement reflects the repulsion operating between the centromeres of daughter chromatids in mitosis, or between the paired centromeres of a meiotic bivalent.

Although there are known instances where chromosome autonomy appears to be the most feasible explanation of movement, Darlington's electrostatic hypothesis is unsatisfactory because of its initial assumptions regarding the nature of spindle fibers, and because, experimentally, there is no evidence of forces of this nature. Similar arguments may be advanced against those hypotheses dealing with diffusion and streaming phenomena; like the electrostatic hypothesis, they are little more than descriptions of the events occurring without a corresponding correlation with the changing appearance of other cellular components.

Quantitative data on anaphase movement of chromosomes has provided what appears to be a satisfactory solution to the problem (Bělař 1929; Barber 1939; Ris 1943, 1949; Hughes and Swann 1948). Although some differences of interpretation have arisen, there seems to be no longer any doubt but that the movement of chromosomes to the poles, at least in animal cells, is brought about by a shortening of longitudinal oriented spindle elements and by elongation of the spindle body. In the primary spermatocytes of the grasshopper and the bearberry aphid, Tamalia, the two processes occur simultaneously, giving an unbroken curve when the distance between centromeres is plotted against time (Fig. 7–20). In the embryonic cells and secondary spermatocytes of Tamalia, and in the primary spermatocytes of the bugs Protentor and Thelia, the two processes are distinct in time, giving a curve of two S-shaped components separated by a plateau. The first portion of the curve represents the movement due to the shortening of the spindle elements, the second to the elongation of the spindle which pushes the daughter plates farther apart. Even in the grasshopper, where the processes are coincident, it is possible to suppress one without affecting the other (Ris 1949). Thus, chloral hydrate (0.08%) inhibits the elongation of the spindle but does not affect the shortening of the spindle elements, a fact that further demonstrates the composite structure and function of the spindle.

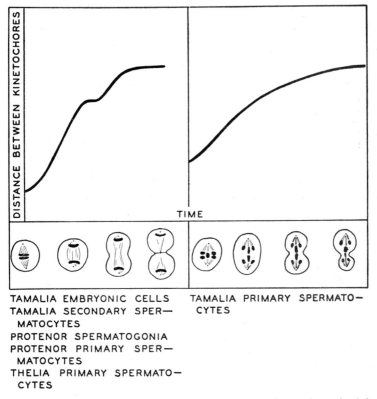

DISTANCE BETWEEN KINETOCHORES

TIME

TAMALIA EMBRYONIC CELLS
TAMALIA SECONDARY SPER—
MATOCYTES
PROTENOR SPERMATOGONIA
PROTENOR PRIMARY SPER—
MATOCYTES
THELIA PRIMARY SPERMATO—
CYTES

TAMALIA PRIMARY SPERMATO—
CYTES

Fig. 7–20. Anaphase movement in various types of cells as determined by the distance between centromeres. Left, the plateau which appears in the curve separates the early movement of the chromosomes caused by the shortening of the chromosomal fibers from the later movement caused by spindle elongation. Right, the plateau is lacking, and all movement is due to spindle elongation (Ris 1943).

Ris has also postulated that the differences in temporal separation between shortening of the elements and elongation of the spindle are related to the type of centromeres present, i.e., whether diffuse or localized. The broad chromosome with a diffuse centromere would tend to delay swelling of the spindle more so than would a chromosome with a localized one, and consequently would delay elongation as well.

The phrase "shortening of the spindle elements" is a noncommittal one, and implies no known physico-chemical mechanism. Bělař believed that the chromosome became attached to the continuous fiber *(Leitfaser)* by means of a traction fiber *(Zugfaser),* and that the initial movement involved a poleward gliding action of the chromosome on the continuous fiber. Later movement involved the expansion of the interzonal region or *Stemmkörper.* Ris, however, has found no evidence for the existence of a *Stemmkörper,* but suggests that the elongation of the spindle results from the fact that it swells and stretches. Hughes and Swann, on the other hand, suggest that the shortening of the elements is an expression of a contractile mechanism with the chromosomes being pulled to the poles. Their studies with polarized light have revealed, also, a more definite molecular orientation at the poles of the spindle than at the equator; the centers, therefore, would be the origin of orienting forces that shape the spindle from isotropic protoplasm.

The flexibility of the cell membrane of an animal cell lets elongation of the spindle and the cell take place. The relative inflexibility of the plant cell wall at the time of division would not permit elongation of the cell, and there is consequently no evidence that an elongation of the spindle does occur.

It is likely that all anaphase movement in plant cells results from the shortening of spindle elements. The converse is true for other cells. In the primary spermatocytes of Tamalia, no shortening of the elements occurs, and anaphase movement is entirely due to elongation of the spindle (Ris 1943). A similar situation holds for the lepidopteran Orgyia, whose chromosomes seem to possess no chromosomal fibers (Cretschmar 1928).

Following the completion of anaphase movement in animal cells, cleavage cuts the cell in two. This is controlled by elongation of the spindle; where elongation fails, no cleavage furrow appears (Ris 1949). Unequal lateral bulging of the spindle occurs if the spindle swells as usual, but the chromosomes fail to separate (a stickiness of chromosomes induced by x-rays will produce this phenomenon). The chromosomes are apparently attached to the poles by fibers, but their stickiness prevents a clean separation and, indirectly, an elongation. In plant cells, this is circumvented by the formation of a cell plate that cuts the cell into halves.

CHAPTER 8

Crossing Over and Chiasma Formation

The preliminary discussion of crossing over in Chapter 4 emphasized aspects of the problem that clarified many of the discrepant phenomena encountered in early genetic studies. Aiding in the establishment of the Chromosome Theory of Inheritance, the early studies clearly showed that crossing over occurred in the four-stranded stage of meiotic prophase, that it was preceded by a synapsis of homologous chromosomes, and that by a reciprocal exchange of chromatin material it led to the breaking up of linkage groups. Blocks of genes rather than single loci were exchanged whenever a crossover occurred, and the phenomenon of interference explained why the points of crossing in any single pair of homologues were spatially distributed in a more or less orderly fashion.

Crossing over, however, still remains as one of the central problems of cytogenetics, partly because the mechanism of crossing over has not been completely solved, and partly because it is a phenomenon subject to considerable variation—often unpredictable—by many intrinsic and extrinsic factors. Any postulated scheme to account for crossing over must perforce include and explain these variables that have been encountered. Although the Darlingtonian hypothesis (Darlington 1937a), to be explained later, has been widely accepted because of its logical simplicity, it is quite evident that it must be viewed with skepticism even though, as Sturtevant (1951a) reluctantly points out, no wholly satisfactory substitute is at hand.

A definition of terms becomes necessary at this point. It has been customary for geneticists and cytologists, following Darlington's views, to equate a *chiasma* and a *chromatid exchange*. The former term, tracing back to Janssens (1909), is descriptive, and refers to a cytologically demonstrable change of partners between two pairs of chromatids without specifying the nature of the change at any level, i.e., equational or reductional, or indeed whether a transfer of chromatin has been made. Cooper's (1949) discovery of chiasmata in the males of Drosophila, which undergo no crossing over, emphasizes that the one-to-one correspondence of these two phenomena is no longer unequivocally admissible. The common practice, therefore, of counting chiasmata as a means of establishing the minimum number of exchanges per chromosome or per cell loses much of its certainty, even as the process of terminalization makes the establishment of the original position and number of chiasmata uncertain. A *chromatid exchange,* on the other hand, is the immediate result of crossing over, i.e., the exchange of two non-sister chromatids followed by their subsequent cross reunion to give new linkage combinations. The detection of chromatid exchanges therefore is by genetical, not by cytological, means. In what follows, these terms will be used as defined.

ORIGIN OF CROSSOVER CHROMATIDS

Since crossing over occurs when the chromosomes are longitudinally double, and hence when the paired homologues are in the four-strand stage, it involves *chromatids* and not whole chromosomes. This hypothesis, which was established on an experimental basis by Bridges (1916), following Janssens' (1909) cytological study of chiasmata, provides a ready explanation for the fact that two linked genes, regardless of their genetic separation, rarely show more than 50 percent crossing over between them. As Figure 4–11 indicates, the four possible types of non-sister chromatid exchange will, for each type, yield two crossover, and two non-crossover chromatids. When a non-crossover chromatid is recovered among the testcross progeny in a linkage experiment, its origin may therefore have been from a pair of homologues that did not undergo genetic exchange, or from a pair that underwent crossing over one or more times.

The kinds of chromatids recovered from a double exchange will vary according to how the chromatids involved in the first exchange are related to those involved in the second exchange. This is illustrated in Figure 4–12. A count of the types of chromatids recovered from double crossovers reveals that the ratio of non-crossover chromatids to singles to doubles is 1:2:1. For the sake of convenience, the types of double exchanges have been designated two-, three-, and four-strand exchanges, the designations indicating the number of different chromatids involved at the two points of crossing over. Two kinds of three-strand double exchanges are therefore to be expected.

With more than two exchanges per chromosome pair, the chromatid relationships become complicated, but they can be shown to be produced in predictable ratios (Table 8–1).

A specific example will serve to indicate how this procedure may be utilized in dealing with experimental material. Bridges (Morgan, Bridges, and Schultz 1935) studied crossing over throughout the X-chromosome of *D. melanogaster,* making use of nine well-spaced loci to give eight sections in which crossing over could be detected. The data from a total of 16,136 flies are given in Table 8–2.

As indicated, the recovered chromatids do not give a clear picture of the exchanges that gave rise to them. The crossover data can, however,

TABLE 8–1

**Ratios of crossover and non-crossover chromatids
recovered from various types of exchanges.**

Exchanges ——*Recovered single chromatids with relative frequencies*——

	Non-Crossovers	Singles	Doubles	Triples	Quadruples
None	1				
1	1	1			
2	1	2	1		
3	1	3	3	1	
4	1	4	6	4	1

TABLE 8–2

**Summary of Bridges' data on crossing over
in the X-chromosome of D. melanogaster
(Morgan, Bridges, and Schultz 1935).**

Chromatid types in terms of crossing over	Number of individuals	Percentage of individuals
Non-crossover	6,607	40.9
Single	7,555	46.8
Double	1,913	11.9
Triple	61	0.4
Quadruple	0	0.0
Total	16,136	100.0

be converted into exchange data by making use of information dealing
with the relative frequencies of chromatid types to be expected (Table
8–1). When this is done (Table 8–3), the origin of the chromatid cate-

TABLE 8–3

**An analysis of the recovered chromatids from Bridges'
data in terms of the number of exchanges which
they represent (Weinstein 1936).**

No. chromatids recovered	Non C.O.		Single C.O.		Double C.O.		Triple C.O.		Percent of Exchange
		6,607		7,555		1,913		61	
0 exchange	1	904							5.6
1 exchange	½	3,912	½	3,912					48.5
2 exchanges	¼	1,730	½	3,460	¼	1,730			42.9
3 exchanges	⅛	61	⅜	183	⅜	183	⅛	61	3.0

gories becomes clearer, and a better understanding is gained of the over-all
frequency of exchanges in a particular chromosome. The single and double
exchanges are found to be the origin of the great majority of recovered
chromatids, with the non-exchanges and triple-exchanges being relatively

infrequent. This procedure for calculating the origin of the recovered chromatids is of course predicated on the assumption that a crossover at one locus between any two non-sister chromatids does not influence in any way the chromatids that might cross over at another locus in the same chromosome. Such interference is known as *chromatid interference,* but so far as the Drosophila studies show, it is non-operative. Hence crossing over between two loci cannot exceed 50 percent. There are indications, however, that chromatid interference is operative in some organisms (see later), leading to frequencies greater than 50 percent.

POSITION OF CROSSING OVER

A precise determination of the position of crossing over in respect to chromosome distances can only be made after the genes have been located on a cytological map, since physical and genetical map distances are not interchangeable units of measurement. The most convenient point of reference in all such problems is the centromere, particularly since there is good evidence that the centromere exerts a marked influence on the rate of crossing over in its neighborhood, and since a crossover on one side of the centromere is without influence on one on the other side. A wealth of evidence indicates that the crossover frequency per unit of physical distance varies throughout the chromosome.

In a relatively crude way, this can be demonstrated in Chromosomes II and III of *D. melanogaster,* by reference to the genetical map (Fig. 4–13). The left arm of Chromosome II is approximately 55 map units long. The gene *purple* (*pr*), 0.4 crossover units from the centromere, is one-fourth of the distance from the centromere to the end of the chromosome as judged by somatic chromosome lengths. *Black* (*b*), 6.4 units from the centromere, occupies a position close to the middle of the arm. It is apparent, therefore, that the frequency of crossing over increases as one approaches the middle of the chromosome arm, and is greatest in the distal half of the chromosome which has a map length of 48.2 units.

A similar situation holds for the right arm of Chromosome III, which has a length of 58.5 units. *Pink* (*p*^{p}), 1.5 units from the centromere, is located in the proximal one-seventh of the arm. *Stripe* (*sr*), at 14 units, is in the middle. Since the remaining distal half of the right arm of III contains 44.5 crossover units, the majority of exchanges must occur distally. By the same token, loci physically close together in the central portions of the arms would show a proportionally greater spatial separation on the genetical map.

The origin of the discrepancies between the genetical and cytological maps is clearly to be sought in the spatial distribution of crossing over. It is more frequent in the center of the arms, in Drosophila at least, than it is at the ends or near the centromere, thus shortening or extending the genetical map as crossing over is less or more frequent per unit of chromosome length.

Cytological maps can also be constructed from salivary chromosomes, but they possess a disadvantage in that they do not give a true picture of the large heterochromatic portions adjacent to the centromeres of the three major chromosomes in *D. melanogaster*. Their detailed structure, however, permits a more accurate mapping of the loci, and also makes it feasible to determine whether local differences in crossover frequencies exist, a study manifestly impossible with somatic chromosomes. That such local patterns of crossing over are found is indicated by a comparison of the cytological and genetical distances from *y* to *fa* in the left end of the X-chromosome (Table 8–4). Clearly, from these data, the *rst-fa* region is one of relatively high crossing over. The *w-rst-fa* region, located in four, possibly five, detectable bands, has the same crossover frequency (1.5%) as the *y-pr-w* region, made up of 75 bands (Fig. 8–1). Whether this is the result

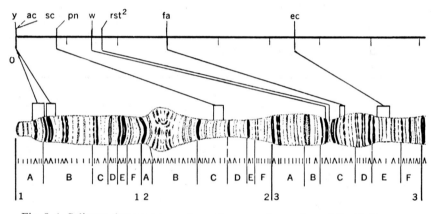

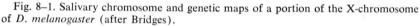

Fig. 8–1. Salivary chromosome and genetic maps of a portion of the X-chromosome of *D. melanogaster* (after Bridges).

of mechanical weaknesses in the chromosome—as, for instance, intercalary heterochromatic regions—or to inherent differences arising out of the mechanism of crossing over, is not clearly evident.

McClintock (1943) has found a region of similarly high crossing-over frequency in Chromosome 9 of maize. Gene *C* (*colored aleurone*) is located at 26 crossover units from the end of the short arm of the chromo-

---

TABLE 8–4

A comparison of crossover frequencies as a function of distance (band number) in the y — fa region of the X-chromosome. Number of bands based on Bridges' (1935) salivary chromosome maps.

Interval	Number of bands between genes	Map distance	Percent C.O. per band
y — pr	57	0.8	0.014
pr — w	18	0.7	0.038
w — rst	2	0.2	0.1
rst — fa	2	1.3	0.65

some, and lies in the fifth or sixth chromomere from the end. The chromomeres are extremely minute, but gene *yg-2,* which is located within the terminal chromomere, is 19 crossover units from *C.* This in itself suggests that within this region, crossing over is higher per physical unit of length than it is in other parts of the arm. Additional data, however, demonstrate this to a striking degree. Chromosome 9 can be made deficient for a number of terminal chromomeres. The extent of the deficiencies ranges from the loss of the terminal chromomere up to a loss of four chromomeres (Fig. 6–5). The deficient chromosomes are not pollen-transmissible. Therefore, if the deficient chromosome, in a plant heterozygous for the deficiency, carries the dominant gene, and the normal chromosome carries recessive *c,* any normal chromosome transmitted by the pollen parent, and carrying the dominant *C,* will have resulted from a crossover between *C* and the end of the chromosome. This can be detected by placing such pollen onto the silks of a plant homozygous for *c.* The percentage of crossing over can be determined directly from the ratio of colored to colorless kernels, and Table 8–5 gives the data so derived.

TABLE 8–5

Relationship of crossing over between gene C and the end of the chromosome as a function of the length of the crossover segment (McClintock (1943).

Deficiency	Percent crossing over	No. of kernels examined
Deficient for 4 chromomeres		
df. 1297 A — 2	0.016	6130
" 1278 A — 4	0.052	1923
" 1501 A	0.52	5748
" 1559 B — 2	0.72	1383
" 1463 — 2	0.94	9743
Average	0.449	
Deficient for 3 chromomeres		
df. 1265	1.25	5830
Deficient for 2 chromomeres		
df. 1533 A	3.07	8791
Deficient for 1½ chromomeres		
df. 1507	8.33	4566
Deficient for 1 chromomere		
df. 1509	17.06	3826
df. 1512 D — 2	21.1	1639
Average	19.08	

It is apparent that the greater the length of the terminal segment in which crossing over may occur, the greater is the frequency. The relationship is not strictly linear, however. Loss of the terminal chromomere has but little reductional effect on crossing over (ca. 2%), but removal of an additional half of the adjacent chromomere causes an abrupt drop in frequency. This may have resulted from the loss of a segment within which crossing over is highly localized, or it may be simply a function of the length of chromatin available for crossing over.

Other data indicate that the gene *Dotted* lies seven crossover units distal to *yg-2;* thus there must be a very high frequency of crossing over within the terminal chromomere (Rhoades 1945). Rhoades (1939) has also shown that a similar situation obtains for Chromosome 2 in maize, and it would appear that in this respect Drosophila and maize differ markedly from each other if the crossover data from the X-chromosome are used for comparative purposes. The right end of Chromosome II of Drosophila, however, has a relatively high frequency of crossing over per micron length of salivary gland chromosome.

Bridges (1937), in arriving at this conclusion, has utilized the *coefficient of crossing over* to make comparisons between linkage maps and salivary chromosome lengths. If the total length of all of the salivary chromosomes (1180 microns) is divided by the total map distance (279 units), then the average ratio is one map unit per 4.2 microns of salivary chromosome length. The measured distance between *plexus* (*px;* 100.5) and *Minute 33a* (*M33a;* 108.0) in the right arm of Chromosome II is 18.5 microns, giving a ratio of one map unit to 2.5 microns (18.5/7.5). The coefficient of crossing over (4.2/2.5) is therefore 1.7, and crossing over is approximately 70 percent freer than in the set of chromosomes as a whole. If one narrows this down to the *px-bw* (*brown;* 104.5) region, 4.0 map units equal 7.0 microns of chromosome length, giving a coefficient of 2.4, or one map unit to 1.75 microns of length.

By way of contrast, the crossover circumstances in the right arm of Chromosome II can be compared with those obtaining in the *y-w-rst-fa* region in the X-chromosome. According to Bridges' 1935 salivary map, the *y-w* region is about 25 microns in length, and the *w-rst-fa* region about 3 microns (Fig. 8–1). Since each region has a map distance of 1.5 (Table 8–4), the coefficients of crossing over are 0.26 and 2.0, respectively. On the other hand, the next 25 microns of chromosome length to the right of *fa* represent a map distance of 10 crossover units, with a coefficient of 1.7.

Although the cytological and genetical maps cannot yet be accurately compared along their entire length, there are clearly marked differences in the coefficients of crossing over for the various regions of the chromosomes. This is indicated in Table 8–6 for almost the entire X-chromosome, although a different measure of chromosome length is utilized. How much reliance can be placed upon these methods of comparison, however, remains a moot question, largely because critical comparisons between salivary and meiotic chromosomes are lacking.

Mather (1936, 1938) and Charles (1938) have considered in detail problems relating to the spatial distribution of crossovers in *D. melanogaster,* and to the mechanisms involved in the determination of the spacings. Recognizing that the centromere (or its adjacent heterochromatin) has a

TABLE 8–6

Location of loci studied on the basis of 100 units for the X-chromosome with the frequency distribution of crossing over in single exchange tetrads between loci in absolute values and in terms of the frequency per 1/100 of chromosome length within the sections (Bridges' data from Charles 1938).

Locus	Locus on genetic map	C.O. frequency per section	C.O. frequency per 1/100 of chromosome length within sections
sc	2.2		
		2.57	0.195
ec	15.4		
		6.48	0.727
cv	24.3		
		5.95	0.850
ct	31.3		
		11.63	0.722
v	47.4		
		7.41	0.432
s	64.1		
		10.60	0.658
f	80.5		
		2.60	0.226
car	92.0		
		1.25	0.250
bb	97.0		

pronounced effect on crossing over, and that when changes in crossing over occur due to altered internal or external conditions, these changes are most generally expressed in the centric region, Mather has concluded that the centromere exerts a determining role in the spacing of crossovers along the chromosome arms. Thus, the frequency of crossing over in any region of the chromosome arm (in V-shaped autosomes the arms are independent of each other insofar as crossing over is concerned) is a function of the distance of that region from the centromere. Also, since Mather believes the centromere plays the determining role in crossing over, it is further assumed that there is a time sequence of crossing over which proceeds from the centromere in a distal direction. The most proximal crossover would therefore form first, followed by others more distally located.

Charles' (1938) analysis of Bridges' data (Table 8–6) reveals, however, that although there is an orderly distribution of exchanges from the centromere to the end of the chromosome, there is an equally orderly distribution from the end of the chromosome to the centromere. The free end of the chromosome may, as a consequence, be equally instrumental in determining the spacing of crossovers. Charles finds no support for a temporal seriation of crossovers that begins at the centromere.

SISTER CHROMATID CROSSING OVER

It has been generally assumed in the past that no crossing over takes place between sister chromatids during meiosis. In normal rod chromosomes this type of event would pass unrecognized since it would not alter the crossover relationships between non-sister chromatids; in ring chromosomes, however, it should be possible to detect sister-chromatid crossing, and the evidence to date from Drosophila studies indicates that it does not occur.

The evidence most frequently cited to oppose the hypothesis that sister-chromatid crossing does occur is that obtained from the frequencies of homozygosis in attached-X females (Beadle and Emerson 1935), although additional supporting data is derived from the study of ring chromosomes in Drosophila (Morgan 1933) and of the Bar locus (Sturtevant, 1925, 1928). On the basis of random distribution of crossing over between the four strands of an attached X-chromosome, there are six possible combinations of these four strands and the frequency of homozygosis cannot exceed 16.7 percent. If only non-sister-strand crossing over takes place, the frequency can rise to 25 percent when one exchange occurs, 12.5 percent for two exchanges, and 18.75 percent for three exchanges (Sax 1932b), and the fact that homozygosis can exceed 16.7 percent (Fig. 4–16) has been interpreted as proving that little or no sister-strand crossing over takes place (Beadle and Emerson 1935). As Schwartz (1953a, b) points out, the evidence is valid only under certain circumstances; and in light of data obtained from a study on ring chromosomes in maize, it seems necessary to revise our ideas regarding the occurrence of sister-strand crossing over. Schwartz (1954) has further suggested that somatic crossing over in attached-X females of Drosophila is interpretable on the basis of sister-strand crossing over occurring in conjunction with non-sister-strand crossing over. Brown and Welshons (1955), however, have been unable to confirm Schwartz's data, so that the validity of the hypothesis remains in doubt.

The ring chromosome, X^{cl}, in Drosophila shows no sister-strand crossing over when studied in heterozygous state with a rod chromosome (Morgan 1933). If sister-strand crossing over occurred in the ring, dicentric double-sized rings would be produced which would be eliminated in oögenesis much as is an inversion bridge (Fig. 8–2). This would lead to a decrease in the number of non-crossover rings recovered in the progeny, but since Morgan found the frequency of non-crossover rings to be equivalent to the frequency of non-crossover rod chromosomes, the conclusion was drawn that such crossing over did not occur.

The extensive studies of McClintock (1938a, 1941a, b) on ring chromosomes in maize, as well as the data of Braver and Blount (1950) on the ring X-chromosomes in Drosophila, indicate that at least in somatic cells dicentric, double-sized rings occur, and the likelihood is that these arise from sister-strand crossing over. It is clear, however, that they can also arise by the division or replication of a ring chromosome containing a twist in the initial strand. In this sense, the chromosome can be viewed as

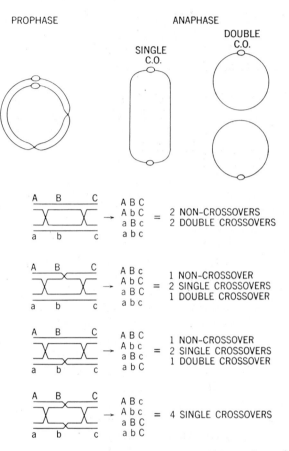

Fig. 8–2. Consequences of odd (single) and even (double) numbers of sister-strand crossovers in a ring chromosome (above), and the relation of non-crossover to cross-over chromatids when odd and even numbers of sister-strand crossovers are associated with a two-strand double crossover (below). Compare the ratios of non-crossovers to single crossovers to double crossovers (4:8:4) with that in figure 4–12.

a Moibius ring the inner and outer faces of which are continuous with each other because of a half-twist in the strand.

Schwartz (1953a), however, has provided what appears to be reasonable evidence that sister-strand crossing over does occur in the meiotic cells of maize when a ring chromosome (derived from nearly the whole of Chromosome 6) exists in heterozygous state with its homologous rod chromosome. When a single non-sister-strand crossover takes place between the ring and the rod chromosomes a bridge forms at anaphase I unaccompanied by a fragment. When two exchanges are formed in the bivalent, the configurations formed in anaphase I and II will depend upon whether the double crossover is of a two-, three-, or four-strand type (Fig. 8–3). On the assumption that there is no chromatid interference, and that

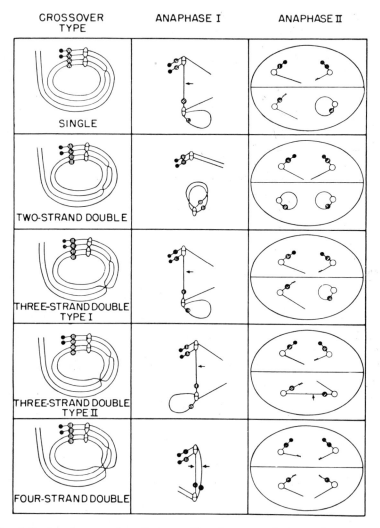

Fig. 8–3. Anaphase configurations resulting from crossing over between a ring chromosome and its rod homologue (chromosome 6 in maize). Arrows indicate positions of breakage of anaphase bridges while wavy ends indicate freshly broken regions of the bridge (Schwartz 1953).

the types of double crossovers occur with equal frequency, then the frequency of anaphase I and II bridges will provide a clue as to the events that occurred at the time of crossing over.

Thus, from the four types of double crossovers there should be the same frequency of anaphase II single bridges (from three-strand, Type II) as there are double bridges in anaphase I (from four-strand doubles). The data in Table 8–7 indicate that this equivalence does not hold, the difference being nearly threefold in favor of the single anaphase II bridges.

Furthermore, 59 percent of the anaphase I cells showed single bridges, these arising from single crossovers and from both types of three-strand doubles. If the four types of double crossovers are formed with equal frequency, i.e., if there is no chromatid interference, then the single bridges in anaphase I arising from three-strand doubles should be twice the frequency of double anaphase I bridges arising from a four-strand double crossover, or 26 percent ($13\% \times 2$). This leaves 33 percent of anaphase I single bridges due to single crossovers.

TABLE 8–7

Meiotic anaphase configurations observed in a strain of maize heterozygous for a ring and a rod chromosome (Schwartz 1953a).

| | —————Anaphase I————— | | | | —————Anaphase II————— | | | |
| | | | | | | (daughter cell pairs) | | |
	Single bridge	Double bridge	No bridge	Total	Single bridge	Double bridge	No bridge	Total
No. of cells	368	81	171	620	166	47	262	475
Percent	59	13	28	100	35	10	55	100

On the basis that sister-strand crossing over is frequent, and that odd numbers of sister-strand crossovers in the ring, and associated with single non-sister exchanges, will also yield single bridges in anaphase II while even numbers will not be detected, Schwartz has calculated that one-half of these cells (16.5%) will yield single bridges in anaphase II. These, together with the 13 percent resulting from Type II three-strand doubles, will give 29.5 percent, which is not greatly different from the 35 percent observed. Sister-strand crossovers associated with double non-sister crossovers do not alter the frequency of bridges in anaphase I or II (Fig. 8–2), and can therefore be disregarded.

The question that remains to be answered is whether such crossing over occurs between the sister strands of normal rod chromosomes, or whether they are peculiar to ring chromosomes in maize, and to attached-X chromosomes in Drosophila. If so, the circumstances of ring chromosome behavior may provide a clue as to the mechanism of crossing over, a point that will be discussed later in this chapter.

FACTORS AFFECTING CROSSING OVER

It was early recognized that crossing over was a variable phenomenon, subject to change by a number of environmental factors. Genetic maps, therefore, should be based on crossing over that takes place under certain specified conditions. This, of course, can be done only with organisms that can be grown to maturity under controlled laboratory conditions, and to date, Drosophila is the only organism that has yielded such accurate information. The map distances in *D. melanogaster* are computed from data collected from organisms raised at 25° C. This is also possible with the bread mold, Neurospora, although the data are by no means as extensive.

The extrinsic and intrinsic factors that govern the degree of crossing over have been much investigated, and the data obtained must inevitably be accounted for in any hypothesis bearing on the mechanism of crossing over.

Effect of sex. It is well known that there is no crossing over in males of *D. melanogaster* except under unusual experimental conditions (Whittinghill 1937, 1947). The same holds true for the female of the silkworm, *Bombyx mori*. In organisms in which crossing over is regularly found in both sexes, the frequency of recombination between any two genes may be identical in the two sexes (or in the anthers and ovaries of plants) as in the garden pea, higher in females than in males, as in the mouse and the rat (Dunn 1920; Castle 1925), or higher in males than in females, as in the pigeon (Hollander 1938). It has been pointed out by Haldane (1922) that where linkage differentials exist between the sexes, it is the heterogametic sex in which crossing over is lowered in frequency, or absent, and this is borne out by available data in animals where the chromosomal sex mechanism is known.

Data derived from linkage studies in chromosome 5 of maize are of interest because of the hermaphroditic nature of the plant (Rhoades 1941b). The data (Table 8–8) are obtained from the male and female flowers of the same plant, but it should be recognized that the environmental conditions at the time of crossing over were not controlled since meiosis in male and female flowers does not take place at the same time. The gene order and map loci of chromosome 5 are as follows:

$$\frac{a_2 \qquad bm \qquad bt \qquad\qquad\qquad pr}{0 \qquad 6 \qquad 8 \qquad\qquad\qquad 31},$$

with the centromere being between, and adjacent to, *bm* and *bt*. It is clear that for all regions studied crossing over is higher in the male than in the female sporocytes. There is also a strong suggestion that the regions neighboring the centromere show a greater percentage increase in crossing over. This may be related to the pycnotic nature of the centric region of chromosome 5 since a number of studies have provided data which suggest that crossing over in regions in or adjacent to heterochromatin is much more affected by environmental changes than is crossing over in euchromatin.

TABLE 8–8

Summary of crossover data for regions in Chromosome 5 in maize. The centromere lies between genes Bm and Bt (Rhoades 1941b).

Sex	Crossover percentages			
	$A_2 - Bt$	$Bt - Pr$	$A_2 - Bm$	$Bm - Pr$
Male	16.5	35.4	15.6	33.8
Female	9.7	30.3	9.1	24.4

It is not certain to what extent a linkage differential between the sexual cells of maize might be present in other chromosomes. The *Su-Tu* region of chromosome 4, the *Lg-B* region of chromosome 2, and three regions of chromosome 10 show no sexual differences, while the *C-Sh* region of chromosome 9 has been variously reported as having a higher, a lower, and an identical recombination rate in female cells as compared to male (Rhoades 1941b). None of these regions, however, lies conspicuously close to the centromere. Since the meiotic processes, and hence crossing over, in the anthers and ovaries of maize do not go on simultaneously—microsporogenesis precedes megasporogenesis—it is uncertain whether the linkage differentials reported are due to intrinsic or extrinsic factors.

Effect of age. Bridges (1915) early demonstrated that crossing over in *D. melanogaster* varied markedly with the age of the female. Collections of eggs were made over three periods of ten days each, and the region tested being the *b — pr* section of Chromosome II. These two genes, according to Bridges' genetic map, lie six map units apart. Recombination data for the first ten-day period revealed a crossover frequency of 5.9 percent, which dropped to 1.8 percent during the second ten-day period, and which then rose to 3.8 percent for the third ten-day period. An initial high rate of recombination is therefore followed by a marked fall, after which a second maximum is encountered.

It is to be noticed that the genetic region tested lies close to the centromere, which is medianly located in Chromosome II. That this region is particularly susceptible to the effects of aging has been shown for the three major chromosomes of Drosophila (Bridges 1915, 1927; Plough 1917, 1921; Stern 1926; Bergner 1928). The Chromosome III study of Bridges (1927) is particularly interesting since it makes use of the entire chromosome, appropriately marked and therefore amenable to analysis of multiple crossing over as well as of percentages of total recombination. The chromosome used is marked as follows:

ru	*h*	*D*	*st*	*p^p*	*ss*	*e^s*
0	26.5	41.0	44.0	48.0	58.5	70.7

A considerable section of the left arm of Chromosome III extends beyond *e^s* (*sooty*), while *ru* (*roughoid*) lies at the extreme distal end of the right arm. The centromere lies between *st* (*scarlet*) and *p^p* (*peach*). The percentages of recombination for specific crossover regions are given in Figure 8–4. It is apparent, when the total recombination values are calculated, that two minimal periods of crossing over occur, the first at approximately 11 days and the second at 25 days. The variability in crossing over within the different chromosome regions can best be appreciated by reducing the data into terms of percentage decreases and when calculated as the percentage difference between the initial high and first minimum (Table 8–9).

Region *st — p^p* contains the centromere and shows the greatest effect with age. Regions *p^p — ss* and *D — st* lie adjacent to, and on either side of,

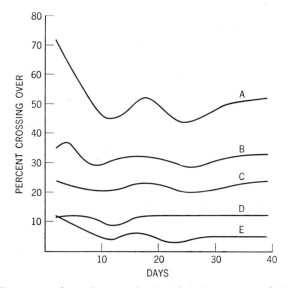

Fig. 8–4. Frequency of crossing over in the third chromosome of *D. melanogaster* as a function of the age of the female. A, total crossover frequency; B, *ru-D* region; C, *ru-h* region; D, representative of both the *h-D* and *ss-e^s* regions which are approximately equidistant from the centromere in the left and right arms, respectively; E, *p-ss* region. The general shapes of the curves are similar except that in B, the depression in crossover frequency occurred at nine rather than at eleven days (redrawn from Bridges 1927).

TABLE 8–9

**Variability in crossing over in Chromosome III
of D. melanogaster with aging
(Bridges 1927).**

Section	*Percent crossing over:* *Initial high—first minimum*	*Percent decrease*
st — pᵖ	5.6 — 0.5 = 5.1	91
pᵖ — ss	13.4 — 4.2 = 9.2	69
D — st	1.7 — 0.6 = 1.1	65
Total	71.7 — 45.7 = 26.0	36
h — D	12.7 — 8.4 = 4.3	34
ss — eˢ	12.8 — 8.8 = 4.0	31
ru — D	36.1 — 29.8 = 6.3	17
ru — h	25.6 — 21.2 = 4.4	17

the centromere and show comparably large decreases, while those at the end of the chromosome arm, *ru — D* and *ru — h*, exhibit the least effect.

Obviously the effect of age is to decrease the over-all ease with which crossing over occurs. Does it also alter the spatial distribution of crossovers, or the distance between successive crossovers (internode length)? Bridges demonstrated that internode length varied greatly. Thus in the *ru — h* region, for the initial high period, of the 187 crossovers obtained

34.8 percent were coincident with other crossovers, the remainder being single crossovers. At the first minimum period, only 12 percent of the 281 crossovers were similarly coincident. It is apparent therefore that the average map distance between double crossovers is much greater at the minimal period than at the initial high.

Effect of temperature. Plough (1917, 1921) and Stern (1926) have demonstrated that, like aging, temperature very greatly affects the frequency of crossing over, with the magnitude of effect being greatest in the neighborhood of the centromere. Plough used Chromosome II marked as follows:

$$
\begin{array}{ccc}
b & pr & c \\
\hline
48.5 & 54.5 & 75.5
\end{array}
$$

The centromere lies very close to the right of *pr*. Flies reared at a series of temperatures provided the crossover data shown by Table 8–10.

TABLE 8–10

Crossing over in D. melanogaster (Chromosome II) as a function of temperature (Plough 1917).

Temperature	Number of flies	—Percentage crossovers—	
		b — pr	*pr — c*
9° C	995	13.6	25.8
13°	2,972	17.5	27.2
17.5°	2,870	8.2	23.0
22°	15,000	6.0	19.6
29°	4,269	8.7	22.5
31°	3,547	18.2	26.7
32°	4,376	15.4	26.5

It can be clearly seen that the same general trend is exhibited by the two regions studied, but that the $b - pr$ region, lying close to the centromere, is most strongly affected. The phenomenon is obviously not a simple chemical reaction following Van't Hoff's law, where a $Q_{10} = 2$ would be expected for every 10° C rise in temperature. To ascertain more effectively the time of effect of temperature as it relates to oögenesis, Plough varied the temperature during the time of hatching and breeding. If the females were exposed to high temperatures before hatching, their first offspring (approximately 140) showed the effects of a higher rate of crossing, but if exposure was not given until after emergence, the effect did not appear in the offspring until approximately 250 eggs had been laid. By thus fractionating the temperature exposures and the successive broods, it was possible genetically to point to earliest oögenesis as the time of crossing over. This has since, of course, been amply confirmed cytologically.

Plough, curiously enough, was unable to obtain a temperature effect on crossing over in the X-chromosome. At that time the effect of the centromere was not known; of the genes employed, the one closest to the centro-

mere was *forked* at 56.7, which is approximately 10 units away. No appreciable temperature effect would have been noticed since it has a tendency to diminish as the genes studied lie farther and farther away. Stern (1926) later showed that the X-chromosome behaves like Chromosome II in its reaction to age and temperature. The effect, however, was in the *Bar —
bobbed* region immediately adjacent to the centromere.

Effect of centromere. The studies previously discussed point to the centromere as a region of high variability insofar as crossing over is concerned. Is this because the centromere controls crossing over, this control being age- and temperature-sensitive, or is the variability related to the rather large sections of heterochromatin located adjacent to the centromeres on all of the major chromosomes of Drosophila?

The effect of the centromere is indicated by the Drosophila experiments of Beadle (1932) and Graubard (1932). The former made use of a translocation involving the III and IV chromosomes, which was subsequently obtained in a homozygous state. The changes made were as follows with the centromere indicated by the crossbar, and points of breakage by arrows:

Normal III   *Normal IV*

ru	*h*	*th*	*st*	↓ *cu*	*sr*	*e^s*	*ca*
0	26.5	43.2	44.0	50.0	62.0	70.7	100.7

Translocated chromosomes

The genes *ru* to *st,* as a result of the translocation, remain unchanged relative to the centromere of Chromosome III, while the remaining genes, and in particular *cu,* are placed closer to the centromere of Chromosome IV. The effect of this on crossing over is indicated as follows with the percentages of crossing over indicated between the genes:

Normal	*ru*	*h*	*th*	*st*	*cu*	*sr*	*e^s*	*ca*
		27.5	21.3	0.4	6.2	13.3	11.6	35.0

Homozygous translocation	*ru*	*h*	*th*	*st*		*cu*	*sr*	*e^s*	*ca*
		29.1	21.2	0.8			0.9	2.8	32.2

The crossover percentages in the successive regions from *ru* to *st* remain essentially unchanged. The displacement of *cu* to close proximity of the IV centromere markedly reduces the *cu — sr* and *sr — e^s* crossover frequencies. The *e^s — ca* region, being in the distal region of the arm, shows little variation. Clearly, proximity to the centromere alters the rate of crossing over, and it is apparent that the bunching of genes on the genetic maps of the X, II and III chromosomes does not mean that they are physically closer to each other, but simply that crossing over is reduced in these areas. Graubard (1932, 1934), through the use of an inversion, confirmed Beadle's results, making it quite clear that it is the positions of the genes, and not the genes themselves, that determine the frequency of crossing over.

Effect of heterochromatin. Mather (1939) has attempted to determine whether the crossover variability in the vicinity of the centromere is conditioned in any way by the rather large blocks of heterochromatin known to be located in the centromeric regions of all of the major chromosomes of Drosophila. The experiment was carried out on an X-chromosome in which a piece of heterochromatin had been inserted in a median position. The data obtained, although not conclusive, indicated that heterochromatin is more unstable than euchromatin in its response to environmental variables. It should be noticed, however, that all other regions that have shown a varying response to age and temperature lie in distinctly euchromatic portions, although bordering on heterochromatin, with the exception of *bb* in the X-chromosome, which is in heterochromatin.

Interchromosomal effects. All present theories of crossing over, with the exception of that proposed by Belling, are based upon mechanical considerations, and all imply that crossing over between one pair of chromosomes is independent of that occurring simultaneously between other homologous chromosomes. Sturtevant (1919), however, had early pointed out that such was not the case. A decrease in crossing over between one pair of homologues, due to the presence of a heterozygous inversion, increased the frequency of crossing over in non-homologous and unrelated pairs of chromosomes in the same cell. It appeared therefore as if a certain amount of potential energy were available for crossing over within each meiotic cell; if one pair of homologues did not utilize its allotted amount, other pairs could draw from the reserve to increase their frequency of crossing over. This interchromosomal relationship of crossing over was placed upon a somewhat more quantitative basis by Schultz and Redfield (see Morgan, Bridges, and Schultz 1932, 1933) and Glass (1933), independently, in *D. melanogaster.* MacKnight (1937) has shown that a similar effect holds for *D. pseudoobscura,* but there is no confirmatory evidence from other organisms.

The data of Schultz and Redfield will serve to illustrate the phenomenon. Crossing over in Chromosome II was studied at the same time that crossing over was reduced in (1) the X-chromosome by the *ClB* inversion, (2) in Chromosome III by the *Payne* inversion, and (3) in both the X and the III by the simultaneous presence of the *ClB* and *Payne* inversions. The results obtained are given in Table 8–11.

The *ClB* inversion is somewhat more effective than the *Payne* in in-

TABLE 8–11

Crossing over in Chromosome II of D. melanogaster as modified by the presence of the ClB and Payne inversions (Schultz and Redfield, from Morgan, Bridges, and Schultz 1933).

Cultures	Number of Flies	Regions tested (C.O. in percent)						Total C.O.
		al — ap	ap — b	b — pr	pr — c	c — px	px — sp	
Control	2894	10.3	27.7	3.5	16.2	20.0	3.5	80.2
ClB	1776	12.4	29.0	9.3	21.7	·23.5	5.9	101.8
Payne	2519	14.2	29.7	5.8	18.9	25.3	6.0	99.9
ClB + Payne	1652	18.5	37.3	12.4	31.7	29.9	7.8	137.6

creasing the total crossover frequency in Chromosome II, but this is gained through the medium of large increases in the regions adjacent to the centromere, $b — pr$ and $pr — c$. The two inversions, acting simultaneously, are roughly additive in their effect. It is of interest to note that, unlike the action of age and temperature, the interchromosomal effects are even expressed at the distal ends of the arms, px and sp being 45.5 and 52 map units respectively from the centromere.

In a series of subsequent experiments (Steinberg 1936, 1937; Steinberg and Fraser 1944) dealing with the same problem, a number of interesting, if unexplained, facts have come to light.

When autosomal inversions are tested for their effects on crossing over in the X-chromosome (Steinberg 1936), or X-chromosome inversions for their effects on crossing over in Chromosome III (Steinberg and Fraser 1944), it becomes obvious that each inversion possesses its own unique specificity of action. Figure 8–5 illustrates this point. The *Payne* inversion (Chr. III) increases crossing over in the X-chromosome uniformly, while the Chromosome II *Curly* inversion exerts a small but measurable effect from *cv* (13.7) to *f* (56.7) and an effect of considerable magnitude from *cv* to *y* at the distal end of the chromosome. The X-chromosome inversions (12 in number) tested against Chromosome III varied greatly in magnitude of effect. Four had no effect that was detectable. Of the remaining eight that were effective, their specific influences were such that no correlations could be drawn between the magnitude of the effect of each on crossing over in Chromosome III and the size of the inversion, the positions of the inversion limits, or the amount of intra-inversion crossing over. Since it had previously been shown that crossing over is not necessarily reduced in an inversion (Sturtevant and Beadle 1936), it would not appear that a simple reduction in crossing over in one chromosome pair can account for the increase in other non-homologous pairs.

The increase in Chromosome III crossing over was generally the result of an increase in multiple-strand crossing over, but with no accompanying change in interference values. Only one inversion, y^4, effected a reduction in interference. The greatest effects, like those found by Schultz and Red-

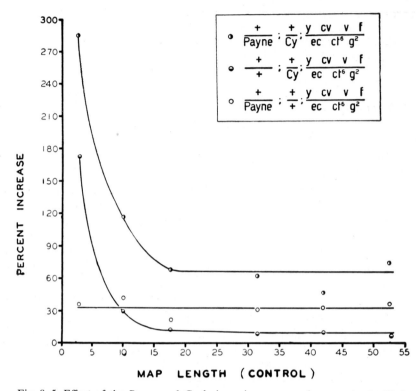

Fig. 8–5. Effect of the *Payne* and *Curly* inversions on crossing over in the X-chromosome of *D. melanogaster*. Abscissa represents the control map length in individuals lacking the inversions; the ordinate represents the percent increase obtained by the three inversion combinations indicated in the square (Steinberg 1936).

field (1951), were in the neighborhood of the centromere, and it may well be, as they postulate, that heterochromatin is influential in determining these effects. No distal increases were found.

Steinberg (1937) has also shown that when an inversion is tested for its effect on crossing over in two other chromosomes, it does not affect them equally. This can be seen in the following data where the increases in crossing over produced in non-homologous chromosomes are expressed as decimal fractions:

Inversion	X-Chr.	Chr. II	Chr. III	Total
ClB	——	0.38	0.46	0.84
Curly	0.22	——	0.49	0.71
Payne	0.33	0.55	——	0.88

When these data, however, are converted into ratios that permit a direct comparison between length of chromosome (from gonial cells) and magnitude of effect, it appears that the effect of an inversion on crossing over in a non-homologous chromosome is approximately proportional to the length of the affected chromosome. If the X-chromosome is arbitrarily given the length of 100, and the others are scaled to it, the following data are obtained:

Chromosomes	X/II	X/III	II/III
Ratio of size	$100/145 = 0.69$	$100/175 = 0.57$	$145/175 = 0.83$
Ratio of effect	$0.33/0.55 = 0.60$	$0.22/0.49 = 0.45$	$0.38/0.46 = 0.83$

No other chromosomal aberrations have been studied so intensively for their interchromosomal effects on crossing over, although translocations produce similar deviations (Schultz and Redfield 1951). Nor have homozygous inversions been tested in similar fashion. The latter study could be of aid in testing the hypothesis of Steinberg and Fraser (1944) that the interchromosomal effect on crossing over is a position effect; a position effect should not disappear with homozygosity.

Inversions are not alone in their effect on crossing over. Schultz (see Morgan, Bridges, and Schultz 1933) has shown that a Y-chromosome added to an XX female of D. *melanogaster* has a marked effect on crossing over in the D^3-H region of Chromosome III. This region extends from 41.0 to 69.5 and includes the centromere.

In XXY females Bridges (1916) has shown that the usual distribution of chromosomes in meiosis was such that X or XY eggs were produced. Apparently the X-chromosomes paired normally, and the Y was distributed at random. Occasionally, however, XXY daughters were produced that had received both X-chromosomes from their XXY mother; the distribution of the chromosomes therefore was XX and Y. A study of these exceptional daughters showed that no crossing over had occurred between the X-chromosomes. Non-disjunction had led to the inclusion of both X's into a single egg. In normal XX sisters of the XXY mothers, a D^3-H recombination value of 10.3 was regularly obtained. When the chromosomal distribution was X and XY, and crossing over had taken place between the X's, a value of 17.09 was found, indicating that the presence of the Y raised the frequency of crossing over 70 percent. Among the exceptional daughters, however, the crossover rate jumped to 33.34. In other words, the presence of the Y, plus the absence of crossing over between the X's, markedly raised the frequency in a non-homologous chromosome. No immediate explanation for this rise in crossover frequency is obvious, although heterochromatin is suspect whenever the Y-chromosome is involved.

There remains a strong possibility that the interchromosomal effects on crossing over are not actually increases *per se,* but are due rather to the elimination of low-crossover chromosomes. The preferential retention of high-crossover chromosomes would lead to an apparent increase, but selection rather than an increased rate of crossing over would be involved. This is suggested by the data of Cooper, Zimmering, and Krivshenko (1955) who showed that increased autosomal heterozygosity in the form of inversions brought about an increased rate of non-disjunction and loss of X-chromosomes. Such losses are reflected in an increased number of dominant lethals and patroclinous males, whereas an increased rate of crossing over would be expected to reduce X-chromosome losses. The fact that autosomal inversions do not affect interference values (the y^4 inversion appears to be an exception) fits into Cooper's hypothesis; it is uncertain, however, on the basis of the preliminary results published, whether this hypothesis can account for all interchromosomal effects on crossing over, e.g., the D^3-H results mentioned above.

Effect of aberrations. The internal rearrangements of a chromosome, when existing in a heterozygous condition, would be expected not only to alter the linear order of genes in the affected chromosome, but to alter the frequency of crossing over between it and its normal homologue. Frequent reference was made in the early Drosophila literature to crossover suppressors, which reduced or eliminated recoverable recombination types among the offspring. These were shown to be inversions for the most part when in 1933 the study of salivary gland chromosomes became an accepted part of genetical investigations. In Muller's now famous *ClB* stock, the crossover suppressor, *C*, has been shown to be an inversion that includes the middle two-thirds of euchromatin lying between *echinus* and *fused*, a distance of nearly 54 map units.

The effect of inversions on crossing over has been investigated most thoroughly in *D. melanogaster* (Sturtevant and Beadle 1936). Figure 8–6

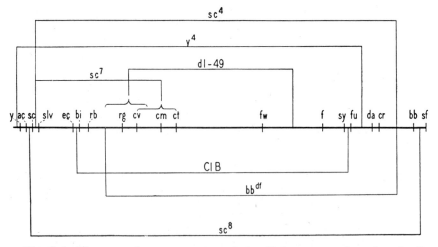

Fig. 8–6. Diagrammatic representation of the X-chromosome inversions in *D. melanogaster* used by Sturtevant and Beadle (1936) in their study of crossing over within inversions.

illustrates the inversions studied in the X-chromosome, with the limits of the inversions indicated with respect to neighboring genetic loci. With the chromosome properly marked with mutant loci, crossing over can be followed both within, and to the left and right of, a particular inversion. From such studies certain facts emerge, which can be summarized as follows:

1. Females homozygous for inversions show no reduction for crossing over except as the genes are moved nearer to, or away from, the centromere.

2. Single crossovers within inverted sections are rarely recovered. This results from a selective orientation and failure of breakage of the first meiotic inversion bridge so that broken chromatids are not included in the egg nucleus (Fig. 8–7). Cytological confirmation of these genetically predicted events has been made in Sciara (Carson 1946). Only non-crossover, or two- and three-strand double crossover, chromatids can be recovered, and these can be recognized in appropriately marked chromosomes. If, however, a chromatid bridge is formed at the second meiotic division, the egg nucleus may or may not receive a deficient chromosome which would lead to inviability. Such an event is rather rare with a typical X-chromosome and would not lead to a marked mortality of eggs, but Novitski (1952) has shown that if an X-chromosome has an added arm in the form of a translocated piece of the Y-chromosome, structurally aberrant X-chromosomes are delivered to the egg nucleus from either the first or second division, and considerable inviability of fertilized eggs results.

3. Crossing over is markedly decreased in adjacent uninverted regions to the left and right of the inversion limits. For example, females heterozygous for the *dl-49* inversion, which lies roughly in the middle of the X-chromosome, showed a reduced crossing over between y and ec from approximately 5.5 percent to 0.56 percent. To the right of the inversion the rate of crossing over is considerably higher. Females heterozygous for the *sc-7* inversion show no crossing from ct (20.0) to the left of the inversion, as would be expected since the left limit of the inversion lies close to the end of the chromosome. From sn (21.0) to lz (27.7) the frequency is reduced to 1.6 percent. From lz to v (33.0), however, the normal frequency of 5.5 is obtained, while from v to f (56.7), the frequency was 24.9.

Novitski and Braver (1954), on the other hand, have demonstrated that the degree of reduction of crossing over inside and outside of an inversion is a function of the kind of chromosome being studied. They constructed a tandem metacentric compound X-chromosome, i.e., the two arms are similar but in tandem rather than being reversed as in the attached X-chromosome (Novitski 1954), with one arm having in it the *dl-49* inversion. Crossing over within the inversion was reduced about 25 percent as compared to that occurring in a normal sequence, but there was little interference with crossing over outside the inversion. Novitski and Braver postulate that the difference in crossover interference by inversions is re-

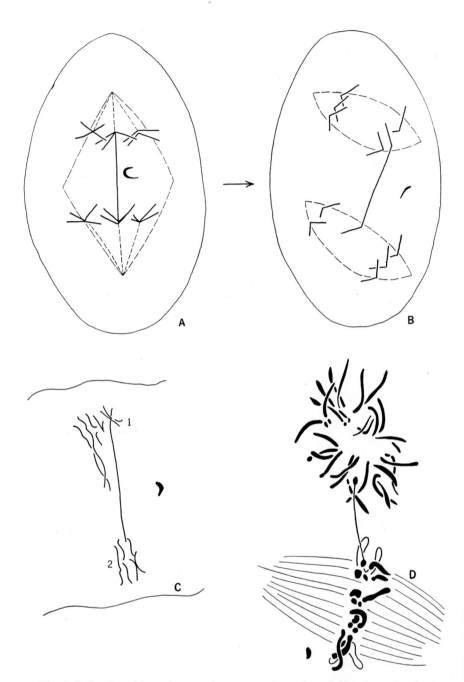

Fig. 8–7. Results of inversion crossing over and anaphase bridge formation in the eggs of Drosophila or Sciara. A, B, bridge formation at anaphase I and II to demonstrate the manner by which the bridge fails to be included in the functional nucleus; C, metaphase II in the egg of *Sciara impatiens* showing the bridge hung between the outer (1) and inner (2) nuclei (redrawn from Carson 1946); D, metaphase II in the embryo sac of *Lilium testaceum* illustrating the same phenomenon (redrawn from Darlington and LaCour 1941).

lated to pairing differences, and that the reduction is not caused by the formation of an inversion loop so much as it is by the interruption and consequent failure of euchromatic pairing. When heterochromatin is available to initiate and facilitate pairing, little reduction in crossing over is observed.

4. Crossing over within the inverted sections is decreased in inverse proportion to the length of the inversion, i.e., the shorter the inversion the greater the reduction. Since only double crossovers of the two- and three-strand variety are recoverable in the offspring, their frequency should be a measure of the amount of crossing over within the inversion. The data of Sturtevant and Beadle (1936) indicate that this frequency is positively correlated with the length of the inversion. Consequently an inversion does not necessarily reduce crossing over within the inverted section, an important fact to be considered in any interpretation of the interchromosomal effects on crossing over, but the number of recovered crossover chromatids is limited to those coming from two- and three-strand doubles.

In addition to a study of crossing over in females heterozygous for particular inversions, it is also possible to consider those females heterozygous for two inversions, one in each X-chromosome. Such an arrangement can, if the two inversions overlap, or if one is included within the other, give a central region common to both. The latter condition is represented by the *sc-4/dl-49* combination, *dl-49* lying completely within *sc-4*. As might be expected, no recoverable crossovers are obtained even though it is likely that some single crossovers do occur. A single crossover would give large deficiencies and duplications, and inviability would result (Fig. 8–8). The *sc-4/y-4* combination, shown in the same figure, is of particular interest

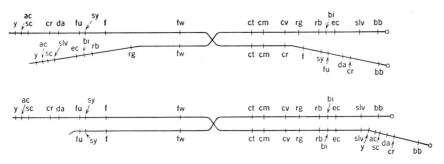

Fig. 8–8. Pairing and crossing over between the *sc-4* and *dl-49* inversions (above) and between the *sc-4* and *y-4* inversions (below). The crossover products of the *sc-4/dl-49* combination will lead to inviability since one chromatid will have the *cr-f* region duplicated while lacking the *slv-rg* region; the other chromatid will possess the complimentary duplication-deficiency. In the *sc-4/y-4* combination, one chromatid will lack the *y-cr* region, the other chromatid will have this region duplicated; the deficient chromatid is male lethal, but may survive in occasional females, while the duplicated chromatid does not affect viability to any appreciable extent. The heterochromatic regions in the vicinity of *bb* are not indicated (after Sturtevant and Beadle 1936).

since a single crossover will give a chromosome deficient for *y, ac-sc,* and *cr* which is male lethal, but which permits occasional females to survive, and a chromosome duplicated for the same regions which is viable in both sexes. It is obviously a method for increasing the number of genes in the chromosomes.

The effects just described hold for inversions in Drosophila, but it is apparent that a fundamental difference exists between the situation in this genus and that in maize (Rhoades and Dempsey 1953). In maize broken chromatids are produced from inversion bridges in Chromosome 3 at both meiotic divisions, are regularly transmitted to the egg nucleus (i.e., to the basal megaspore), and may be viable if the acentric fragment resulting from inversion crossing over is not too extensive in length. These conditions are somewhat similar to those described in Drosophila when the X-chromosome is two- rather than one-armed (Novitski 1952), and Chromosome 3 in maize is essentially metacentric. Crossing over within the inversion is greatly reduced, genetic recombination being effected only by infrequent double crossovers, but recombination between a gene within the inversion and one proximal to it is significantly increased rather than reduced. It is difficult to comprehend such an increase in terms of any present hypothesis of pairing or crossing over.

The fact that a translocation involves the reciprocal transfer of chromatin sections between non-homologous chromosomes implies that an alteration of crossover frequency is to be expected because of the difficulties involved in complete synapsis of all portions of the affected chromosomes. Cytological examination of the synaptic relationships of translocations at pachynema in maize, and in the salivary gland chromosomes of Drosophila, frequently shows non-association of homologous regions. This presupposes a reduction in crossover frequency, since synapsis of homologous parts is a prerequisite for crossing over. This phenomenon has been studied in some detail in *D. melanogaster* (Dobzhansky 1931, 1934).

Using a variety of translocations, Dobzhansky has shown that the greatest reduction in crossing over is in the neighborhood of the breaks, and that the reduction becomes less pronounced as sections of the chromosome more remote from the points of breakage are tested. However, the data also reveal that a translocation in one arm of a V-shaped chromosome exerts little or no effect on the frequency of crossing over in the other arm. This, of course, is to be expected on the basis that there is no interference across the centromere. On the other hand, when the break is at the centromere for both chromosomes involved, crossing over is markedly reduced throughout the length of both chromosomes, and especially in the region of the centromere. Table 8–12 provides typical examples of the changed crossover frequencies found. Translocations *a* and *b* of Chromosome III involve sections of the left arm, while translocations *c* and *d* involve only the right arm.

TABLE 8–12

**Differences between the normal frequencies of crossing over in
Chromosome III and those resulting from various
translocations (Dobzhansky 1931).**

Internal		Control Value	Translocations			
			a	*b*	*c*	*d*
left arm	$ru - h$	23.7	17.2	21.2	26.9	29.1
	$h - D$	13.7	2.9	5.9	15.4	14.8
	$D - th$	1.1	0.2	0.2	1.5	1.1
	$th - st$	0.8	0.2	0.3	0.9	0.9
centromere region	$st - cu$	8.0	6.6	4.6	4.5	5.9
right arm	$cu - sr$	15.4	16.6	17.1	3.7	12.6
	$sr - l^s$	10.3	11.7	10.0	7.5	8.9
	$e^s - ca$	31.0	31.0	31.0	28.9	20.2

A variety of kinds of duplications is possible in that the duplicated piece of chromatin may be in tandem as in the case of *Bar;* a duplicated fragment may have its own centromere and thus act as a fragment or supernumerary chromosome; an end piece may be attached to the same chromosome; or an end piece may be attached to a different chromosome. Each will affect crossing over in a manner peculiar to itself.

Rhoades (1931) first demonstrated in Drosophila that a piece of Chromosome II, translocated to the Y-chromosome, and acting as a duplication, reduced the amount of crossing over in the normal second chromosomes with which it was partially homologous. Dobzhansky (1934) has studied the phenomenon in some detail, utilizing duplications of varying length derived from the left end of the X-chromosome (Fig. 6–6). Of these 112, 134, and 102, which are fragment chromosomes, are similar except for the specific amount of chromatin duplicated. 101 is different in that the *bb* region adjacent to the centromere is present. 105 and 138 have different portions of euchromatin duplicated in such a manner as to make the X two-armed. T-3 and T-7, being added to the end of the Chromosomes III and II respectively, may be tested as duplications or as translocations. 126 has an internal portion of the X-chromosome inserted in the centric region of Chromosome III.

A comparison of the effects of 112, 102, and 105 indicates that as the length of the duplication is increased, the over-all reduction is similarly greater (Table 8–13). 126, being in Chromosome III, and probably less free to interfere because of limited mobility, has a smaller and perhaps not significant effect. It is apparent, however, that although the greatest reduction is in the region duplicated, the effect is not confined to this area, but extends generally throughout the X-chromosome. 138 has a markedly different effect from 105. The latter produces a decrease through the entire chromosome. 138, on the other hand, has no effect from *y* to *s,* but induces a high reduction for the regions adjacent to the centromere from *s* to *car* (Table 8–14).

TABLE 8–13

Crossing over in the X-chromosome and in the presence of duplications 112, 134, 102, 105, 126 (Dobzhansky 1934).

Interval	Control	112	134	102	105	126
y — ec	6.05	5.88	2.48	5.00	2.25	4.68
ec — cv	10.47	10.43	7.14	6.28	3.35	8.72
cv — ct	11.38	11.26	6.28	7.37	3.55	10.54
ct — v	15.95	15.36	13.59	10.79	5.46	14.99
v — g	11.13	11.18	9.04	8.69	8.06	10.60
g — f	12.86	13.31	12.79	11.45	10.38	13 06
f — Bx	5.25	5.41	4.26	3.32	3.69	2.40
Total (*y — Bx*)	73.08	72.83	55.58	52.90	36.74	64.99

TABLE 8–14

Influence of duplication 138 on crossing over (Dobzhansky 1934).

	y — cv	*cv — ct*	*ct — v*	*v — s*	*s — f*	*f — car*
Control	8.82	6.50	10.76	7.76	14.98	6.77
Duplication	8.15	7.01	10.00	7.62	3.40	1.24
Difference (percent)	−8	+8	−7	−2	−77	−82

TABLE 8–15

Crossing over in the X-chromosome and in the presence of T-3 and T-7 translocations and duplications (Dobzhansky 1934).

		y — ec	*ec — cv*	*cv — ct*	*ct — v*	*v — g*	*g — f*
Control		4.07	7.22	6.37	13.64	12.38	9.70
Translocation	T–3	0.42	0.64	2.80	10.57	11.38	13.41
Duplication	T–3	1.60	4.15	4.65	11.64	11.19	10.69
Translocation	T–7	0.0	1.34	3.25	11.67	10.39	9.35
Duplication	T–7	1.30	3.27	2.65	9.32	10.68	11.67

T-3 and T-7 make possible a direct comparison between the effects produced by a duplication and by a translocation (Table 8–15). When used as a translocation, the reduction is greatest. The effect on crossing over in Chromosome II is very much less marked, although the *sp* end, where the duplicated segment is attached, shows some decrease.

These data have led Dobzhansky to propose the hypothesis that the reduction in crossing over results from a process of competitive pairing. The hypothesis holds for inversions, translocations, or duplications. In essence, it suggests that the pairing blocks, whatever their size might be, compete in synapsis for pairing partners. Where the chromosomes are homologous, the zipper action of synapsis brings the homolgous regions together once pairing has been initiated. A two-by-two association occurs. With a change in homology, however, brought about by an inversion or translocation, or with a particular region represented in triplicate, a competition for pairing segments results in a lowered degree of synapsis. This is confirmed cytologically. Since crossing over is dependent upon a previous synaptic condition, a lowered frequency results.

It is of interest to note that crossing over rarely occurs between the normal chromosomes and the duplicated fragment (Dobzhansky 1934). In triploids, however, no reduction in crossing over occurs (Bridges and Anderson 1925, Redfield 1930, 1932). In the X-chromosome, for example, crossing over is reduced in the middle, but increased at the ends (see below). This has the tendency of freeing the process of crossing over from the effects of the centromere, and making the frequency of crossing over more nearly a function of actual linear distance between the genes than a function of distance from the centromere.

A tandem duplication would probably be expected to interfere with crossing over in relation to its size, a longer duplication having a greater effect than a short one. The *Bar* "gene," however, which is associated with a duplication of seven bands in the 16A region, produces no effect on the rate of crossing over in the neighboring $g — f$ region (Sturtevant 1928), although within the $f — fu$ region it increases the crossover frequency from 2.5 to 3.5 units in homozygous *Bar* females. The addition, therefore, of seven bands contributes one unit of crossover distance to the X-chromosome. In maize, however, a small duplication or a deficiency creates, possibly because of non-homologous pairing, a greater disturbance in crossing over than might be suspected through knowledge of similar-sized aberrations in Drosophila. Thus, Stadler and Roman (1948) have shown that cytologically undetectable deficiencies can lead to considerable reductions in crossover frequencies.

While crossing over would be completely lacking in the section covered by the deficiency, it is likely that it would also tend to reduce the frequency somewhat in its immediate neighborhood because of the difficulties of synapsis. The phenotype *Notopleural* (*Np*) is due to a deficiency in the right arm of Chromosome II (Fig. 6–2), with its limits extending from 58.7 to 60.2, and covering a loss of 50 recognizable bands (Bridges, Skoog, and Li, 1936). When crossover values from *cn en/Np* and *blo en/Np* females obtained (*cinnabar* 57.8; *engrailed* 62.0; *bloated* 59.0), a local reduction of 1.5 units was found on an average. The deficiency itself removes about 5 microns of the salivary chromosome length, and this amounts to approximately 4.4 percent of the right arm. Since the genetic length of this arm is 52 units, a reduction of 2.3 percent in crossing over would be expected if crossing over were equally distributed, but with crossing over being relatively lower in this region, the reduction is also lower.

CROSSING OVER IN POLYPLOIDS

The problem of crossing over in polyploids is obviously more compli-cated than in diploids because of the added number of chromosomes which can pair in such a manner as to form multivalents. A study of the problem is experimentally most feasible in autopolyploids, where the known homologies of the chromosomes are established. Allopolyploids, having bivalent formation, would behave essentially as diploids, although dupli-cate loci may be present to complicate the picture. As contrasted to a diploid, which has crossing over taking place at the four-strand stage, an autotriploid would have the process occurring at the six-strand stage, an autotetraploid at the eight-strand stage. Newton and Darlington (1930) demonstrated that even though three or more homologous chromosomes may be present in a single meiotic cell, at any particular level only two of the chromosomes can synapse with each other. Since synapsis precedes crossing over, an exchange of genes is still, as in diploids, a process taking place between two of the four or more associated chromatids.

On the other hand, added chromosomes could well be expected to alter the regional frequencies of crossing over because of competition develop-ing between the chromosomes for pairing regions. The fact that in auto-triploids, for example, two of the homologues may synapse in one region is no guarantee that these two chromosomes will be paired along their entire length to the complete exclusion of the third homologue. This is supported by cytological data, for in autopolyploids multivalent associations occur regularly.

Only the data obtained from a study of autotriploids in *D. melanogaster* will be considered in detail since that obtained from autotetraploids in plants (Lindstorm 1936; Little 1945) is more complicated while adding little in the way of supplementary information.

In the X-chromosome. Crossing over in the X-chromosomes of triploid females exhibits a regional difference from that found in the diploid female. A marked increase in frequency of crossing over is found in the distal regions, accompanied by equally marked decreases in the central portion of the chromosome (Table 8–16).

TABLE 8–16

Comparison between triploid and diploid crossing over for
the X-chromosome (Bridges and Anderson 1925).

Region	Triploid Crossover Value	Diploid Crossover Value	Ratio T/D
y — rb	14.3	6.9	2.07 : 1
rb — lz	11.3	22.8	0.50 : 1
lz — dy	3.9	10.1	0.39 : 1
dy — B	8.2	16.2	0.51 : 1

The region immediately adjacent to the centromere, however, was not tested, so that it is not certain whether any alteration in the frequency of crossing over in triploids is to be expected for the proximal portions of the X-chromosome. An additional fact established was that coincidence values were unusually high, indicating that interference distances were reduced and that double crossovers occur with greater freedom than in diploids.

In the II and III chromosomes. Redfield's 1930, 1932) data on crossing over in Chromosomes II and III of triploid females agree with that of Bridges and Anderson in revealing marked regional differences as compared to diploid values (Table 8–17), but disagree in showing strong distal decreases and marked proximal increases. It would appear, therefore, that in the autosomes of triploids the centromere has a lesser influence on crossing over in its neighborhood than it does in diploids, giving a triploid genetic map with different gene spacings than those characteristic of the diploid (Fig. 8–9). Regions in the diploid where genes are more

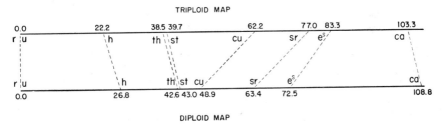

Fig. 8–9. A comparison of the diploid and triploid linkage maps for the third chromosome of *D. melanogaster*. Dotted lines connect similar loci (Redfield 1930).

closely spaced are lengthened in the triploid; where more distantly spaced in the diploid, they are brought somewhat closer together in the triploid. According to Redfield, the triploid genetic map more acurately represents the physical spacing of genes on the chromosome.

The discrepancies between the data of Bridges and Anderson on the one hand, and that of Redfield on the other, may have resulted from the fact that the former calculated their crossover values from exceptional diploid females that received both X-chromosomes from the mother, while Redfield derived her data from diploid females that obtained only a single II or III chromosome from the mother. Because homozygosis increases as one passes from the centromere distally, a correction factor is necessary for a proper evaluation of the data. This cannot be done for Redfield's data because of the absence of exceptional females. When applied to that obtained from the X-chromosome, it reveals that in the neighborhood of the centromere crossing over is comparable in triploids and diploids, but even more greatly accentuated in the distal regions for triploids than is revealed by the data of Bridges and Anderson (Rhoades 1933a).

In XX X triploids. The experiments of Beadle (1934, 1935) provide

TABLE 8–17

Comparison of triploid and diploid crossover values for Chromosomes II and III (Redfield 1930, 1932).

Region	Triploid Crossover Values	Diploid Crossover Values	Ratio T/D
	Chromosome II		
al — dp	8.3	10.0	0.83 : 1
dp — b	16.2	27.2	0.59 : 1
b — pr	7.4	5.7	1.30 : 1
pr — c	27.1	19.2	1.41 : 1
c — px	13.0	22.1	0.59 : 1
px — sp	4.4	5.7	0.77 : 1
	Chromosome III		
ru — h	19.5	25.3	0.77 : 1
h — th	14.9	15.3	0.97 : 1
th — st	1.2	0.4	3.00 : 1
st — cu	21.2	5.6	3.79 : 1
cu — sr	14.6	14.0	1.04 : 1
sr — es	6.1	8.9	0.69 : 1
es — ca	18.0	34.3	0.52 : 1

Note. Centromere in Chromosome II lies just to the right of *pr,* and between *st* and *cu* in III.

an interesting corollary to those of Bridges and Anderson in that attached-X triploid females ($\widehat{XX}$ X) were used. This provided only one free chromosome, the other two being bound by their centromeres. Pronounced increases in crossing over were found proximally in both the X and $\widehat{XX}$ gametes that were recovered, with a slight but significant increase in the distal portion (Fig. 8–10). The proximal region which showed a marked rise in crossing over (from *forked* to the centromere, Regions 1 and 2 in Table 8–18) was not tested by Bridges and Anderson, so a direct comparison of the entire length of the chromosome in XXX and $\widehat{XX}$ X females cannot be made, but Beadle found no significant decreases for the mid-portion of the chromosome.

In XXX females, there was randomness of crossing over between any two of the three chromosomes at any particular region. In $\widehat{XX}$ X females, a non-randomness was clearly apparent. Considering the arms of the attached-X chromosomes as *a* and *b,* and the free chromosome as *c,* the ratio of *a — b* crossovers to *a — c* or *b — c* is as 60.2:52.6:48.0, indicating that *a* and *b* cross over more frequently with each other than does *a* with *c* or *b* with *c.* The difference, however, was due largely to a greatly increased crossover frequency between *a* and *b* chromosomes in the *f*-centromere region, since all regions distal to *f* were more or less at random. The randomness of crossing over between the three chromosomes, in the

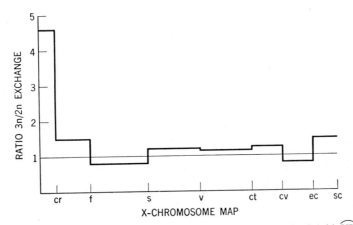

Fig. 8–10. Relation of crossing over in the X-chromosome of triploid $\widehat{XX}$ X D. *melanogaster* to that in diploids. Straight line, diploid standard; broken line, average crossover values for X and $\widehat{XX}$ gametes (after Beadle 1934).

proximal region, is indicated by the ratio of recurrent to progressive double crossovers. The former are those where the two chromosomes crossing over at one locus are similarly involved at another locus, whereas the latter are those doubles in which the second crossover does not involve the same two chromosomes as did the first crossover. Beadle found that the ratio of recurrents to progressives was 98:96. This is in agreement with the data of Bridges and Anderson, and with that of Redfield, and clearly indicates that pairing of the three chromosomes in two-by-two association is quite at random.

CROSSING OVER BETWEEN X- AND Y-CHROMOSOMES

Genetic experiments in the various species of Drosophila are conducted on the assumption that germinal crossing over does not occur in males. For all general purposes the assumption is valid, for where crossing over does occur in males, it can generally be traced to somatic crossing over, which takes place in the spermatogonial cells rather than in the sperma-tocytes (Whittinghill 1937, 1947). This conclusion is based on the fact that when crossing over occurs it is detected by the occurrence of clusters of similar crossover chromatids, indicating a gonial origin, and that there is no interchromosomal effect on the frequency by heterozygous inversions.

Gonial crossing over between the X- and Y-chromosomes of D. melano-gaster has been detected in $\widehat{XX}$ Y females (Kaufmann 1933) and in XY males (Stern and Doan 1936; Neuhaus 1936, 1937; Lindsley 1955). In all cases it appears that the crossovers involved the heterochromatic por-tion of the X-chromosome adjacent to the centromere. This is the only region of the X that is homologous with the Y-chromosome. It appears from Neuhaus' (1937) data that the X can cross over with either the short

TABLE 8–18

Comparison of frequencies of crossing over in triploid attached-X females
of D. melanogaster in X and $\widehat{XX}$ gametes as compared
with the diploid standard (Beadle 1934)

Region	———Triploid———		Diploid
	X gametes	$\widehat{XX}$ gametes	
1 and 2	46.8	36.2	18.0
3	23.1	20.3	28.0
4	22.8	23.6	20.0
5	27.0	32.4	26.0
6	14.4	15.8	12.6
7	10.8	11.3	13.6
8	25.2	21.2	13.6

or the long arm of the Y. When an exchange occurs between the X and the short arm of the Y, the crossover can be either to the right or to the left of the gene *bobbed* (*bb*), but crossovers with the long arm of the Y are only to the right of *bb*, i.e., between *bb* and the centromere. The X is therefore homologous with two separate regions of the Y-chromosome. The distal regions of the long arm of the Y-chromosome do not appear to be homologous with any known portion of the X. Lindsley's data, obtained through the use of inversions involving the heterochromatic region of the X, indicate that there are possibly five segmental homologies between the X and the Y, but that pairing and exchange are conditioned by non-homologous but heterochromatin-specific forces.

It has also been shown that the frequency of detachment of $\widehat{XX}$ chromosomes in females by an exchange with a Y is not altered by autosomal structural heterozygosity, making it reasonably certain that the process is mitotic rather than meiotic (Cooper 1946b).

Some organisms, however, exhibit a partial sex-linkage of certain genes. It occurs where the Y is not completely heterochromatic, and where the euchromatic portion of the Y is homologous with a similar region in the X. Absolute sex-linkage is found only for genes that lie in the non-homologous, or differential, portions of the X- or Y- chromosomes, which undergo no crossing over. In man, for example, genes are known that follow an absolute X-linkage and an absolute Y-linkage pattern, as well as a partial sex-linkage pattern of inheritance. The fish Lebistes and the plant Melandrium show a similar pattern of linkage.

SOMATIC CROSSING OVER

Crossing over in most organisms appears to be restricted to germinal tissue where it is associated with reduction division in the formation of male or female gametes. In *D. melanogaster,* however, crossing over takes place in somatic tissues, although at a frequency much rarer than that found in germinal tissues (Stern 1936). Its rarity in other organisms, and its relatively high frequency in Drosophila, is undoubtedly due to the unusual synapsis that occurs between homologous chromosomes in somatic cells (Metz 1916), and that can lead to the formation of chiasma-like configurations (Kaufmann 1934). However, artificially produced diploid nuclei in the mycelia of *Aspergillus nidulans* and *A. niger* seem to undergo a somatic "meiosis" leading to segregation of genes but without reduction to a haploid state (Pontecorvo 1952, 1953). It may well be that somatic crossing over is more widespread than it is customarily believed to be, but that it is detected only under carefully controlled conditions of experimentation.

Bridges (1925) has earlier postulated the elimination of certain X-chromosomes from the somatic cells of females heterozygous for a number of genes as the result of the presence of a *Minute-n* locus located in the eliminated X-chromosome. Since the recessive genes were in the non-eliminated X-chromosome, females that were otherwise wild type exhibited mosaic spots characterized by the recessive phenotypes.

Stern, seeking an explanation of the phenomenon, discovered that the mosaicism was caused not by the elimination of certain chromosomes, but by somatic crossing over followed by a normal mitotic segregation of chromatids. The genes *y* and *sn* (singed bristles) were used because, against the wild-type background of a heterozygous female, the homozygous or hemizygous *y* and *sn* could be readily recognized.

In a typical experiment, involving the use of a $\dfrac{y \quad +}{+ \quad sn}$ female, the mosaicism was generally expressed as twin spots of relatively equal size, one exhibiting the *y* phenotype, and the other the *sn* phenotype. Less frequently only *y* spots were found, and still more rarely only *sn* spots. These could readily be explained (Fig. 8–11) by assuming that the twin spots arose by a crossover in the four-strand stage between *sn* and the centromere,

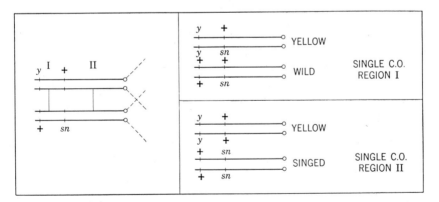

Fig. 8–11. Somatic crossing over in *D. melanogaster*. Single crossing over between *y* and *sn* (Region I) can only yield single yellow spots; single crossing over between *sn* and the centromere (Region II) yields twin spots; single *sn* spots can arise only through double crossing over in Regions I and II (after Stern 1936).

the *y* spots by a crossover between *y* and *sn,* and the *sn* spots by a double crossover between *sn* and the centromere and between *y* and *sn.* The less frequent occurrence of single *y* spots is explicable on the basis of the short map distance between *y* and sn. The double crossovers are understandably rare. The size of the spots would be dependent upon the time in development at which the crossover occurred.

Additional experiments by Stern have shown that other factors exert an influence upon somatic crossing over: (a) the phenomenon is not restricted to the X-chromosome, being found also in the autosomes, (b) the various *Minute* loci, of which there are many, increase the frequency of somatic crossing over to the right of *sn,* and these loci exert varying degrees of effect, the sex-linked *Minutes* being more effective in causing increases than the autosomal *Minutes,* (c) the Chromosome III *Minutes* exhibited a peculiar specificity in that they limited somatic crossing over to the arm in which they were located, (d) somatic crossing over occurred in males as well as females, although less frequently, (e) it takes place within heterozygous inversions leading to chromatin bridges, and between a ring-X and a normal X-chromosome, and (f) temperatures of 30° C, as compared to 25° C, decreased somatic crossing over (Stern and Rentschler 1936). This last effect is in distinct contrast to the usual increase in germinal crossing over produced by high temperatures. The independence of germinal and somatic crossing over is indicated by the observation that the *C3G* gene, which practically eliminates meiotic crossing over in females of *D. melanogaster,* has no effect on the frequency of somatic crossing over (Le Clerc 1946).

Schwartz (1954, 1955a) has also considered the problem of somatic crossing in $\widehat{XX}$ chromosomes. It is considerably lower in frequency than in unattached X-chromosomes, even in the presence of the autosomal *Minute, M(3)y,* but it is greatly enhanced by aging the $\widehat{XX}$ mothers prior to mating. It is believed that this is due to sister-strand crossing over, as suggested by Brown and Hannah (1952) in their study of instability of ring chromosomes in Drosophila, but the importance of Schwartz's study is in the strong indication that it is the newly formed chromatids that are involved in the crossovers between homologous arms, with the sister-strand crossovers occurring between one old and one new chromatid (Fig. 8–12). Although this is an attractive hypothesis, Brown and Welshons (1955) have been unable to confirm Schwartz's data that somatic crossing over is increased by aging the females.

UNEQUAL CROSSING OVER

Crossover data gathered from many sources indicate that when an exchange takes place between homologous chromatids it does so at loci that correspond exactly with each other in location. Such a precise mechanism guarantees that the number of genes per chromosome remains the same

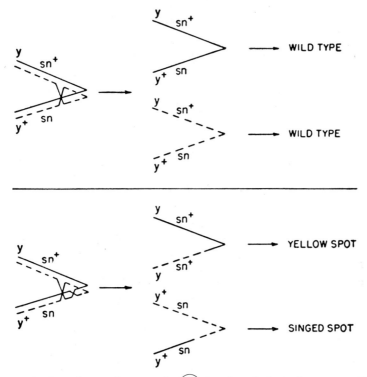

Fig. 8–12. Somatic crossing over in X͡X females of *D. melanogaster*. (Above, crossing over between newly formed chromatids (broken lines); below, same as above, but with a sister-strand crossover occurring between an old and a new chromatid (Schwartz 1953b).

regardless of the number of times it may undergo exchange, and it must indicate that synapsis which precedes crossing over must be equally exact, homologous genes pairing with homologous genes.

Were the mechanism of crossing over less specific as regards corresponding levels in the two crossover chromatids, it would be expected that internal deficiencies and duplications would be far more frequent than they are known to be. This has been made strikingly evident by the now-classical case of the *Bar* "gene" in the X-chromosome of *D. melanogaster*. *Bar* was considered earlier to be an example of a highly mutable locus, reverting to wild type or to a more extreme *Bar (Bar-double)* with a frequency far higher than that known for other loci. *Bar* was different from other genes, however, in the fact that the "mutation," whether to normal or to *Bar-double*, was always accompanied by crossing over in its vicinity (Sturtevant and Morgan, 1923). It has since been shown genetically and cytologically (Fig. 6–7) that *Bar* is associated with a tandem duplication, not being a mutation in the strict sense of the word, and that its "mutability" is a consequence of unequal crossing over (Sturtevant 1925).

When females of the constitution $\dfrac{+\ B\ +}{f\ B\ fu}$ (*forked,* 56.7; *Bar,* 57.0; *fused,* 59.5) are crossed to homozygous recessive males, normal or *Bar-double* offspring, which constitute a very low percentage of the population, are always $f +$ or $+ fu$. This can only mean that crossing over occurs between f and fu whenever a *Bar* "mutation" arises. Also *Bar* males never produce reverted or *Bar-double* individuals among their offspring, as would be expected in the absence of crossing over. Figure 6–7 diagrams the mechanism involved. Apparently the left section in one homologue pairs with the right section of the other, and crossing over in this conjugated section leads to a normal chromosome with one section (a reversion) and a *Bar-double*-chromosome with three like sections.

Although *Bar* itself is not a true mutation, mutations can occur at the *Bar* locus (Sutton 1943). *Infra-Bar* is such a mutation. It is similar but distinguishable from *Bar,* and like *Bar* it reverts to normal or to *infra-Bar-double* through unequal crossing over. However, *Bar* cannot be recovered from *infra-Bar* except by mutation.

In order for unequal crossing over to occur, the duplicated and adjacent segments must be in a tandem order. The failure to detect unequal crossing over in the many suspected cases of duplication in *D. melanogaster* arises from the fact that the great majority appear to be of the reverse type, *Bar* apparently being an exception (Bridges 1935; Lewis 1945). The *A* locus in maize, however, is an apparent tandem duplication (Laughnan 1955), with the *alpha* and *beta* components of the locus being independently recoverable by unequal crossing over.

TETRAD ANALYSIS IN NEUROSPORA

In an earlier discussion on the origin of crossover chromatids, it was pointed out that non-crossover and single-crossover chromatids could be derived from bivalents in which multiple crossing over had occurred. In Drosophila, the problems of origin are handled on an indirect statistical basis rather than by direct analysis of all the chromatids recovered from a single meiotic cell. The data so analyzed have indicated that chromatid interference is non-operative in Drosophila, and that two-, three-, and four-strand double crossovers occur in frequencies expected on the basis of randomness.

These problems can be approached directly in the red bread mold, *Neurospora crassa,* since from a single ascus, all four chromatids from any tetrad can not only be recovered, but recovered in serial order to provide information as to the numbers and types of crossovers that occur. The manner of division and segregation is indicated in Figure 8–13. There is good evidence that the ascospores do not, as a rule (less than 1 percent of the time), slip past each other in the ascus, so that isolation of the asco-

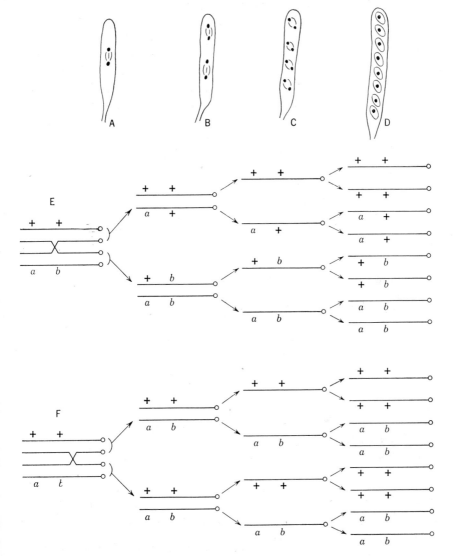

Fig. 8–13. Meiotic divisions and segregation in Neurospora. A, anaphase I; B, anaphase II; C, anaphase of the post-meiotic mitosis; D, mature ascus with eight ascospores; E, behavior of one pair of homologous chromosomes and segregation of two pairs of genes (*a* and *b*) when the crossover is between the genes. The first division is equational for gene *a*, reductional for gene *b*, while the second division is the reverse. F, same as E except that the crossover is between gene *b* and the centromere, giving an equational first division and a reductional second division for both genes. The serial order of chromatids as they will be reflected in the serial order of the ascospores in the ascus except for very occasional slipping of ascospores past each other.

spores in order and the determination of their genotypes will provide clues as to the events taking place at the time of crossing over. Also, since the homologous centromeres regularly segregate from each other in the first division (however, see Perkins 1955 for discrepancies), the distance from the centromere to any gene can be determined. Distances between linked genes can be determined directly by the crossover frequencies.

The methods and technical difficulties of mapping the seven linkage groups in *N. crassa* have been considered in detail by Houlahan, Beadle, and Calhoun (1949) and by Barrett, Newmeyer, Perkins, and Garnjobst (1954). Papazian (1952) and Perkins (1955) have also dealt with tetrad analysis, while McClintock (1945) and Singleton (1953) have clarified the cytological status of the species. The results indicate that crossing over in Neurospora does not differ appreciably from that taking place in other organisms, the principal difference with Drosophila being the existence of a marked non-randomness in the types of double crossovers (Lindegren and Lindegren 1937, 1939, 1942; Whitehouse 1942). If no chromatid interference is operative, the frequency of two-, three-, and four-strand double crossovers is in the ratio of 1:2:1. Positive chromatid interference would lead to an excess of three- and four-strand doubles, while negative interference would lead to an excess of the two-strand type. Both types of interference occur in *Neurospora crassa* (Lindegren and Lindegren 1942), but most striking is the fact that an excess of two-strand doubles occurs in two of the chromosomes tested when the two exchanges occur symmetrically on either side of the centromere; in other regions of these chromosomes, the first exchange may lessen the chances of the second exchange occurring between the same two chromatids. In *N. sitophila,* an excess of three-strand doubles is found across the centromere (Perkins 1955).

The Neurospora crossover data also furnish evidence of a negative chiasma interference; a marked excess of double, triple, and quadruple crossovers were found. These results are paralleled by an excess of two-strand doubles in the silkworm Bombyx, and an excess of four-strand doubles in Viola and in certain mice to give more than 50 percent recombination (Whitehouse 1942).

It is difficult to explain these patterns of crossing over by any of the current hypotheses regarding crossing over, although the Belling hypothesis (see later) would favor an excess of two-strand doubles as opposed to the three- or four-strand types. It is evident, however, that Neurospora is a particularly favorable organism for studying the dynamics of crossing over, particularly since suitable linkage groups can now be constructed.

RECOMBINATION IN BACTERIA AND VIRUSES

The nature of hereditary changes in micro-organisms such as bacteria or viruses has long been a subject of debate. The supposed haploid character and lack of knowledge of a sexual phase have, until recently, prohibited a genetic analysis of variation, without which a classification of hereditary changes into gene mutations, chromosomal abnormalities, or cytoplasmic inheritance cannot be made.

It is true that the bacterial cell has been shown to possess a Feulgen-positive nucleus-like structure, but despite considerable study the cytological picture is still in some doubt (DeLamater 1951, 1953; Bisset 1951, 1952, 1955). On the other hand, the size of these cells is such that the failure to clarify and identify chromosome structure and number with certainty should occasion no surprise, for the chromosomes must be exceedingly minute. That mutations do occur in micro-organisms, however, and that they are similar in nature to the mutations of higher organisms, is inferred from their permanency, recombination, reversibility, and frequency of induction by mutagenic agents (Lederberg 1948; Tatum and Perkins 1950).

A critical test of the validity of the mutation hypothesis in micro-organisms was provided by the discovery that an exchange of genes can take place in bacteria and bacterial viruses (bacteriophages) when two strains of dissimilar genetic constitution are brought together. These findings serve to bring the micro-organisms into genetic conformity with the higher plants and animals, although at the present time it is premature to attempt a complete construction of the hereditary mechanism as it exists in the bacterial cell or the virus particle.

Recombination in the colon bacterium, *Escherichia coli,* was established through the ingenious work of Lederberg (Lederberg and Tatum 1946; Lederberg 1947, 1948; Lederberg, Lederberg, Zinder, and Lively 1951; Hayes 1953). The technique consists essentially of plating a heavy mixture of two nutritionally-deficient, multiple-mutant, but dissimilar, strains of *E. coli* on an agar medium lacking the specific requirements for growth. The marker genes include those governing bacteriophage and antibiotic resistance and susceptibility as well as distinctive biochemical syntheses. The medium is such that the original strains cannot develop individually. When the two strains are mixed, however, occasional colonies appear, in a frequency of $1:10^6$, which are nutritionally wild type in that supplementary factors are not needed for growth. These are *prototrophs* in contrast to the *auxotrophs* which are nutritionally deficient. The frequency of prototrophs, while generally very low, is still far higher than can be accounted for on the basis of the coincident reverse mutation of several independent genes.

The conclusion to be drawn, therefore, is that some form of "sexual" mechanism permits an exchange of genetic material, with the prototrophs being one class of recombinant progeny. The complementary class, which would be deficient for several nutritional factors, cannot be recovered on a minimal medium. Since the genes determining bacteriophage and antibiotic resistance or susceptibility can be tested independently of those determining biochemical syntheses, the fact that they too fit into the more or less conventional concept of gene recombination is added proof that the heritable material in the bacterial nucleus undergoes genetic recombination. Support for this concept is provided also by the demonstration that prototrophs recovered from a mixture of three marked strains show the characteristics of two, but never of all three, strains, thus ruling out the possibility that a diffusible chemical factor is responsible for the formation of recombinant types.

The establishment of consistent linkage groups in *E. coli* has proven to be extremely difficult, but there is no doubt that some genes are linked, and that their behavior in the coupling or repulsion phases follows segregative expectations to provide partial linkage maps. Hayes (1953) has indicated that at least three linkage groups exist. This is supported by De-Lamater's (1953) cytological work, but only provisional acceptance of three as a haploid number is warranted at this time because of the equivocality of the cytological studies, and the inconsistencies and variations in linkage expression (Lederberg and Tatum 1954).

Diploid heterozygous cells that undergo continued segregation have been isolated, and cell-progeny lines have been studied (Zelle and Lederberg 1951), but some genes show segregation from a heterozygous state while others do not. In particular, the genes *Mal* and *S* seem always to be hemizygous while other loci are heterozygous (Lederberg 1955a), suggesting a preferential post-zygotic loss of the *Mal-S* segment in what was otherwise a diploid cell.

It is now clear that genetic recombination in bacteria involves a sexual mechanism not too unlike that in higher forms in that conjugation of cells occurs, followed, very likely, by the fusion of nuclei and then by meiosis. Isolated progeny show that recombination of genetic materials has gone on, but a striking difference from higher forms is that recombinant progeny are such as to suggest a one-way transfer of genes. An agent or factor "*F*," of unknown nature, determines sexual compatibility. Those bacteria possessing *F* (designated *F⁺*) are donor cells, those lacking it (*F⁻*) are receptor cells, and the genetic transfer is from *F⁺ to F⁻* cells. The *F⁻* cells yield not only recombinant progeny, but are also transformed to an *F⁺* genotype. On the other hand, *F* can be transferred from *F⁺* to *F⁻* cells without accompanying genetic transfer. In some instances *F* may be transferred to all of the F⁻ cells, but in only 3 to 4 percent of the time is this transfer accompanied by genetic recombination (Hayes 1953). Hayes states that *F⁺* appears to be a temperate bacteriophage, but this has not been conclusively demonstrated (Lederberg 1955a; Cavalli, Lederberg and Lederberg 1953). *F* cannot be separated from the cells that possess it, and cell fusion is necessary for the transfer of F or genetic materials.

Sexual compatibility in *E. coli,* therefore, depends upon the presence or absence of F. $F^- \times F^-$ crosses are incompatible, $F^+ \times F^+$ are capable of crossing to a limited extent, and $F^+ \times F^-$ to the greatest extent. Under most experimental conditions F appears not to be a genetic locus in that it does not appear linked to any other genes, and this is supported by the observation that F^+ cells can under certain conditions be depleted of F. They then behave as F^- cells. However, the studies of Wollman and Jacob (1955; Adams 1955) suggest that the F factor may actually be a locus on the bacterial chromosome.

Using a variant of F^+ called Hfr, which increases the rate of recombination 1000-fold over that obtained with F^+, recombination frequencies of the order of 1 to 10 percent of the initial number of Hfr were obtained. In a particular strain of E. coli, Hfr affects the recombination rate of the linked genes T L Az V_1 Lac Gal (threonine and leucine requirements, azide sensitivity, Virus T_1 sensitivity, lactose and galactose fermentation), but is without effect on the unlinked gene S^s (streptomycin sensitivity). From a cross between strain HFr T^+ L^+ Az^s $V_1{}^s$ Lac^+ Gal^+ S^s and strain F^- T^- L^- Az^r $V_1{}^r$ Lac^- Gal^- S^r, the T^+ L^+ S^r recombinants could be selected by plating the cells on a medium lacking threonine and leucine and containing streptomycin (S^r, streptomycin resistance). These recombinants could then be tested for other genes obtained from the Hfr parent, and of the T^+ L^+ S^r group, 90 percent were Az^s, 75 percent $V_1{}^s$, 40 percent were Lac^+, and 25 percent Gal^+.

In order to understand the basis of the peculiar recombinant ratios, Wollman and Jacob interrupted the maturing process at particular intervals. They found that there was a 10-minute lag period before any recombinants appeared. Following the lag period, the T^+, L^+ and Az^s locus appeared simultaneously, the $V_1{}^s$ locus at 11 minutes after mating, the Lac^+ locus about 18 minutes, and the Gal^+ at 29 minutes. This not only suggests that the genes are in a linear order in the linkage group, but that they enter the $F-$ cell in a predetermined order with a sufficiently slow rate of entrance to permit interruption of the process at various stages of completion of the mating events. This again suggests the involvement of a bacteriophage vector similar to that operative in Salmonella (see below), but the process of recombination, unless occurring between fragments of linkage groups in successive order, is exceedingly difficult to comprehend at the present time. Lederberg (1955a, b), in fact, raises objection to the interpretation of Wollman and Jacob that there is a serial transfer of genetic material in fertilization, believing that any fractional heterozygotes obtained are due to post-meiotic loss of broken linkage groups rather than to pre-meiotic additions.

Salmonella typhimurium, another bacterium, is similar to E. coli in that genetic recombination yields prototrophs from mixtures of auxotrophic cultures (Lederberg, Lederberg, Zinder, and Lively 1951; Zinder and Lederberg 1952; Zinder 1953, 1955; Lederberg and Edwards 1953;

Demerec, Blomstrand, and Demerec 1955). For example, two auxotrophic strains, 2A and 22A, when mixed on minimal agar yield prototrophs in a frequency of $1:10^5$; other strains possess a reduced or an enhanced capacity for similar change. Furthermore, and as in *E. coli,* genetic transfer is a one-way proposition, in this instance from 2A to 22A.

Two differences separating the two systems are immediately evident. In *S. typhimurium,* cell contact or even cell mixing is not necessary, the transmissive vector being separable from lysed cells to give an active preparation containing a filtrable agent (FA) (strain 2A thus would be $FA+$ donor cells, strain 22A the $FA-$ receptor cells); and genetic transfer appears to involve only single genetic loci, or at best two closely linked loci, instead of whole linkage groups. The transmissive vector is a bacteriophage. Such a system is also present in *E. coli,* with the temperate bacteriophage P1 acting as the transmitting agent (Lennox 1955). Genes responsible for biochemical syntheses, fermentation patterns, antibiotic resistance, and antigen types have been successfully transferred, but only one at a time. The transmitted unit seems therefore to be smaller in size than that in the *E. coli* sexual system, but the size of the unit may be determined not by what is transmitted but by what is incorporated into the host linkage group. This phenomenon has been called *transduction*. Studies on a group of cystine-requiring mutants (Demerec, Blomstrand, and Demerec 1955) indicate that the unit incorporated may, in some instances, be smaller than a single genetic locus, but nevertheless large enough to be responsible for the transduction of a single allele. This particular aspect of the problem, however, has important bearing on the structure of a genetic locus, and further consideration of it will be deferred until a later chapter.

The manner of incorporation of a chromosomal fragment by transduction from a donor to a receptor cell has not been clarified. Since the major portion of the genetic material of the donor cell is not represented in the segregant cells that arise after transduction, it must be assumed (1) that, if incorporated as a whole haploid complement into a zygote, then most of the transmitted genotype is eliminated prior to or during reduction, or (2) that only a portion was contributed initially. Figure 8–14 indicates several possible ways of incorporation of a fragment into a host chromosome at the time of chromosome duplication. The incorporation could be direct or by means of a double crossover. No critical evidence yet available permits a choice between these two possibilities.

The transduction phenomenon found to be operative in *S. typhimurium* possesses certain features similar to the *transformations* that take place in the pneumococcus bacteria (Zinder 1953; Hotchkiss 1951, 1955; Euphrussi-Taylor 1951, 1955). In transduction it has been impossible as yet to separate the genetic material donated by a cell from the bacteriophage vector that transmits it, leaving doubt as to whether the transduced material is an integral part of the bacteriophage or whether the bacteriophage acts

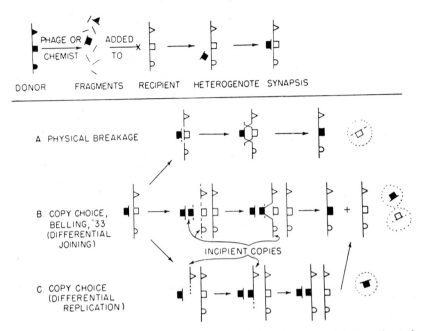

Fig. 8–14. Possible means whereby transduced fragments, carried by a bacteriophage or introduced as a transforming principle, may be incorporated into a bacterial host chromosome. Top, preliminary stages of fragmentation and introduction of fragments into recipient cell; A, B, and C, the three means by which incorporation could take place (Lederberg 1955).

simply as a carrier that brings genetic material into the recipient cell at the time of infection. The transduced material must, however, be within the viral protein envelope, since enzymes do not affect the transduced material or the ability of the virus to bring about transduction.

The situation in the pneumococci is somewhat clearer. No bacteriophage vector is involved, and the *transforming principle* has been extracted in highly purified form and shown to be a desoxyribosenucleic acid (DNA). As in transduction, the transforming principle consists of specific genetic loci contributed by, and extractable from, a donor cell which then becomes incorporated into a host cell as heritable material. In a genetic sense, it is the replacement of a host allele by a corresponding allele from the donor cell, the host cell neither gaining nor losing genetic loci but simply replacing one allele with another.

The loci exchanged are always homologous. In general, single genetic loci are involved in any transformation, and only single cells rather than whole cultures are transformed, but Hotchkiss (1955) has indicated that linkage may be involved in some transformations. Thus the loci for streptomycin resistance and mannitol fermentation are associated far more frequently in transformation than would be expected on the basis of coincident double transformation by single independent units of DNA. The size of the DNA molecule necessary to bring about transformation is not known with certainty, but many agents—x-rays, nucleases, and others—that degrade DNA also lessen its biological activity as measured by the frequency of transformations.

Clearly, transduction in *S. typhimurium, E. coli* and *Shigella dysenteriae* (Lennox 1955), and transformation in pneumococci and *Hemophilus influenzae* (Zamenhoff 1952) have much in common. Zinder (1953), in fact, speaks of the "infective heredity of bacteria," and the active role of DNA in all three systems is indicated by the demonstration that bacteriophage infection of a bacterial cell involves only entry of the DNA of the bacteriophage, the protein envelope being left behind (Hershey and Chase 1952). From what has been stated above, however, there is no certainty that recombination of hereditary units in bacteria and in higher forms involves events or structures of like nature. Both are based on the concepts of linked genes and the exchange of homologous parts, and these similarities are sufficient to suggest that bacteria have chromosomes that behave in a manner not unlike those of other species. Because of the infective basis of genetic exchange in some bacteria, as contrasted to fertilization, crossing over, and meiosis in higher species, some reservation must still be attached to any consideration of the mechanism of recombination (Sturtevant 1955). Recombination in the bacteriophages also poses problems when an attempt is made to fit the genetic events in these "organisms" into a general scheme applicable to all species.

The phenomenon of recombination in bacteriophages was discovered by Delbrück and Bailey (1946), and the known loci in the T4 type, which infects *E. coli,* fall within three linkage groups having a total map length of approximately 100 units (Fig. 8–15). Three linkage groups are also known in the T2 type (Hershey and Rotman 1949), but whether these can be equated with three separate chromosomes, as illustrated by Burnet (1955), is equivocal. In any event, a linear arrangement of genetic units is evident, and these can be recombined to give recombinant as well as parental progeny. As in other species, the frequency of recombinants to parental types provides a measure of linkage strength.

The recombination system of bacteriophages can be visualized in the following manner. When a single bacteriophage particle infects a bacterium, only the inner DNA contents are injected. The bacteriophage then assumes a non-infective vegetative condition in which replication of the virus and recombination of the hereditary units takes place (Doermann 1953). The viral particles eventually mature and lyse the bacterial cell, and from ten to several hundred new bacteriophages are liberated, the number depending upon the period of growth in the bacterial cell prior to lysis.

If but a single virus has infected the bacterium, the progeny possess the parent genotype, except when a mutation has occurred. With double infec-

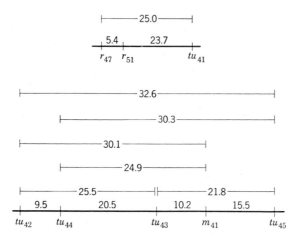

Fig. 8–15. Linear order of loci in the linkage groups of the T4 bacteriophage. Linkage group I is not represented, and consists to date of only a single mutant, r_{48}. Linkage group II is represented at the top, with the numerical values indicating the recombination percentages between linked loci. It is this linkage group which has been investigated in detail by Benzer (see Figs. 12–1, 12–3, and 12–4). Linkage group III is indicated at the bottom. Mutant symbols are m = minute placques; r = rapid lysis; tu = turbidity of plaque (redrawn from Doermann and Hill 1953).

tion by two particles of dissimilar genotype, recombinant as well as parental types are recovered at lysis. The freqeuncy of recombination will approach 50 percent for unlinked markers (Doermann and Hill 1953), or may be as low as 0.013 percent for very closely linked genes (Benzer 1955). Table 8–19 illustrates the results obtained from a three-factor cross in a T2 type bacteriophage. Essentially the same results are obtained if one studies the types and frequencies of progeny from a single lysed bacterial

---

TABLE 8–19

Progeny from a three-factor linked cross in bacteriophage T4 (Doermann 1953). Class B consists of single recombinations between m and r, C between r and tu, and D double recombinations between m and r, and r and tu.

Category	Class	Genotype			Total plaques	Percent
Parental	A	m	r	tu	3467	33.5
		$+$	$+$	$+$	3729	36.1
Recombinant	B	m	$+$	$+$	520	5.0
		$+$	r	tu	474	4.6
Recombinant	C	m	r	$+$	853	8.2
		$+$	$+$	tu	965	9.3
Recombinant	D	m	$+$	tu	162	1.6
		$+$	r	$+$	172	1.7

Note. The probability of double recombinations (B + D) (C + D), assuming no interference, is 2.7 percent. The observed (D) is 3.3 percent, suggesting a negative interference.

cell, or the pooled progeny from many lysed cells. However, it has been shown that the frequency of recombination increases as the period of growth prior to lysis increases (Levinthal and Visconti 1953).

Of particular interest is the observation that if a bacterium is infected by three genotypically dissimilar bacteriophages, recombinant progeny can be obtained that possess marker genes derived from all three parental types (Hershey and Rotman 1949). This piece of information, together with that discussed above, has led Visconti and Delbrück (1953) to propose an hypothesis which, in the main, satisfactorily accounts for recombination.

The hypothesis assumes—and Doermann (1953) has demonstrated this to be true—that the bacteriophages on entering the cell become non-infective and vegetative. These multiply as units, the replicated units mate in pairs repeatedly, and at random with respect to pairing partner. Exchange of genetic material occurs during the mating process. Eventually the replicated and recombined particles mature by being transformed from a non-infective to an infective state. As a mature particle, the bacteriophage does not appear to multiply or to mate. Maturation therefore depletes the mating pool, and at the time of lysis all of the particles are mature. An average of five matings per vegetative particle can account for the frequency of recombinants obtained.

The Visconti-Delbrück hypothesis satisfies most of the experimental situations encountered to date in recombination studies. The physical state of the linkage groups at the time of mating and the mechanism of recombination are not known, and it is not certain that haploid-diploid phases are involved. On the other hand, it is not unreasonable to assume that a situation analogous to that known from other forms holds in the bacteriophage.

There remains, however, one observation that did not fit into the above hypothesis. Hershey and Chase (1951) discovered that about 2 percent of the progeny released from a doubly-infected bacterium were heterozygous for a particular pair of alleles. The proportion of heterozygotes, i.e., 2 percent, does not seem to depend upon the genes in question, but analysis reveals that heterozygosity exists for only small segments of the linkage map at any one time. Thus, a single bacteriophage may be heterozygous for an r locus but not for an h locus if these are normally not closely linked. If the genes are closely linked, such as the $h — r^{13}$ pair, heterozygosity may involve both loci. This situation brings to mind the hemizygous-heterozygous diploids of $E.$ $coli$ (Lederberg 1955a), although how close the parallel is remains uncertain.

It appears therefore that heterozygosity involves the carrying of a fragment of the linkage group in addition to the entire genetic complement, suggesting that replication of the linkage groups may be by fragments rather than by whole units. Recombination of these fragments to form whole linkage groups at the time of maturation could account for recombination, as proposed by Levinthal (1953).

Recent studies by Levinthal (1953, 1954) and by Doermann, Chase, and Stahl (1955) have clarified the role of the heterozygotes and the replication process. It now appears that the heterozygotes result from the mating of unlike viral particles in the bacterial host cell, and that heterozygosity is due to the fractional replication of linkage groups in such a way that overlaps occur to give duplicate loci in some parts of the genetic system. The heterozygotes are interposed in time between the original infecting bacteriophages and the recombinant progeny, and about 2 percent of the released progeny still possess a heterozygous state. This very strongly suggests that the linkage group are not replicated as a whole, but in parts (Doermann's partial-replica hypothesis). As such, these fragments of linkage groups enter the pool of vegetative particles to become incorporated into a maturing bacteriophage before they have had the opportunity to link themselves to the remainder of their usual linkage group. After infection of another bacterium they reveal their heterozygous nature during multiplication. This interpretation complements, but does not supplant, the Visconti-Delbrück hypothesis.

In appraising the genetic systems operative in bacteria and bacteriophages it should be recognized that there is a very natural tendency to force the experimental facts into a pattern that has been developed from a knowledge of such forms as maize and Drosophila. The microbial geneticists, however, have been justifiably cautious in broadly interpreting their data in conventional terms. So far as recombination is concerned, the many similarities make the fit a natural one; on the other hand, the dissimilarities, together with the recognized evolutionary plasticity of organisms, inject a note of restraint into any consideration of a generalized scheme of recombination explaining the genetic behavior of all organisms. It may well be that the microbial geneticists have chanced upon a mechanism that is without parallel in species where a haploid-diploid alternation of states is an established condition.

THE MECHANISM OF CROSSING OVER

No completely satisfactory hypothesis has been advanced to account for the manner by which the recombination of genes, or crossing over, takes place. As previous sections in this chapter have indicated, any proposed mechanism must explain a process influenced by many intrinsic and extrinsic factors at the same time that it remains a very precise system of reciprocal chromatin exchange. For purposes of reorientation, it will be well to recapitulate the conditions under which crossing over takes place:

(1) In higher organisms it takes place during meiotic prophase, al-

though Matsuura (1950), on the basis of cytological evidence, places its occurrence in late metaphase or anaphase of the first meiotic division. Crossing over also occurs in the somatic cells of Drosphila and in the mycelium of certain fungi (Pontecorvo 1952). At present, only a guess can be hazarded as to the period in the life cycle of bacteria or bacteriophages when recombination takes place.

(2) It is preceded in higher forms and in fungi by the synapsis of homologous chromosomes; the circumstances in lower forms are not yet known, although it is logical to assume that an analogous process is involved.

(3) It involves an exchange of chromatin between two of four chromatids. These are generally non-sister strands, but sister-strand crossing over may also take place (Schwartz 1953a, b, 1955a).

(4) It is precise to an extreme in having the two points of exchange between chromatids lie at identical loci, the exceptions being when unequal crossing over occurs in tandem duplications or when, very rarely, nonhomologous exchange takes place.

(5) Crossing over is associated with patterns of interference, which vary in strength along the length of the chromosome.

(6) It exhibits general as well as specific patterns of localization, which vary from organism to organism.

(7) Lastly, crossing over is affected by such diverse factors as genotype (Levine and Levine 1955), temperature, age, sex, proximity to centromere, amount of heterochromatin, and chromosomal aberrations. The latter may be either in the chromosome being tested or in a non-homologous chromosome.

The hypotheses that have been advanced to account for crossing over are of three types: (1) the *classical hypothesis* of Sax, and its later variant, the *neo-classical* hypothesis of Matsuura and Haga; (2) the partial *chiasmatypy hypothesis* of Janssens and Darlington; and (3) the *Belling hypothesis,* which considers crossing over and chromosome replication to be intimately related. White's (1954) "frontier" theory is not appreciably different from that of Darlington.

The classical, or two-plane, hypothesis (Sax 1932b) is based on the assumption that a chiasma does not represent a crossover; rather, crossing over results when a chiasma is ruptured, and a reunion of broken ends brings about recombination (Fig. 8–16). When the synaptic attraction of pachynema lapses, and diplonema ensues, the loops of each bivalent are considered to be alternately reductional and equational, but with the centric loop always being reductional. When reductional, sister chromatids are associated with each other on either side of a loop; when equational, nonsister chromatids are associated. As the chromosomes contract and the loops bow out, a strain is imposed which ruptures the two chromatids at the point of the chiasma. The subsequent reunion of ruptured ends would result both in the loss of a chiasma and the induction of crossing over.

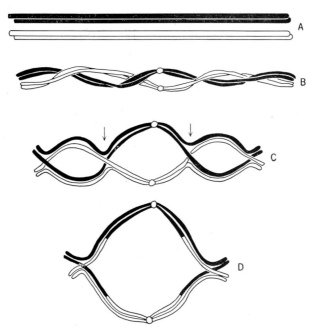

Fig. 8–16. Classical, or two-plane, theory of crossing over. The paired homologues are shown separately (A); relationally coiled in pachytene (B); and opened up in diplonema (C), with the centric loop showing paired sister chromatids, adjacent loops with paired non-sister chromatids, and four chiasmata present but with no crossing over as yet. Crossing over is assumed to take place at the regions indicated by the arrows to give the metaphase configuration (D). According to this theory chiasmata are lost when crossing over takes place, thus reducing the number of chiasmata from four to two.

A more recent modified version, the *neo-classical* hypothesis (Matsuura 1940, 1950; Haga 1944), postulates that the cytologically-observed chiasma bears no relationship to genetical crossing over. Chiasmata are thought to be due to the chance opening out of loops between paired chromatids, but since it is considered that an equational or a reductional opening out is equally probable at any position along the length of the chromosome, including the centric portion, an alternation of reductional and equational loops would give rise to chiasmata. The chiasmata, which generally are not greatly reduced in frequency as meiosis progresses from diplonema to metaphase, and which would necessarily be reduced if the classical hypothesis were valid, are simply resolved by the separation of chromosomes at anaphase I. To bring crossing over into the picture, Matsuura has suggested that this takes place when a relational spiral of chromatids is transformed into a parallel spiral system at anaphase I. This means crossing over would occur in a detectable fashion only when non-sister chromatids were associated at anaphase, but it would also mean at least one crossover for every coil. This suggests a far higher crossover frequency than is believed to obtain. Because of this, the neo-classical hypothesis has gained very little general acceptance.

The partial-chiasmatypy, or one-plane, hypothesis was originally proposed by Janssens (1909, 1924) to account for the origin of chiasmata. It has been elaborated upon and supported by others, notably Darlington (1934b, 1935, 1937a), and in its present form the hypothesis has been widely accepted because it so beautifully integrates cytological with genetical observations. The chiasma is considered to be the cytological equivalent, and consequence, of crossing over between non-sister chromatids, i.e., the exchange of chromatin leads to the formation of a chiasma (Fig. 8–17).

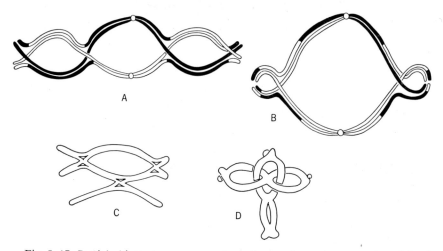

Fig. 8–17. Partial chiasmatypy, or one-plane, theory of crossing over. A and B of Fig. 8–16 are also applicable here, but in A of this figure crossing over has already occurred to give rise to four chiasmata. In B, some terminalization of chiasmata has taken place. C, a type of trivalent, and D, interlocked bivalents, both of which would be impossible according to the classical hypothesis, since this hypothesis assumes diplotene loops to be alternately reductional and equational. C and D, which have been observed, provide convincing proof that a chiasma is the cytological equivalent of a crossover (C, after Darlington 1930; D, after Mather 1938).

Since crossing over is accompanied by an exchange of chromatin, as Stern (1931) and Creighton and McClintock (1931) have demonstrated, the relationship of the chiasma to crossing over has rounded out the cytogenetical picture. On the other hand, Cooper (1949) has shown that chiasma-like structures are formed in the neuroblast cells and in the spermatocytes of *D. melanogaster* where crossing over does not occur (Fig. 8–18), suggesting (1) that a chiasma is not unequivocally the consequence of crossing over, and (2) that some chiasmata may form by the opening up of equational loops as postulated by Sax's classical hypothesis. The weight of evidence, however, favors the assumption that a chiasma and a crossover are but different expressions of an exchange of chromatin (Brown and Zohary 1955).

The relationship between chiasmata and crossing over in maize is illustrated in Table 8–20. With each chiasma being an exchange between two of the four paired chromatids, each corresponds to 50 map units of genetical crossing over. An average of two chiasmata per bivalent would give a map length of 100 units. It is therefore possible to calculate map distances from chiasma frequencies. The observed crossover lengths for each of the ten chromosomes (Chromosome 1, being the longest, has been given an arbitrary pachytene length of 100, the other nine being scaled to it) are lower than the lengths calcu-

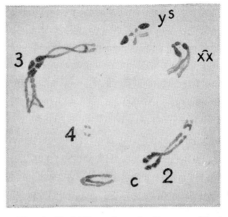

Fig. 8–18. Midprophase in the neuroblast cells of $\widehat{XX}$ Y^s females of *D. melanogaster*, showing somatic pairing and chiasmata, particularly in the attached-X and third chromosomes. Y^s is a modified Y chromosome, and *c* represents the secondary constriction, unassociated with nucleolar formation, in the left arm of chromosome 2. The dark-staining regions are centric heterochromatin (Cooper 1948).

lated from the chiasma frequency, but this is to be expected on the basis of unmapped regions of the chromosomes and double crossovers. The expected total crossover length is 1350; in 1934, when Darlington first made his calculations, the observed total crossover length was 618, but by 1950 this had been increased to 904. There is, consequently, an approach to the one-to-one correspondence of chiasmata and crossovers as the chromosomes become better mapped. This point of view is further supported by Beadle's (1932a) study of chiasma frequency and crossing over in a translocation complex in maize. In a particular interstitial segment, located between the centromere and the point of translocation, 20 percent chiasma frequency was associated with 12 percent crossing over. However, the assumption is made that there is an equal probability of adjacent-1 and alternate segregation of chromosomes from the translocation ring of 4, an assumption which may well be valid but which has not yet been so established. We are left, as a result, with highly suggestive, but no absolutely critical, data on this important point, although the more recent study of Brown and Zohary (1955) are in good agreement with Beadle's earlier findings.

If the position is taken that a chiasma is evidence of crossing over, the question remaining concerns the manner by which crossing over takes place. Two general hypotheses have been advanced: the torsion hypothesis of Darlington (1935, 1937a), and the Belling (1933) hypothesis which correlates crossing over with reproduction of the new chromatids.

TABLE 8–20

Correlation of pachytene length, chiasma frequency, and crossover length in Zea mays (Darlington 1934b).

Number of chromosome	Pachytene length	Chiasma frequency	Crossover length		
			Calculated	Observed 1934	Observed * 1950
1	100	3.65	187	102	156
2	86	3.25	163	58	128
3	78	3.00	150	92	121
4	76	2.95	148	80	111
5	76	2.95	148	44	72
6	53	2.20	110	52	64
7	61	2.45	123	50	96
8	61	2.45	123	20	28
9	53	2.20	110	52	71
10	44	1.95	98	68	57

* From Rhoades (1950).

The torsion hypothesis considers that the two homologues are relationally coiled about each other. Being undivided, they are attracted to each other as a pair to satisfy a two-by-two association. The longitudinal cohesion and paired equilibrium will be upset, however, when the new chromatids are formed, for the two-by-two association will now be between sister chromatids rather than between homologues. The attraction between homologues is replaced by a repulsion which forces them apart, but since they are relationaly coiled about each other, a torsion is developed which eventually breaks two non-sister chromatids. The relational coiling is undone, and the torsion relieved, by the movement of broken chromatids, and when the broken ends rejoin, if the rejoining is between non-sister strands, a crossover occurs.

It should be realized that the torsion hypothesis of crossing over is but a part of the more general *Electrostatic Theory of Chromosome Behavior* put forth by Darlington (1937a), a theory which postulates the existence of electrostatic forces of attraction and repulsion. Experimental demonstration of these forces has not yet been made, and their existence has been frequently questioned, e.g., terminalization can be explained equally well by means other than the repulsion forces postulated by Darlington (Swanson 1942b). The torsion hypothesis is consequently less attractive today than when it was originally proposed.

Belling (1931b, 1933) proposed that crossing over was the result of an exchange between new chromatids during the period of their formation (Fig. 8–19). He considered that the new chromomeres were formed first alongside their respective sister chromomeres, and that the interconnecting

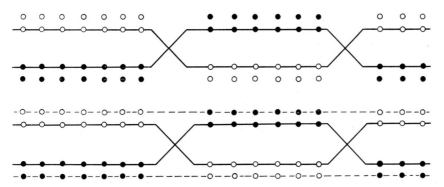

Fig. 8–19. Belling's theory of crossing over which considers crossing over to be related to the reproduction of the chromosome. Above, the chromomeres have replicated, but the inter-chromomeric connections have not yet been made. Below, after the new inter-chromomeric connections are formed, with crossing over accomplished. Solid circles, paternal chromomeres; open circles, maternal chromomeres; solid line, old connections; dotted line, new connections. According to this theory, reproduction of a new chromatid is a two-step affair, and leads only to single crossovers and to 2-strand doubles; sister-strand crossovers could transform 2-strand doubles into 3- and 4-strand doubles as suggested by Schwartz (see Fig. 8–2).

fibers formed later. If a relational coil existed between homologues, the interconnecting fibers could form between non-sister chromomeres, thus producing a crossover. A possibly more sophisticated manner of stating this now, since chromomeres seem to be but a reflection of a differential coiling pattern rather than discrete bodies of variable size, is that the chromosome reproduces itself by the formation of partial replicas, and that these are then joined to form a new chromatid. When two crossovers occur, however, such a system, which restricts crossing over to the newly formed chromatids, could give rise only to two-strand doubles, whereas in Drosophila, at least, three- and four-strand doubles are known to form with a frequency equal to the two-strand type.

The difficulty of explaining the origin of three- and four-strand doubles by the Belling hypothesis can be circumvented if it is assumed that sister-strand crossing over can occur between the two non-sister crossovers (Figs. 8–2 and 8–3), such an event converting two-strand doubles into three- and four-strand types. As indicated in an earlier section, Schwartz (1953b, 1955a) has shown that this hypothesis is in keeping with experimental facts insofar as somatic crossing over in attached-X females of D. melanogaster is concerned. These data suggest that sister and non-sister strand crossing over are different phenomena, possibly occurring at different times.

The manner by which sister strands cross over, a process that involves a new and an old chromatid, remains an enigma, but the recombination of genes as a phenomenon related to the replication of the chromosome gains support from the infective type of heredity known in bacteria and bacteriophage, where parts of a linkage group become incorporated into the genetic apparatus of the host cell (Fig. 8–19). It is difficult to comprehend such a phenomenon on a torsional basis, but reasonable if one considers a process of replication to be involved.

It will be evident that the present discussion of crossing over, which tentatively favors the Belling hypothesis, assumes that the chromosomes prior to synapsis are single, whereas earlier statements have suggested that the chromosomes, on the basis of cytological observations, are double or multi-stranded in leptotene. A reconciliation of these seemingly opposite points of view is at the present time difficult, but the conflicting data serve to emphasize that our knowledge of chromosome structure, of its method of replication, and of the mechanism of crossing over, is far from complete.

CHAPTER 9

Variations in Chromosome Behavior

The preceding chapters about mitosis and meiosis have indicated that each is exceedingly complicated. At a morphological level either process serves as a beautiful example of biological integration in both time and space. If enough were known about the cell in division, presumably the same degree of integration would be found at the chemical and physical levels as well.

The fact that cell division is not a unitary process, however, means that the steps that normally occur in orderly succession are subject to disturbance and open to attack. Knowledge gained from studying disturbed cells can provide a better understanding of the factors involved, and of their relation to one another. One approach would be to subject the cell to various influences: mitotic drugs, radiations, various temperatures. The degree of specificity of these agents' action upon the individual features of division will determine their usefulness. This approach will be taken up in the following chapter. The other approach, and the one to be discussed here, would be to examine the variations in cell division that occur normally in untreated materials.

The latter approach is useful for two reasons. In the first place, the natural causes of upsets in cell and chromosome behavior can be examined, as well as their consequences to the particular individual and to the population at large. And secondly, we get a clearer picture of the limits of the variation the process of cell division can undergo without upsetting the ultimate goal of the process, that namely of producing two daughter cells from one mother cell. In an evolutionary sense, the approach also permits us to visualize the extreme flexibility of the process, for innovations and their complementary compensatory mechanisms in cell divisions are often sufficiently bizarre to strain the imagination even while we must recognize them as characteristic of whole groups or orders of organisms. Many of these facts and observations cannot, as yet, be incorporated into the general body of cytogenetical knowledge with the same assurance that we put together a jigsaw puzzle. Manifestly, our knowledge is still inadequate to permit us to do this, even assuming that we have all of the puzzle fragments, yet at the same time we must proceed on the assumption that each

291

piece will fall into place when the less detailed parts of the puzzle are completed.

SOMATIC SEGREGATION

Plants and animals exhibiting different genotypic characters in various parts of the same individual have been frequently described. The patterns of variation may be almost infinite in variety: color striping in fruits and flowers, mosaicism in insect larvae, gynandromorphism in animals, and variegated fur and feather patterns have been reported. In plants that can be vegetatively propagated, many of the altered characteristics have been sufficiently large to permit the establishment of clonal lines by cuttings, budding, or grafting, and many horticultural varieties owe their origin to these methods of propagation.

The origin of variations has been equally varied. Some originate non-genetically (in a Mendelian sense), such as those arising from viral infections or from cytoplasmic factors affecting the chloroplasts in plants. Others, presumed to be genetic, may arise in different ways. Among the causes the following may be listed: chimaeras in which tissues of different genetical or chromosomal constitution lie adjacent to, or overlap, each other; endomitosis and somatic reduction which alters the chromosome complement of the cell; abnormal fertilizations to give gynandromorphs or mosaics; somatic crossing over which reveals hidden heterozygosity; chromosome elimination or fragmentation; and gene mutations. The direction of gene mutation may be from recessive to dominant, or vice versa. However, the direct cause of somatic variation may be ascertained only when the segregation involves known genes whose behavior can be followed, and for this reason the cases to be considered will be restricted to those where adequate genetic evidence indicates that the probable cause of the variations is chromosomal. Somatic segregation can therefore be defined as *the process that gives rise at a somatic cell division to two genetically dissimilar cells*. Those types of change leading to spontaneously formed aberrations will be discussed in the following chapter, although they could equally well be considered here.

Chimaeras. A chimaera may be described as *an organism, usually a plant, that is not genetically uniform throughout* (Chittenden 1927; Cramer 1954). It consequently reflects past instability of the organism, or of part of the organism. The term, however, has with the passage of time taken on a more restricted usage, and chimaeras are now thought of as *those plants having genotypically distinct tissues lying adjacent to one another*.

Generally speaking, most chimaeras described in the literature are those easily recognized by their distinct morphological appearance, but with the finding of chimaeras recognizable only at the cytological level it becomes clear that morphological differences may be lacking in some chimaeral organisms. A mosaic is probably the nearest zoological equivalent of a chimaera, although the term "mosaic," particularly in a genetic sense, is used botanically to describe a chimaera that arises through repeated genetic change to give rise to irregular patterns of morphology. Since it is tissues rather than individual cells that are involved in the ultimate expression of a chimaera (although a cellular basis is obvious), there have been three general types recognized, with their plan of organization reflecting to a certain extent their mode of origin and pattern of development. These three are the *sectorial, periclinal,* and *mericlinal* types (Fig. 9–1).

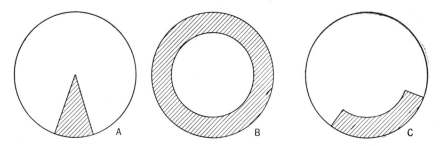

Fig. 9–1. Diagrammatic representation of the three types of chimaeras. A, sectorial; B, periclinal; C, mericlinal. The chimaeras may be genetic or chromosomal in origin, and are generally recognized by an altered phenotype.

As the name would indicate, a sectorial chimaera has a pie-shaped segment of tissue extending from the epidermis in toward the center of a leaf, stem, or root, and united laterally on either side to a genetically or cytologically different tissue. These sectors are comparatively stable, and grow forward as the organ enlarges or elongates. Branches or lateral roots arising from these sectors may vary widely in the composition of their tissues, depending upon where the branch or root initial arises in relation to the sectored portion. If the plant can be propagated asexually, it is possible to isolate and produce plants composed wholly of mutated tissue.

The periclinal chimaera is probably the most stable, since it is characterized by an entire layer of tissue, one, two or more cells in depth, surrounding a particular organ. Frequently the periclinal chimaera may have only an outer epidermis genetically different from the remainder of the tissue; in other instances the chimaeral section may be an inner tissue, either central in location or sandwiched between two normal layers.

The mericlinal type is probably the most commonly found, although also the most unstable insofar as perpetuation is concerned. Only the superficial epidermis is generally involved, and this only part way around the organ. Since this layer can only give rise to itself during growth, it can enter into the formation of neither sporogenous tissue nor branch or root initials.

Many chimaeras believed to be sectorial are probably of the mericlinal type since they can arise through the mutation of any cell giving rise to epidermal tissue, while the other two involve a particular apical cell whose successive derivatives go to form a segment of an organ. It is unlikely that whole tissues undergo mutation or change to produce chimaeras.

Chimaeras of a spontaneous sort have been frequently reported, particularly in fruits and flowers. Unless such changes include the sporogenous tissue, they cannot be perpetuated. On the other hand, chimaeras are readily produced, with grafting being a commonly used method. The Solanum chimaeras have been of special interest in this regard, and it has been possible to obtain from grafted areas shoots that possess an epidermis of one species overlying a central core of another species. Studies of tissue interactions become possible through techniques of this sort, as well as the study of diffusible gene or cytoplasmic products.

The chromosomal chimaeras, in which distinctly different karyotypes are recognizable, are of more immediate interest to the cytologist. These have been described in Nicotiana, Solanum, Datura, and Crepis. Those in Datura, for example, were induced by treating the germinating seed with colchicine (Satina, Blakeslee, and Avery 1940; Satina and Blakeslee 1941). The three germ layers could be recognized according to the degree of induced polyploidy, and all the chimaeras were of the periclinal type. Since the induction of polyploidy in any particular germ layer could not be predicted, the 68 chimaeras studied showed various combinations of 2n, 4n and 8n layers in which one, two or three layers were polyploid. Since the size of the resting nuclei corresponds roughly to the degree of ploidy, interphase as well as dividing cells could be used to determine the extent and nature of change. The use of tissues modified in this way for morphogenetic studies is obvious, and Satina and Blakeslee (1941) have made excellent use of the Datura chimaeras in various problems of development.

Brumfield (1943b) has employed a somewhat different approach to the study of morphogenesis through the use of chromosomal chimaeras. Exposing the roottips of Crepis or *Vicia faba* to x-rays induced viable chromosomal aberrations—mostly translocations—in meristematic tissue, providing a means of "tagging" a single apical cell, and of determining after certain periods of time the kind and extent of tissues arising from this cell. Most of the chimaeras produced were sectorial, and the changed chromosome complement was found in cells of the root cap, epidermis, cortex, and central cylinder (Fig. 9–2). Usually about one-third of any cross section of the root was affected, suggesting that at most three apical cells gave rise to the entire root behind the apex. The absence of periclinal chimaeras in this study stems from the method of treatment and the type of tissue exposed to x-rays. In Datura, it is more likely that whole tissues rather than single cells were raised to a particular degree of ploidy by colchicine. Brumfield's approach, on the other hand, complements the method of Satina and Blakeslee in that it provides a means for the detection of cell lineages. It has the disadvantage of being applicable only to those tissues that have cells in active division.

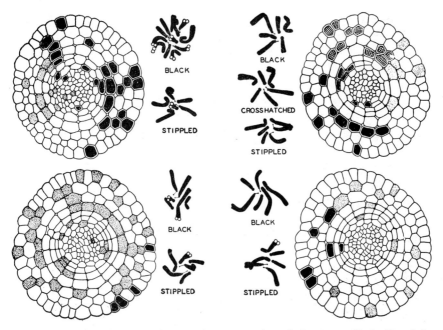

Fig. 9–2. Chromosomal chimaeras in the roottips of *Crepis capillaris*. Top left, sectorial chimaera of diploid (stippled and tetraploid (black) cells; top right, sectorial chimaera of three different karyotypes produced by x-rays; bottom left, mericlinal chimaera of two karyotypes; bottom right, sectorial chimaera of two karyotypes (Brumfield 1943b).

ENDOMITOSIS AND SOMATIC REDUCTION

There was a belief, expressed frequently in the older literature, that polyploid cells occurring sporadically in an otherwise diploid organism were to be regarded as anomalies, stemming possibly from accidents in the mitotic mechanism. The very frequent occurrence of aneuploid and highly polyploid cells in malignant tissues (Fig. 9–3) has tended to focus attention on such findings since this change in chromosome number seemed a possible cause of malignancy, and the repeated observations of such cells have in recent years provided the impetus for a more systematic study of the phenomenon (Levan and Hauschka 1953; Tjio and Levan 1954b; Hsu 1954a, b). The result has been that we now have a far better, even if not a complete, understanding of what may happen to the nuclei of nondividing cells during the process of differentiation and development.

The belief that all the cells of an organism must have, barring rare accidents, the same genic and chromosomal constitution was a logical outgrowth of the Chromosome Theory of Heredity (Huskins 1947), but from an embryological point of view it was difficult to conceive of differentiation occurring in an organism whose cells were of like hereditary character, regardless of the tissue in which they were found. It is now known in

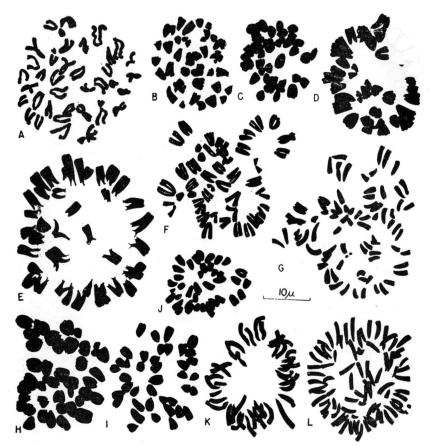

Fig. 9–3. Endomitoses in an ascites tumor (TA3 adenocarcinoma) of the mouse. A–C, normal early, middle and late prophases; D–H, metaphases of endomitotic cells; I–L, normal metaphases (Levan and Hauschka 1953).

insects, where the study of polyploid cells has been most complete, that the entire process of histological change is associated with an orderly change in the chromosomal complement of the constituent cells, with each organ having its own characteristic degree of ploidy. This need not be a uniform degree of ploidy, but rather a uniform pattern, since some organs or tissues may be composed of but a single type of cell while others may present mosaics of different cells having different degrees of ploidy. To what extent histological differentiation is influenced by the degree of ploidy remains to be determined, since the correlation, while evident, is not understood, but the more or less regular occurrence of polyploid cells in the tissues of both plants and animals has dissipated the old concept that these cells were to be regarded as anomalies.

It has been known since 1905 (Nemec) that the distended nuclei in the vascular tissues of the roots of some plants were polyploid even when the meristematic cells were clearly diploid, but it remained for Jacobj and Geitler to provide quantitative information on the subject. The studies of Jacobj (1925) were made on nuclear volumes. When the nuclear volume in any one tissue was plotted against frequency, the curve was found to be not a continuous one, but rather one characterized by many maxima, which in turn could be shown to correspond to exact doublings of the nuclear volume. It was shown that the fusions of adjacent cells of nuclei could not account for the phenomenon. Jacobj reasoned that there was a rhythmical growth and inner division of the nuclear components, unaccompanied by a nuclear division. Hertwig (1935) showed the same phenomenon to occur in the growth of the nurse cells in the Drosophila ovary, with six or seven maxima being encountered. The proportionalities involved were striking since the nuclear volumes corresponded to cells having 2-, 4-, 8-, 16-, 32-, 64- and 128-ploid constitutions if it was assumed that with each doubling of the chromosome complement there was a corresponding doubling of the nuclear volume.

It remained for Geitler (1937, 1939a, 1941) to clarify the situation cytologically and to give the phenomenon a name. This study was done primarily on the various tissues of the water strider, *Gerris lateralis,* the male of which has a chromosome number of 21 in somatic cells. The odd chromosome is that which determines sex, the male being an XO type, and in somatic cells it is deeply heteropycnotic. It is therefore possible to determine directly the polyploid nature of any cell by counting the number of pycnotic bodies in its nucleus (Fig. 9–4). In the salivary gland, the cells possess giant nuclei, and the ploidy of these was as high as 512 and 1024. Moreover, Geitler showed that the process of formation of the polyploid cells paralleled quite exactly, up to a certain stage, the nuclear behavior of normal somatic cells having a diploid constitution. The chromosomes contract through coiling, and exhibit the usual increase in stainability as prophase progresses. At late prophase, however, the process stops, but the chromatids of each chromosome separate from each other autonomously, and begin to unravel. The nuclear membrane does not break down. No spindle, and hence no metaphase plate, is formed, and there is no hint of anaphase movement, but the partial mitosis has effectively doubled the chromosome number of the cell. The fact that some cells have an exceedingly high chromosome number indicates that a cell may go through the process a number of times. Geitler termed the process *endomitosis,* the connotation being that somatic polyploidy of this sort is bound up with the process of mitosis, however incomplete it may be, which provides for the reduplication of the chromosomes and their separation. The term *endopolyploidy* is merely descriptive of the fact without implying the mechanism involved, as is the similar term *polysomaty.*

It is now clear that chromosome reduplication can occur without an ad-

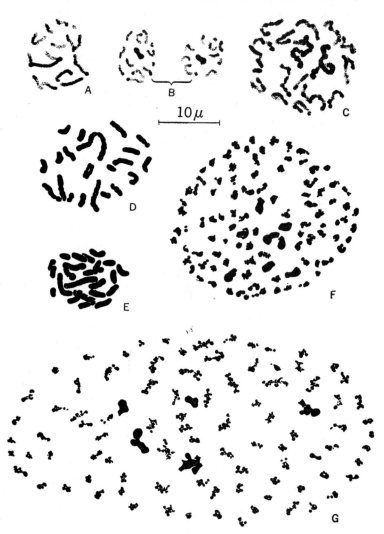

Fig. 9–4. Endomitosis in the somatic cells of the water strider, *Gerris lateralis*. A, 2n prophase, and B, 2n telophase, in connective tissues of the male; C, 4n prophase in the female; D, 4n early metaphase in the male; E, 4n early metaphase in the female; F and G, 16n prophases. The X-chromosomes are heteropycnotic in prophase, and determinations of the degree of ploidy are made by counting the number of heteropycnotic X-chromosomes (Geitler 1939a).

ditional separation of the sister chromatids. In this case, the result is a polytene (many-stranded) chromosome in a cell that retains its diploid character. It is not certain in this case that nuclear doubling follows, since it is difficult to determine the exact degree of polyteny. The general concept of the salivary gland chromosomes of Drosophila is that they are polytene in nature, while other examples are the nurse cells in Drosophila (Painter and Rheindorp 1939) and the intestinal cells of the larval mosquito (Berger 1938, 1941; Grell 1946).

Actually, the distinction between the two end results—somatic polyploidy with normal-stranded chromosomes and polyteny in a diploid cell—seems to be but a matter of degree, and as White (1954) points out, the formation of the polytene nature of the salivary-gland type of chromosome (which is also found in other tissues of dipteran insects) is but a special case of the much more general phenomenon of endopolyploidy. In the nurse cells of Drosophila there are what might be considered to be transitional stages between endomitosis and polyteny. The earlier doublings of the chromosome structure leave the chromatids closely associated in discrete bundles, corresponding in number to the original chromosomes. Later reduplications leave the chromosomes much more loosely associated, although even in the cells with the highest degree of doubling there still remains evidence of the discreteness of the bundles.

In a later study, White (1946b) has shown that although it is recognized that chromosome doubling is at the basis of both processes, it is feasible to retain the terms separately since both polyteny and polyploidy can be found to co-exist in the same cell. The salivary gland of the gall midge, Lestodiplosis, is made up of the usual type of cell containing polytene chromosomes found in other members of the Diptera. But the gland has, in addition, a single giant cell, measuring 150 by 220 microns, at the ascending portion of the salivary duct, which contains the salivary type of polytene chromosome but in a polyploid number (32-ploid). Whether polyteny came first, to be followed by polyploidy, or vice versa, is not known, although Bauer (1938) claims, from a study of the nurse cells of the Muscidae, that a polytene nucleus can be converted into a polyploid one by longitudinal division of the chromosomes without loss of polyteny. The fact that the polytene chromosomes in the giant cell of Lestodiplosis are smaller in diameter than those in adjacent salivary gland cells does not contradict the hypothesis of Bauer; on the other hand, the ability of a polytene chromosome to divide endomitotically to give double the number of chromosomes, seems to be proven conclusively by the studies of Berger (1938) and Grell (1946) on the larval ileum of the mosquito, Culex pipiens. Although we shall consider their work primarily from the point of view of somatic reduction in chromosome number (see later), they have shown that cells containing polytene chromosomes are able to undergo cell division, and that polyteny can be transformed into polyploidy by the falling apart and subsequent segregation of multiple-stranded chromosomes into their component parts.

Endomitosis has been studied rather extensively in plants, particularly in roottips where the process of differentiation can be rather accurately studied as a progressive event extending from the root apex where meristematic cells are undergoing division back through the zone of elongation to the zone of maturation. Berger's (1941) study in Spinacia, where polysomaty is confined to the periblem, is particularly instructive, and it could be shown that there is a definite progression (from the tip of the root toward the differentiated region) from diploid cells to those that are tetraploid, but with the chromosomes existing in pairs ($4n$), to $4n$ cells with the chromosomes unpaired, to $8n$ with the chromosomes again paired. The evidence indicates that in differentiated cells endomitosis is a regular and constantly occurring process, with the endomitotic division of chromosomes taking place during interphase. In the tapetal cell of Spinacia (Witkus 1945), a similar condition exists, but with the degree of ploidy reaching only a tetraploid condition. In Allium, tetraploidy seems to be the highest degree reached, with such cells being found in the mesophyll of the cotyledon and in the cortex of the transition region between the root and shoot of seedlings.

Huskins and his co-workers (Huskins 1948; Huskins and Steinitz 1948) have made a concentrated attack on the problem of polysomaty and its relation to differentiation. They have used, among other plants, *Rhoeo discolor,* a monotypic genus having a number of heterochromatic bodies (prochromosomes and/or nucleoli) which can be followed in the interphase stages. These increase in number in the differentiated tissues of the root, and, as Geitler had shown, the increase arises through abortive mitoses in which cell division is absent. The restituted nuclei formed following such mitoses are polyploid. This was shown to be actually the case by inducing these cells to undergo a mitosis by the application of indole acetic acid; the chromosome number could then be determined directly. When this was done, it could be shown that the production of polytene chromosomes is not uniform for all chromosomes of a single nucleus, i.e., some chromosomes are more polytene than others, or for all the cells of a tissue, and instead of abrupt doublings in the number of strands there is a gradual change from diploidy to tetraploidy, and from tetraploidy to octoploidy. This gradual change, if caught before the completion of the entire process of doubling, will give both tissues of mixed ploidy and cells with an uneven degree of polyteny in the individual chromosomes. Mickey (1946, 1947) has also shown this type of *mixoploidy* to be true for the spermatogonia in the testes of the grasshopper, Romalea.

Although the relationship between differentiation and polysomaty has been discussed by a number of authors (see Huskins and Steinitz 1948), the relationship is not clear. Cells having a secretory function, as those in the salivary glands, are either polyploid (as in Gerris) or have chromosomes of a polytene nature (as in Drosophila), but the wider occurrence of polyteny or polysomaty suggests that a different interpretation must be in order. Huskins (1947) suggests that polysomaty or polyteny will occur in any non-dividing cell that maintains an active metabolic existence, and that the simplest interpretation one can apply would be that genes, in carrying out their active functions, accumulate chromatin as a by-product, and that this accumulation shows itself in the reproduction of the chromatin strands. On this basis, the longer a cell remains active without dividing, the greater will be the degree of polyteny or polysomaty.

This point of view cannot be definitely established at the present time, but what is probably more important from Huskins' studies is the question he raises: how is the zygotic number of chromosomes maintained? The answer seems to lie in the fact that it is in the actively dividing tissues that the original number is maintained, and it would appear, as a first observation at least, that the zygotic number is maintained only when cell division is synchronized with the reproduction of the chromosomes. If the latter proceeds at a faster rate, or if cell division is missing altogether polysomaty or polyteny will arise; if, however, cell division goes on faster than chromosome reproduction, or if cell division comes in after polyploidy has been achieved, somatic reduction will occur. We now know this to be the case in some tissues.

Although reduction divisions are normally associated with the formation of germ cells in animals, and of asexual spores in the case of the higher plants, somatic reduction divisions are known to occur. In plants, the divisions take place sporadically and, so far as can be determined, without any relation to a regular developmental process or structural differentiation; in the few reported instances of somatic reduction in animals the process is regular in *Icerya purchasi* and in Culex, possibly sporadic in other forms.

Hughes-Schrader (1925, 1927) first described a regular somatic reduction in the cottony-cushion scale, *Icerya purchasi*. This species is known to produce normal males and females as well as functional hermaphrodites. It is in the latter that somatic reduction takes place during differentiation of male cells in the core of the developing gonad. The mechanism of reduction in these hermaphrodites, which in all other respects resemble normal females, is not known, but the chromosomes in the haploid nuclei can be identified as a complete haploid set. Rapid proliferation of these cells produces a mass of haploid tissue, the cells of which become primary spermatocytes. These later undergo a single equational division to produce two sperm cells each, the process being identical to that taking place in the spermatocytes of the normal haploid males. The outer cells of the gonad develop into ovarial tissue, with a reduction division producing reduced eggs much as in the normal females. Occasionally a diploid cell becomes trapped in the mass of haploid tissue. Such a cell may initiate proliferation and development much as do normal diploid cells in ovarial tissue, even to the point of having nurse cells surrounding an early oöcyte, but these trapped cells soon degenerate and disappear.

Reduction divisions have been studied in the iliac epithelium of *Culex pipiens* by both Berger (1938, 1941) and Grell (1946). During the later larval life of the mosquito, and for a few hours during pupation, the iliac epithelium grows by an increase in cell size. No cell multiplication is involved. The cells initially have a diameter of 3–4 microns, but these dimensions gradually increase until at metamorphosis the greatest diameters are between 10 and 17 microns. Formation of the imaginal epithelium commences at about the eighth hour of pupal life and is complete by the twelveth to the fourteenth hour; it is during this time that the reduction divisions take place, with the imaginal epithelium being derived by cell division from the larval iliac epithelium rather than from regenerative cells or imaginal discs. The diameter of the newly formed imaginal epithelial cells is smaller than that of the iliac cells from which they arose.

It had been known for some time that multiple chromosome complexes were formed in the mid-gut cells of the mosquito. The gradual increase in size of nuclei during larval life indicated that the process of chromosome reduplication was going on, but it was not until cell division in these highly polyploid cells was studied that it was realized that reduction divisions were taking place. The onset of metamorphosis finds the ileum composed of a few large cells, the size being related to the degree of polyploidy. Polyploidy, however, is attained by a repeated duplication of the chromonemata during a protracted resting stage so that endomitosis, in the sense of Geitler, does not occur. Mid-metamorphosis finds cells of many sizes, while the end of metamorphosis leaves very few cells of large size, most being quite small.

The reduction divisions take place in the following manner: in prophase, a gradual condensation of the chromatin leads to the formation of three pairs of thick chromosomes ($n = 3$ in the mosquito), each of which has two to 32 strands. By late prophase, these have fallen apart into their constituent units, after which it appears that homologous strands unite by a process of somatic synapsis, and reach the metaphase plate in this condition. The larger cells have 24 or 48 of these pairs arranged on a plate. Anaphase sets in and the chromosomes separate from each other without a further longitudinal division taking place, to give daughter cells having a reduced number of chromosomes. Later divisions exhibit the same behavior, i.e., prophase condensation into thick strands, separation of these into the individual strands, synapsis of apparently homologous strands, and then separation of these to effect further reduction. Eventually the cells of the imaginal epithelium have 12 or 24 chromosomes ($4n$ or $8n$) instead of the 48 or 96 initially present at the onset of metamorphosis.

It would appear therefore that the process of chromosome duplication that gives rise to cells of a polyploid nature is followed by a compensating mechanism that progressively halves the chromosome number. Berger suggests that this is a means of effecting a very rapid metamorphosis of certain tissues, but although polyploid cells have been described in many insects it is not known how widespread this mechanism may be.

Berger's interpretation of the cytological events in the mosquito have not gone unchallenged (White 1954), but the further studies of Grell leave no doubt as to the correctness of the original studies.

Huskins (1948) and Huskins and Steinitz (1948) have attacked the problem of somatic reduction and segregation in the roottips of Allium and Rhoeo. They induced cells to divide that ordinarily would never do so by applications of indole acetic acid, and showed that many tissues are of a polyploid nature, having become so through an endomitotic process. Occasional cells were found that were haploid, and this led to an experimental approach to the induction of somatic "meiosis." Ribose nucleic acid, or its sodium salt, used in concentrations of 1–2 percent for 6–12 hours, effectively increased the frequency with which somatic reduction divisions took place. These divisions resemble those occurring in meiotic cells in that synapsis occurs, and paired homologues come to lie on the metaphase plate. Whether there is any genetic consequence to such divisions, arising out of somatic crossing over and segregation, remains to be determined.

GENETIC CONTROL OF CELL DIVISION

Wherever adequate genetic data have been obtained, the general features of inheritance in both plants and animals have been found to be remarkably constant. In the vertebrates, for example, there appear to be no deviations from a straightforward Mendelian type of inheritance when single genes are studied, and the same can be said of many other forms. This fact has, of course, enormously simplified the study of inheritance since the basic principles can be derived from experiments on favorable organisms, and the conclusions drawn can then be generally applied with reasonable surety to the great majority of species which do not lend themselves to laboratory study. To be sure, differences exist, but in the main the physical features of meiosis—synapsis, crossing over, and segregation—are sufficiently constant to permit generalizations to be made from the cytological fact to the genetical interpretation, and vice versa. This has been made apparent in the preceding chapters where a variety of species have been discussed in our examination of the underlying facts of inheritance and their physical bases.

Cell division, therefore, whether it be mitotic or meiotic, can be viewed as a series of events coordinated in both time and space to give an orderly end result: two similar daughter cells if mitotic, or a variety of gametes if meiotic. It is logical to assume that the entire process of cell division is under rather exacting control by certain genes or groups of genes even though this would be impossible to determine were it not for the fact that genes mutate, and through their mutation give rise to variations that can be followed cytologically, and tested genetically. Even where departures from some assumed normality exist, and these departures characterize an entire group of related organisms, e.g., the dog roses or the gall midges, it must be assumed that these fixed abnormalities are genically controlled, and have risen to their present bizarre state by the processes of evolution. This assumption must be made since reproduction of the species goes on and competition can be withstood.

In this section, however, only those abnormalities will be discussed whose genetic control has been established as the result of single gene changes. Their importance from the point of view of cellular mechanisms is great. They serve as a beautifully controlled experiment in which a single phase of cell division is disturbed, and from this disturbance the investigator can first of all visualize the interdependence of the various parts and processes of the cell in the successful completion of cellular division, and secondly determine the relative importance of the various steps in an analysis of intracellular mechanisms.

Mitosis. As one might expect, variations in cell division caused by mutant genes are much more frequent in meiosis than in mitosis. The former is a more complicated process, with more opportunity for irregularities to be expressed. More important is the fact that gross upsets in somatic divisions would soon lead to death of the affected cells, and eventually to death of the organism. Elimination of these genes from a population would presumably proceed at a fairly rapid rate. It is only when somatic disturbances are relatively innocuous in their effects, or are expressed only infrequently or in a non-vital portion of the body, that the organism can survive and the circumstances of disturbance be studied.

The detection of somatic variations can be made best where genetic markers or sexual characters can be clearly followed to give an indication of the events which have taken place. Genetically conditioned gynandromorphism (i.e., a somatic mixture of male and female parts) is a case in point, and a clear-cut example has been found in the larvae of the silkworm, *Bombyx mori* (Goldschmidt and Katsuki 1927, 1928). Determined by a single gene, gynandromorphism, together with somatic mosaicism, arises during the process of fertilization as the result of polar nuclei, as well as the egg nucleus, being penetrated by sperm. Since the male of the silkworm is the homogametic sex, all of the sperm contain an X-chromosome, yet they may be genetically different if derived from a heterozygous individual. The polar nuclei will contain either an X- or a Y-chromosome, but whatever the case, the egg nucleus will be different, i.e., if the polar nucleus contains a Y-chromosome, the egg will bear the X as the result of segregation, or vice versa. The polar nucleus, after fertilization, sinks back into the now-fertilized egg, and apparently plays an equivalent role with the zygotic nucleus in development. The way is thus paved for the forma-

tion of mosaic individuals, with the mosaicism being expressed for autosomal as well as for sexual characters.

Mosaicism of a different type has been studied in *D. melanogaster,* and
it may well be that this type is far more often the cause of mosaicism than
is generally realized. This is the type of mosaicism due to somatic crossing
over. Presumably the somatic pairing of chromosomes characteristic of
dipteran species makes it initially possible, but the peculiar relationship of
the many *Minute* factors to the location and the incidence of somatic crossing over is a most puzzling phenomenon (Stern 1936). Somatic crossing occurs in the absence of *Minute* factors, but with a much lower frequency,
and when *Minute* factors are present, each tends to influence somatic crossing in a particular way. In general, the *Minutes* increase somatic crossing
most in the arm of the chromosome in which they are located, with the sex-
linked *Minutes* being more influential than the autosomal ones. *Minute-n,*
for example, which is located in the X-chromosome, strongly affects the
frequency of somatic crossing over to the right of singed (21.0), less so
the left of this locus. Other *Minutes* are less specific, but where a series of
linked genes have been used in a single experiment, it could be demonstrated that crossing over was more frequent near the centromere than at
loci further removed from it. An extra Y-chromosome has the effect of
increasing the frequency, although the frequency in females is generally
higher than in males of similar genetic constitution.

It is difficult to visualize how the *Minute* factors, most if not all of them
being deficiencies, produce their effects. It may well be that crossing over,
meiotic or somatic, will vary according to the protein framework of the
chromosome, as White (1954) suggests, and that the *Minutes,* through
their action on the cellular milieu, lead to such alterations either specifically
in the chromosome in which they are located, or in the nucleus in general.
Since the effects are more pronounced near the centromere, the role of
heterochromatin becomes suspect. It may well be that the heterochromatic
regions become stickier because of the genetic action of the *Minutes,* and
that this stickiness is more pronounced in the chromosome containing the
Minute factor than in other chromosomes in the same nucleus. If such a
situation occurred during somatic synapsis, the opportunity for somatic
crossing over would be enhanced.

Another well known instance of genetically controlled somatic aberrations is that described in *D. simulans* (Sturtevant 1929; Wald 1936). The
claret gene, a Chromosome III recessive, produces its major effect, other
than modifying eye color, in meiosis, causing aberrant spindle formation
and considerable egg inviability because of irregular segregation and
chromosome elimination. The effects, however, are carried over into
somatic tissues, since a high percentage of exceptional individuals and
gynandromorphs appear among the relatively few progeny produced. It

was at first believed by Sturtevant that the abnormal results could be explained by the elimination of one of the X-chromosomes during the maturation or early cleavage divisions, but Wald was able to show that in addition to the aberrant divisions which caused scattered nuclei to appear there was also the addition of scattered chromosomes back into deficient nuclei during the early cleavage divisions. That is, during the maturation divisions the X-chromosome (the fourth chromosome could also be followed, and shown to behave similarly) sometimes failed to pass to the poles, and instead formed a separate nuclear membrane about itself. This nucleus later united with the nucleus undergoing cleavage, and the single chromosome passed to one or the other of the two poles. If this took place during the first cleavage division, a gynandromorph was produced, and the deficient tissue would invariably lack the maternal X- (or fourth) chromosome. (Eggs lacking a II or III chromosome would die since both chromosomes are necessary for spindle formation.) The *claret* gene affects spindle formation in meiosis and the cleavage divisions in the female only; it is without effect except for eye color in the male. A gene in *D. melanogaster,* apparently homologous with the *claret* gene in *D. simulans,* is without effect on that species, although an x-ray induced mutant, called *claret-non-disjunctional,* has been found in *D. melanogaster* which produces the same abnormalities as does the *simulans claret* (Lewis and Gengarella 1952).

Another somatic variation, genetically controlled, is that found by Beadle (1931, 1933a) in a particular strain of maize. A recessive gene, *polymitotic divisions,* is responsible for the condition. Meiosis in this strain is normal, a regular tetrad of microspores being formed. As the first microspore division approaches, the chromosomes contract to a meiotic-like appearance, and chiasma-like formations have been observed. The chromosomes do not divide, however, but cell divisions occur in rapid succession to separate the chromosomes into smaller cells. Many of the cells have but a single chromosome in them, and since as many as five divisions may occur to give 32 cells, others may be completely devoid of chromosomes. Sterility, of course, is complete. Approximately 10 percent of the embryo-sacs are viable and provided with the normal haploid complement of ten chromosomes, suggesting that the action of the gene is less severe during embryosac formation than during the formation of the male gametophyte.

Meiosis. A fairly large number of genetically determined meiotic abnormalities have been described (Darlington 1937a, Table 62). These affect pairing, crossing over, contraction and size of chromosomes, spindle formation—in fact, almost every conceivable aspect of meiotic behavior capable of being disturbed. For the most part, the effects of these genes have been most thoroughly studied in the microsporocytes of plants. Here the disturbances are readily detected, with pollen sterility providing the first indication of some more deep-seated abnormality, but it would appear also that microsporogenesis is more easily upset than is megasporogenesis.

This is shown by the fact that most of genic effects grouped among the "male sterility" types have an exclusive male expression, the production of viable embryo sacs being unimpaired. Presumably the vulnerability of the male gametophyte stems from the relatively unprotected haploid existence as opposed to the protected embryo sacs, but this cannot provide the complete answer since many of the genes have their expression during the meiotic process itself. Only a few of the many abnormalities will be mentioned here.

Beadle's studies in maize revealed a number of meiotic disturbances which have proven to be of considerable interest. One of these, called *asynaptic* (Beadle 1930, 1933b), affects the formation of bivalents with the result that most of the chromosomes arrive on the metaphase plate as univalents rather than as bivalents. Examination of the microsporocytes in diakinesis show cells having from ten to no bivalents. Congression of the univalents onto the metaphase plate, and the later distribution of them at anaphase, is highly irregular, but enough viable male gametes are formed to permit a study of crossing over in homozygous asynaptic plants. The fact that pachytene and even zygotene pairing is very poor in these plants led Beadle to suspect that crossing over had been greatly interfered with, but Rhoades (1947) has found, on the contrary, that crossing over is much higher than normal. Asynaptic maize produces both haploid and diploid gametes. Undoubtedly the haploid gametes were derived from those microsporocytes having a minimum number of chiasmata compatible with regular segregation; the origin of the diploid gametes, however, is obscured, although it is possible that they were derived from those meiotic cells in which no chiasmata had formed, the first meiotic division was suppressed, and the 20 univalents divided as in a mitotic cell. Yet crossing over was higher than normal in both the haploid and diploid cells, and the most striking difference was the great increase in the frequency of double crossovers. Thus in the *ws-lg-gl* region of Chromosome 2 the ratio of double crossovers in asynaptic and normal strains was about 25:1, while the genetic length of these two regions was increased about one-third in the asynaptic strain. Comparable results were obtained with the *c-sh-wx* region in Chromosome 9.

Clearly then the situation in asynaptic maize is rather anomalous in that crossing over occurs with a high frequency but without the usual formation and detectable appearance of chiasmata. The time of crossing over is not known, but there is good evidence for believing that the absence of chiasmata is not due to a very rapid rate of terminalization. Presumably crossing over could occur in a pre-meiotic cell division (similar to gonial crossing over in Drosophila), but there is no evidence to suggest that clusters of similar crossover chromatids are recovered. Similar genetic conditions governing asynapsis are also known to exist in Datura (Bergner, Cartledge and Blakeslee 1934), and in Crepis (Richardson 1935), but the crossover situation in these forms has not been studied as it has in maize.

Both the size (volume) and shape of the chromosomes at meiosis are dependent upon events occurring before metaphase. Although little is known about what might be involved in altering chromosome size within a single species, it has been shown in both Secale (Lamm 1936) and *Lolium perenne* (Thomas 1936) that this feature is under genetic control. As Figure 9–5 shows, the segregants from a particular strain of Lolium

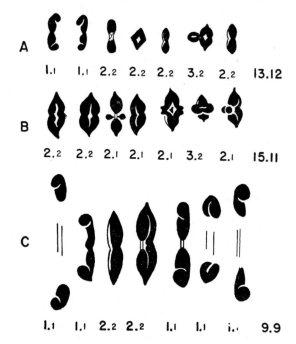

Fig. 9–5. Metaphase and early anaphase bivalents in three plants of the perennial rye grass, *Lolium perenne,* showing differences in chromosome size and chiasma frequency. A, female parent of both B and C. Figures represent the frequencies of total number of chiasmata to the number which are terminal (Thomas 1936).

exhibit metaphase chromosomes of two different sizes even though the gene content of the two segregants must be assumed to be similar. It is perhaps easiest to consider that the extra-genic material on the chromosomes differs in amount, but our knowledge of the chemical makeup of the chromosomes is too sketchy at the moment to make this anything but sheer speculation.

Chromosome shape can be readily altered experimentally by various environmental agents, but two well known studies have shown that the length of the chromosomes, and the distribution of chiasmata, at metaphase can be influenced by certain genes. The garden stock, *Matthiola incana,* normally has a short chromosome, and the chiasmata in the bivalents are strongly terminalized (Lesley and Frost 1927). A mutant long-chromosome form shows the chiasmata to be largely interstitial, a circumstance which can be attributed either to a precocious metaphase that interrupted coiling and also terminalization, or to a slower tempo to the coiling process. Both would give the same end result. These circumstances are closely paralleled by a siutation found in the sweet pea (Fig. 7–10), except that in this species the long-chromosome form with interstitial chiasmata is normal, and the short-chromosome form abnormal (Upcott 1937). In addition, the short-chromosome form is also male-sterile, and the cause seems to be related to a slower rate of another development since metaphase I is reached when the anthers have progressed beyond the size characteristic of this stage of microsporogenesis.

Clark's (1940) study in maize serves to illustrate the changes that can be genetically induced in the structure of the spindle. Arising from the result of exposure to ultraviolet light, the gene *divergent* (*dv*), when homozygous, causes the spindle in pollen mother cells to take an abnormal form. The usual picture obtained is that of a spindle that diverges and flares at the poles rather than one that converges to form a biacuminate structure. In some extreme cases the spindle elongates greatly, and in doing so, follows the contours of the cell. The result is that several nuclei rather than one are formed in telophase. The second division which follows is therefore abnormal, since each nucleus, regardless of the number of chromosomes it may contain, forms its own spindle which may or may not be divergent in character.

More than four spores are sometimes formed from each microsporocyte, but when only four result, many of these are multinucleate. The microspore division may also show divergent spindles, although with a much lower frequency. Pollen sterility is of course to be expected, but the fact that a study of seven plants showed that the range was from 13 to 90 percent suggests that the expression of the *dv* gene is altered by various environmental factors, or that the genetical background in which it is found determines its degree of effectiveness in altering spindle shape.

A last instance of the genetic control of a particular step in meiosis in plants may be mentioned, that, namely, of multiploid sporocyte formation in barley (Smith 1942). In normal strains of this species, the pollen mother cells contain seven bivalents. In a single strain, however, and particularly in the lateral florets, Smith found pollen mother cells with 14, 21, 28, 56, 112 and higher numbers of pairs of chromosomes (Fig. 9–6). Apparently cell walls are absent in these cells, and syncytial masses of cytoplasm are formed which include all or part of the contents of a single anther locule. Whether cell walls are ever formed, or whether they disappear in early prophase, is not clear, but fusion of the masses takes place prior to synap-

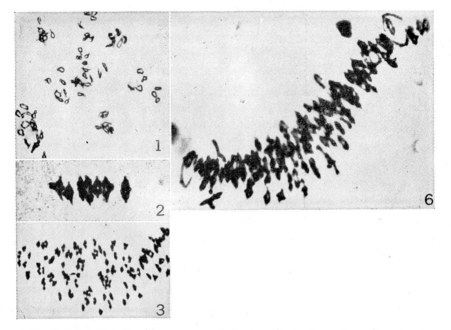

Fig. 9–6. Multiploid microsporocytes in barley due to the action of a recessive gene. 1, diakinesis, with clear boundaries between cells lacking; 2, metaphase I in a normal barley plant; 3, metaphase I in a multiploid sporocyte showing about 112 pairs of chromosomes; 6, metaphase I from same plant pictured in 3, showing 113 bivalents and 4 quadrivalents (Smith 1942).

sis since in many instances multivalent formation was found. Fusion of metaphase plates also seems to occur, with the result that tremendously long plates, often wavy in appearance, are formed in the syncytium. Anaphase movement seemed to be unhindered, even when the metaphase figures were highly abnormal, yet the length of the spindle seemed to vary but little. As a consequence, it seems unlikely that the spindle was biacuminate, being rather similar to the divergent type described by Clark.

In *D. melanogaster,* several genes lead to meiotic abnormalities. One of these, known as the *C3g* gene, is a Chromosome III recessive which prevents crossing over, and leads to much primary non-disjunction in homozygous females (Gowen 1928, 1933). It is without effect in the male. More unique, however, is the "sex-ratio" gene found in wild populations of *D. pseudoobscura* and *persimilis* (Sturtevant and Dobzhansky 1936). It is known in other species of Drosophila (Gershenson 1928) but whether the mechanism is the same in all cases is not known. When present in males, it leads to an abnormally high frequency of daughters (over 90%) among the offspring, irrespective of the genetic makeup of the mother. The cytological explanation lies in an abnormal spermatocyte division (Fig. 9–7). There is no pairing between the X and the Y, and the X at

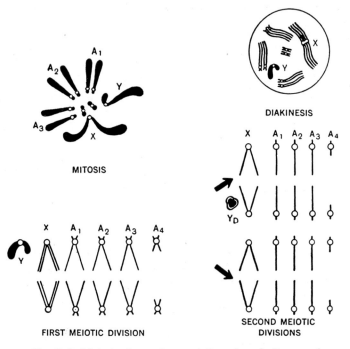

Fig. 9–7. Meiosis in a "sex-ratio" male of *D. pseudo-obscura*. A_{1-4}, autosomes; X splits in both meiotic divisions; Y is heteropycnotic and eventually disintegrates (Y_D) (White 1954 after Sturtevant and Dobzhansky 1936).

diakinesis is seen to be split twice. Thus it contains four chromatids instead of the usual two, and it divides at each meiotic division. Each sperm from such a division consequently carries an X, which then fertilizes X-bearing eggs to give daughters only. The Y does not divide, and although it passes to one of the poles in the first division, it eventually becomes enclosed in a separate vesicle and degenerates. Occasionally a cell division allows for inclusion of the Y into a sperm (some sperm have no X-chromosomes while others have both X and Y), and from these arise the relatively rare sons.

The gene is without effect in females. How the cytological situation is determined in males is unknown, although in cases where the sex-ratio gene has been found, it is in association with inversions. It has been suggested (Darlington and Dobzhansky 1942) that an increased nucleination of the X causes its anomalous behavior, a suggestion arising out of the fact that the frequency of sons is lower at 16.5° C than at 25° C (Darlington postulates that the amount of nucleic acid in the chromosome is affected by temperature).

Segregation of the sex chromosomes in males of the cotton stainer,

Dysdercus koenigii, is of interest in this regard although nothing is known about its genetic control (Ray-Chaudhuri and Manna 1952). In a sense, it is the opposite of that in Drosophila males bearing the sex-ratio gene. Dysdercus males have an XY sex mechanism, and the X and Y do not pair. Although each is bipartite, and orientation on the metaphase plate as univalents is such as to suggest that an equational division will ensue, the X goes to one pole undivided, the Y to the other. In the second division, the centromeres remain undivided, and no equational division takes place; instead the X (or Y) passes precociously to one pole or the other. Half of the sperm therefore lack a sex chromosome, and evidence indicates that these are non-functional. Division of the sex chromosomes does not take place until the first cleavage division.

MALE STERILITY

Male sterility in plants is of unusual interest not only because of the different causes that can give rise to it, but because of its intrinsic value to the plant breeder. From an experimental point of view, male sterility can of course be studied only in plants that have functional egg cells, or where the condition is determined by a recessive gene. Undoubtedly male sterility occurs in animals as well but, except in hermaphroditic species, the opportunities for a genetic analysis would be completely lacking.

The occurrence of this phenomenon in plants has been noted many times, and current interest in male sterility, particularly in species of a commercial value, stems from the fact that these individuals having non-functional male cells can be successfully employed for the production of hybrid seed with its attendant hybrid vigor. As Rick (1945) has pointed out, the advantages of using male-sterile mutants are several: emasculation is unnecessary; there is no danger of contamination from selfing; they are frequently easy to identify in the field because of their greater vegetative growth (this is particularly true for tomatoes); and since they usually are determined by single recessive genes, they would constitute 50 percent of a backcross progeny and would therefore be easy to obtain in sufficient numbers for the commercial production of hybrid seed.

Male sterility is, of course, characterized by the lack of production of viable male cells. Obviously this can be caused by a variety of events that interfere with the formation of normal pollen grains, and as a number of studies have shown, the disturbing event can occur anywhere along the sequence of steps from pre-meiotic stages through to the production of normal-appearing, but inviable, pollen grains. For example, 20 different male-steriles have been described in maize (Emerson, Beadle, and Fraser 1935). The study of male-sterile mutants in the tomato by Rick (1945) indicates clearly that while the end result is the same, the determining cause may be variable. Thus, in four male-sterile (ms_{1-4}) plants the following behavior was observed: ms_1 passes through the initial stages of meiosis, but collapse of the pollen mother cells is complete by diakinesis; ms_2 has a normal meiotic behavior, but the microspores degenerate shortly after the formation of tetrads; ms_3 shows an impaired development of the sporogenous tissue prior to the beginning of meiosis, although a few cells manage to continue on through metaphase I and telophase I; ms_4 exhibits a fairly normal meiotic behavior although the cells enter meiosis rather irregularly. The time of cellular breakdown was consequently less precise, but no cells reached viable maturity. Lesley and Lesley (1939) have also reported a case of male sterility in tomato in which degeneration of the male cells did not take place until just prior to maturity, but in this instance two recessive genes are known to be involved.

The mutants in tomato discussed by Rick were fertile insofar as the production of seed was concerned, although seed production was poorer in ms_3 than it was in plants of later generations derived from ms_3. Five other mutants, which like the four male-sterile forms were diploid in nature, were both male- and female-sterile. One plant was known to be asynaptic in the pollen mother cells, and presumably so in the embryo-sac divisions; the others, though sterile, had normal meiosis in the pollen mother cells, with the microspores degenerating at later stages.

Failure to set seed was found to be caused by two types of embryo-sac abnormalities (Rick 1946). In the *collapsed* type, the four megaspores are produced normally, but degeneration sets in at some stage before the mature embryo sac is formed. Hypertrophy of the inner integumentary cells may occur. This type is, however, more apt to characterize the sterile triploids and tetraploids than it is the genetically sterile diploids. The latter usually possess what is known as the *substitution* type in which no megaspore mother cell differentiates, and no gametophyte develops. Rather, the nucellar apex in which the megaspore mother cell would normally arise remains as a group of undifferentiated cells which persist until the flower is matured. The inner integumentary cells may hypertrophy, but the outer tissues of the ovule develop normally.

The strains of tomato that were both male- and female-sterile are the exception rather than the rule, for most male-steriles are completely female-fertile. This is particularly true in maize where all of the male-steriles that are genetically determined show no female inviability.

PREFERENTIAL SEGREGATION OF CHROMOSOMES

Segregation of a particular chromosome in meiosis, both in regard to the specific pole attained and to any particular non-homolgous chromosome with which it assorts, is generally at random. Maintenance of this randomness is a necessary condition if Mendel's second principle of inheritance is to hold. Although linkage imposes certain restrictions of greater or lesser severity on the randomness of genic assortment, Carothers' study of heteromorphic homologues in a number of grasshopper species provided physical proof of the randomness of assortment of whole chromosomes.

The mechanism for such segregation is to be found of course in the behavior of bivalents. In most plants and animals, bivalents are maintained until the beginning of anaphase as a consequence of chiasma formation. Orientation of any pair of homologues on the metaphase plate is only in relation to the longitudinal axis of the spindle rather than to any particular pole, and is likewise independent of any second pair of homologues. We have therefore come to regard as "normal" those genetic and cytological systems that more or less conform with Mendelian expectation, and these relationships, plus the fact that in many organisms failure of chiasma formation is often followed by non-disjunction, have been generalized into the "chiasma hypothesis of metaphase pairing" (Darlington 1929).

The hypothesis cannot be universally applied, however (Cooper 1944, 1945), and the realization has been gradually formed that the assortment of chromosomes, whether at random or not, can be governed by a number of mechanisms not all of them associated with chiasma formation (e.g., *Dysdercus koenigii*). The causal basis of many of these mechanisms still remains to be elucidated, although there can be no doubt that the meiotic processes exhibit a wide range of flexibility.

Non-random disjunction of sex chromosomes. Where an XO or a multiple sex chromosome condition exists, some mechanism other than normal bivalent formation and segregation must come into operation to insure the regular distribution of sex determinants to the poles. In such forms as represented by the grasshoppers, where an XO:XX sex mechanism is present, the X-chromosome in the male is heteropycnotic, and it passes precociously to one or the other of the poles in anaphase I. Separation of the chromatids of the X-chromosome takes place in the second division. The reverse behavior, namely splitting of the X in the first division, with segregation occurring in the second division, occurs in only a few organisms, notably the coccids, the dragonflies, and the firefly Photinus.

In the coccid Llaveiella, a unique variation of X-chromosome behavior has become established. In this form, the X splits in prophase into two chromatids which fall apart and may become enclosed in entirely separate vesicles. At the first division, the two chromatids behave as individual chromosomes, with the chromatids splitting again and the daughter halves (half-chromatids) passing to opposite poles. In the second division, however, the two half-chromatid X's come together, pair intimately, and then pass to one pole as a unit.

In a somewhat different way, Seiler (1921) has shown that segregation of the X-chromosome can be influenced by the environment. In the lepidopteran species, *Talaeporia tubulosa,* the X passes into the polar body when the temperature is normal or below normal. At high temperatures, however, and in overripe eggs, the X has a strong tendency to remain in the egg. Since the female of Talaeporia is the heterogametic sex, the temperature at the time of the first meiotic division has a marked effect on the sex ratio.

Where an XY sex chromosome mechanism is present, and the X and Y possess few or no homologies between them, their regular segregation must depend upon some other mechanism than that regulated by chiasma formation. This must be true in the male Drosophila where no crossing over exists. Darlington (1934a) proposed that the X and Y are invariably joined by two chiasmata in the vicinity of the centromere, and that these, being always reciprocal, counteract each other insofar as genetic exchange is concerned, but at the same time insure the regular segregation of these two components.

The incorrectness of the "reciprocal chiasmata" hypothesis has been shown by Cooper (1944), and it is now apparent that chiasma formation or, indeed, metaphase pairing is not a necessary feature of regular segregation. This is true in many insect forms such as the mantids, certain flies, and a number of true bugs. In the mantids (Hughes-Schrader 1943a) there is a physical approximation of the homologues to each other, but no chiasmata are formed (Fig. 9–8), but in certain other insects conjunc-

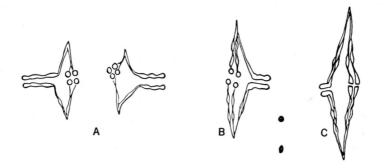

Fig. 9–8. Anaphase I bivalents in spermatocytes of the mantid, Callimantis, separating without evidence of previous chiasmata (Hughes-Schrader 1943).

tion may be only at a distance, or the homologues may unite only briefly at their ends (touch-and-go pairing) (Fig. 7–7).

An interesting variation of this behavior has been described by Wilson (1925) in the coreid bug Metapodius. Bivalents are formed between most of the homologues, but the small "m" chromosomes do not pair in any way. Instead they arrange themselves in the center of the metaphase plate, clearly separate from each other, and along the vertical axis of the spindle. From this point they segregate normally. Clearly this is a special mechanism for insuring segregation in the absence of pairing.

The role of heterochromatin in insuring normal disjunction is indicated by the studies of Sandler and Braver (1954). Different types of XY and XYY males of *D. melanogaster* were tested for loss of both X- and Y-chromosomes. The types differed by the amount and distribution of heterochromatin in the X-chromosomes. Losses of chromosomes occurred most frequently when the homologies between the chromosomes were greatly reduced, suggesting that disjunction is related to pairing in the heterochromatin and is unrelated to centric pairing.

Where multiple sex chromosomes exist, special conditions must be set up to guarantee proper distribution of the sex determinants whether chiasmata are formed or not. White (1954) gives many examples of these forms, but two examples will suffice. Corresponding to the XO type, we find an X_1X_2O male in the spiders, or an $X_1X_2X_3X_4O$ male in the aphid *Euceraphis betulae*. In each case, the X's go to the same pole in the absence of pairing partners. These have probably arisen from the simpler XO type in which the mechanism of segregation had probably been previously established, with the maintenance of the mechanism a necessity if survival of multiple sex chromosome types is to be preserved. Where a Y is found along with multiple X's, as in many of the assassin bugs (family Reduviidae), the X's segregate from the single Y. Figure 9–9 illustrates how this

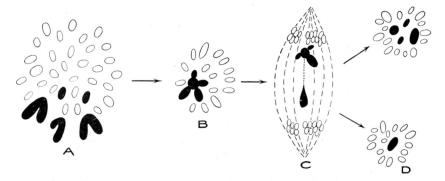

Fig. 9–9. Behavior of the $X_1X_2X_3X_4Y$ chromosomes in the beetle *Blaps lusitanica*. A, spermatogonial metaphase; B, metaphase I with the X's and the Y chromosome forming a multivalent; C, anaphase I with the X's segregating from the Y; D, second division metaphases. Sex chromosomes in black, autosomes in outline (modified from Wilson 1925).

is accomplished in the tenebrionid beetle, *Blaps lusitanica,* although in this instance the possibility of multiple Y-chromosomes has not been ruled out. Whether chiasmata are formed is also not known.

Cooper's (1946a) study of the segregation of the X_1X_2Y trivalent in males of *D. miranda* serves as an example of how such preferential distributions may take place (see also Hughes-Schrader 1943a, for behavior of X_1X_2Y trivalents in male phasmids). Both X's pair with the Y-chromosome, and both segregate from it as the result of proper orientation on the metaphase plate. The efficiency of this type of segregation approaches nearly 100 percent, yet no chiasmata are formed. In fact, even in females in *D. melanogaster,* where chiasmata are usually formed between the two X-chromosomes, those sex bivalents devoid of chiasmata can disjoin in a normal fashion, indicating that the lack of chiasmata in a species where crossing over is a normal event need not necessarily lead to meiotic irregularity (Cooper 1945).

The type of orientation at meiotic metaphase of the sex trivalent in *D. miranda* also has a direct bearing on the mechanism of secondary non-disjunction in *D. melanogaster.* Bridges (1916), it will be recalled, found that exceptional females, arising from non-disjunctional (primary) eggs and having an XXY composition, produce a number of exceptional offspring. This phenomenon he called *secondary non-disjunction.* He postulated that there was an active competition between the two X's and the Y for pairing partners, and that when any two of these three chromosomes formed a pair, the third was excluded and left as a univalent to assort at random. Secondary non-disjunction would therefore take place when an X and a Y paired, and the remaining X, by chance, passed to the same pole as the segregating X. Even if one of the X's paired with the Y in all oöcytes, the maximum amount of secondary non-disjunction, according to Bridges' hypothesis, would not exceed 50 percent. Actually in XXY females, where the X's are structurally homologous with each other, the frequency is slightly over 1 percent.

However, in certain XXY females which were also heterozygous for X-chromosome inversions, Sturtevant and Beadle (1936) found that secondary non-disjunction values were as high as 63 percent, leading Cooper (1948a) to believe that trivalent formation, together with an imposed non-random segregation similar to that in *D. miranda,* was operative. Since both arms of the Y in *D. melanogaster* are partially homologous with the X (Neuhaus 1937), trivalent formation is possible, particularly if such pairing is fostered by reducing the extent of pairing in euchromatic sections of the X by the presence of inversions. The experimental results of Cooper, designed to test this hypothesis, and based upon the use of various X-chromosome inversions as well as one-armed Y's, were well in accord with the idea that high frequencies of secondary non-disjunction can be traced to the formation of trivalents followed by a directed segregation. The greater the structural heterozygosity of the two X's, the greater the frequency of secondary non-disjunction, i.e., the Y becomes a more acceptable pairing partner as pairing between the X's decreases. Likewise the frequency of secondary non-disjunction is reduced if a one-armed Y is used, this abbreviated chromosome providing only one region with which one or the other of the X's can pair. In support of this is the observation of Sturtevant (Morgan and Sturtevant 1944) that structural heterozygosity in the autosomes will tend to reduce secondary non-disjunction. This is to be expected since such autosomal heterozygosity will increase crossing over in the X's, and hence lower the frequency with which the X's pair with the Y.

Segregation of chromosome IV in Drosophila. Triplo-IV females in *D. melanogaster* are viable and fertile, and it is possible to test whether random segregation of these three IV chromosomes occurs. If the three chromosomes are labelled A, B, and C (Fig. 9–10), and if randomness of segregation prevails, the three patterns of segregation, AB/C, AC/B, and BC/A, should be found in equal numbers. Evidence that a preferential segregation of IV chromosomes exists was first found in a stock in which the females had two normal IV chromosomes plus a duplication which possessed a IV chromosome centromere and distal end, with a piece of the X-chromosome inserted between them (Sturtevant 1936). The known loci of the IV had been removed. The two IV chromosomes segregated to opposite poles in 95 percent of the cells, but the duplication showed a definite preference for one of them. When different IV chromosomes were

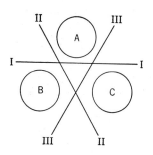

Fig. 9–10. Types of segregation possible when three IV chromosomes are present in *D. melanogaster* (after Sturtevant 1936).

tested in various combinations (26 different ones were used), it was evident that a series could be arranged such that the duplication showed a higher preference for any IV chromosome higher in the series than it did for any below it. Expressed differently, any chromosome in the series sought the haplo-pole more frequently than did those lying above it in the series. Thus, if A was higher in the series than B, the duplication was more frequently segregated with A than with B, the latter, conversely, being found more frequently at the haplo-pole. When triplo-IV females were tested (the duplication being replaced by an intact IV), the same seriation held. Again, if the three chromosomes are represented as A, B, and C, with A higher in the series than B, and B higher than C, then the segregation AB/C was more frequent than AC/B, and this more frequent than BC/A. A significant deviation from 33.3 percent for any segregation would, of course, indicate that preferential behavior was operative.

A satisfactory explanation for this phenomenon is difficult to formulate. If one assumes that two of the chromosomes pair, and the third segregates at random, then the maximum frequency to be expected is 50 percent, i.e., if A and B always paired and C passed at random to one or the other pole, AC and BC should be equal in frequency. However, most of the frequencies obtained by Sturtevant were considerably higher or lower than 50 percent, the frequency depending upon the particular combination of IV chromosomes used. Sturtevant therefore suggested that a more likely explanation would be trivalent formation, with two of the chromosomes segregating from the third. If so, preferential segregation must have been preceded by preferential pairing or preferential orientation on the metaphase plate. The fact that the duplication behaved similarly to the IV chromosomes high in the series suggests that the basis of preferential behavior must lie in the centromere of the particular IV chromosome (or its adjacent chromatin). The known loci in these chromosomes were shown to be without influence on segregation. Roman's (1947a, b) studies on the preferential behavior of the B-chromosomes in maize, and similar studies by Crouse in Sciara (both discussed later), also indicate the importance of the centromeric region on segregation, without providing a clue as to the essential property of the region involved. The results of Novitski (1954) and Sandler and Braver (1954), however, suggest that centric heterochromatin rather than the centromere *per se* may play a decisive role in segregation.

Non-random disjunction due to chromosomal aberrations. The effect of inversions on disjunction has already been discussed, and it need only be pointed out that single crossing over within an inversion leads to the elimination of the crossover chromatids in the eggs of Drosophila. The bridge resulting from such crossovers becomes suspended between the two newly-formed nuclei, and only those chromatids that do not cross over within the inversion (except for two- and three-strand doubles) have an opportunity of being included in the functional egg nucleus. The directed segregation occurs at the second meiotic division, as Sturtevant and Beadle (1936) demonstrated genetically, and as Carson (1946) confirmed cytologically in Sciara.

The loss of all chromatids to give nullo-X eggs results when four-strand double crossovers occur within X-chromosome inversions. However, Novitski (1952) has shown that this holds true only when the X-chromosome is telocentric. If one of the X-chromosomes has an additional arm in the form of the short or long arm of the Y, the frequency of nullo-X eggs is greatly reduced even though broken chromatids are lethal; when both X's have additional arms, nullo-X eggs are practically eliminated. These observations are supported by a study of maize inversions in which it was shown that broken chromatids from inversion bridges are delivered to the basal megaspore (Rhoades and Dempsey 1953).

A further point of interest in the work of Sturtevant and Beadle is the fact that when an inversion is present in one of the arms of an attached-X stock, ring chromosomes should result 50 percent of the time when a crossover occurs within the inversion, assuming of course that the rings are viable. However, the frequency of ring to attached-X chromosomes recovered was higher than 50 percent, a finding also confirmed by a similar study by the Russian workers, Sidorov, Sokolov, and Trofimov (1935, 1936). This suggests that preferential recovery of rings as opposed to non-rings was involved.

Recently Novitski (1951) has gone into the problem of such non-random disjunction, making use of attached-X chromosomes heterozygous for an inversion that would yield, on crossing over, ring chromosomes deficient for no region, thus eliminating the possibility of zygotic inviability entering in to complicate the picture. The data obtained were similar to those found by the previous workers, and indicate a very large excess of ring chromosomes and a deficiency of attached-X chromosomes. Novitski has also shown that the differential recovery of these two chromosome types cannot be accounted for by sister-strand crossing over, chromatid interference, or differential frequencies of two-, three-, or four-strand double crossovers. Rather it would appear that at first anaphase, as the two X-chromatids are progressing toward the region of the functional egg nucleus, the ring chromosome, being smaller, lies furthest away from the metaphase plate. In this position it has a greater chance of being segregated in the second division to the nucleus that will become the egg nucleus.

To test whether a smaller chromosome has a better chance of entering the functional egg nucleus, Novitski employed several scute inversions which differ slightly in their rearrangement of chromatin. When inversions sc^4 and sc^8 are combined in the same female the crossover product sc^4sc^8 (Fig. 9–11) is deficient for the *bobbed* region plus a section of hetero-

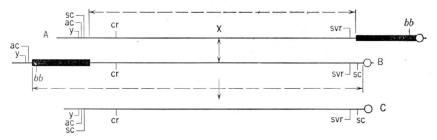

Fig. 9–11. Diagrammatic representation of the inversions sc⁴ (A) and sc⁸ (B) together with the crossover product sc⁴ — sc⁸ (C), which lacks the *bb* locus and a large portion of the centric heterochromatin (black). The centromere is represented by a circle and the crossover region at X. The extent of the inverted portion in each chromosome is indicated by the dashed line (after Sturtevant and Beadle 1936, and Novitski 1951).

chromatin (Muller's block A), thus giving a chromosome only about two-thirds as long physically as a normal X, although of nearly similar genetic length to a normal chromosome. Since this chromosome can be readily identified by the use of properly marked sections, the frequencies of the various types recovered could be determined. When this was done, and due correction made for lethal combinations of chromosomes, it was again found that the smaller chromosome was recovered in a pronounced excess. When a similar cross was made, using scute inversions that gave crossover products of equal length, a 1:1 ratio of the expected types was obtained, indicating that the excess of the crossover product sc^4sc^8 must be either a function of the left end of this chromosome from which the block of heterochromatin is missing, or simply its physical dimensions which in some unknown manner determine which chromosome shall enter the functional egg nucleus.

It cannot yet be said that the preferential recovery of certain chromosomes discussed above is thoroughly understood. Even less can be said about the factors governing chromosomal segregation in translocation heterozygotes, although such preferential segregations have long been recognized. In translocation heterozygotes, a ring of four chromosomes can, on the basis of a random distribution of two chromosomes to each pole, give two heteroploid unbalanced types to every orthoploid (balanced) type. Yet in such genera as Oenothera or Datura, the pollen fertility is quite high even though the translocation complexes may contain as many as 14 chromosomes (Cleland and Oehlkers 1930; Cleland 1936). Alternate chromosomes go to the poles in a very large majority of cases, and Marquardt (1948) feels that the survival of these types is due to the fact that the chromosomes are either physically short or that crossing over is cut down in the interstitial regions by the disturbance caused by the translocation or by heterochromatin. The chiasmata in these species are therefore strongly terminalized by metaphase, with few interstitial chiasmata being present, and the ring or chain is quite maneuverable on the metaphase plate. Emerson (1936) has shown that there are interstitial segments in Oenothera in which crossing over can take place, but that in genetic terms these are very short, and pairing is infrequent. *Rhoeo discolor,* a monotypic genus having a chromosomal situation similar to the Oenotheras in that a ring of 12 chromosomes can be formed, has a higher degree of pollen sterility, but it is quite likely that those forms having a high degree of fertility, despite their complicated chromosomal heterozygosity, have the type of orientation under fairly rigid genic control.

This is strongly suggested by studies of Rhoades (personal communication). He has produced a translocation between Chromosomes 3 and 5 in maize, with Chromosome 3 being broken through the centromere in such a manner as to give each arm a functional centromere. One arm of 3 has a fragment of Chromosome 5 attached to it (designated 3^5); the other arm has another fragment of unknown origin attached to it (designated 3^x). Consequently in a plant possessing a normal 3, together with both parts of the fragmented 3, a three-chromosome configuration will result if pairing is complete. In one strain of maize the translocation complex gives rise to a high degree of pollen sterility since the 3^5 and the 3^x chromosomes go to opposite poles with high frequency, and the normal 3 behaving more or less at random. In another strain, however, disjunction in the trivalent is such that in 95 percent of the pollen mother cells the normal

3 goes to one pole, and the two other fragment 3's go to the opposite pole. Pollen fertility consequently is high. In this instance it is known that the segregation is under genetic control.

In both Drosophila and maize attempts have been made to determine the causes of non-random segregation in translocation heterozygotes. In Drosophila, Dobzhansky (1933) and Glass (1935) early recognized that a differential segregation of chromosomes from a ring of four tended to favor the recovery of orthoploid types through alternate segregation, and that this was a problem of segregation rather than one of the differential viability of orthoploid versus heteroploid zygotes. Dobzhansky was led to believe that the conditions determining segregation at metaphase related to the synaptic process, while Glass postulated that the axis of separation, determined to a certain extent by the equality or inequality of arm lengths, was the influential factor. Later studies by Brown (1940) and Pipkin (1940) strongly suggest that disjunction in the female at least is determined by the presence of chiasmata. Both $3 - 4$ and $2 - 3$ translocations were studied, and although structurally these are very different types, orthoploid disjunction was aided by the presence of chiasmata.

Burnham's (1949) study of crossing over in interstitial regions of maize translocations involving Chromosome 6 with its nucleolar organizer, permits the identification of all types of segregation, whether alternate, adjacent-1, or adjacent-2, because of the nucleolar situation in the spore quartets. Like Brown and Pipkin, he concludes that the equality or inequality of the axes of the translocation complex has no effect of segregation, but that in rings of four, low crossing over permits alternate segregation 50 percent of the time. High crossing over practically eliminates adjacent-2 segregation from rings of four, and there is little or no adjacent-2 segregation from chains of four regardless of the degree of crossing over. In none of the many translocations studied, however, did the pollen fertility drop much below 50 percent, and it would appear that whatever directed segregation exists in maize favors alternate segregation of chromosomes.

The studies of Hughes-Schrader (1943a, b) and of Östergren (1951) throw some light on how a chain or a ring of more than two chromosomes can maneuver on the spindle to establish a configuration that allows for alternate segregation to give orthoploid gametes. In the male phasmid, the X_1-X_2-Y trivalent forms a chain of three, and during prometaphase orientation (which includes the premetaphase stretch) the arrangement of the three centromeres as regards the poles can be various. If the two X's orient to one pole and the Y to the other pole, this arrangement persists until anaphase movement brings about the proper segregation. However, an X and the Y may initially orient to one pole and the other X to the other pole, or the X's may go one to each pole with the Y hung between them. In any event, a reorientation takes place on the spindle with one or more of the centromeres shifting their position until both X's are now directed to the same pole and the Y to the other. Half-spindle fibers are present prior to the reorientation, but it would appear that these must dissolve and reform if the centromeres shift their position.

Clearly, then, the chromosomes are not fixed immediately in position once they are within the sphere of influence of the spindle, but they can adjust to predetermined conditions which one must presume are genetically controlled. Economy of space on the spindle must also come into play, and with a cumbersome structure such as a ring of four or more chromosomes, the zig-zag arrangement providing for alternate segregation is probably the most efficient. Östergren believes that this comes about by a co-orientation of multivalents on the metaphase plate which involves first an orientation of the active side of the centromeres to the poles, a mutual interaction between adjacent centromeres such that they are directed toward opposite poles, and an active pulling of the centromeres by the poles. Orientation of a ring of chromosomes would begin by one chromosome's responding to the pulling action, with this movement setting into action a chain of events that would lead to the progressive orientation of the remaining members of the ring. Flexibility of the ring would improve the chances of proper orientation, and one consequently finds that those forms having a high degree of alternate segregation possess few or no interstitial chiasmata. Östergren (1949a) has considered the forces necessary to bring about these movements, but as yet these can not be considered more than speculations.

Preferential segregation in maize and rye. Mention has already been made of the fact that preferential segregation of the B-chromosome occurs in maize. As Roman (1947a) has demonstrated, non-disjunction of the two chromatids of a B-chromosome occurs in the second division of the microspore with the result that of the two sperm cells produced, one generally has no B-chromosomes while the other has two. This was suspected when it was shown that plants having only a single B-chromosome could give rise to offspring having none or two; plants having two B-chromosomes frequently gave offspring having more than two such chromosomes.

Roman traced the cause of preferential segregation to the centromere (or its adjacent heterochromatin) of the B-chromosome. A translocation was obtained between the B-chromosome and Chromosome 4 of the A set, with the piece from Chromosome 4 translocated to the B-chromosome portion carrying the dominant gene *Su* (starchy). The translocation homozygote, TB-4a, therefore has the composition shown in Figure 9–12. Crosses are made to the homozygous recessive stock *su su,* (sugary). If TB-4a is used as the female stock, all of the kernels are *Su su,* or heterozygous starchy. Non-disjunction does not occur in the embryo sac. If used as a male, however, one-half or more of the kernels were sugary. This would indicate a deficiency of the B⁴-chromosome carrying starchy. On

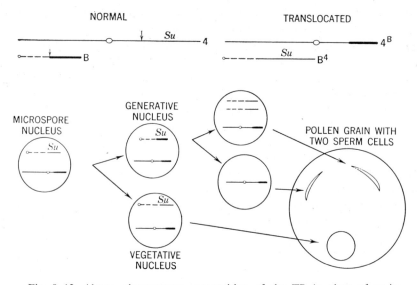

Fig. 9–12. Above, chromosome composition of the TB-4a plant of maize with the normal 4 and B chromosomes as well as the translocated 4^B and B^4 types indicated. Below, non-disjunction of the B^4 chromatids at the second microspore division to give sperm of different chromosomal compositions. The B^4 chromosome is marked with the *Su* (starchy) gene so that its presence or absence can be detected from the phenotype of the endosperm (after Roman 1947a).

the basis that the two sperm cells have an equal chance of fertilizing either the egg or the fusion nucleus of the endosperm, this would then mean that every sugary kernel carried an embryo whose chromosome composition should include a normal Chromosome 4, a translocated Chromosome 4^B, and two B^4 chromosomes. Twenty-four plants grown from sugary seeds showed this composition, and cytological examination of the microsporo-cytes of the sugary plants left no doubt that the extra chromosomes were of the B^4 type. Twenty-seven plants grown from non-sugary seed showed 24 lacking the B^4-chromosome, but otherwise carrying the normal 4 and the translocated 4^B. The other three plants were translocation heterozygotes which resulted from normal disjunction. The fact that more than one-half of the kernels were sugary indicates further that the sperm carrying the two B-chromosomes is more likely to unite with the egg nucleus than it is with the endosperm fusion nucleus (Roman 1947b). The reason for this preferential fertilization is unknown.

The cause of non-disjunction of the B-chromosome in maize in the second microspore division seems to reside in the centromere or its adjacent regions. This is suggested by Roman's data as well as by earlier data from a study of fragment chromosomes derived from the B-types (Randolph 1941a). The "F" fragment, which consists of a B-type centromere and a very minute amount of attached chromatin, undergoes a similar behavior, suggesting that the B-type centromere is responsible for the aberrant process. Roman proposes that the position of the centromere may have something to do with the inability of the B-chromosome to disjoin properly. The B-centromere is terminal or nearly so, whereas those of the A set are interstitial. When, however, a telocentric chromosome is formed from a member of the A set, as Rhoades (1940) has done with Chromosome 5, this chromosome consisting of the short arm can form isochromosomes. The frequency is higher on the male side than on the female, and genetic tests show that the formation of the isochromosome from a single telocentric type is a post-meiotic process, with non-disjunction carrying both arms into the same nucleus. To be sure, this is somewhat different in end result from the non-disjunction of the B-chromosomes, but it suggests that the aberrant behavior of the terminal, or nearly terminal, centromere is responsible for both. Whether this is an intrinsic property of the centromere, or of the adjacent heterochromatin (see below), remains to be determined.

The situation in rye, as described by Muntzing (1946b), differs as to mechanism. This plant has been found with three types of fragments: (1) a standard fragment with a long and a short arm, (2) an isochromosome derived from the long arm, and (3) an isochromosome derived from the short arm. At early anaphase of the first post-meiotic division, the standard fragment lags between the two anaphase groups of chromosomes, and has the appearance of a bivalent with two chiasmata localized near the centromere. The centromeres pull apart from each other, but the chromatids are prevented from disjoining by a heterochromatic block in the long arm, although the short arms also remain attached to each other. As the spindle stretches, the non-separating chromatids pass to the generative cell in a large majority of the cells. The large isochromosome behaves similarly, with the exception that there are now two heterochromatic blocks, one on each side of the centromere, which obviously hinder separation. Like the standard fragment, it passes to the generative cell. The small isochromosome, however, disjoins regularly suggesting that it has no segment of chromatin to hinder anaphase movement.

At present one can only speculate as to the mechanism. Assuming that the obstructing piece of the chromosome is heterochromatic, its failure to divide could result either from a localized stickiness of the chromatin which resists the anaphase pull of the centromeres, or from an improper longitudinal cleavage of the chromosome into chromatids at this point. In any event, in rye as in maize, we have examples of chromosomes that behave normally in all divisions, both meiotic and mitotic, except one. Being in the germ line, the detection of the aberrancy is possible, and one must assume that some environmental or physiological circumstance in the cell at the particular microspore division conditions the fragment chromosomes to behave in a manner different from those of the normal set. In maize, the aberrant process is restricted to the male side; in rye, there also appears to be some non-disjunction of fragments in the ovules, but the phenomenon has not been as clearly localized as to the particular division involved.

A by-product of this research was the realization that the preferential segregation of the B-chromosomes provided, through translocation with members of the A set, an excellent means of determining linkage groups. Twenty different translocation complexes are needed for this type of linkage determination (each arm of the ten A-chromosomes would need be translocated to a B-chromosome) and several of these have been obtained for genetic study (Rhoades 1955). A plant containing the recessive gene to be located serves as the seed parent, and pollen is used from a plant carrying the A-B interchange with the dominant alleles present in the A-B chromosome possessing the B centromere. The deficient progeny, i.e., those lacking the B-chromosome with its portion of an A-chromosome, will show the recessive trait if the locus of the gene is distal to the break in the A-chromosome. The use of *su* in the TB-4a cross just described provides an illustration of the method for locating recessive genes.

Chromosome 10 in maize has also been of considerable interest because of its influence on preferential segregation (Rhoades 1942, 1952). Two forms of Chromosome 10 are known: the type most commonly found and whose behavior is normal in all respects, and an abnormal type morphologically distinguishable from the normal 10 by a large heterochromatic knob at the end of the long arm plus a characteristic chromomeric pattern adjacent to the knob. When either of these chromosomes is studied in a homozygous state, segregation is perfectly normal, and good Mendelian ratios are obtained for any genes on this chromosome. In plants heterozygous for the abnormal Chromosome 10, i.e., having one normal 10 and one abnormal 10, distorted ratios are obtained, and it is found that 70 percent of the megaspores contain the abnormal Chromosome 10. This departure from randomness is not a function of any particular gene found on the chromosome, but is related strictly to the knobbed portion. Preferential segregation also occurs for any genes linked with the knob, and since the two types of chromosomes cross over with each other, genes on the normal 10 would be affected in distribution in proportion to the amount of crossing over between the specific gene and the knob.

In maize the basal megaspore in the linear tetrad becomes the functional embryo sac. The abnormal 10 must therefore be distributed to the basal megaspore with a relatively high frequency. Since the genetic length of the long arm of Chromosome 10 is such that at least one exchange is regularly formed in the arm, this means that at anaphase I the segregating Chromosome 10's would each contain a chromatid with a knob and one without. Preferential segregation presumably occurs then in anaphase II, and the abnormal 10 chromatid passes to the lower pole to be included in the nucleus of the basal megaspore.

A clue to the reason for this departure from random Mendelian segregation is obtained from a further peculiarity induced by the abnormal Chromosome 10. As indicated in Chapter 5, this chromosome also causes the appearance of neo-centromeres, i.e., regions of the chromosomes that take over, at least partially, the functioning of the normal localized centromere. Rhoades (1952) has shown that anaphase movement of the neo-centromeres is precocious to that of the normal centromere, and that in anaphase II as well as in anaphase I the abnormal 10 chromatid with its neo-centromere passes quickly to the pole nearest to it. This movement may occur before the other chromosomes normally separate in anaphase, and if so, the normal chromatid passes to the opposite pole when its centromere begins to function. If such a precocious movement of the neo-centromere of abnormal 10 occurred in anaphase I, and the orientation of chromatids was maintained until the next division, then the neo-centromere of the abnormal 10 would be nearest to the lower (the upper also) pole, and would consequently be in a position to begin its anaphase II movement precociously to the lower pole. When no crossovers or a two-strand double crossover form in the long arms of the heterozygous bivalent, segregation of the knobbed chromosome from its knobless partner would take place in the first division, and the opportunity for preferential segregation in the second division would be lacking.

In addition to being segregated preferentially itself, abnormal 10 also induces a non-random segregation of other chromosomes possessing knobs (Longley 1945). In plants homozygous for normal Chromosome 10, knobbed chromosomes are unaffected in their distribution, but if abnormal 10 is present in the heterozygous state, all knobbed chromosome are affected, presumably by the same mechanism by which abnormal 10 itself is preferentially segregated. That is, the knobs of other chromosomes are set into action by abnormal 10 and become neo-centromeres, precocious in their anaphase movements in meiosis. When genetic tests are set up to follow the distribution of the knobbed chromosomes, genes closest to the knobs show the greatest distortion in Mendelian ratios. Thus, in Chromosome 9, which possesses a knob in the short arm, and also the genes *C*, *Sh* and *Wx,* with *Wx* being nearest the centromere and *C* nearest the distal knob, the *C* locus showed the greatest degree of preferential segregation, *Sh* was somewhat comparable, while *Wx* was little disturbed.

It would appear from Rhoades' study that the determining influence in the preferential segregation of abnormal 10 emanates initially from the localized centromere of this chromosome rather than from some intrinsic property peculiar to the knob itself. This is suggested by the observation that a fragment chromosome, possessing a knob but not a centromere, does not produce a neo-centromere in the presence of abnormal 10. It is as if some substance capable of transmitting centromeric properties flows from the centromere along the arm to the knob where it localizes itself in sufficient amounts to impart a neo-centromeric function to the knob.

CHROMOSOME DIMINUTION AND ELIMINATION

In the presentation of the elementary facts of cytology and genetics it is usually stated that the chromosomal compositions of the germinal cells and of the cells of the soma are equivalent. In plants this is particularly true since the same meristematic cells that give rise to the vegetative organs at one stage of the life cycle can give rise, at a later stage, to the sporogenous tissues in which meiosis occurs. The fact that vegetative propagation is used to establish a clonal line of plants is practical proof of this underlying assumption. In many animals, however, the germ line is established very early in the embryonic development of the individual, and although these cells need not be isolated from the soma in a physiological sense, they can be considered to be so genetically. It has now become quite clear that the somatic cells of many species may undergo cytological changes of various sorts—some random, some peculiar to various organs—even while the germ cells or their progenitors may preserve the original chromosomal constitution. From an evolutionary point of view, this is a necessary condition since the constancy of the species is dependent upon the constancy of behavior of the cells of the germ line.

The soma of an animal, on the other hand, represents an evolutionary dead end, lost from a population with the death of the individual, and any changes occurring in it affect only that individual. Even so, the somatic changes in chromosomal composition, unless they are accidental in nature, must be reasonably regular and not so drastic as to cause genetic unbalance in the cells in which these changes occur. It is not surprising, therefore, that the somatic variations in chromosome number and form are characteristic of the various tissues involved, and exhibit a species specificity. It was Boveri who first pointed out that in *Ascaris megalocephala* the chromosomal composition of the soma and the germ line was not identical, and it has since been found to be a regular occurrence in a number of species, particularly in certain groups of insects. The variations are, however, not confined to the soma; equally dramatic changes are known to occur in the cells of the germ line. Some are sufficiently dramatic as to approach the bizarre.

In Ascaris it is possible to trace with accuracy the separate formation of the germ line. At the two-cell stage of the embryo, the stem-cell which is to give rise to the germ line can be distinguished from its companion blastomere which will divide to produce only somatic cells. The first division of the zygote is a normal one (Fig. 9–13), and the two long chromosomes with their club-shaped ends are clearly visible. At metaphase, the middle section of each chromosome is attached to the spindle, while the

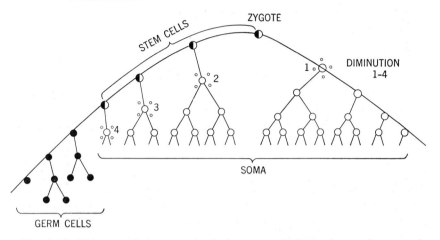

Fig. 9–13. Diagram of the process of chromosomal diminution as it occurs in the early cleavage divisions of Ascaris (after Wilson 1925).

ends dangle free in the cytoplasm. At the second division, the two cells will behave differently. The progenitor of the somatic cells reaches metaphase in a normal manner, but at anaphase the two chromosomes lose their heavy ends while the central portions fragment into a number of smaller chromosomes. The resultant cells are smaller than the stem-cell, and their nuclei are both smaller and stain less deeply as a consequence of the chromatin diminution that has taken place. All subsequent divisions of these cells will show the numerous smaller chromosomes on the metaphase plate, and these will behave henceforth as entirely individual chromosomes each possessing its own centromere.

The stem-cell, at the second division, divides normally, but the two daughter cells have different potentialities. One remains as the stem-cell; the other behaves as did the other somatic cell in that it undergoes chromatin diminution and chromosome fragmentation. This process goes on through the fifth cleavage and until the 16-cell stage of the embryo is reached. At this stage, the remaining stem-cell sinks into the interior of the mass of cells where it becomes the primordial germ cell. Here it multiplies by normal somatic division to give rise to the cells of the gonad. This process insures that only the germ cells receive the total mass of chromatin present in the fertilized zygote.

The significance of the diminution process remains obscure, but it seems quite clear that the discarded ends of the chromosomes are of heterochromatin. The presence of this heterochromatin is not necessary for the development of the soma; it seems reasonable to assume that it is necessary for the formation of germ cells even though it is not possible to ascribe any positive function to it. The chromosome number of the germ cells remains two (in var. *univalens;* four in var. *bivalens*); there is some uncertainty as to the exact number of the small chromosomes. From 52 to 72 have been reported for var. *univalens,* and from 62 to 144 for var. *bivalens,* and there is no certainty that the number is the same for the two sexes. Since it is quite certain that each possesses its own centromere, the larger chromosomes of the germ line are most certainly polycentric. The same type of chromatin diminution takes place in other species of the Ascaridae, but appears to be absent in other families of nematodes.

Diminution is also believed to occur in the beetle Distycus and in certain of the Lepidoptera, although in these organisms, elimination of the chromatin comes at later stages in development (Wilson 1925). In Distycus, it apparently occurs in the gonad, with the last four divisions in the germ line producing but one primary oöcyte for each 15 nurse cells. Only the oöcyte retains all of the chromatin. In the Lepidoptera, the diminution does not take place until the maturation divisions of the egg. Whether these eliminations are similar to the loss of heterochromatin in Ascaris remains to be shown. There is the possibility that they may involve the loss of particular chromosomes, as is the case in the dog roses, Sciara, and the gall midges, rather than the ends of chromosomes.

The dog roses, *Rosa canina,* and their relatives, are pentaploid species of hybrid origin. Their somatic number of chromosomes is 35 (the basic number for the genus *Rosa* is 7), and in both micro- and macro-sporogenesis seven pairs of homologous chromosomes in the form of bivalents and 21 univalents arrange themselves on the metaphase plate in meiosis (Täckholm 1922; Gustafson 1944). The seven bivalents, which form chiasmata and presumably undergo crossing over, segregate regularly to give each pollen grain and embryo sac a complete set of chromosomes. The 21 univalents, however, behave quite differently depending upon the type of cell. In the microsporocytes the bivalents divide first, and pass to the poles, to be followed later by the univalents which have divided equationally. Passage of the univalents to the poles is accompanied by some irregularity, and occasional chromosomes fail to be included in the telophase nucleus. The process is similar in the second meiotic division: the daughter bivalents separate regularly while the univalents attempt to divide again. A greater degree of irregularity ensues, and the majority of them fail to reach the poles. These are lost in the cytoplasm. Most of the microspores that can undergo the division to form the tube and generative nuclei contain seven, eight, or nine chromosomes, and of these the ones possessing the seven chromosomes derived from the seven original bivalents have a better chance of surviving and functioning because of their balanced complement. Occasional aneuploid plants have been found, indicating that some unbalanced pollen grains take part in fertilization, but these plants are exceptions rather than the rule.

In megasporogenesis, the seven bivalents are likewise formed, but the univalents, instead of segregating irregularly as in the microsporocytes, are precociously grouped at the micropylar end of the spindle. Here they are joined by the seven segregating chromosomes, and together they are included in the telophase nucleus. The second division proceeds regularly to give a linear tetrad of two large megaspores in the micropylar position with 28 chromosomes, and two small megaspores, each containing but seven chromosomes. One of the two large megaspores forms the functional embryo sac. On fertilization by a seven-chromosome sperm, the somatic number of 35 is restored.

Obviously genetic segregation in the dog roses can occur only for those genes located in one of the seven pairs of homologues. So far as the univalents are concerned, inheritance is strictly maternal, since these are transmitted as a block through the embryo sac. Their apparent lack of homology with the seven basic chromosomes and with themselves precludes any crossing over. With the exception of a few 14- and 28-chromosomes species, the *canina* group of roses are generally characterized by the system just described. Darlington (1937a) has called this a semi-clonal type of inheritance, analogous to the Oenothera translocation complexes in that it permits a hybrid to breed true. The dog roses can freely hybridize, and it appears that the seven pairs are rather constant throughout the group. If so, it is probable that these maintain fertility and constancy of type while the univalents provide a source of variation. However, it can also be argued conversely that the univalents provide what amounts to an asexual method of inheritance while the bivalents permit recombination to occur.

Cytogenetics of Sciara. The lower Diptera, of the suborder Nematocera, show a wide variety of meiotic abnormalities which have been established as family characteristics (White 1946b, c). In the families Tipulidae (crane flies), Limoniidae, Cylindrotomidae, Culicidae (mosquitoes), and Chironomidae (midges), spermatogenesis is normal in that chiasmata are regularly formed between bivalents. In the Bibionidae (March flies) and Scatopsidae (Scatopsids) bivalents are formed, but there are no chiasmata, and presumably there is no crossing over. In the Sciaridae (fungus gnats) and the Cecidomyidae (gall midges), spermatogenesis has become highly involved, and a bizarre behavior characterizes both groups. There is as yet no certain knowledge of the evolutionary significance of these peculiarities of chromosome behavior, nor of their method of origin, but they are of sufficient interest to be worthy of some attention.

The genus Sciara possesses a chromosomal mechanism so unique as to place it apart from other sexually functioning organisms. Its peculiarities have stimulated much investigation, with the result that despite its devious methods of cell division, the chromosome cycle and the type of inheritance is reasonably well known. All species of the genus behave in much the same manner, and the description to be given of *S. coprophila* is fairly representative.

In most organisms there is present in every cell of the body at least one member of each pair of chromosomes. This of course results from the contribution by the egg and sperm of equivalent sets of chromosomes to the zygote. In the germ line of Sciara, however, there is present, in addition to the basic set of four pairs of chromosomes, an anomalous chromosome or chromosomes distinctive in appearance and behavior. These are the *limited chromosomes,* so called because of their restriction to the germ line. They are apparently devoid of genes in the usual sense of the word, and they can be recognized during the growth of the nurse cells and of the primary spermatocyte by their heteropycnotic appearance. During the early cleavage stages of the embryo, they are eliminated from the somatic nuclei and extruded into the cytoplasm where they disintegrate.

Oögenesis in Sciara is normal in all respects, the chromosomes undergoing synapsis, crossing over, and segregation in regular fashion. It is only in the male that the peculiarities of segregation and behavior are found. This initially becomes apparent with the unequal contributions to the zygote by the egg and the sperm. The egg pronucleus contains a haploid set of chromosomes consisting of an X, three autosomes, and one or more limited chromosomes. Genetic evidence indicates that these may be of paternal or maternal derivation, segregation in oögenesis apparently being at random. The sperm, however, contributes, in addition to one or more limited chromosomes, two sister X-chromosomes and three autosomes, all of maternal origin.

Figure 9–14 indicates the manner by which these aberrancies arise in Sciara. The first spermatocyte division is essentially a monocentric mitosis, which separates the maternal homologues from those of paternal origin. The chromosomes seem not to congress and orient onto a metaphase plate

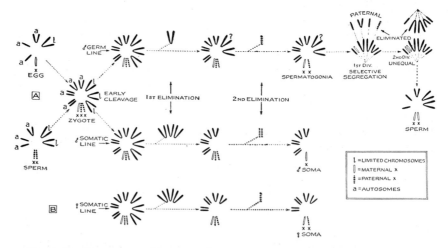

Fig. 9–14. Chromosome history during somatic development and gametogenesis in the male *Sciara coprophila,* and during somatic development in the female. Oogenesis follows a regular course (Crouse 1943 after Metz).

as is customary, but begin anaphase movement from what appears to be a prophase condition and position. The maternal chromosomes move to the single pole while the paternal ones back away from the pole, although their centromeres are directed poleward. This is true for the X-chromosome and the autosomes only; the limited chromosomes, whatever their origin, pass with the maternal X and autosomes in the secondary spermatocyte. The paternal chromosomes which have moved away from the pole are collected into a tiny bud that later pinches off and disintegrates. Males of Sciara therefore never transmit traits of a paternal origin.

The division in the single remaining secondary spermatocyte is also anomalous and unequal. It is essentially an equational division except for one chromosome which is precocious in its appearance and behavior. The spindle, unlike that of the first division, is bipolar, and the chromosomes reach the metaphase plate in normal fashion. The precocious chromosome, however, passes to one pole before anaphase movement has commenced for the remaining chromosomes, and since it is longitudinally divided both halves pass to the same nucleus. Anaphase movement of the remaining chromosomes then takes place, giving two nuclei of unequal constitution. The cell bearing the two halves of the precocious chromosome becomes a functional sperm; the other degenerates. Through means of translocations between the X-chromosome and the autosomes, Crouse (1943) has demonstrated that the precocious chromosome is the X-chromosome, and that it is the centromere (or its adjacent chromatin) that is responsible for its early passage into the functional sperm nucleus.

Elimination of the limited chromosomes from the soma follows a constant and unique pattern. As stated earlier, the zygote contains three X-chromosomes (two of paternal origin), three pairs of autosomes, and one or more limited chromosomes (three are indicated in Figure 9–14). This complement is maintained through only the first few cleavage divisions. At the fifth or sixth division, the limited chromosomes are eliminated. They go through what is an apparently normal prophase contraction, and reach the metaphase plate along with the other chromosomes. Their centromeres divide, and begin anaphase movement, but the distal ends appear unable to separate cleanly into two chromatids. As a consequence, the limited chromosomes are left in the middle of the spindle, and are not included in the daughter nuclei. Presumably some precisely determined upset in the chemistry of these heterochromatic bodies is responsible for their inability to divide, but there is no indication of this until anaphase movement sets in. White (1954) suggests that the situation may be similar, or is at least analogous, to the behavior of the Y-chromosome in the sex-ratio males of Drosophila.

At the seventh or eighth cleavage division there is a further elimination of chromosomes from the soma. In this instance it is the paternal X-chromosome that is involved, and the method of elimination is very similar to that which removes the limited chromosomes. The circumstances differ, however, depending upon whether the soma is to become male or female, a circumstance which is dependent upon the female that produced the eggs (see below). If destined to be male, elimination of two X-chromosomes, both of paternal origin, takes place; if female, only one X-chromosome is deleted from the complement, and this again is of paternal origin. The male soma consequently is XO, the female XX.

After the germ cells have migrated to their future gonadal site, there is a third elimination, this time that of the extra paternal X-chromosome. The method of elimination in this case differs, however, from those previously described. According to Berry (1941), elimination takes place from resting nuclei, and the X-chromosome moves directly through the nuclear membrane into the cytoplasm where it disintegrates. There must be an elimination of one or more of the limited chromosomes in the germ line as well, although this has not been cytologically described. This assumption is necessary since the number of limited chromosomes remains fairly constant from one generation to another even though the sperm transmits a full complement of limited chromosomes in addition to those that come through the egg. The male and female germ cells consequently are identical in chromosomal constitution, and it must be assumed that the germinal tissue becomes ovary or testis according to the constitution of the soma.

It remains to account for the mechanism by which zygotes identical in chromosomal constitution develop into males or females. It appears from the genetic studies that have been done, that the male is of no importance in the determination of sex. *S. coprophila* generally produces unisexual broods, and it appears that the male producers differ from the female producers in the type of X-chromosomes in the mother. On the basis that the two types of females are present in populations in equal numbers, it has been assumed that the female-producing are heterozygous (XX′), the male-producing ones homozygous (XX). No difference has been detected cytologically between the two types of X-chromosomes, and it may be that the difference is merely a genetical one. In any event, it is the genetical composition of the mother that determines the type of somatic elimination that will accur, and that in turn will determine the sex. Bisexual strains of Sciara, however, are known, and even in the so-called unisexual strains, an occasional male is produced in an otherwise female brood, and vice versa. In *S. ocellaris* there is a cytological difference between the unisexual and bisexual strains, one of the autosomes possessing a terminal centromere in the former, while in the latter it is interstitially located. Whether this can account for the difference in the sexuality of the broods must remain a moot question, particularly since it is an autosome that is the basis of karyotype difference.

Cytology of the gall midges. The Cecidomyidae are taxonomically close to the Sciaridae, and there is likewise a striking similarity in the very aberrant chromosome cycles of the two groups at the same time that there are equally striking divergencies in meiotic behavior (Reitberger 1940; White 1950). As in Sciara, there are two types of chromosomes in the Cecidomyids—the basic set of S-chromosomes which is found in both somatic cells and in those of the germ line, and the E-chromosomes which, like the limited chromosomes of Sciara, are confined to the germ line, and are eliminated from the soma in the early cleavage divisions. The number of E-chromosomes varies widely from species to species. Where in Sciara two or three limited chromosomes may be found (they are even absent in some species as *S. reynoldsi*), in the gall midges which have been studied by White the number ranges from 16 (in *Trishornomyia helianthi*) to as high as 56 (in *Oligarces paradoxus*).

The elimination of the E-chromosomes during the early somatic divisions is based on the position of embryonic nuclei. Those lying in the yolk cytoplasm eliminate all of their E-chromosomes while the polar nuclei, destined to become the germ line nuclei, retain the full zygotic complement of chromosomes (Fig. 9–15). The manner of elimination is much as it is in Sciara. The S- and E-chromosomes show no difference in form or behavior until anaphase. At this time, the S-chromosomes separate cleanly and pass to the poles. The E-chromosomes, however, initiate a poleward movement at their centromeres, as evidenced by the fact that these regions open out and show a tension, but the chromatids fail to separate along the arms. As a consequence, the E-chromosomes become suspended between the two poles, and are not included in the telophase nuclei. White suggests that interlocked coils, or some sticky matrical material, prevents their separation. The latter suggestion has much in its favor since heterochromatin, of which presumably the E-chromosomes are composed, has a tendency to become sticky under certain conditions.

The time of elimination of the E-chromosomes, although early in embryonic development, is variable from species to species. In Miastor, the genus in which this phenomenon of elimination was discovered many years ago, it takes place at the third or fourth cleavage division; in Monarthropalpus at the fifth cleavage. In Oligarces, two eliminations occur: at the third or fourth division, 55 of the 56 chromosomes pass into the cytoplasm, while a single one is lost at the sixth, seventh, or eighth division.

It is presumed by White that sex determination in the Cecidomyidae is similar to that obtaining in the Sciara group. If so, there must be an additional elimination of certain of the S-chromosomes in the male soma since this has a different chromosome number from that of the female. For example, Miastor has 48 chromosomes in the germ line, 12 in the cells of the female soma and six in the male soma. In *Taxomyia taxia,* there are 40, eight, and six respectively, with 32 being eliminated in the soma of the female and 34 in that of the male.

In order for the elimination process to be responsible for the determination of sex, there must be, in the soma of the male at least, an elimination

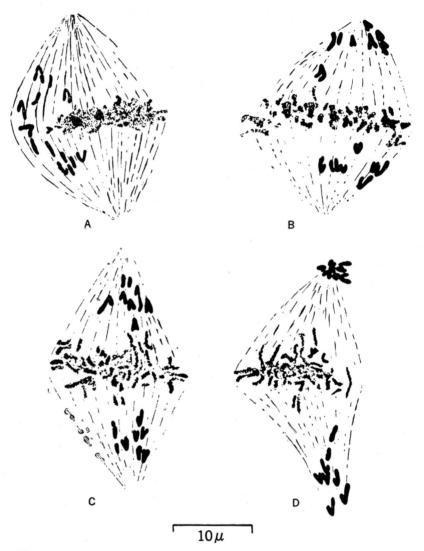

A   B

C   D

10μ

Fig. 9–15. Elimination-mitoses at the fifth cleavage division in the embryo of the cecidomyid, *Monarthropalpus buxi* (White 1950).

of specific X-chromosomes. The X-chromosome complement of Taxomyia can therefore be represented as AA BB X_1 X_2 for the male, and AA BB X_1X_1 X_2X_2 for the female, with AA and BB being pairs of autosomes and X_1 and X_2 being sex-determining chromosomes. The male soma is consequently of the XO type, with sex determination arising through the specific elimination of an X_1 and an X_2 chromosome. Their elimination has not been observed directly, however. The reported occurrence of unisexual as well as bisexual broods in some species suggests that the gall midges, as Sciara, may have different types of X-chromosomes which influence the nature of the broods.

The general features of spermatogenesis are similar throughout the group of gall midges studied by White. In the early prophase stages of meiosis, the S-chromosomes are generally heteropycnotic, the E-chromosomes diffuse (Fig. 9–16). This difference in stainability disappears by the time meta-

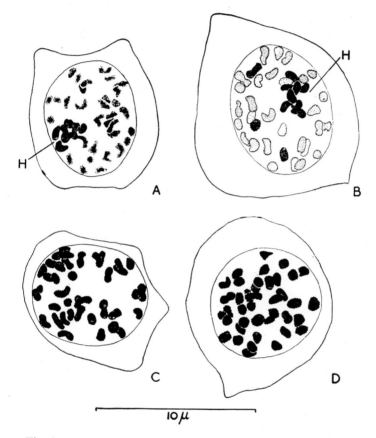

Fig. 9–16. A and B, early, and C and D, late meiotic prophases in a male cecidomyid, *Taxomyia taxi;* H, groups of 8 heteropycnotic chromosomes which are distinguishable in early stages but not in later ones (White 1947).

phase I has been reached. The usual meiotic prophase stages are lacking, however. No synapsis occurs, and consequently no chiasmata and no bivalents are formed. The meiotic spindle develops in prometaphase, and it is cone-shaped, having an acuminate tip and a broad base. Such a spindle has been described as unipolar in Sciara, but White suggests that it is possibly bipolar, with the tip of the cone being a normal active pole and the base a diffuse passive pole. This suggestion stems from the fact that two nuclei are regularly formed and the cell wall cuts through the spindle elements, but since the mass of chromosomes at metaphase aggregate at the broad base, one would have to assume that the metaphase plate and the diffuse pole are one and the same thing (or occupy the same position), or that the chromosomes are aggregated at the diffuse pole, that there is no metaphase plate, and that movement of the chromosomes which segregate is from one pole to the other. At the present time, the unipolar nature of the spindle seems a more likely and reasonable interpretation.

In any event, as the spindle elongates, a haploid set of S-chromosomes passes to the acuminate pole while the E-chromosomes and the other haploid set of S-chromosomes remain at the passive pole. Unequal cyto-kinesis gives two unequal daughter cells with nuclei of different sizes. The second meiotic division involves only the smaller of the two secondary spermatocytes. Its chromosomes divide equationally to give two haploid cells which are eventually transformed into sperm. The larger "residual" cell, containing the remainder of the chromosomes, does not divide again and does not form sperm. In Miastor, exactly 1024 sperm are formed by the male during its lifetime (White 1946c); these of course arise from 512 primary spermatocytes. Whether such precision exists in other species of the group is not known.

The general scheme outlined above holds for Miastor and Taxomyia, and the sperm for each species would contain, respectively, six and four chromosomes, while the residual cell would contain 42 and 36. In Mo-narthropalpus, however, about half of the chromosomes are distributed to the active pole in spermatogenesis, and it would appear therefore that in some species, the E- as well as the S-chromosomes can be transmitted by the sperm. Correlated with the inclusion of E-chromosomes into the func-tional sperm of Monarthropalpus (this also occurs in *Rhopalomyia sabinae* and *Oligotrophus pattersoni*) is the heteropycnotic nature of some of the E-chromosomes. It is these that pass with the S-chromosomes to the active pole while the more diffuse E-chromosomes remain at the base of the spindle to be included later into the residual cell. It would thus appear that prophasic heteropycnosis of the E-chromosomes in some manner deter-mines their anaphase behavior; the same cannot be said of the S-chromo-somes, however, since all are heteropycnotic although only a haploid set passes to the active pole.

It will be recalled that in Sciara genetic evidence revealed that the sperm transmits only chromosomes of a maternal origin, the paternal ones being pushed off into a bud cell during spermatogenesis and lost. The similarities of division, and the close taxonomic relationships of the gall midges to Sciara and its allies, would suggest that the type of segregation of maternal from paternal chromosomes holds for both groups, but in the absence of genetic data, and because of the inability to distinguish cytologically the maternal from the paternal chromosomes, the identity of the haploid set passing to the active pole remains unknown.

Oögenesis in the gall midges, like megasporogenesis in the dog roses, results in the retention of a haploid set of S-chromosomes plus all of the E-chromosomes in the functional egg nucleus. The X-chromosomes form bivalents, and presumably undergo crossing over and segregation. Together with the E-chromosomes, they line up on the metaphase plate, with only a haploid set of S-chromosomes passing into the polar body. Whether the E-chromosomes split equationally in the first, second, or in neither meiotic division is not known, although in meiotic prophase they are longitudinally divided into chromatids. Some regularity regarding their inclusion into the egg nucleus must be assumed to insure the constancy of chromosome number from individual to individual within a species, and it is most likely that the equational split of the E-chromosomes takes place in the second meiotic division.

On the other hand, some difficulty is encountered in accounting for the constancy of the chromosome number in Monarthropalpus. If, as the somatic nuclei would suggest, the haploid number of S-chromosomes is four, and the sperm transmits a number (24) of E-chromosomes as well as those of the S-type, then some compensatory mechanism must exist in oögenesis to keep the germ-line chromosome number from changing with each generation. Since this number is approximately 50, the egg nucleus must contain in the neighborhood of 22 chromosomes rather than 46. How this distribution is effected remains to be determined, but if one assumes that chromosome distribution in spermatogenesis and oögenesis is similar, it is only necessary to assume further that it is the "residual" nucleus in oögenesis that becomes the functional egg nucleus to give complementary types of gametes.

CYTOLOGY OF THE COCCIDS (COCCOIDEA-HOMOPTERA)

In an earlier chapter dealing with chromosomal behavior, frequent mention was made of the contributions to cytology emerging from studies of the coccid chromosomes. These chromosomes, at the same time, because of their unusual behavior and structure, have presented equally challenging problems. Their establishment as successfully functioning entities forces one to recognize that the division of chromosomes and cells is, despite its marvelous integration, a mechanism of extraordinary flexibility. As Hughes-Schrader (1948b) points out in a recent review, the unusual features of coccid cytology cannot be viewed as abnormalities, but rather as variations within cytological limits far wider than our knowledge of more common organisms would, earlier, have led us to consider possible. It seems desirable therefore to present a more unified picture of coccid cytology than was afforded by the scattered references made earlier.

Somatic mitosis. Basically, the departure from a normal course of cell division, as exemplified in the onion roottip cells or in those of the white-fish blastula, stems from the possession by the chromosomes of diffuse rather than localized centromeres. As a consequence, the chromatids separate from each other, and pass to poles in anaphase as parallel structures rather than as V's, J's, or rods. Similarly, as we shall see, the diffuse centromere also determines metaphase orientation and the formation of chromosomal fibers.

Somatic mitosis is similar through the coccid group, and the description given also holds for the single spermatocyte division in those species having haploid males (e.g., Steatococcus). Prophase begins in an essentially normal fashion, but the chromatids undergo a separation as soon as an evident coil is established in them. This is followed by a lateral separation of half-chromatids, and by metaphase each chromosome consists of four parallel strands (Fig. 9–17), each clearly separated from the others, and each

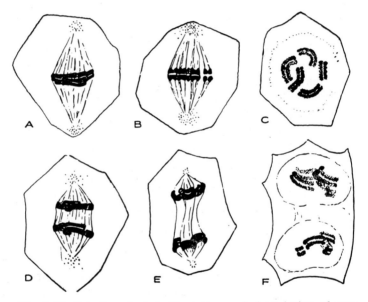

Fig. 9–17. Somatic mitosis in Nautococcus. A, lateral view of metaphase; B, same except for the chromosome to the right of the spindle which is seen in end view as consisting of four half-chromatids; C, polar view of metaphase with clearly separated chromatids; D and E, anaphase; F, telophase with the half-chromatids separated (Hughes-Schrader 1948b, and used with the permission of Academic Press, Inc.).

possessing a coiled structure. No relational coil is present, suggesting that a paranemic rather than a plectonemic arrangement of the strands was present earlier. [Manton (1945) believes this to be true also in certain plant materials although it appears to be in opposition to other observations.] In a chromosome with a localized centromere such a separation of chromatids and half-chromatids would not be possible since the centromere does not divide until early anaphase. The diffuse centromere, however, appears to offer no such obstacle to separation.

At metaphase the chromosomes lie parallel to the metaphase plate, with a sheet of chromosomal fibers extending from their poleward surfaces and converging at the pole. Whether any surface of the chromosome, presented to the poles, could form fibers cannot be answered; it can only be said that the chromosome has no series of differentiated loci corresponding to a linear grouping of many localized centromeres, and that its properties of movement appear to be diffused over its entire surface. Also, any fragment, induced or spontaneous, is capable of metaphase orientation and anaphase movement.

Anaphase disjunction is parallel, with a bending of the tips of the chromosomes toward the pole in late stages. Telophase reorganization is normal, and it must be assumed that the separated half-chromatids entering the telophase nucleus become once more closely associated with their sister strands before prophase comes on again.

Meiosis. Meiosis in females of the coccid group is basically similar to that of the more primitive male type except where parthenogenesis enters in to complicate the picture. These considerations will, however, be deferred to a later chapter dealing with these specific topics, and here only the male types will be discussed. The classification of male types set up by Hughes-Schrader (1948b) will largely be followed.

Puto, a genus in the family Ericoccidae, represents what is probably a primitive type of meiosis in males. Having an XX — XO type of sex mechanism, the chromosome number in females is $2n = 14$, in males $2n = 13$. Synapsis may be assumed to have taken place since diakinetic bivalents in the form of rods or crosses are found (Fig. 7–8). It is not known whether the chiasmata present represent previous chromatid exchanges; in any event, the chiasmata are completely terminalized by metaphase, at which time the chromatids and half-chromatids of each chromosome are discernible as separate entities. Each bivalent therefore is eight-stranded.

No repulsion exists between homologous chromosomes at metaphase such as appears in bivalents having localized centromeres in each homologue. In fact, as Figure 7–8 illustrates, each chromosome rather than the bivalent as a whole orients on the spindle, and the first division is equational, at least for such crossover regions as may be present. In interkinesis, the two chromatids of a dyad move apart from each other, uncoil slightly, and then approach each other to pair again. The second meiotic division is similar to that of the first except that for non-crossover regions, the division is reductional. The division, whether reductional or equational, is therefore the reverse of that found in the more commonly studied organisms. This system of division and segregation was first analyzed by Ris (1942) in the bearberry aphid, and it is thought by Oksala (1943) to hold for the Odonata, a quite unrelated group of insects in which the centromeres are of the conventional localized type.

The males of Puto, in common with the males of other coccid species, form multinucleate spermatids. This is brought about by the fusion of the cytoplasmic masses of the four products of meiosis.

Meiosis in Matsucoccus (family Margarodidae) resembles that in Puto except for the sex chromosomes. In the females $2n = 40$, in the males 34. There are consequently six X-chromosomes which in the male appear as univalents. These condense precociously to form a ring in the center of the metaphase plate, around which the more slowly condensing autosomes come to lie. The X-chromosomes move as a unit to one of the poles in anaphase, with an equational split taking place in the second division. Spermatid nuclei therefore contain either 14 or 20 chromosomes.

The iceryine type of meiosis, characteristic of coccid members of the tribe Iceryini, is essentially an adaptation to the haploid condition of the males. Presumably, somewhere along the line of evolution of this group, the physiological block for development of an unfertilized egg was removed since the males develop parthenogenically. The haploid number of chromosomes is two. Meiosis in the iceryines has but one division, and that is of course equational to give two haploid nuclei. Cytoplasmic division, a remnant of which preceded the fusion of the four products of meiosis in Puto, is here completely suppressed, and a binucleate spermatid is formed directly.

The iceryine spindle is entirely of nuclear origin. The nuclear membrane may in fact persist until late anaphase in some species, and at the poles it is pushed out into acuminate tips by the developing spindle.

Before passing to the more evolved types of meiosis it will be well to mention the rather strange manner by which the iceryine sperm are formed. Each binucleate spermatid develops two cytoplasmic *anlage* which will elongate to form the tail. Into these pass the two nuclei, one to each tail. At this time the spermatid nuclei are in the form of a delicate network, having despiralized during telophase. As the chromosomes move into the tail, with the shorter chromosome always preceding the longer one but terminally united to it, they condense, but as the tail elongates the chromosomes apparently despiralize again, at least partially. This is followed by a last condensation which leaves the chromosomes about the length they were in meiotic prophase. By this time the sperm tail has become detached from the spermatid body, in which the empty nuclei can still be seen. Clearly, this behavior, as Hughes-Schrader points out, suggests that the chromosomes have inherent capabilities of movement quite independent of any spindle mechanism, and that the order of migration into the tail must be determined by some peculiarity of the chromosome ends.

The fourth type of coccid meiosis, the Llaveiine type, is found in the closely related genera Llaveia, Llaveiella, and Protortonia, and in Nautococcus, all members of the family Margarodidae. Meiosis in the females is rather orthodox, but extreme specialization characterizes the males. The first evidence of it, in Llaveia, is the vesiculation of the nucleus. The two bivalents and the single X-chromosome condense in separate vesicles, with the X condensing precociously to the others. Synapsis presumably precedes vesiculation. If asynapsis takes place, as it does occasionally in this genus, the separate univalents may be in lobes of a single vesicle or in independent vesicles, but since the first division is equational, no meiotic irregularity follows. As in the meiotic types just described, the movement apart of chromatids in telophase, and their secondary pairing in interphase and prophase of the second division, is characteristic, with secondary pairing serving as a stabilizing factor to offset asynapsis.

The meiotic spindle also presents new features. From the outer edge of each chromatid, i.e., the opposite side from the pairing faces, a flange of chromosomal fibers arises in premetaphase as the vesicle walls disappear. When the separate flanges from the two halves of a bivalent press together, they form a mass of fibers having the shape of a megaphone, flaring at their apex (Fig. 9–18). The fibers in each bivalent are first formed without reference to any pole (since there is none) or to each other, but later they orient in parallel fashion to form a bipolar figure with flaring poles. Obviously the spindle has a composite origin. The chromosomal fibers shorten in anaphase as the equational separation goes on, and the interzonal connective becomes a tubular affair which further elongates to push the chromosomes apart. The second division is similar except that the X-chromosome forms no spindle fibers. Rather it is passively moved to one pole, without further division, by being caught in the fibers of one of the autosomes.

In *Nautococcus schraderae,* the meiotic events are similar to those in Llaveia except for a rather pronounced asynchrony in the anaphase separation of chromatids in the two members of the bivalent. The chiasmata are resolved completely before metaphase, and the homologues may lie some distance from each other. In some instances, however, two chromosomes, dividing asynchronously, may have a fusion of spindle elements, to give a linear aggregate of four chromatids (Fig. 9–18).

The independence of the individual parts of the chromosomes reaches a greater degree of expression in Llaveiella. The four half-chromatids of each chromosome are clearly evident, being arranged in linear order in the tube-like spindle elements. The feature of asynchrony may, on occasion, reveal eight elements from a single chromosome, thus indicating that the individual chromosome at metaphase I is an eight-part structure. In most organisms this feature, if present, would not be revealed because of the intimate coiled nature of the chromosomes and the undivided centromere, but asynchrony and the diffuse centromere permit a greater freedom to the parts present. The unique automomy of the chromatids finds a striking

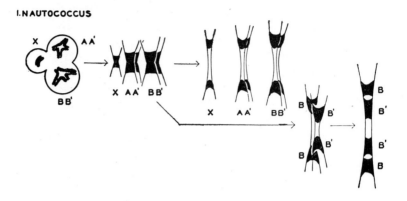

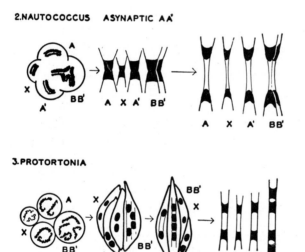

Fig. 9–18. Formation of spindles in two genera of coccids. 1, the sperma-tocyte nucleus of Nautococcus is vesiculated, synapsis of autosomal homologues is regular, terminalization is complete, flaring spindle elements are formed by each chromosome, and anaphase disjunction is regular except where spindle elements fuse as with the B chromosome pair; 2, same as above except that the A pair of autosomes is asynaptic; 3, fusion of spindle elements in Pro-tornia is regular (see Fig. 9–19) with the chromatids of one pair of homologues, in this instance those of the B pair, being forced in between each other to insure a normal equational separation (Hughes-Schrader 1948b, and used with the permission of Academic Press, Inc.).

expression in the X, which during meiotic prophase has its two chroma-tids, each with half-chromatids visible, in separate vesicles. Yet the X always behaves as a unit, dividing and segregating as do the other chromo-somes.

In *Prototonia primitiva,* the unusual circumstances of coccid meiosis reach full expression (Fig. 9–19). All of the chromosomes are dissociated

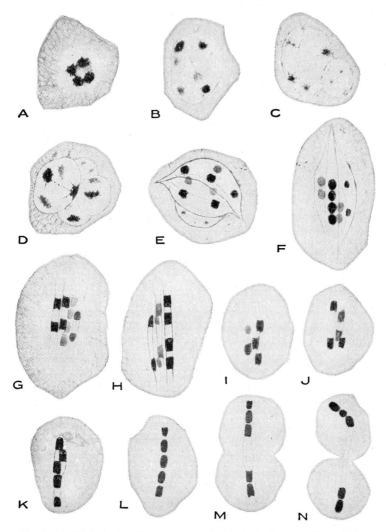

Fig. 9–19. Meiosis in *Protortonia primitiva*. A–D, meiotic prophase, illustrating the vesiculation of the nucleus; E and F, establishment of bipolarity of the nucleus and formation of spindle elements; G and H, anaphase I; I–K, fusion of spindle elements in interphase to give a linear aggregate of the five chromosomes as indicated in L; L, the aggregate consists of the undivided X and the separate chromatids of the two autosomes; M and N, anaphase II with the X terminal in the upper group in M and central in N. The chromatids of the two autosomes must alternate in the linear aggregate in order that each spermatid receives its proper chromosomal complement, and K illustrates how this is brought about (Hughes-Schrader 1948b, and used with the permission of Academic Press, Inc.).

into chromatids during the premeiotic telophase, leaving ten free chromatids from the five chromosomes of the diploid set. Four vesicles are formed, one containing four elements, three containing two each. It does not seem likely that synapsis or chiasma formation has taken place, although a residual attraction between chromatids keeps them from being irretrievably mixed up. This is certainly true for the smaller pair of autosomes, each of which lies in a separate vesicle. The vesicles then assume a biacuminate form (this is reminiscent of the intranuclear spindle of the iceryines), become appressed together, and form within each spindle element with the chromatids in linear aggregates. In the second division, the independence of the chromatids, followed by a secondary pairing, is strikingly shown by the fact that the X-chromatid may find its way between two homologous chromatids to give a linear aggregate of three. The identity of the X in this situation is made certain by its negative heteropycnosis.

The orientation of the four chromatids in the large vesicle into a linear aggregate poses a special problem. If the first meiotic division is equational, as it certainly is for the other coccid chromosomes, then the two central chromatids must be from one chromosome, and the two end ones from the other homologue. Figure 9–18 illustrates how Hughes-Schrader believes this to have arisen to insure that the division is truly equational.

The lecanoid type of meiosis, represented here by *Phenacoccus acericola,* retains many of the coccid features while introducing three new ones. In the first place, asynapsis is complete (even as in Protortonia) at the same time that a compensatory mechanism insures proper segregation; secondly, the two haploid sets of chromosomes are, from the blastula stage on, sharply differentiated from each other by a difference in condensation; and thirdly, half of the sperm degenerate. The males and females of the lecanoids are diploid, with the $2n$ number in Phenacoccus being 12. In meiotic prophase of the males six of the chromosomes are heavily condensed at one side. At metaphase, all 12 are similar in appearance, and anaphase separation is equational. In the second division, however, six chromosomes, presumably those from the earlier heteropycnotic set, clump together while the remaining six do not aggregate. Spindle fibers form from the clumped six, a unipolar spindle arises, and these chromosomes move to the single pole. The nucleus formed is heavily pycnotic, and eventually, in the quadrinucleate spermatid, disintegrates. The remaining more normally behaving chromosomes develop into a nucleus, and since there are two in each spermatid, only two functional sperm are formed.

The situation in *Gossyparia spuria* is even more bizarre. The diploid number is 28, and in the female 14 bivalents are regularly formed, but in the male 14 of the chromosomes are clumped into a heteropycnotic mass in the meiotic prophase as seven bivalents. The remaining 14 condense more slowly, and remain as univalents (Fig. 9–20). At metaphase I, the spindle shows 14 univalents and seven bivalents, and segregation takes place by the univalents dividing equationally, the bivalents reductionally. In the secondary spermatocytes, the seven dyads derived from the bivalents remain condensed, form a unipolar spindle, move to the single pole and there

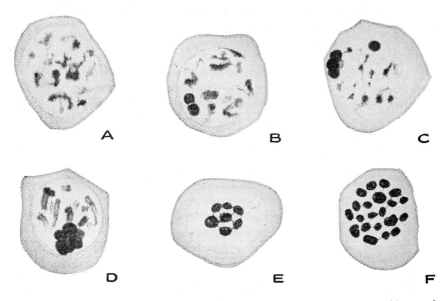

Fig. 9–20. Meiosis in *Gossyparia spuria*. A, early prophase with no evidence of heteropycnosis; B–E, condensation of 7 heteropycnotic bivalents; F, metaphase I with 7 bivalents and 14 univalents (Hughes-Schrader 1948b, after Schrader, and used with the permission of Academic Press, Inc.).

fuse into a pycnotic mass which, in the spermatid, later degenerates. The remaining two clumps, each of 14 normal chromosomes, round into nuclei, and eventually are transformed into functional sperm. It seems clear that *G. spuris* is a tetraploid since other related genera have 2n chromosome numbers of 10, 12, and 14. This fact alone, however, does not explain the peculiar behavior of the 14 heteropycnotic elements according to Hughes-Schrader (see, however, White 1954), and a further study of related genera is needed before an understanding can be had.

Polar bodies in development. Before taking leave of the coccids, with their wealth of interesting cytological features, another peculiarity, this time in the females, may be mentioned. This concerns the active participation of the polar bodies in development. This was first discovered by Schrader (1923) in *Pseudococcus citri,* and has been confirmed in other related forms.

Usually the polar bodies play no role in development, although as mentioned earlier in this chapter the mosaicism found in some strains of the silkworm arises from fertilized polar bodies sinking back into the egg to contribute to somatic development. In *P. citri,* a polar nucleus is formed by fusion of the polar bodies, and it is triploid, having 15 chromosomes. The polar nucleus divides, usually three times, to give rise to derivatives having 15 chromosomes each. These fuse in pairs, or with one or two cleavage nuclei, to produce nuclei having 25, 30, or 35 chromosomes. These giant nuclei then divide endomitotically to give still larger nuclei with 50 to 70 chromosomes. At this stage, the nuclei take in a fungal symbiont (which passes from one generation to another through the egg) and become primary mycetocytes. In turn, these divide to form the mycetome organ of the adult organism. Later endomitotic divisions in the mycetocytes may bring the chromosome number up to as high as 200.

CHAPTER 10

Spontaneous and Induced Chromosomal Aberrations

Sufficient mention has been made of the use of various chromosomal aberrations for the investigation of cytological and cytogenical problems to indicate that these are of invaluable aid as working tools. Certain studies would scarcely be possible without the use of aberrations; and in fact so important are they that several laboratories maintain numerous cytologically distinguishable stocks of Drosophila and maize which are available to those who wish to use them in experimental work. They provide, in essence, intracellular devices by which the behavior of the chromosomes, particularly in meiosis, can be controlled. In this chapter, however, we will be concerned with their production rather than with their use.

The study of aberrations, and an appreciation of their usefulness in genetic work, had its origin in the late 1920's when Muller made use of the famous ClB technique in his early radiation experiments. The perfection of this technique, which is based on the use of an inversion to prevent crossing over in the X-chromosome of female Drosophila, led to the discovery that x-rays cause gene mutations in very appreciable numbers. This discovery was followed by parallel studies of Altenburg (1928) who showed that the frequency of translocations was also increased by ionizing radiations. Stadler's (1928) work in maize and barley demonstrated that the same situation holds for plants. Since then the field of radiobiology has become one of the most active areas of cytogenetic research, fostered as it has been in late years by the development of new sources of radiation and by an awareness of the possibilities of radiation damage to large segments of the population either through sudden exposure to atomic explosions or from chronic exposure to continual low doses of radiation. It was natural that studies of the effects of radiation were first concentrated on the genetical and cytological aspects; these are the most readily discernible, and good quantitative data could be obtained. Later, the extension of these studies to biochemical levels within the cell has given a far better idea of the subtle but at the same time widespread nature of radiation damage, and the information has provided a sounder basis for radiation therapy at the same time that it has enabled us to obtain a deeper insight into the workings of the living cell.

SPONTANEOUS ABERRATIONS

The induction of chromosomal aberrations by experimental means offers the opportunity of further inquiry into the nature of those changes that occur spontaneously. We know, for instance, that the genera Oenothera and Rhoeo are characterized by remarkably complex systems of translocations, and that within the species of Drosophila there appear to be relatively few translocations at the same time that there are numerous paracentric inversions, with some species having them more prevalent than others, and further, with some chromosomes within a single species more likely to contain inversions than other chromosomes in the same nucleus. The grasshoppers, as a group, are almost free of inversions in nature, although heteromorphic pairs of homologues, arising presumably from other types of aberrations, are fairly common. How do these arise, what is their frequency in nature, what is their survival value under various conditions of competition, what are the conditions favoring their production? These, and other questions, are difficult to answer; yet it is quite certain that aberrations play a role in the evolution of organisms, and from this point of view the problem of aberration production is of intrinsic interest.

The study of spontaneous changes in chromosome structure can be made only in organisms where large numbers of cells can be studied with ease. The low rates of change make this a necessary condition, and the most satisfactory quantitative studies have been those done on Tradescantia (Giles 1940a, 1941; Steffensen 1953, 1955) and on Allium (Nickols 1941).

Every organism presumably has its own rate of spontaneous chromosomal change, a rate governed by both intrinsic and extrinsic factors. Giles was particularly concerned in his studies with the rates of change in different species of Tradescantia and in interspecific hybrids between certain species. *T. paludosa* and *T. canaliculata,* both diploid species ($2x = 12$), and the F_1 and F_2 hybrids were examined. The frequency of aberrations in the species, judged by examination of the chromosomes in the microspore division, was quite low (Table 10–1), but this frequency was increased threefold in the F_2 hybrids. Variation among the 21 F_2 offspring suggested that genetic factors governing the stability of chromosomes in the parent species had undergone segregation in the F_1 hybrids, while the greater frequency in the hybrids as a group indicated that hybridity itself was a cause of instability. These facts alone remove any doubt that the aberrations are the result of naturally occurring radiations; in fact, as indicated in the preceding chapter, the daily dose of radiation received by these plants was about 1800 times too low to account for the observed frequencies.

Giles later extended this study to include triploid and tetraploid plants of the same genus. The triploid plants were interspecific hybrids produced by crossing a diploid *T. paludosa* with a tetraploid *T. canaliculata*. In the diploid species the frequency of breaks in the chromosomes was 0.06 per-cent, a figure that agrees with the 0.04 percent found in the earlier study.

TABLE 10–1

**Frequency of spontaneous aberrations in
Tradescantia (from Giles 1940a, 1941).**

Plant	No. chromosomes examined	Total breaks	Percent breaks
Non-hybrid diploids	7,574	2	0.04
F₂ plants (21)	70,447	81	0.12
Diploids	10,408	6	0.06
Triploids	19,447	115	0.71
Tetraploids	10,024	8	0.11

The tetraploid species showed a frequency of 0.11 percent, while the aver-age of six triploid plants was 0.71 percent. Thus the frequency in the triploids was about six times as great as in the tetraploid and about 12 times as great as in the diploid. If considered on a cell basis, the ratio of aberrations in the diploid, tetraploid, and hybrid triploid plants was 1:2 :12, with 5.5 percent of the cells in the triploid showing aberrations of one sort or another.

These results clearly indicate the importance of genic stability in con-trolling the behavior of chromosomes. Since the somatic number of chromo-somes in the triploid is 18, with trivalent formation at meiosis a general rule (Giles 1941), the distribution of chromosomes to the reduced micro-spores is such that each cell can contain from six to 12 chromosomes. Cells with in-between numbers of chromosomes are unbalanced, and many are inviable. The conclusion that genic unbalance is responsible for the high frequency of aberrations in these cells is borne out by the observation that the frequencies of aberrations in roottip mitoses are essentially the same in all of the plants. In these cells there is of course no unbalance. A somewhat similar study in triploid forms of Tulipa indicates again a high rate of spontaneous breakage (Darlington and Upcott 1941).

The role of nutrition in maintaining the stability of the chromosome has also been demonstrated in Tradescantia (Steffensen 1953, 1955). Spontaneous breakage is greatly increased when calcium and magnesium are deficient in the culture medium in which the plants are grown. Such conditions also increase the sensitivity of the chromosomes to x-rays. The role played by these divalent ions in maintaining the integrity of the chromosome has not been ascertained, but Mazia (1954a) has further shown that salivary gland chromosomes are broken into small fragments when subjected to the action of versene, a chelating agent that binds calcium.

Another factor governing the production of spontaneous aberrations is age, and the simplest procedure for investigating this problem is to examine cell division in the growing roottips of seeds of varying ages. Nickols' (1941) study was done on the commercial onion, *Allium cepa*. Even for seed of the same age, although not necessarily stored under the same conditions, there was considerable variation, the range in percent aberrations in five varieties being from 1.6 to 13.0. Where seed of the same variety, but of different ages, could be studied, the oldest seed generally showed the highest frequency of aberrations (Table 10–2). One can assume that in the cells of dormant seed, a constant production of aberrations goes on (Levan and Lotfy, 1949). Undoubtedly temperature and humidity during storage affect this rate, although the mechanism of spontaneous breakage of chromosomes remains unknown. It is a common observation that some sources of *Vicia faba* seeds show an abnormally high rate of broken chromosomes in the primary and lateral roots of the germinating seed, with 57–70 percent of the cells often being affected. This is particularly true for American-grown seeds; English seeds appear to be relatively free of such aberrations.

TABLE 10–2

Frequency of spontaneous aberrations in seed of varieties of Allium Cepa stored for different periods of time (from Nichols 1941).

Variety	No. chromosomes examined	Total aberrations	Percent aberrations
Yellow Strassburg '35	5120	26	0.50
" " '36	5184	11	0.21
" " '38	4000	5	0.12
Sweet Spanish '36	9376	69	0.73
" " '39	5024	8	0.15

A suggestion that dehydration may be a factor in increasing the frequency of aberrations comes from the observation that even in onion varieties having a fairly high frequency of aberrations in roottips from germinating seed, no aberrations were found in roottips produced from bulbs of the same variety.

The plants seem to be able to outgrow the effects of aberrations and to reduce their frequency in later divisions. As Table 10–3 indicates, there is a reduction in frequency as the root elongates, although Nickols points out that even in a plant six months old, the frequency remains much higher than that found by Giles in roottips of Tradescantia. This difference can probably be attributed to the genic characteristics of the two genera. In other forms, however, abnormal dividing cells are fairly common. This is particularly true of certain rapidly dividing malignant tissues such as various strains of the ascites mouse tumor, where fragmentation, abnormal anaphases, and highly polyploid cells are frequent (Levan and Haushka, 1953). Some strains of the ascites tumor appear to be relatively free of such aberrancies.

TABLE 10–3

Frequency of spontaneous aberrations in Allium Cepa var. Prizetaker in successive stages of development of the root (from Nichols 1941).

Length of root	Cells analyzed	Percent aberrations
2–5 mm.	450	10.4
7–9 mm.	58	6.6
10–12 mm.	138	5.8
25–30 mm.	190	2.1
80–100 mm.	116	1.7

In meiosis, where the forces acting on the chromosomes are more varied in nature and possibly in strength, one might expect to find relatively greater frequencies of spontaneous breakage, but to date the only reasonably complete studies appear to be those made in the sterile polyploid grass hybrid, *Bromus Trinii* × *B. maritimus* (2n = 49) (Walters 1950, 1951), mutant strains of maize (Beadle 1932c; Jones 1937; 1940; McClintock 1951, 1953), Scilla (Rees 1952), Paeonia (Marquardt 1952), and Paris (Haga 1953). A high frequency (1.1/cell) of chromatid bridges was found at anaphase I in the Bromus hybrid, and these could not be related either to meiotic pairing or to chiasma formation since both phenomena were of quite low occurrence. Apparently the breaks occurred in univalent chromosomes sometime during prophase and after chromosome duplication, since only chromatid (and not chromosomal) aberrations were found. That the state of univalency of the chromosomes seems to be responsible, although in what way is not certain, is indicated by the fact that in the colchicine-induced allopolyploid *B. Trinii* × *B. maritimus* (2n = 98) fertility was high, meiosis regular with few univalents, and breakage much reduced. Walters suggests that a possible interaction between the *Trinii* and *maritimus* genomes sets into motion processes that lead to the breakage of chromatids, but as yet no experimental or observational evidence provides a clue as to the nature of these processes, although other studies such as those of Sears (1952a, b) in wheat again point to the instability of univalents in meiosis.

In the maize strain investigated by Beadle, the occurrence of spontaneous aberrations is governed by a recessive gene, *sticky*. Located in Chromosome 4, this gene, when homozygous, is responsible for the induction of aberrations in all tissues with the result that the plants are dwarfed, and streaks of altered phenotypes appear in the leaves, stalks, reproductive parts, and endosperm. Many changed chromosomes have been seen in mitotic cells. At anaphase I, the chromosomes adhere to each other, hence the designation *sticky,* and the aberrations arise from the rupturing that occurs during anaphase movement. A marked increase in spontaneous mutations has also been observed in offspring from *sticky* plants. Precisely what change has occurred to bring about the sticky and consequently unstable chromosomal and genic condition is not known, although it seems not too farfetched to assume that an altered nucleic acid condition is the basic cause.

Jones (1937, 1940) has also described endospermic alterations in maize which undoubtedly stem from spontaneous chromosome change. As in the *sticky* strain, these are under genic control. The rate of change is sufficiently high to be detected cytologically (Clark and Copeland 1940). It would appear that reciprocal translocations between non-homologous chromosomes are formed, producing twin spotting in the endosperm as the result of somatic segregation, as well as other changes that lead to unstable broken ends of chromosomes. As will be described below, these lead to a cyclic alteration which, in properly marked chromosomes, can be detected by the mosaic pattern produced in endosperm or foliage parts.

Probably the most remarkable case of genetically controlled production of aberrations is the *Dissociation-Activator* (*Ds-Ac*) system discovered in maize by McClintock (1950a, b, 1951, 1953). The striking genetic effects of this system will be described in a later chapter, but the cytological effects produced include deficiencies, duplications, inversions, translocations, and ring chromosomes. The system, which was discovered during a study of the behavior of broken ends in Chromosome 9, consists of two single chromosomal units. These are extragenic in the sense that they function, and are recognizable, only through their action on other genes and loci, and there is reason for believing that they are heterochromatic in nature. However, their location in the chomosomal complement can be determined through linkage studies. What is most remarkable is the fact that they can move in the chromosomes from one location to another. The first-discovered and standard location of *Ds* is proximal to *Wx* on Chromosome 9, but has been located in other regions of the same chromosome as well as in other chromosomes; presumably it can enter or leave the chromosome complement at any position, a phenomenon McClintock has called "transposition." *Ac* has no standard position, but like *Ds* it is also capable of transposition to any chromosome.

As a two-unit system, *Ds* initiates changes in genic expression and *Ac* determines when these changes will occur (see Chapter 12). *Ds* is without effect in the absence of *Ac*. It is the transposition events that are of cytological interest, for when transposition takes place a break occurs at the location of *Ds,* and any aberration formed always has one break at the former location of *Ds* (Fig. 10–1). The transposition of *Ds* from one location to another and the induction of a break at the location of *Ds* are therefore coincident with each other. They are further related to certain somatic cells and at very precise developmental stages. This is believed to be true for *Ac* as well, but is somewhat more difficult to determine.

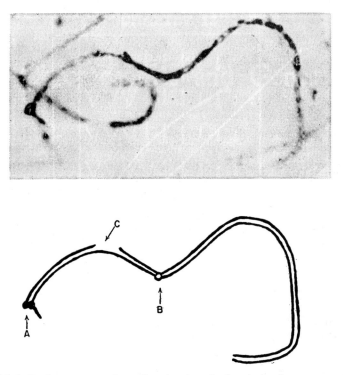

Fig. 10–1. Pachytene stage in maize showing the break in chromosome 9 when *Ds* is located at its standard position in one homologue and absent in the other. In the diagram, A indicates the terminal knob, B the centromere, and C the observed break (McClintock 1951).

So far as the mechanism that leads to transposition is concerned, McClintock (1950b) suggests that this may result from a stickiness of the heterochromatic *Ds* locus during the cell cycle, and that stresses during chromosome movement lead to breakage at *Ds*. *Ds* can be transposed to another site in the complement, as a block of heterochromatin, and the site it occupied heals to reveal no detectable loss, or it may lead to the formation of an aberration if other broken ends are available with which it might illegitimately heal.

The size of the *Ds* and *Ac* units is not known with certainty, and they may actually vary in size even as it is known that each unit can have varying influences on genic expression, but there is suggestive evidence that the *Ac* locus may be associated in one instance with a cytologically detectable deep-staining chromomere in the short arm of Chromosome 9 (McClintock 1950b).

It is difficult to determine whether the spontaneous breakage of chromosomes in other species results from the operation of a system similar to the *Ds-Ac* situation in maize. Maize is, of course, particularly favorable for the detection and study of such a system, but now that McClintock has clarified and explained the maize situation, it may well be that other species exhibiting genic instability will be found to be governed by analogous units of determination.

Breakage-fusion-bridge cycle. McClintock's (1938a, b, 1941a, b, c, 1942, 1944) classical studies on the behavior of ring and dicentric chromosomes in maize has led to a clarified picture of the behavior and fate of unstable chromosomes. These changes, forming the so-called breakage-fusion-bridge cycle, are of two types, depending upon the kind of chromosome and the tissue in which these chromosomes are found. They are further distinguished by the type of reunion that occurs.

The first concerns the behavior of ring chromosomes in somatic tissues. Such chromosomes, generally produced through x-radiation although they may arise spontaneously, do not maintain themselves unaltered through successive cell generations, and, by use of a ring marked with dominant genes against a recessive background, McClintock (1938b) has shown that the ring may increase in size by duplication of sections of the original ring, decrease in size by loss of sections, be lost entirely, or be present in increased numbers. To accomplish one or the other of the first two possibilities, the ring must obviously break. One might assume that breakage of the ring, followed by healing of the broken ends, would lead to the formation of a rod chromosome, but such has never been observed to have happened. Although breakage is known to occur, both spontaneously and induced, ring chromosomes produce only ring chromosomes.

Figure 10–2 indicates how the ring chromosomes behave in somatic tissues. If a ring chromosome reproduces itself to form two ring chromatids that can separate cleanly from each other in anaphase, no alteration in structure is to be expected. However, in some instances the divided ring chromosome forms a continuous, double-sized, dicentric ring, a condition that could arise through sister-strand crossing over or through replication while in a twisted state; in other instances, two interlocking rings result. If the latter are to be included in their respective telophase nuclei, at least one of the rings must break; reunion of the broken ends in the telophase or resting nucleus apparently always occurs. No change in ring size results although the interlocked rings may be delayed in anaphase separation, thus providing a mechanism for loss, or they may both find their way into one or the other of the two sister nuclei.

When the continuous ring is formed, the position of rupture is variable. Three possibilities are indicated in Figure 10–2, and each will lead to different genetic consequences depending upon the loss or duplication of the genic regions involved. Clearly, the larger the ring at the time of chromatid duplication, the greater will be the frequency of continuous or interlocking rings, and the greater will be the degree of mosaicism. Smaller rings, however, stand a greater chance of being lost. The instability of ring chromosomes can therefore be readily appreciated.

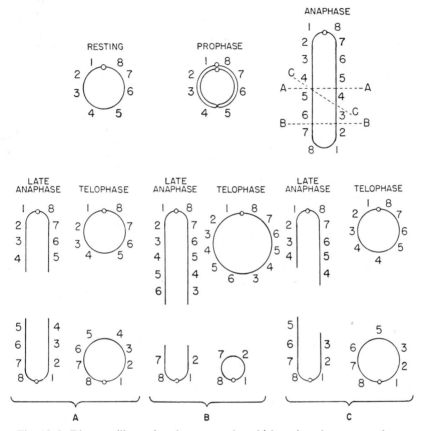

Fig. 10–2. Diagram illustrating the manner by which a ring chromosome becomes altered in size and genetic constitution. Upper left, a ring in an undivided resting state; upper middle, a replicated ring with a "crossover" between sister strands; upper right, a double-sized dicentric ring with A, B and C representing three possible breakage situations in anaphase; lower half, the consequences of the three possibilities at late anaphase and telophase. The numerals indicate the individual parts of the ring. The union of the broken ends of the ring in telophase occurs prior to the replication of the ring, and the entire cycle is an example of the chromosomal type of the breakage-fusion-bridge behavior (after McClintock 1941).

The above can be considered the *chromosome type* of breakage-fusion-bridge cycle, since the reunion of broken ends in the telophase nucleus involves functionally undivided chromosomes rather than chromatids. The *chromatid* type can occur in both meiotic and somatic tissues, and is most easily understood by considering the origin as well as the fate of these

aberrant chromosomes. McClintock (1941c), making use of a rearrangement in Chromosome 9 of maize (Fig. 10–3), has developed a method
for the formation of a chromosome that is dicentric at the same time that

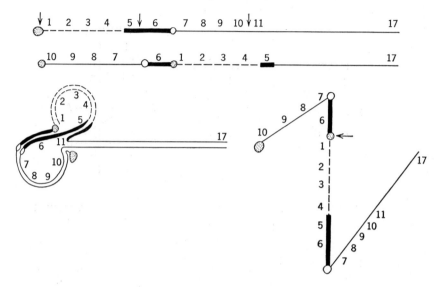

Fig. 10–3. Rearrangement in chromosome 9 of maize with the pachytene and
anaphase I configurations. Top, normal chromosome 9 with the points of breakage
marked with arrows; immediately below, rearranged chromosome 9; left, pachytene
configuration when complete pairing takes place between the heterozygous homologues; right, anaphase I dicentric bridge formed when crossing over occurs in the
1 to 4 region. If breakage of the bridge occurs at the point indicated by the arrow,
a chromosome with a broken end but with a full complement of genes will result
(redrawn from Rhoades 1955, after McClintock).

the full complement of genes is present. Breakage in certain places at anaphase will leave the genic complement complete, yet each chromosome
will possess a broken end. Fusion of sister chromatids takes place by
prophase of the next division, and this again leads to the formation of a
dicentric chromosome (Fig. 10–4). This type of breakage-fusion-bridge
cycle will continue in gametophytic tissue so long as the change in genic
content is not sufficiently great to cause death of haploid cells.

If such chromosomes succeed in passing through the several divisions
leading to the formation of sperm cells, they can be introduced either into
sporophytic tissue by fertilization of an egg, or into endospermic tissue
through union with the fusion nucleus. In sporophytic tissue, the broken
ends heal and the cycle ceases; in the endosperm, the cycle continues, as
evidenced by the mosaicism that can be induced. However, a broken end
in the egg can unite with a broken end introduced by the sperm, and the
dicentric chromosome produced goes through the chromosome type of
breakage-fusion-bridge cycle (McClintock 1942). Why the same broken

chromosome behaves differently in different tissues is not known, but is probably to be explained by the different physiological conditions of the two tissues.

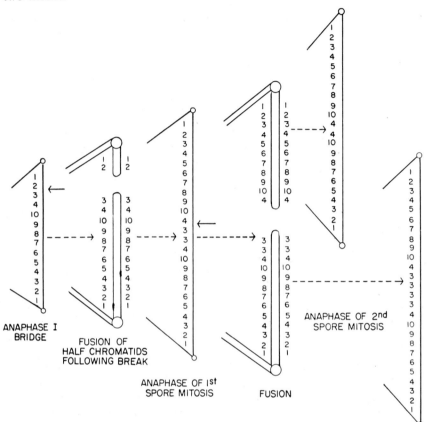

Fig. 10–4. Diagram of the chromatid type of breakage-fusion-bridge cycle as it occurs in gametogenesis following formation of a dicentric chromatid by crossing over within an inversion. Position of breakage is indicated by solid arrows. The breakage-fusion-bridge cycle would continue in the formation of endosperm, but would cease when a gamete containing a broken chromosome enters into fertilization to form the zygote (Rhoades 1955, after McClintock).

Crossing over in normal chromosomes can sometimes give rise to the chromatid breakage-fusion-bridge cycle. One such case is that involving Chromosome 6 in maize, which carries the nucleolar organizer in its short arm (McClintock 1941b). Chiasmata are formed only infrequently in this arm, but when they are, terminalization through the nucleolar region is prevented, presumably by the nucleolus itself or by the heterochromatic nucleolar organizer. If the force of terminalization is sufficiently strong, rupture at the position of the organizer occurs, fusion takes place between the two chromatids, and a bridge is formed at anaphase. Translocation of the nucleolar organizer region to the long arm of another chromosome, thus providing for more frequent crossing over, leads to a very high frequency of anaphase bridges.

Another type of aberration involving fusion of broken chromatids is that which follows non-homologous crossing over in univalents (McClintock 1941b). Univalents fold back upon themselves to pair non-homologously, in which position they may also undergo crossing over. Inversions, acentric rings and rods, and centric rings can be produced, and this process may well be the origin of a portion of such aberrations as occur spontaneously, particularly in organisms with unbalanced complements of chromosomes.

Other dicentric chromosomes occurring in various species have been described by Sears and Camara (1952) in wheat, by Darlington and Wylie (1953) in hyacinths, and by Koller (1953) in a rat tumor. That described by Sears and Camara is particularly interesting in that its behavior at meiosis indicates that the two centromeres are of varying strengths. Originating from an isochromosome for the short arm of Chromosome VII in *Triticum aestivum*, the dicentric has a structure that gives a ratio of 30:10:1 for its three parts. At meiosis it generally behaves as a bivalent, with the two centromeres opposing each other. The sub-terminal centromere, however, fails to function properly, and the entire dicentric passes to one of the telophase nuclei. The second meiotic division is essentially mitotic in character, and the two centromeres of each chromatid pass to the same pole. The weakness of the sub-terminal centromere is only evident when it is opposed by the stronger one, and the inherent weakness, which appears intrinsic rather than positional, may stem from the fact that having arisen as an isochromosome by misdivision, it may actually lack some of the substance of a normal centromere without, however, having lost completely its power of movement.

Behavior of telocentric chromosomes. It has been suspected for some time that all normally behaving chromosomes are two-armed, i.e., that an arm must end with a piece of chromatin rather than with a centromere. An apparent exception is the type of chromosome Cleveland (1949) has described in the Protozoa, and it may well be that stability here is achieved by virtue of the fact that the centromere is more or less permanently attached to the centriole. In other organisms telocentric chromosomes are unstable, and their relative infrequency in nature probably stems from the fact that they are rapidly eliminated from a population in which they might arise by chance.

Rhoades (1940) has described in detail the behavior of such a telocentric chromosome, which arose in a strain of maize trisomic for Chromosome 5. This chromosome lacks the long arm, and is terminated with a centromere (whether all or part of the centromere is present is not known).

Since the gene *bm* (brown-midrib) is located close to the centromere in the short arm, its loss can be followed in somatic tissue. If streaks of aberrant tissue extend into the tassel, study of the altered chromosome can be made at pachynema. It was apparent that changes in the chromosome appeared with some frequency. Smaller telocentric fragments, small chromosomes with subterminal centromeres, and isochromosomes have been found; the isochromosomes probably arose by misdivision of the centromere, but the origin of the other types is not known. It is also uncertain why a terminal centromere should be unstable, unless it is assumed that the material composing the centromere is basically unstable, and must consequently be inserted into chromatic material, which orients its plane of division and imparts to it a condition of stability.

INDUCED CHROMOSOMAL ABERRATIONS

The past quarter century has witnessed a tremendous amount of research dealing with the cytological effects of various radiations. The literature on the subject is voluminous and often confusing, but through their response to various radiations much has been learned of the behavior and structure of chromosomes. Many of the aberrations have been produced especially for the investigation of other problems—position effect, dosage effects, cytological mapping—but a large part of the information gained has given us a better understanding of how radiations affect the living cell. The frequencies and types of aberrations have proven to be effective yardsticks for the cytological assay of radiation damage, and these data, together with those from comparable genetical and physiological studies, have provided some idea of how the individual cell may be killed or altered—temporarily or permanently—by radiations.

The practical importance of these studies from the point of view of medical therapy and radiation protection is obvious, yet no less intriguing are other more fundamental problems of cellular structure and function that can be elucidated through the use of radiation technique. Muller (1928), Altenburg (1928), and Stadler (1928) initiated the work that has led to the quantitative considerations of radiation effects, and the more recent and comprehensive results are to be found in volumes by Lea (1955), Nickson (1952), Bacq and Alexander (1955) and Hollaender (1954, 1955), and in a review by Catcheside (1948).

More recently, it has been found that cytogenetical effects similar to those induced by radiations can also be induced by chemical means. The pioneering studies of Auerbach and Oelhkers on mustard gas and urethane, respectively, have been followed by many others, and a wide variety of seemingly unrelated chemical compounds have been shown to be very effective mutagenic agents. Their actions are not always similar, and a number of the chemicals appear to be more specific in their action on chromosome breakage than the ionizing radiations commonly employed.

The hope exists that chemical agents of known specific action will be found to be mutagenic in a specific and directed manner, possibly with the high degree of specificity exhibited by antigens, but no clue points with certainty to the realization of this hope.

The effective radiations. The radiations capable of inducing cytological aberrations may conveniently be classified as *ionizing* and *non-ionizing*. Alpha, beta, and gamma rays from radioactive sources, x-rays, protons, and neutrons are of the ionizing type, while ultraviolet radiation of effective wavelengths, i.e., between 1850–3000 A, is non-ionizing.

The ionizing radiations achieve their effects by virtue of the fact that they are themselves particulate, or that they eject ionizing particles from atoms they strike or within which they are absorbed. The ionized atoms, or ions, are not randomly distributed in the irradiated substance, but tend to lie in tracks, the length of which is dependent upon the initial speed of the ionizing particle (i.e., its initial energy) as well as on its mass. Thus, a proton and an electron, having the same energy, will produce the same rate of ionizations along a track, but the proton will travel considerably greater distances because of its greater mass. The spacing of ion pairs along the track will also depend upon the energy and mass (magnitude of charge) of the ionizing particle, and as the particle is slowed down by its passage through matter, collisions will be more frequent and the ion pairs will tend to be closer and closer together, producing at the end of the track a "tail" of dense ionization. Consequently alpha particles and protons are more densely ionizing than are the electrons ejected by x-rays and gamma rays. As will be pointed out later, there is every reason for believing that the ionizing radiations produce their effects as the result of paths of ionization, and that the denser the path the more effective the radiation, at least within certain physical limits.

Ultraviolet radiation is non-ionizing, being capable only of raising, through excitation, atoms and molecules to higher energy states. Dissociation of certain molecular bonds is possible under such conditions. On an energy basis, ultraviolet is far less efficient in producing structural aberrations in chromosomes than are the ionizing radiations, but this disadvantage is offset by the fact that ultraviolet is selectively absorbed by the nucleoproteins of the chromosome, and that monochromatic wavelengths of relatively high purity can be obtained for comparative studies of effectiveness. Information as to the absorbing elements in the chromosomes can be obtained from such studies. Monochromators having a relatively high output of energy from high-pressure mercury arcs of capillary bore are necessary for the isolation of wavelengths in the 2–3000 A region, but a ready source of energy of 2537 A is available from the low-pressure mercury vapor lamps commonly employed for sterilization purposes.

Doses of x-rays, gamma rays, beta rays and alpha rays are commonly measured in roentgen (r) units, this being the dose of radiation that produces 1 e.s.u. of charge in 0.001292 grams of air ($= 1$ cm^2 of air at standard temperature and pressure). In terms of ionization, 1 r produces about two ionizations per cubic micron of tissue. Beta rays, which are streams of electrons, are measured in terms of rep (roentgen equivalent physical), with one rep being that unit of energy absorption equal to 93 ergs/gram of tissue. One rep is consequently equal to 1 r unit of x-rays.

Measurement of neutron doses are somewhat more difficult, and several energy units have been employed. In America, the n-unit has been commonly used, and it is equivalent to 2.5 r units of x-rays or gamma rays. The v-unit of L. H. Gray is made equivalent in energy dissipation to 1 r unit of x-rays, and by the conversion of all doses of ionizing radiation, regardless of type, into rep, comparisons of biological effectiveness can conveniently be made.

For a more complete account of the physics of biologically effective radiations the student is referred to Lea (1955).

General effects of radiation on cells. In addition to the frequency of aberrations, radiation damage to a cell can be assessed by a variety of other means, e.g., depression of mitotic activity, depression in the synthesis of desoxyribosenucleic acid, a variety of morphological changes, and the stickiness of metaphase and anaphase chromosomes.

The depression of mitotic activity by radiations has been studied in a variety of organisms. An accurate determination of the magnitude of the effect is quite complicated when tissues such as the cornea of a vertebrate or the roottips of plants are studied, because there may be a latency in the appearance of the effect and because recovery of cells may take varying periods of time, depending upon the dosage employed and the sensitivity of the cells being studied. The studies of Carlson (1950, 1954; Carlson and Hollaender 1944) avoid these difficulties, however, since use is made of the neuroblast cells of grasshopper embryos, which can be examined and followed under the light microscope. They confirm, in general, studies made on tissues, at the same time that they reveal marked differences in sensitivity of the stages of the cell cycle.

Inhibition of mitosis can be observed with as little as 4 r of x-rays, yet 8,000 r will permit some neuroblast cells to pass through an entire, even if abnormal, cell cycle. Figure 10–5 indicates the depression caused by 15 r of x-rays and 6000 erg/cm^2 of 2537 A ultraviolent radiation. With x-rays there is a compensatory wave of cell division following the depression, which indicates a stoppage of cells at a critical stage. These delayed cells then go through division as a group to give an apparent increase in mitotic rate. The critical period has been identified as a late prophase stage just prior to the breakdown of the nuclear membrane. Cells that have passed this stage are not greatly delayed except as an induced stickiness of the chromosomes impedes chromatid separation; those that have not yet reached the critical stage show a reversal of mitotic behavior in that they regress to an earlier prophase stage. If the dosage employed is low, cells entering mitosis are not prevented from doing so, and these, together with the repressed cells, then go through mitosis as a group to account for the compensatory rise in mitotic count.

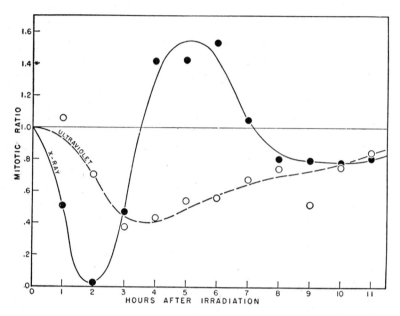

Fig. 10–5. Comparison of the effects of ultraviolet (2537 A) and x-rays on cell division in the neuroblast cells of the grasshopper embryo. A mitotic ratio of 1.0 is considered to be normal. 6000 ergs/cm² of ultraviolet, 15 r of x-rays (Carlson and Hollaender 1944).

During the compensatory period, when the mitotic rate is above normal, one is consequently dealing with a mixture of cells that have been irradiated at different times during the cell cycle. Unless the circumstances of regression are known and accounted for, an erroneous impression of cell sensitivity and mitotic stimulation would be gained from these data. A similar study of irradiated microspores in Tradescantia supports Carlson's opinion of a critical stage in prophase (Beatty and Beatty 1954), whereas earlier studies (Giese 1947) indicated that the sensitive period varied from organism to organism. The sensitive period in Tradescantia, however, is in mid rather than late prophase.

Figure 10–5 indicates that ultraviolet radiation does not have the same effect. No compensatory rise is encountered, and early rather than late prophase was found to be most sensitive (Carlson and Hollaender 1944). From late prophase on, doses as high as 36,000 ergs/cm² had little effect on mitotic inhibition. Ultraviolet of this wavelength is absorbed strongly in the nucleic acids of the cell, but no critical evidence is available to indicate whether absorption in the DNA of the nucleus or the RNA of the cytoplasm is responsible for the inhibition. Protein absorption, however, is indicated by the fact that ultraviolet of 2250 A inhibits to a greater extent than does that of 2537 A, and inhibition of spindle formation is suggested (Carlson and Hollaender 1948). With x-rays, part of the inhibition at least is indirect in that oxygen is a necessary factor for full expression of the effect (Gaulden, Nix, and Moshman 1953).

Although the data on radiation-induced mitotic inhibition obtained from neuroblast cells and Tradescantia microspores are in good qualitative agreement with those obtained from widely different tissue and species sources, it is quite clear that the sensitivity of cells from different species varies enormously. Micro-organisms in particular are highly radioresistant even during cell division. Embryonic and meristematic tissues, on the other hand, are highly radiosensitive as to mitotic inhibition. Tissue differences as to sensitivity are indicated in Figure 10–6, but since these curves are

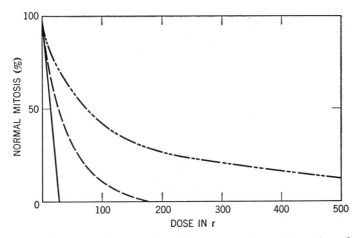

Fig. 10–6. The relation of dose of radiation to maximum depression of mitotic activity. Solid line, grasshopper neuroblast cells; broken line, cells in the developing retina of the rat; dot-dash line, chick fibroblasts (redrawn from Carlson 1954).

derived from different experiments in which culture conditions and the stages of division at the time of exposure may have varied, no valid conclusion can be drawn as to the exact degree of sensitivity. In general, however, it can be stated that the more active a tissue is mitotically and metabolically the more radiosensitive it is likely to be. In the same organism, meiosis would be more inhibited than mitosis, and in Tradescantia the order of sensitivity, from high to low, of cells in division would be microsporocytes, microspores, roottip cells, and pollen tubes.

The ultraviolet studies (Carlson and Hollaender 1948) suggest that absorption by the proteins of the cell, particularly by that protein portion destined to become incorporated into the spindle, is one of the initiating causes of mitotic inhibition. Undoubtedly other cellular metabolic functions are also impaired by radiations. This is indicated by the observation that relatively low doses of x-rays (140 *r*) inhibit the synthesis of DNA in Vicia roottips and bring about mitotic delay (Howard and Pelc 1953). Since only cells entering mitosis synthesize new DNA, any interference with the mechanism involved would bring about delay. The synthetic period appears to be in late interphase, and an analysis making use of radioactive P^{32} incorporated into DNA indicates that the delay occurs in the period just prior to synthesis. The delay is therefore brought about by failure of cells to enter the synthetic period rather than by interruption of synthetic processes already going on. These studies do not contradict those carried out on neuroblast cells and microspores, but merely indicate that interference with any metabolic process necessary for cell division will lead to inhibition. The sensitive period will vary according to inhibiting agent and the type of cell being investigated.

Another general effect of radiation on dividing cells is the appearance of clumped chromosomes at metaphase and an irregular separation of chromatids at anaphase. Termed the *physiological* or *primary* effect of radiation (Marquardt 1938), the chromosomes appear to be pycnotic or "sticky," similar in fact in appearance to the chromosomes in the *sticky* strain of maize. At metaphase the sharp boundaries between the chromosomes are lost, and an "agglutination" takes place shortly after the radiation ceases. Stickiness will persist for a length of time that is dependent on the dose (Fig. 10–7). Late prophase stages appear to be the most susceptible, and

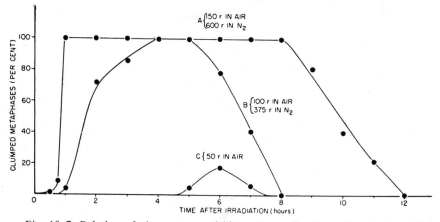

Fig. 10–7. Relation of chromosome stickiness (pycnotic clumped metaphases) in Tradescantia microspores to dose and to time after radiation, with exposures being made in air and in nitrogen (Swanson and Johnston 1954).

the effect persists through, but apparently does not prevent, anaphase movement. Chromatin bridges, however, are formed when the chromosomes fail to separate, and fragmentation of the chromosomes can result from the stresses of anaphase movement. Darlington (1953) has suggested that the stickiness arises from the DNA on the surface of the chromosome, which has been depolymerized and hence rendered more fluid by the radiation, a suggestion rendered plausible by the known effects of radiation of DNA *in vitro* (Taylor, Greenstein, and Hollaender 1948; Sparrow and Rosenfeld 1946). The degree of stickiness produced by a given dose of x-rays is dependent on the oxygen concentration in much the same manner as mitotic delay and chromosome breakage (Swanson and Johnston 1955).

Structural changes. The particular problem being investigated will determine in most instances the organism best suited for study, and while many organisms have been studied, certain ones have come to be regarded as conventional. Drosophila salivary gland chromosomes were early used for cytogenetic investigations, and their large size permits a more exacting study of minute as well as gross changes. Furthermore, these can be evaluated against, and correlated with, a vast background of genetical information which more than offsets the difficulty and tediousness of the salivary chromosome technique. Only viable changes can be observed, however, for after irradiation of either eggs or sperm the inviable aberrations are eliminated through failure of the eggs to hatch or the larvae to complete development. Also, many aberrations involving the large sections of heterochromatin cannot be detected cytologically, although they can be recognized by appropriate genetics tests.

Maize, because of its suitable pachytene stage and many genetical markers, compares favorably with Drosophila, at the same time that it possesses the disadvantages of losing many aberrations in the gametophytic stages of the male cells. The endosperm, however, being triploid, can withstand considerable genetic loss with impunity, and a wealth of favorable markers are available for study.

Meiotic changes are best studied in organisms with few but large chromosomes, the most favorable of which are Trillium, Tradescantia, various species of Lilium, and members of the Orthoptera. Where problems of penetration are important, as they would be with ultraviolet radiation, alpha particles, or very soft x-rays, the pollen tube chromosomes of Tradescantia, grown on an agar-lactose medium, and the neuroblast cells of the grasshopper embryo, offer a ready solution.

For a quantitative study of structural changes induced by radiation, the microspore chromosomes of Tradescantia and the roottip cells of *Vicia faba* are by far the most suitable materials for study. The former is particularly so because of the ease of obtaining large numbers of cells for comparative purposes. The changes to be described, therefore, will be largely taken from the Tradescantia studies even though it is recognized that certain aberrations such as paracentric inversions or reciprocal translocations readily escape detection. Roottips of Vicia, or of *Allium Cepa,* are more suitable, however, when chemical agents rather than radiations are being employed, since penetration of a chemical into the nucleus can be carried out in a reasonably quantitative fashion. Most of the techniques of preparing these materials for study are described by Darlington and La Cour (1942).

In Tradescantia, and in other organisms as well, the structural changes can be classified into *chromatid* and *chromosome* types. The former arise from the exposure of cells after the chromosomes are effectively double—presumably from later resting stages and early prophase to metaphase—and the chromatid rather than the whole chromosome is the unit of breakage. Chromosome aberrations are produced in resting cells, and at this stage the chromosomes behave as though they are effectively single-stranded. Customarily, chromatid studies are made 20 to 24 hours after radiation, while the 72–96 hour period is used for the observation of chromosome breaks. A transition stage exists when both types of aberrations may be present in the same anthers or even in the same cells, but the time of appearance and the duration of this stage is a function of the season of year (i.e., temperature and possibly light conditions). For plants grown in greenhouses but not under strict control of temperature, the transition stage is about 30 hours after exposure during the summer months, and at about 48 hours during the winter. The stage may last for six to 20 hours depending upon the season.

The classification system of Catcheside, Lea, and Thoday (1946) will be used in describing the aberrations in Tradescantia. These are shown diagrammatically in Figures 10–8 and 10–9, and both metaphase and anaphase configurations are given. Scoring of slides, however, is customarily done at metaphase to avoid the effect of anaphase stresses on weakened chromosomes, as well as to determine chromatid relations which are lost at separation.

The *chromatid deletion* (Fig. 10–8) is seen as an interruption in one of the chromatids of a split chromosome. Up to metaphase, the acentric portion remains attached to its sister chromatid either in its original position or, by rotation, somewhat out of alignment. At anaphase, the deleted portion is usually freed and does not undergo movement to one or the other of the poles; it may, however, remain attached to the remainder of the chromosome by a slender thread, presumably of matrical substance. It is believed from a variety of evidences that many more chromatid breaks are actually produced than are observed, and that their number is reduced by restitution (i.e., they rejoin in the original way and hence escape detection). It has been estimated (Lea 1955) that only about one out of 20 of the original breaks actually remains to metaphase, at which time the broken ends are "healed" and are no longer capable of restitution or recombination (i.e., uniting with other broken ends to produce structural aberrations).

Isochromatid deletions involve the rupture of both sister chromatids at approximately the same locus, and four different configurations are possible, depending upon the sister reunions that occur. Thoday (1953) has

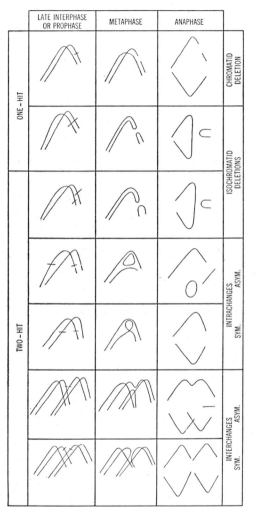

Fig. 10–8. Chromatid aberrations induced in late interphase or early prophase when the chromosomes, so far as their response to radiation is concerned, are longitudinally double, and their appearance at metaphase and anaphase of mitosis. The position of breaks is indicated by short crossbars, and the one- or two-hit character of the aberrations is noted (after Sax 1940).

shown that in *Vicia faba,* the degree of sister reunion is a function of the stage of division, being greatest just before metaphase and becoming progressively less at earlier prophase stages. Such a relationship does not appear to be present in Tradescantia. At anaphase a chromatid bridge will be formed if sister reunion of the proximal broken ends has occurred. Loss of the acentric portion will take place whether or not sister reunion has occurred.

Since isochromatid deletions involve the breakage of two chromatids, it is theoretically possible to have the breakage of both at the same time by a single path of ionization, or of each individually by two different paths of ionizations. Quantitative relationships to dosage, to be described later, reveal that both kinds occur, and these can be conveniently referred to as "one-hit" and "two-hit" types, the term "hit" referring to the path of ionization presumed to be responsible for the initial breakage. By the same token, the chromatid deletions referred to above are consequently "one-hit" aberrations.

The above types of aberrations are commonly called *simple breaks;* they are frequently found following x-radiation in Tradescantia. *Compound aberrations* are those resulting from the recombination of two or more chromatid or isochromatid breaks, and they are clearly of the "two-hit" variety. The resulting combinations, collectively called *chromatid exchanges,* are various and often intricate in nature when high doses of radiation are used, but only the more usual types need be described.

The exchanges may be both *interchanges* and *intrachanges,* and either *symmetrical* or *asymmetrical.* Interchanges involve the recombination of broken ends of two different chromosomes, intrachanges the broken ends in the same chromosome. If symmetrical, recombination among broken ends is of the nature of a crossover in that pieces of chromatids are reciprocally exchanged in such a way that no dicentric chromatids or acentric fragments are formed. The association of sister chromatids preserves such aberrations up to metaphase, however, and they are not dissolved until anaphase. If, on the other hand, the recombination is asymmetrical, the resulting configuration is different for interchanges as compared to intrachanges. With interchanges, a dicentric chromatid and an acentric fragment result, and a chromatid bridge will form at the following, or a later, anaphase. An asymmetrical intrachange, if between the two arms, will produce a ring chromosome and an acentric fragment, neither of which can survive indefinitely. Isochromatid and chromatid-isochromatid exchanges, both inter- and intra-types, have been observed, but they are relatively rare compared to those that have been described. Of all the exchanges possible, interchanges are considerably more frequent than intrachanges, while asymmetrical exchanges are somewhat lower in frequency than symmetrical ones.

Chromosome aberrations, produced in chromosomes that are effectively single so far as their response to radiation is concerned, are of four types: *polycentrics, rings, interstitial* and *terminal deletions* (Fig. 10–9). The polycentrics, usually seen as *dicentrics* or *tricentrics,* are simply asymmetrical interchanges, while rings are asymmetrical intrachanges. An acentric fragment, appearing double at metaphase, accompanies each of these aberrations.

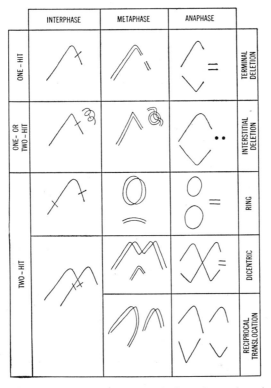

Fig. 10–9. Chromosomal aberrations induced in interphase when the chromosomes, so far as their response to radiation is concerned, are longitudinally single, and their appearance at metaphase and anaphase of mitosis. The position of breaks in interphase is indicated by short crossbars, and the one- or two-hit character of the aberrations is noted (after Sax 1940).

Anaphase movement of asymmetrical exchanges is varied. The dicentrics may separate cleanly, be interlocked, or form double bridges. The rings may also separate cleanly or be interlocked, or a single large dicentric ring may result. When tri- or quadri-centrics are produced, their anaphase behavior is likely to be quite complicated.

The visual distinction between interstitial and terminal chromosome deletions is not a certain one. Arbitrarily, the latter, which are presumably one-hit aberrations, are those that are longer than the diameter of the chromatid (although they can of course be shorter, too), and when divided longitudinally the two acentric chromatids can be seen lying parallel to each other. The interstitial deletions, on the other hand, are generally acentric rings of various sizes formed by the recombination of broken ends. Many of these are quite minute, and while the larger ones are very likely to be two-hit aberrations, there is a strong possibility that some are one-hit types formed by a single path of ionization (Rick 1940).

In Tradescantia, as with other organisms in which dividing cells are irradiated and studied, certain aberrations cannot be detected. Symmetrical chromosome inter- and intrachanges and paracentric inversions cannot be recognized in the microspore division or in roottip cells unless the exchange of chromatin is sufficiently unequal in size to alter appreciably the size of the chromosome or to shift the position of the centromere. Pericentric inversions could be recognized only if a shift in the position of the centromere occurred as the result of two breaks that were not equidistant from the centromere.

Many of the aberrations described would of course lead to the death of haploid cells because of loss or unequal distribution of essential chromatin. If viable, they can be observed in the meiotic cells of offspring from irradiated parents, and studies from Drosophila and maize indicate that inversions and reciprocal interchanges are commonly induced. In diploid tissues, most of the asymmetrical aberrations and deletions induced in genetic cells would cause death of cells (in Drosophila these would be grouped under the term "dominant lethals"; in maize, "embryo abortions") either through loss of chromatin or through interference with cell division. In tissues such as meristematic roottips, these aberrations would tend to be eliminated, and succeeding cell divisions would have fewer and fewer aberrations persisting.

All of the aberrations described are readily induced by ionizing radiations. Ultraviolet radiation, however, is neither as efficient in terms of energy in fragmenting chromosomes nor as effective in inducing as wide a range of aberration types. This is indicated by studies in maize, Drosophila, and Tradescantia, but there are some discrepancies still to be resolved. Early studies in maize (Stadler and Uber, 1942) and Tradescantia (Swanson 1940a, 1942c, 1943a; Swanson and Stadler 1955) indicated that only chromatid deletions were produced after UV exposure, and that there was an absence of inversions, translocations, and isochromatid deletions. Recent data, on the other hand, indicate otherwise. Fabergé (1951) has demonstrated, through a study of maize endosperm mosaics, that UV readily induces the same complex aberrations as does x-rays, while Kirby-Smith and Craig (1955), using dehydrated pollen of Tradescantia, have shown that isochromatid deletions and exchanges as well as chromatid deletions are readily induced by UV. It may well be that chromosomes in dehydrated pollen respond differently to UV than the same nuclei in the prophase of the pollen-tube division (the stage irradiated by Swanson), but the fact that internal deficiencies apparently of two-hit origin can be induced in Drosophila (Slyzinski 1942) suggests that the earlier belief of non-rejoinability of UV broken ends is incorrect, and that an end, no matter how it is broken, can reunite with another similarly broken end. This is also borne out by a study of UV-exposed ring chromosomes in maize (Schultz 1951) as well as by the results of Kirby-Smith and Fabergé.

A further type of structural change that has been observed involves a smaller subdivision of the chromosome than the chromatid. Nebel (1936) pointed these out early in a study of irradiated meiotic chromosomes of Tradescantia, and *half-chromatid* deletions and exchanges have been observed in the pollen-tube chromosomes of the same genus following exposure to both x-rays and UV (Swanson 1947). More recently La Cour and Rautishauser (1953), Crouse (1955), and Sax and King (1955) have demonstrated their formation, particularly in chromosomes irradiated in late prophase or early metaphase, while Slyzinski (1950) has shown that irradiated embryos of Drosophila may reveal alterations involving strands that are less than one-sixteenth the diameter of the chromosome. It would appear that the chromosomes are multi-stranded, although in most cases they respond to radiations as though they were either single- or double-stranded. The formation of half- or sub-chromatid breaks is disputed by Östergren and Wakonig (1954), who consider that only chromatid breaks are possible, and that matrical distortions are responsible for the effects described by others.

From these observations it is clear that radiations are not sufficiently delicate to determine the multiplicity of chromosome structure, and that breakage by radiations in the form of chromatid and chromosome breaks must involve more than one or two longitudinal segments of the chromosome. The question of when the chromosome is longitudinally replicated cannot, therefore, be answered through irradiation experiments with any degree of certainty—even though it is recognized that a reasonably sharp distinction, with a period of overlap, can be made between chromatid and chromosome aberrations. To what extent mosaics in Drosophila, arising from x-ray or mustard-gas treatment, may be resolved in terms of a multi-stranded chromosome in the sperm head, remains to be satisfactorily determined (Auerbach 1950, 1951).

The results obtained from the irradiation of the sperm of Drosophila do not differ appreciably from those described in Tradescantia. The different methods of detection, however, complement each other. Thus, while only viable aberrations can be detected in salivary gland chromosomes—and most of these are lethal when homozygous (Schultz 1936, Kaufmann 1954), indicating that irreparable damage has been done to the genetic constitution of the chromosome by the radiation—these aberrations can be examined in much more detail than in Tradescantia. Kaufmann (1943), for example, has described a complex rearrangement involving 32 separate breaks and reunions, an impossible accomplishment in plant chromosomes.

Distribution of breaks. The distribution of breaks involved in aberrations in Tradescantia chromosomes is not at random, there being a greater frequency in the proximal than in distal regions of the microspore cells (Sax 1940; Sax and Mather 1939), while the reverse appears to be true for pollen-tube chromosomes (Swanson 1942c). This would suggest that the initial breaks are non-random in distribution, but it is probably much more likely that the reunion of broken ends is non-random. Since restitution probably restores most of the breaks originally induced, restitution must likewise be non-random. One cannot directly determine the initial break distribution in any organism, but there is no compelling reason for believing that the initial effects of x-rays are non-random. What mechanism is involved in determining the non-randomness of the reunion process is not entirely clear, although Sax (1940) has suggested that it may be stresses imposed by the coiling of chromosomes, initiated possibly in the centromeric regions.

In *D. melanogaster* radiation-induced breaks are distributed among the chromosomes in proportion to their respective lengths, although there is some indication in the X-chromosome that some intercalary regions such as 11A, 12D, and 12E have a higher break frequency than normal (Kaufmann, 1954). These points along the chromosomes may be positions of intercalary heterochromatin, although the Drosophila data, with one exception, indicate little or no difference in breakability of heterochromatin as compared to euchromatin. In *D. virilis,* however, the Y-chromosome, which is totally heterochromatic, participates in exchanges only half as frequently as the X, although the two are of comparable length (Baker 1949). Darlington and La Cour (1945) indicate that heterochromatin in *Trillium* is unbreakable when "charged" with nucleic acid, but this seems unlikely.

In Drosophila and Sciara, the pattern of rearrangements induced by radiation differs between the sexes. In males all possible viable rearrangements seem to occur, but in females the rearrangements are almost exclusively intrachromosomal, i.e., few or no translocations are found (Crouse 1950; Kaufmann 1954). The absence of translocations in females is difficult to explain in view of the ease with which they are induced in other organisms, but it may well be dependent on a pattern of chromosomal distributions in the cell which, because of their distance from each other, precludes the formation of interchanges.

Differential sensitivity among cells and organisms. The factors that determine the sensitivity of chromosomes to breakage by radiations is not understood; Sparrow (1951) has summed up the various factors that may be operative. One of the difficulties encountered is a determination of whether differences in the final aberration frequency stem from differences in initial rates of breakage prior to restitution and reunion, or from differential rates of restitution. As shall be made clear later, the problem is not easy of solution, but the fact remains that different organisms have vastly different susceptibilities, and, to a lesser extent, so do different cells of the same organism.

The latter point is well illustrated by studies of Tradescantia (Sax and Swanson 1941). Of the four types of cells that can be conveniently examined, the order of sensitivity, from high to low, is: microsporocytes, microspores, roottip cells, and generative nuclei in mature pollen grains, with meiotic cells being 20–50 times more sensitive than the generation nuclei. Whether differences in coiling, DNA content, water content, or other factors are responsible, remains to be determined. Smith (1942b), in fact, has shown that a strain of *Triticum monococcum,* differing principally from other strains by a single Mendelian factor, is greatly different in its susceptibility to x-rays.

Considerable study has been devoted to the changing sensitivity of cells during the course of cell division. The pattern of sensitivity in Tradescantia is indicated in Figure 10–10. Breakage at metaphase is practically absent

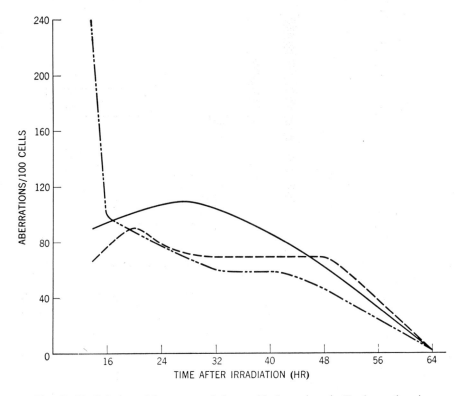

Fig. 10–10. Relation of frequency of chromatid aberrations in Tradescantia microspores to time after radiation. It is not possible to relate stages of mitosis to time after radiation in any precise manner, since the radiation affects the time sequence of division. The time sequence would be greatly shortened if the same study had been carried out in the summer months, when the rate of gametogenesis in the anthers is more rapid (this study was done in February). Solid curve, chromatid deletions; broken line, isochromatid deletions; dash-dot line, chromatid interchanges. Dose, 150 *r* at 50 *r*/min. (redrawn from Swanson and Schwartz 1953).

when observed immediately after radiation, and a peak is reached at about 12 hours, corresponding to exposures made at mid- or late prophase, after which the frequency declines. In this particular study, made when the mitotic cycle was relatively slow, the chromosomal aberrations appeared at 48 hours after radiation and a steady rate of these was soon obtained which persisted for many hours.

The comparative resistance of metaphase chromosomes to breakage is, however, deceptive, for although aberrations cannot be detected initially, they appear at the next division, and it is now quite clear that late prophase and metaphase are the stages most susceptible to breakage by ionizing radiations. This is indicated by Sparrow's (1951) study of meiosis in Trillium microsporocytes (Fig. 10–11). This pattern of sensitivity has been

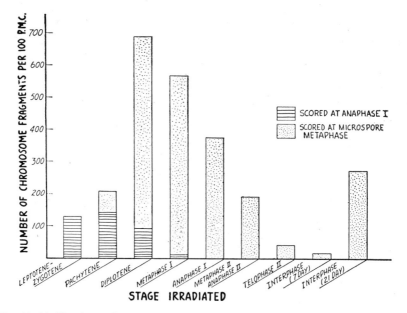

Fig. 10–11. Numbers of chromosome fragments induced by 50 *r* of x-rays at various stages of microsporogenesis in *Trillium erectum* (Sparrow, Moses and Steele 1952).

found in other organisms, both plant and animal, where the immediate as well as the succeeding metaphases can be studied, although again the determining factors have not been identified. With UV, the peak sensitivity in the pollen-tube chromosomes of Tradescantia is reached somewhat earlier than that for x-rays, but these chromosomes cannot be studied beyond the immediate division so that they cannot be compared directly with the more extensive x-ray data from microspore or meiotic chromosomes (Swanson 1943a).

Sax (1942) has shown that the sensitivity of chromosomes depends in part on the presence or absence of a centromere. Chromosomes were first irradiated in the resting stage to produce dicentric and ring chromosomes, plus their accompanying acentric fragments, after which they were irradiated at a later stage to induce chromatid aberrations. The latter were ten times more frequent in centric than in acentric parts when compared on a comparable length basis. Rees (1953) has also produced evidence that suggests a centromeric control of aberration production.

Quantitative results. An understanding of the manner by which radiations induced the breakage of chromosomes has been largely derived from quantitative studies dealing with the dependence of aberration yield on dose and intensity. Such data were early obtained by Sax (1938, 1940) and the more recent evidence has been summarized by Lea (1955), Catcheside (1948), and Giles (1954). The neutron studies of Giles (1940b, 1943) form an important basis of quantitative comparison with the x-ray results, and permitted the development of a comprehensive theory relating the biological effects to both physical and radiochemical data.

Each type of aberration bears a particular relation to the dose of radiation, and some, but not all, exhibit a quantitative relation to the intensity of the radiation. With ionizing radiations, chromatid deletions show a linear relation to dose (Fig. 10–12). At the same time, they are independent of

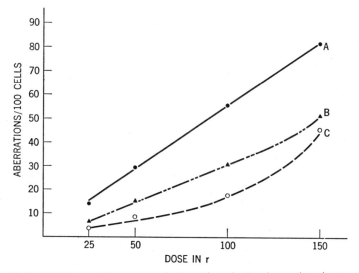

Fig. 10–12. Relation of frequency of aberrations in Tradescantia miscrospores to dose of x-rays. A, chromatid deletions; B, isochromatid deletions; C, chromatid interchanges (Swanson and Schwartz 1953).

intensity (dose rate), the same number being produced per unit of dose whether the intensity is high or low. This type of aberration is consequently considered to rise from a single event, i.e., a single path of ionization, and has been referred to as a one-hit aberration. There appears to be no threshold dose below which they do not occur.

Chromatid and chromosome exchanges, on the other hand, are two-hit aberrations so far as x-rays and gamma rays are concerned. Their relations to dose are such that the dosage curve is non-linear. When high intensities are employed (*ca.* 150 *r*/minute) the aberration frequency is nearly proportional to the square of the dose, but if the intensity is appreciably lower the power of the dose is also lowered. The dose-squared relationship is also obtained if the exposure time is kept constant, with the intensity varied accordingly. It can be concluded therefore that fundamentally the yield of exchanges increases as the square of the dose, and that exchanges arise from two separately induced breaks. Restitution, however, can remove the breaks from participation in the exchange processes if the time between two breaks is long, and this leads in effect to a distortion of the quantitative results unless the dose is given in a short time or unless the same exposure time is employed for all doses.

Isochromatid deletions and interstitial chromosome deletions exhibit a relation to dose intermediate between the one-hit chromatid deletions and the two-hit exchanges. The yield of interstitial deletions increases as the 1.5 power of the dose (Rick 1940), while that for isochromatid deletions lies between 1.0 and 1.5, the value depending on the radiation in question (Kirby-Smith and Daniels 1953; Thoday 1953). These types of aberrations constitute a mixture of one- and two-hit types, and although a further relation to intensity should be expected, this has not been demonstrated to hold (Giles 1954).

When neutrons and alpha particles are used, all aberrations show a linear relation to dose (Giles 1940b, 1943; Kotval and Gray 1947). This holds true for neutrons of varying energies (Conger and Giles 1950) as well as for those released from nuclear detonations (Conger 1954a, b; Kirby-Smith and Swanson 1954). It is believed that these particulate radiations, which are densely ionizing, are capable of breaking more than one chromosome during the passage of a single ionizing particle through the nucleus, and a dose-squared relation would no longer hold.

The effect of intensity on the yield of exchange aberrations is indicated in Figure 10–13. It can be seen that, with a constant dose, there is a gradual drop in yield with x-rays as the intensity is lowered, although this relation is not found with neutrons. Since restitution continually takes place, and since restitution and recombination are competitive processes, fewer and fewer breaks are available at any one time for recombination as the time between their formation is lengthened. The Tradescantia data indicate that a majority of the breaks [91 percent according to the calculations of Lea (1955) and Catcheside, Lea and Thoday (1946)] restitute and fail to be recognized, and that the average time they can remain open is four minutes or less for chromatid aberrations induced in prophase, but considerably longer for chromosomal breaks induced in resting stage (Sax, King, and Luippold 1955). Some small percentage of breaks remain open for much longer, it is believed, while in Vicia roottips (Wolff 1954) the availability of breaks for recombination is of the order of several hours rather than minutes as in Tradescantia. In Drosophila recombination does not take place

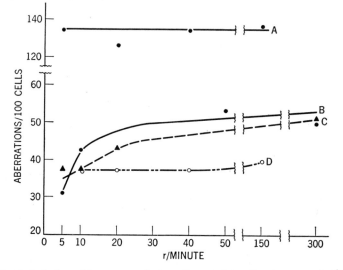

Fig. 10–13. Relation of frequency of aberrations to intensity of x-rays. A, chromatid deletions; B, chromatid interchanges; C, chromosomal interchanges; D, isochromatid deletions. Dose 150 *r* for A, B, and D, 300 *r* for C (redrawn from Giles 1954, after various authors).

until the time of fertilization (Muller 1940; Kaufmann 1954). Lane (1951), on the basis of fractionation experiments, has considered that the decline in aberrations as intensity declines stems largely from the fact that the initial radiation makes the chromosomes more resistant to subsequent exposures, this in turn leading to lowered frequencies of aberrations, but this point of view has not been supported by the data of other workers (Giles 1954).

A space factor is also of importance in the formation of two-hit aberrations. On the basis of quantitative physical methods, Lea (1955) has shown that on an average two breaks must be within one micron of each other in order for them to take part in the formation of an exchange. This relation imposes a restriction on the formation of exchanges, and leads to a certain degree of non-randomness of both distribution and type of aberration.

Earlier studies concerned with the comparative efficiencies of various ionizing radiations indicated that there was but little difference in efficiency between gamma rays and the hard and medium x-rays, but that an increased efficiency as regards breakage of chromosomes was attained when quite soft x-rays were used. Thus in a comparison of the efficiency of monochromatic wavelengths of 1.5 and 4.5 A, a greater frequency of breaks was obtained with the latter, and both were more effective than 0.15 A x-rays.

A drop in efficiency, however, was found with 8.3 A x-rays, but this could be explained on the basis of losses of energy due to absorption (Catcheside and Lea 1943).

These data are in accordance with expectations based on ionization densities and on penetration of the radiation. More recent studies on dry pollen of Tradescantia have shown, however, that clear differences in efficiency can be demonstrated between medium and hard x-rays and gamma rays (Kirby-Smith and Daniels 1953). A ratio of 1.0:0.70 was found when 0.06 A x-rays were compared to gamma rays, while a ratio of 2:1 holds for 0.20 A x-rays as compared to gamma rays. 400 *kev* beta rays were essentially similar in effectiveness to gamma rays emanating from radioactive Co⁶⁰. These findings have been confirmed in the microspores of Tradescantia both with chromosome (Kirby-Smith and Daniels 1953) and chromatid aberrations (Swanson, 1955).

The particulate radiations, i.e., neutrons and alpha particles, are considerably more effective per unit of energy dissipated in tissue than are radiations of the electromagnetic spectrum. The greater the energy of the neutron the less efficient it is (Giles 1943), but Giles and Tobias (1954) in a comparison of x-rays with fast deuterons and alpha particles have demonstrated that the important factor in determining effectiveness is not the type of particle but its rate of energy loss in tissues. As compared to hard x-rays, the neutron-x-ray ratio of biological effectiveness is about 4.5 for chromosome aberrations and somewhat lower (2.7) for chromatid types (Giles 1940b, 1943), but the results of Conger (1954a, b) and Kirby-Smith and Swanson (1954) indicate that neutrons have a considerably higher relative biological efficiency, with the ratio being higher for chromatid than for chromosome aberrations.

There is, however, an inherent technical difficulty in accurately determining the relative biological efficiency of neutrons in that it is almost impossible to remove, or to calculate the amount of, accompanying gamma-ray contamination. This is particularly true when the neutron source is a cyclotron or a nuclear detonation.

Slow neutrons, generated from fast neutrons and moderated by elastic collision to an average energy of 0.025 *ev,* have an efficiency considerably greater than neutrons of 1 *Mev* energy or above (Conger and Giles 1950). Fast neutrons produce their effects by the ejection of recoil protons from hydrogen atoms through a process of scattering, while slow neutrons produce theirs through capture and disintegration within the cell of the unstable compound atomic nucleus that is formed.

Hydrogen, boron, and nitrogen are the principal capturing atoms, which, on disintegration, emit, respectively, gamma rays, alpha particles, and protons. Calculations indicate that of the total *rep* of ionization produced, the hydrogen, boron, and nitrogen reactions yield, respectively, 16, 32, and 52 percent. The fact that the aberration-dosage curves are linear, and that alpha particles and protons are considerably more effective than gamma rays, indicates that the effect of the gamma radiation can be generally disregarded as being important. Conger has, in fact, estimated that the effective radiation from slow neutron exposure is approximately 38 percent alpha particles and 62 percent neutrons. If externally delivered, radiation of this composition would be about five times as effective as an equivalent (in *rep*) doses of x-rays, but when internally generated through the disintegration of unstable atomic nuclei, the ratio is about 15:1, or about three times more effective than external sources. This may result from a non-random distribution of boron and possibly nitrogen in the cell, or it may stem from the transmutation of the unstable elements on disintegration. Conger (1953), for example, has demonstrated that enrichment of the anthers with boric acid increases the normal yield 4–5 times, even though the concentration of boron in anthers is very low.

Ultraviolet is the only non-ionizing radiation capable of fragmenting chromosomes (Swanson and Stadler 1955). Earlier studies indicated that irradiation of pollen-tube chromosomes of Tradescantia produced only chromatid deletions (Swanson 1940a, 1942c, 1943a), giving rise to the impression that breaks induced by ultraviolet light were incapable of reunion, and hence of forming structural rearrangements. The absence of gross rearrangements in Drosophila tended to support this point of view, but the formation of interstitial deletions, some of which must certainly have arisen from two breaks followed by reunion, indicated the incorrectness of this point of view. A study of UV-treated ring chromosomes in maize (Schultz 1951) confirmed the fact that both breakage and reunion are involved, while the more recent studies of Kirby-Smith and Craig (1955) show that when dehydrated pollen of Tradescantia is used, the aberrations formed are not appreciably different, in a qualitative sense, from those induced by x-radiation. More recent studies in maize (Emmerling 1955; Fabergé 1951, 1956) also reveal that ultraviolet radiation is capable of inducing complex chromosomal aberrations. Structural rearrangements, however, are still very low in frequency.

So far as deletions are concerned, the relationship to dosage (at least with 2537 A) is linear (Swanson 1942c), although there is an indication of saturation as the dose is increased. So far as wave-length is concerned, 2537 A is about ten times as effective per unit of energy in inducing deletions as is a mixture of 2967 and 3022 A. The action spectrum for aberrations in the range between 3650 A and 2480 A approximates that for DNA absorption (Kirby-Smith and Craig 1955). This confirms the earlier work of Stadler and Uber (1942) on maize pollen, where terminal deficiencies were shown to follow the same trend with a peak around 2600 A.

On an energy basis, UV is most inefficient compared to x-rays. An exposure of 1000 ergs/mm² of 2537 A radiation to pollen-tube chromosomes in Tradescantia produces 0.1 breaks per cell. This dose delivers, after appropriate reductions for external absorption and penetration, about 10^9 ergs/gram of UV to the nucleoprotein of the chromosome, this being the same energy/gram resulting from 10^7 r of x-radiation (Gray 1953a). Such a dose of x-rays would far exceed the amount of radiation tolerated by pollen-tube chromosomes.

Modifying factors. The early hypotheses regarding the mechanism by which the ionizing radiations induced structural aberrations were based largely on physical consideration (see Lea 1955 and later in this chapter), and the principal factors were considered to be the type, dose and intensity of radiation. Breakage, restitution, and recombination were considered to be the primary biological events, with breakage being dependent on the type and dose of radiation, and restitution and recombination competitive processes determining the final yield of aberrations.

Many experiments were carried out to test these hypotheses, and these have not only clarified and extended our knowledge of radiation effects in general, but they have also indicated that the mechanism of action of radiation and the biological factors involved are considerably more complicated than was earlier supposed. An increase or decrease in yield of aberrations can be brought about by modifying the frequency of breaks, or by disturbing the competition between restitution and recombination, and there are indications that both can be influenced by supplementary environmental treatments.

The fact that aberrations are more frequent in the neighborhood of the centromere, and in centric as opposed to acentric portions of the chromosome, suggests that the frequency of restitution is non-random along the length of the chromosome. That restitution can be influenced by mechanical stresses is also indicated by the fact that centrifugation (2080 *rpm*, Sax 1943; 2300 *g*, Wolff and Von Borstel 1954) and sonic vibrations (9100 cycles/sec., Conger 1948) during the period of x-ray exposure can increase the frequency of exchanges and isochromatid deletions, while colchicine, which presumably interferes with spindle formation, and hence chromosome movement, reduces the yield (Brumfield 1943a). None of these agents as used are effective alone in inducing aberrations.

The results of combined radiation experiments are more difficult of interpretation. Ultraviolet (2735 A) markedly reduces the frequency of aberrations induced by x-rays at the same time that it induces breaks itself (Table 10–4). A pretreatment of Tradescantia pollen-tube chromosomes with UV one hour before x-radiation reduced the yield of all visible aberrations, although the yield of chromatid deletions and exchanges was depressed more than that for isochromatid deletions. A posttreatment with UV reduced the yield of chromatid deletions and exchanges, but did not affect the frequency of isochromatid deletions. The posttreatment effect, together with the fact that UV of this wavelength has a marked effect on the chromosome matrix, suggested that the process of restitution had been favored over that of recombination, possibly because of a greater resistance of the UV treated matrix or because of impaired movement of the chromosomes. The failure of isochromatid deletions to be affected by posttreatment sug-

---

TABLE 10–4

Percentage frequency of chromatid aberrations induced in pollen-tube chromosomes of Tradescantia by x-rays and 2537 A ultraviolet radiation, singly and in combination (from Swanson 1944).

Treatment	Chromatid deletions		Isochromatid deletions		Exchanges	
	observed	expected	observed	expected	observed	expected
x-rays	4.70	—	1.94	—	3.71	—
UV	3.05	—	—	—	—	—
UV + x-rays	3.13	7.75	0.62	1.94	0.00	3.71
x-rays	3.51	—	1.05	—	1.89	—
UV (2 hr.)*	3.17	—	—	—	—	—
UV (2½ hr.)	2.99	—	—	—	—	—
UV (3 hr.)	2.79	—	—	—	—	—
x-rays + UV (2 hr.)	3.29	6.66	1.17	1.05	0.00	1.89
” ” ” (2½ hr.)	2.25	6.49	1.02	1.05	1.43	1.89
” ” ” (3 hr.)	3.72	6.29	1.68	1.05	2.32	1.89

* 2 hr., 2½ hr., and 3 hr. indicates time after germination of pollen when UV was given. X-rays given at 2 hr., so UV followed immediately, 30 mins., and 1 hr. respectively.

---

gested that they are formed immediately on exposure of the chromosomes to x-rays, but the reduction in exchanges and chromatid deletions was a function of the time between x-rays and UV. Confirmatory posttreatment data has also been obtained in Drosophila, gross chromosomal rearrangements being inhibited by UV, but not dominant lethals which are supposed to consist largely of isochromatid-like aberrations (Kaufmann and Hollaender 1946).

The infrared-x-ray combinations are more difficult of interpretation. Infrared alone is ineffective in producing aberrations. In Drosophila, pretreatment with infrared (about 10,000 A) increased the frequency of x-ray-induced viable gross rearrangements, but not that of dominant or recessive lethals. Posttreatment was effective only when applied at the time of fertilization (Kaufmann, Hollaender and Gay 1946; Kaufmann and Wilson 1949; Kaufmann 1954). This would support the contention that the processes of recombination are being favored by infrared, although it is difficult to understand why viable but not inviable gross rearrangements would be increased (the latter would contribute to dominant lethality, which remained unaffected).

In Tradescantia both pre- and posttreatment with infrared increase the yield of aberrations with the exception that posttreatment affects but little the yield of isochromatid deletions (Table 10–5). The major effect in both cases, however, is on exchanges (Swanson and Hollaender 1946; Swanson 1949). Studies, however, reveal that the infrared effect is temperature sensitive (Swanson, Rupert and Yost 1953), with a peak of effectiveness around 12° C, and no effect above 20–22° C (Table 10–6). Further a temperature shock (48° for 30 seconds), interposed between infrared and x-rays (pretreatment), or between x-rays and infrared (posttreatment), effectively removes the infrared effect on Tradescantia chromosomes (Swanson and Yost 1951).

TABLE 10–5

Percentage frequency of chromatid aberrations induced by a combination of infrared and x-rays in Tradescantia (from Swanson and Hollaender 1946). Dose = 47.5 r.

Treatment	Chromatid deletions	Isochromatid deletions	Exchanges
x-rays	2.86	1.72	0.29
infrared + x-rays	5.63	2.68	1.72
x-rays	2.21	2.65	0.28
x-rays + infrared	4.96	2.62	1.89

TABLE 10–6

The effect of temperature in modifying the effectiveness of infrared, given as a pretreatment on x-rayed chromosomes in Tradescantia.

Temperature °C	Percent increase in chromatid breakage
36	5.6
30	—2.6
25	—2.2
23	0.0
21	2.5
18	85.0
15	125.0
12	216.0
7	85.0
2	50.0

These results would suggest that both infrared and x-rays are capable of inducing activated, or metastable, states in the chromosomes (i.e., in addition to the visible changes induced by x-rays) which can be raised to the level of actual breaks by the subsequent action of the other radiation. This interpretation considers therefore that infrared affects the breakage rather than the restitution-recombination processes. Against this interpretation is the fact that no other experiments have indicated that x-rays increase the subsequent sensitivity of the chromosomes (Giles 1954; Kaufmann 1954), so that the actual manner by which infrared affects chromosome breakage in combination with x-rays remains to be determined.

It should be emphasized that infrared in combination with x-rays must act in a different manner from UV, previously considered, and oxygen (see later). The time interval between infrared and x-ray exposures can be very long indeed without any effect on the subsequent yield of aberrations (Swanson 1949), indicating that the effect of infrared on the chromosome is relatively stable at normal temperatures. The results of Yost (1951) on chromosome as opposed to chromatid aberrations are in agreement, although the posttreatments with infrared, even if made when the chromosomes were longitudinally double, produced increases in chromosome rather than in chromatid aberrations. These results are difficult to interpret on any basis. Further, infrared does not affect all types of cells. In Tradescantia, the microspore chromosomes are readily affected, the dry pollen not at all. Roottip cells respond slightly if the infrared is immediately followed by x-rays, but not if a delay in time intervenes between the two radiations. There are some indications that a cell division between infrared and x-rays removes the infrared effect, a circumstance which cannot be tested satisfactorily in Tradescantia microspores.

It might be presumed initially that the effect of infrared on chromosomes was in the nature of a general heating phenomenon. Adequate experiments have been carried out to show that a rise in temperature, brought on by infrared exposure, cannot account for the results observed. Temperature, however, has a decided effect on the final yield of x-ray induced aberrations, with low temperatures during exposure to x-rays increasing the frequency of aberrations (Sax and Enzman 1939). This observation has been widely confirmed, although there is some indication that chromatid deletions are temperature insensitive (Catcheside, Lea Thoday 1946). It has been suggested that temperature affects the recovery process, i.e., at high temperatures restitution goes on at a more rapid rate, and therefore few numbers of breaks are available for the production of exchanges and isochromatid deletions. This may well be the case, to a certain extent, but a portion of the increases in frequency of aberrations at low temperatures arises from an oxygen tension which is higher at low than at high temperatures, and oxygen has been found to play an important role in aberration production (see later). A further indication that temperature plays a role is indicated by the fact that when oxygen is present, the yield of aberrations is high at 0° C., and low at 40° C., but that the reverse occurs when oxygen is replaced by helium (Giles 1954). The effect of temperature is therefore not entirely clear, and it may well be that both restitution and breakage are influenced by temperature, particularly since temperature before or after radiation has relatively little effect.

A major step in an understanding of the mechanism of action of ionizing radiations was made by Thoday and Read (1947), who showed that chromosome aberrations were appreciably reduced when exposures of cells were made under conditions of anoxia. That the presence or absence of oxygen was responsible for determining chromosome sensitivity to ionizing radiations was demonstrated by the fact that hydrogen, argon, or helium could replace oxygen, and the final yield of aberrations was approximately the same (Giles 1954). Furthermore oxygen must be present during exposure to be effective; pre- or post-changes in oxygen tension on irradiated cells were without effect. These findings have been extended to other types of radiation damage, i.e., rates of mitosis, stickiness of chromosomes, lethality, and nucleic acid depolymerization, and it is clear that anoxia is a very effective means of reducing radiation damage (Swanson and Johnston 1955).

The relation of oxygen tension to the frequency of aberrations is given in Figure 10–14. A leveling off is evident after the oxygen tension in air

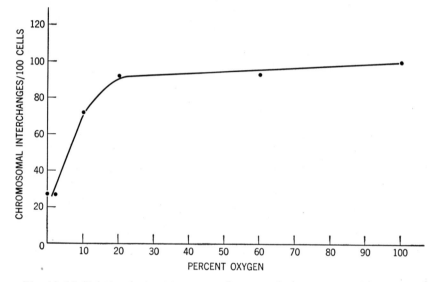

Fig. 10–14. Relation between per cent of oxygen during exposure to x-rays and the frequency of chromosomal interchanges in Tradescantia microspores. Dosage—400 r at 50 r/min. (redrawn from Giles and Riley 1950).

(21%) is reached, after which little increase in aberration frequency is achieved. If the dose is varied, the relationships shown in Figure 10–15 hold for both one- and two-hit aberrations. When chromosome interchanges in Tradescantia are used as a criterion of effect, a reduction factor of about 2.5 is obtained under anoxic conditions as compared to exposure in air when 250 kvp x-rays are employed. This same reduction factor has been found to hold for other radiation-induced phenomena when the quality of radiation remains the same. When chromatid aberrations are studied, however, the reduction factor (which can be conveniently expressed as *effect in air/effect in nitrogen,* or Air/N_2 ratio) is about 2.5 for isochromatid deletions and chromatid exchanges, but only about 1.4 for chromatid deletions (Riley, Giles and Beatty, 1952). This problem has been further studied, and it is now known that the Air/N_2 ratio varies also with stage of division irradiated (Table 10–7). Thus it can be concluded that differential reduction factors are to be expected among the various aberration types,

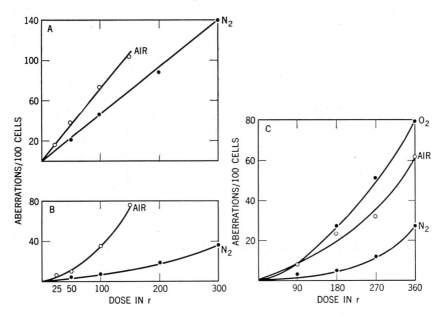

Fig. 10–15. Relation of frequency of aberrations in Tradescantia microspores to dosage when irradiation with x-rays is carried out in air and in nitrogen. A, chromatid deletions; B, isochromatid deletions; C, chromosomal interchanges (A and B redrawn from Swanson 1955; C, from Giles and Riley 1949, Table I).

and that any hypothesis attempting to explain these effects must be flexible to account for these variations in the reduction factor.

This point becomes particularly pertinent since it has been shown that

TABLE 10–7

Variation in Air/N_2 ratios for chromatid aberrations in Tradescantia as a function of the stage of division (from Swanson and Schwartz).
Dose = 150 r.

Hours after radiation	Air/N_2 ratios		
	Chromatid deletions	Isochromatid deletions	Exchanges
8	1.1	2.8	2.9
12	1.1	2.6	2.4
24	1.0	2.3	2.0

the Air/N_2 ratio for aberrations is closely linked to the type of radiation employed. Anoxia has much less of an effect when alpha rays rather than x-rays are employed (Thoday and Read 1949) while neutrons show an intermediate relationship (Giles, Beatty, and Riley 1952). The ion density of the radiation will therefore determine the magnitude of the oxygen effect with the oxygen effect being greater the less dense the ionization (Table 10–8). This effect of quality of radiation is strikingly illustrated when chro-

---

TABLE 10–8

Percentage reduction in total chromatid breakage in Tradescantia as the result of exposure to various radiations in the absence of oxygen (from Swanson 1955).

Radiation	Percentage reduction
Gamma rays from Co^{60}	59
X-rays—250 kvp, 4 mm Cu	48 (58)*
″ —100 kvp, 1 mm Al	43
″ — 50 kvp, unfiltered	36
Neutrons	33*
Alpha particles	0*

* Starred data derived from Riley, Giles, and Beatty (1952) and Giles, Beatty, and Riley (1952).

---

matid aberrations are studied, and the radiations employed are gamma rays and three qualities of x-rays (Table 10–9). The ion density of the radiation per micron of path length increases as one goes from gamma rays to 50 *kvp* x-rays. In air, isochromatid deletions and exchanges increase as the ion density increases, but chromatid deletions have a reverse trend. In nitrogen, the two former types of aberrations are greatly reduced, but the Air/N_2 ratios indicate that exchanges show the greatest reduction with

---

TABLE 10–9

Frequency of chromatid aberrations in Tradescantia induced in air and in N_2 by gamma rays and x-rays (from Swanson 1955).
Dose = 150 r.

Radiation	Atmosphere	Chromatid deletions	Isochromatid deletions	Exchanges
X-rays 50 kvp unfiltered	Air	49.3	84.6	35.3
	N_2	98.2	15.0	9.5
	Air/N_2 ratio	0.50	5.6	1.9
X-rays 100 kvp 1 mm of Al	Air	66.0	62.5	30.5
	N_2	79.3	14.0	7.3
	Air/N_2 ratio	0.83	3.9	2.0
X-rays 250 kvp 4 mm of Cu	Air	78.0	44.0	28.0
	N_2	63.5	16.6	6.0
	Air/N_2 ratio	1.25	2.7	2.3
Gamma rays 1.1–1.3 MeV	Air	96.2	32.5	26.0
	N_2	50.5	14.0	5.0
	Air/N_2 ratio	1.9	2.3	2.3

The header spanning the last three columns reads: Aberrations per 100 cells

gamma rays while the isochromatid deletions the greatest with 50 *kvp* x-rays. Chromatid deletions, on the other hand, have Air/N_2 ratios comparable in trend to those exhibited by the exchanges, but with the soft x-rays (50 and 100 *kvp*) may even be increased rather than decreased. It would appear that isochromatid deletions and exchanges, possibly through a process of partial repair or restitution, are being transformed into chromatid deletions, and thus compensating or even overcompensating for the reduction normally resulting from irradiation under anoxic conditions.

Oxygen can affect the final yield of radiation-induced aberrations in one of three ways (Giles 1954, 1955): (1) by determining the frequency of breaks, this in turn determining the frequency of aberrations, (2) by altering the metabolism of the cell in some manner as to affect the radiosensitivity of the chromosomes, and (3) by favoring recombination, which leads to aberrations, over restitution which restores the original condition of the chromosome.

The third possibility, proposed by Schwartz (1952), is strongly supported by studies in Drosophila where it has been found that loss of ring X-chromosomes, as indicated by disturbed sex ratios, shows no oxygen effect, whereas a striking one would be expected if oxygen tension governed breakage of the ring (Baker and Von Halle 1955). Support for the second possibility is suggested by the changing radiosensitivity of chromosomes during the cell cycle, while it has been shown that both carbon monoxide and carbon dioxide, when combined with air, lead to increases in aberration frequencies (King, Schneiderman, and Sax 1951; King and Schneiderman 1952; Schneiderman and King 1953). How CO_2 acts synergistically with the oxygen in air is problematical, but CO is a cytochrome oxidase poison, and by blocking this enzyme the flavoproteins may be excited to greater activity as terminal oxidases, thus leading to greater hydrogen peroxidase formation. Oxygen alone can produce much the same sort of damage as radiation so far as the production of aberrations is concerned (Conger and Fairchild 1951), and the fact that cyanide will inhibit this effect points once again to a possible role of some as yet unidentified terminal oxidase.

The three possibilities are not mutually exclusive, and through the possible role of H_2O_2 on chromosome breakage, may possess a common denominator. The earlier data, with the possible exception of the information on ring chromosomes, seem to fit most successfully into the hypothesis that oxygen tension, in determining the frequency of aberrations, does so by modifying the rates of breakage (Giles 1954, Swanson 1955, Gray 1953b), but the studies of Wolff, to be discussed later, make it clear that both breakage and rejoining are oxygen-dependent. It is believed that the radiodecomposition of water, and the subsequent formation of H_2O_2 in the chromosome or its immediate vicinity, is responsible for a portion of the breakage of chromosomes by ionizing radiations. The other portion probably results from direct ionization and is uninfluenced by oxygen tension.

It is legitimate therefore to speak of "direct" and "indirect" effects of radiation. The direct effects can be produced in a state of total anoxia, and there is as yet no protection factor that is absolute, nor is it likely that one will be found. The indirect effects, arising from the decomposition products of irradiated water, are at least one chemical step removed from the breakage of chromosomes. Water, when exposed to radiation, is ionized, largely into OH and H radicals, and these interacting with each other, and with dissolved gases, lead to the formation of HO_2 or H_2O_2, both being highly reactive with most organic molecules. Their formation is directly related to oxygen tension when x-rays or gamma rays are used, but largely independent of oxygen tension when the more densely ionizing neutrons and alpha rays are employed. The rate of production of hydrogen peroxide as a function of linear ion density is closely paralleled by aberration production (Fig. 10–16). For this reason the relation of the magnitude of the

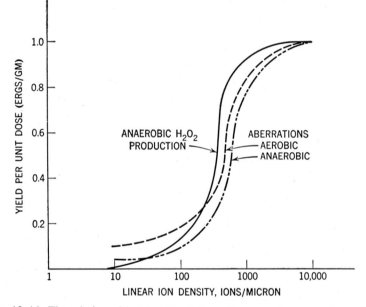

Fig. 10–16. The relation of ion density of the radiation to the production of H_2O_2 in aqueous solutions and to the frequency of chromosomal aberrations (redrawn from Gray 1953b).

oxygen effect to the quality of radiation makes very good sense when viewed in terms of radiation chemistry. The fact that it is the oxygen tension during the time of exposure, rather than before or after, that is important also fits into the hypothesis that the oxygen is part of a reactive system determining the rate of breakage.

The principal chemical reactions in irradiated H_2O are as follows:

$$2\ H_2O \longrightarrow H_2O_2 + H_2$$
$$H_2O \longrightarrow H + OH$$
$$H + O_2 \longrightarrow HO_2 \tag{1}$$
$$2\ HO_2 \longrightarrow H_2O_2 + O_2 \tag{2}$$
$$H + HO_2 \longrightarrow H_2O_2 \tag{3}$$

Other reactions take place which tend to decompose H_2O_2 to H_2O, as well as to remove HO_2, but the three reactions diagrammed indicate that O_2 and H_2 are important in the formation of the supposedly effective H_2O_2 and HO_2. The importance of H in reaction (3) for the formation of H_2O_2 has been demonstrated in water (Ebert 1955), although a similar relation to chromosome breakage remains to be determined. The immediate chemical steps by which these reactants attack the chromosome and cause it to break are as yet unknown, but the role of O_2 in the indirect effect of radiation is well established.

Breakage of chromosomes by chemicals. Before attempting to fit the radiation data into a model system that relates the physical and radiochemical events of radiation to the breakage and reunion of chromosomes, it will be well to consider, in a comparative way, the effects of chemical mutagens on aberration induction. Evidence indicates that radiations are non-specific in their effect on breakage, with points of breakage being distributed at random among the chromosomes and along the respective arms. The non-random distribution of aberrations, on the other hand, results from non-random restitution and recombination. With the discovery that chemicals can induce aberrations (urethane, Oehlkers 1943, 1953; mustard gas and its derivatives, Auerbach and Robeson 1947; Auerbach 1951), the hope has been that chemicals having a specific and limited action may be found to induce specific mutations or aberrations, thus obtaining information of gene and chromosome structure that could not be gained through conventional means.

This hope has not been realized, even though a large array of chemicals have been found to have effects on chromosomes. The active chemicals are not of any particular type, and presumably their action is as variable as their structure. Some, like colchicine, are mitotic poisons, producing a general blockage of mitosis or a destruction of the spindle. Others such as the mustards, diepoxides, and some purine derivatives, are radiomimetic in that their effects simulate those induced by ionizing radiations. Some, however, induce stickiness without breakage, some breakage without stickiness, and some both phenomena (D'Amato 1950; Levan 1951; Kihlman 1951, 1952a, b). Their variableness of action cannot, as yet, be related to their structure or chemical reactivity, but penetration of course is of great importance. As Kihlman points out, the purines fall into two groups: the lipoid- and the water-soluble types. The former have an action on the chromosomes of resting cells since they can penetrate the nuclear membrane; the latter, if effective, may be able to attack the chromosomes only after the nuclear membrane breaks down in late prophase. Their times of effective action might consequently differ.

The problem of penetration of chemical mutagens requires that techniques of exposure be developed. With Drosophila, the mutagen must reach the sexual cells or their progenitors, and techniques of feeding, injection, and exposure to gases (e.g., mustard gas) have been developed. In plants the most feasible approach has been through the use of roottip cells, and both Allium and Vicia have been commonly employed (Levan 1951).

Although a large variety of chemicals, differing appreciably in structure and reactivity, are capable of producing aberrations, attention will be directed only to those that have been studied intensively. These are various mustard gases and their derivatives (HN_2), one of the diepoxides di(2:3-epoxypropyl) ether (DEPE), 8-ethoxycaffeine (EOC), and the anti-auxin, maleic hydrazide (MH). It is not yet possible to say how any of these chemicals affect chromatin to bring about the induction of aberrations, but it is apparent that their actions differ among themselves at the same time that all differ in their action from the ionizing or photochemical radiations. Chemically, MH is more similar to EOC than it is to either DEPE or HN_2. Both MH and EOC are relatively unreactive compounds whereas DEPE and HN_2 have a high chemical reactivity with almost any organic molecule. The mutagenic effect of MH and EOC may possibly be related to the fact that both possess a structural resemblance to the nucleic acid bases: EOC is a purine derivative while MH is a structural isomer of the pyrimidine, uracil. Of these mutagens, MH is the only one having pronounced acidic properties, this being reflected in the strong pH dependence this compound exhibits for effectiveness. It is a powerful mutagen at pH 4.5; at pH 7.0 or above it is relatively ineffective (Kihlman 1956), suggesting that the unionized form of the molecule penetrates more readily than does the ionized form.

In spite of their structural similarity, the mutagenic action of MH bears no closer resemblance to EOC than it does to HN_2 or DEPE. Aberrations induced by MH, HN_2 and DEPE appear eight to 12 hours after exposure, indicating that the time of action, at least in Vicia roottips, is in early interphase (Revell 1953; McLeish 1953). Those induced by EOC appear within two hours after treatment, indicating that it acts in late interphase or early prophase (Kihlman 1955). The relation of effectiveness to temperature follows a similar pattern. Increasing temperature during exposure increases the effectiveness of MH, HN_2, and DEPE; EOC, on the other hand, has a peak effectiveness at 12° C, with diminishing effectiveness at higher and lower temperatures (Fig. 10–17).

On the other hand, the action of EOC and MH, but not that of DEPE, is greatly interfered with by reducing the oxygen concentration during exposure (Table 10–10), while pre- and post-treatments with 2, 4-dinitrophenol, an agent that uncouples phosphorylation from the respiratory

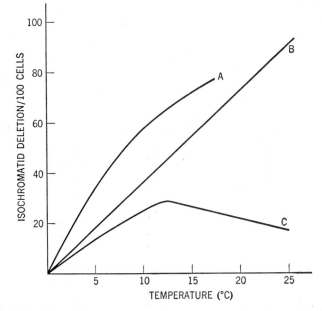

Fig. 10–17. Relation of temperature to the induction of isochromatid deletions in Vicia roottip cells by A, maleic hydrazide; B, di (2:3-epoxypropyl) ether; and C, 8-ethoxycaffeine (Kihlman 1956).

TABLE 10–10

Chromatid aberrations induced in Vicia roottip cells by chemical mutagens in the presence (air) and absence (N_2 = nitrogen) of oxygen (Kihlman 1956).

Mutagen	Atmosphere	Recovery period in hours	———Aberrations/100 cells——— Isochromatid deletions	Exchanges
EOC	air	5½	14.5	94.5
	N_2	”	1.8	2.8
	air	19	71.6	17.0
	N_2	”	2.6	0.8
MH	air	24	66.8	12.8
	N_2	”	18.3	2.8
	air	48	30.0	11.5
	N_2	”	14.0	3.5
DEPE	air	24	44.0	7.5
	N_2	”	44.0	17.0
	air	48	54.0	32.5
	N_2	”	68.0	19.0

cycle, have a variable effect (Table 10–11). These results are difficult to interpret as regards the pathway of action of chemical mutagens, but it suggests that oxidative phosphorylation is in some way related to their mode of action at the same time that it emphasizes that each mutagen is unique in action.

TABLE 10–11

Chromatid aberrations induced in Vicia roottip cells by chemical mutagens when combined wth pre- and post-treatments of 2,4-dinitrophenol (DNP) (Kihlman 1956).

Mutagen	DNP-treatment	Recovery period in hours	Aberrations/100 cells	
			Isochromatid deletions	Exchanges
EOC	———	22	39.5	1.0
	Pre-DNP	”	1.2	0
	———	24	45.0	5.0
	Post-DNP	”	42.0	2.0
MH	———	24	65.0	13.0
	Pre-DNP	”	11.0	2.0
	———	”	72.0	13.0
	Post-DNP	”	15.0	5.0
	———	48	41.0	9.0
	Pre-DNP	”	4.0	3.0
	———	”	48.0	13.0
	Post-DNP	”	63.0	18.0
DEPE	———	24	30.0	6.0
	Pre-DNP	”	16.0	2.0
	———	”	23.0	13.0
	Post-DNP	”	3.0	2.0
	———	48	46.0	21.0
	Pre-DNP	”	67.0	45.0
	———	”	103.0	70.0
	Post-DNP	”	58.0	27.0

Their differences are also emphasized when one considers their specificity of site of action, which leads to a non-random distribution of aberrations (Table 10–12). With the ionizing radiations, it has been assumed that the distribution of breaks in chromosomes is at random as regards particular chromosomes or particular regions of chromosome arms. A non-random distribution of aberrations is further assumed to be the result of non-random restitution and recombination. With chemical mutagens, a non-random distribution of aberrations is strikingly evident, and implies that there are sites on the chromosomes that the chemicals attack preferentially. This can be seen most clearly when the effective concentration of the mutagen is low; the non-randomness tends to disappear when an excess of mutagen is used. In Vicia roottip cells, HN_2 and DEPE produce a heavy concentration of aberrations in heterochromatic segments in the middle of the long arms of the short chromosomes (Ford 1949; Loveless and Revell 1949; Loveless 1953; Revell 1953, 1955). MH-induced aberrations are also localized in heterochromatin, but in this instance the aberrations involve two blocks of heterochromatin lying on either side of the centromere of the long satellite-bearing chromosome (Darlington and McLeish 1951; McLeish 1953). Out of 202 MH-induced aberrations, 194 were localized in one or the other of these two regions. EOC confines its major effect to the same chromosome, but in this case the large proportion of aberrations involve the nucleolar region (Kihlman 1956). As indicated above, the degree of non-randomness of aberrations induced by chemicals is partly a function of the concentration of the mutagen; it is also a function of the time after exposure (Table 10–12), since it is most pronounced 22–24 hours after exposure than it is earlier or later.

TABLE 10–12

Distribution of isochromatid deletions in the chromosomes of Vicia roottip cells after exposure to chemical mutagens (Kihlman 1956).

Mutagen	Recovery period in hours	Nucleolar constriction: long chrom.	Centric hetero-chromatin: long chrom.	Mid. hetero-chromatin: short chrom.	Others
			Aberrations/100 cells		
EOC	22	32.5	0.5	1.0	5.5
MH	24	0	45.0	2.0	10.0
	48	0	10.0	2.0	6.0
DEPE	24	0	3.0	22.0	12.0
	48	1.0	4.0	15.0	25.0

The suggestion has often been made that chemicals and ionizing radiations induce breaks in interphase chromosomes because of their interference with nucleic acid synthesis. No critical evidence proves or disproves this point, but the differential times and sites of action of chemical mutagens, the ability of ionizing radiations to break chromosomes in all stages of cell division, and the differential effectiveness of mutagens and radiations under conditions of anoxia and in the presence of inhibitors of oxidative metabolism, would indicate that an induced disturbance of nucleic acid synthesis cannot account for all parameters that have been encountered. As will be discussed in the next section, it would appear that the chromosome can be attacked through different pathways, although it is possible that chemical mutagens and radiations have a common metabolic pathway which determines, in part at least, the degree of damage inflicted on exposed chromosomes.

Mechanism of induction of aberrations. It is impossible as yet to state with certainty how radiations or chemical mutagens induce aberrations in chromosomes, but Figure 10–18 is an attempt to formalize current notions of interactions at the chromosomal and physical-chemical levels within the nucleus during and after exposure to mutagenic agents. The major steps indicated are known with some degree of certainty, but it seems equally likely that the chain of events will become more complicated as more subtle experimentation is carried out.

At the chromosomal level the two major categories of events are *breakage* and *rejoining,* but each is apparently subdivisible. As to the breakage category, it is unlikely that all breaks consist of fully broken chromatids or chromosomes. Although difficult to assess, the concept of *potential* as distinguished from *actual* breakage (Thoday 1953) gains credence from x-ray-infrared combination studies in Tradescantia (Swanson and Yost 1951) as well as from genetic studies done in Drosophila with mustard gas (Auerbach 1951). So far as radiations are concerned, the linear ion density would probably be the principal factor determining the spectrum of chromosomal damage (Kirby-Smith and Daniels 1953; Swanson 1955), i.e., the greater the linear density the greater will be the ratio of actual breaks to potential breaks, and it seems likely, although difficult to prove, that the oxygen level of the cell would also be a contributing factor in converting potential breaks into actual breaks capable of forming visible aberrations.

The rejoining system can be subdivided into *restitution* and *recombination,* these being competitive processes for the disposal of broken ends of chromosomes in the nucleus. The great majority of breaks undergo restitution, Lea (1955) estimating that only one-tenth are realized as visibly detectable aberrations, but it is as yet uncertain whether restitution involves the repair of potential breaks or the rejoining of actual (open) breaks, or both.

More important, however, for our understanding of the events involved, is the fact that rejoining can be effectively separated from breakage. It has long been known that in Drosophila the rejoining of broken ends is largely delayed until after the sperm enters the egg during fertilization; in Tradescantia, chromatid breaks remain open for a period of four to five minutes on an average, while chromosome breaks may be available for recombination for a period of up to an hour (Sax, King, and Luippold 1955). In Vicia roottip cells the rejoining system can be separated from breakage and dealt with experimentally (Wolff and Atwood 1954; Wolff and Luippold 1955), and it has been shown that the act of rejoining is an energy-requiring event which can be delayed by inhibitors such as 2,4-dinitrophenol, cyanide, carbon monoxide in the dark, and low temperatures.

These studies suggest the involvement of oxidative metabolism, and Wolff has proposed that the energy required for rejoining is derived from energy-rich phosphate bonds generated by oxidative phosphorylation. His studies further show that the oxidative system controlling the process of rejoining is very sensitive to small amounts of radiation, and irradiation under anoxic conditions protects the system from radiation damage. Whether the oxidative system is nuclear or cytoplasmic is not known, although the recent studes of Allfrey, Mirsky, and Osawa (1955) on isolated calf thymus nuclei point to the existence of oxidative processes that generate energy-rich phosphate bonds within the nucleus. These were formerly considered to be confined to mitochondria.

The physical and chemical events depicted in Figure 10–18 represent a modification of an earlier scheme proposed by Latarjet and Gray (1954).

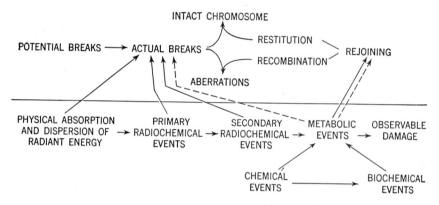

Fig. 10–18. Diagram to illustrate the possible relationship of physical and chemical events in the cell, arising from exposures to radiations or to chemical mutagens, to structural events taking place in the chromosome. Solid arrows indicate possible radiation-chromosomal interactions; broken arrows indicate possible chemical mutagen-chromosomal interactions. See text for explanation.

The principal factors determining the magnitude and the kind of physical events will be the dose, intensity, and quality of radiation. Thus, densely ionizing alpha particles would be expected to induce a different pattern of events, both qualitatively and quantitatively, than that induced by the less densely ionizing gamma rays or x-rays. The radiochemical events, discussed earlier, stem largely from the effects of radiation on water, and oxygen will play an important role in governing the steps involved.

A distinction has been made between primary and secondary radiochemical events; the former may be considered to include the production of short-lived decomposition products of ionized water, the latter the longer-lived peroxides which continue to act after radiation ceases. The continued degradation of irradiated nucleic acid after the cessation of radiation strongly suggests that such relatively long-lived peroxides or peroxide-like derivatives exist, particularly since such derivatives do not form, and the continued degradation does not continue, in the absence of oxygen (Butler and Simson 1955). The identity of the exact nature of the reactants and the reactions, however, remains to be determined.

The studies of Wolff, discussed above, and the data in Tables 10–10 and

10–11 indicate that certain metabolic steps must be considered as a part of the chain of events leading to chromosomal damage. Figure 10–18 shows only a single category of metabolic events, but it is not certain whether radiations and chemical mutagens share certain steps, or whether each has its own unique pathway of reaction.

The chemical and biochemical events shown at the bottom of Figure 10–18 indicate possible ways by which chemical mutagens can act on chromosomes. It would appear that the mustards and diepoxides, being highly reactive agents, have a simple chemical (non-enzymatic) activity first, and only later enter into a biochemical (enzymatic) phase. This is suggested by the fact that DEPE is inhibited in its action to a greater extent by a posttreatment with 2,4-dinitrophenol than it is by a pretreatment. MH and EOC, on the other hand, being derivatives of nucleic acid bases, probably act as anti-metabolites, and enter the chain of events via a biochemical pathway immediately. All of the chemical mutagens discussed eventually involve some part of the oxidative machinery of the cell (Kihlman 1956), and oxidative phosphorylation becomes suspect. However, the fact that cyanide acts on EOC and MH much as does anoxia implicates the cytochrome systems, which so far as is known are located in the mitochondria. It appears, therefore, that interference with any part of the oxidative metabolism of the cell will eventually lead to an interference with the action of a chemical mutagen. On this basis, oxidative phosphorylation can be viewed as one of the terminal steps, with the respiratory oxidative system one or more steps removed.

Any attempt to relate the events occurring at the physical and chemical levels with those taking place at the chromosomal level can only be considered as suggestive. The arrows in Figure 10–18 indicate possible relations. The physical and chemical events associated with radiation govern breakage; there is no compelling evidence suggesting that the metabolic events have any such influence. To be sure, the sensitivity of chromosomes changes with the stages of cell division, suggesting a metabolic involvement, but this variable sensitivity may well be due to the state of the chromosome rather than to any extrachromosomal metabolic system that contributes directly or indirecly to breakage. However, the fact that spontaneous breakage is variable from species to species, and often between individuals of a species, suggests that altered physiological conditions such as those induced by nutritional deficiencies (Steffensen 1953, 1955) may be responsible. The metabolic system, on the other hand, governs rejoining, but since the metabolic events are but a link in the chain of events, the physical and radiochemical events must also affect rejoining, even if only indirectly. It has not been possible to separate breakage and rejoining when chemical mutagens are employed, and for this reason it is considered that they affect both phenomena.

It is obvious from what has been discussed that the production of aberrations, either spontaneously formed or induced by physical or chemical agents, is easy to accomplish but difficult to comprehend in all of its aspects. A further understanding of the problem will require more detailed experimentation and a greater knowledge of the metabolism of the cell and of the chemical structure of the chromosome.

CHAPTER 11

The Chemistry of Nuclei and Chromosomes

The beautiful and impressive regularity of the chromosomes in cell division provides for the formation of genetically identical daughter cells (mitosis) as well as for the distribution of genetic factors to future offspring in predictable fashion (meiosis). The greater part of our present cytological knowledge of these phenomena comes from fixed and stained material, and the concept of permanency of the chromosomes is understandably derived from such studies. But phase microscopy and time-lapse motion pictures of living cells, and, in particular, studies of the incorporation of radioactive materials into the chromosomes, have altered and broadened our points of view, showing that permanency is restricted primarily to the cyclic behavior of cells in division. That is, at a particular stage the same chromosome, with its sequence of genes, makes its reappearance unchanged.

That the chromosome, like the cell or the entire organism, is a dynamic structure must now be faced, and at this level cytology merges with, and becomes indistinguishable from, cell physiology and cytochemistry (Danielli 1953; Mazia 1952; Caspersson 1950; Mellors 1955).

The task that confronts the cytochemist in attempting to characterize the chromosome as a dynamic chemical entity is a formidable one. In its dual role of being the carrier of hereditary materials and the organizer and governor of cellular activity, the nucleus and its parts must be capable of *self-reproduction* or *duplication,* of *mutation* without impairment of duplication, and of *specificity of action* in a genetic sense. In addition chromosome movements such as synapsis, crossing over, and coiling must be accounted for. These phenomena, long recognized cytologically or genetically, have their origin in the chemical makeup of the chromosome, and it is quite apparent that an understanding of them lies beyond the resolving powers of the light microscope.

In approaching these problems from the point of view of relating chemical structure and activity to morphological and genetical function and form, the cytochemist has at his command four major methods of analysis: (1) staining reactions of varying degrees of specificity, (2) photometric procedures for the qualitative and quantitative determination of chemical structure and concentration, (3) enzymatic digestion, and (4) direct chemical analysis following mass isolation of nuclei and chromosomes in an uncontaminated state. These methods, inadequate as they might be at the present time, and unreliable in unskilled hands, have demonstrated that the chromosomes and nuclei consist chiefly of desoxyribose nucleic acid (DNA), ribose or pentose nucleic acid (RNA or PNA), basic proteins of the histone and protamine types, and more complex or non-histone residual proteins containing a good deal of the amino acids tryptophane and tyrosine, and having acidic properties (Table 11–1). All except the histones and protamines are long chain polymers of giant size and possess a structural backbone to which side chains or groups are attached. Their almost universal presence in all types of nuclei, and in all types of organisms from the viruses to higher plants and animals, is a testimony of their vital importance, while their general form suggests that the shape of the molecule is critical to its function. However, no DNA has been found in the tobacco mosaic virus, and RNA is absent, or nearly so, in the bacterial viruses.

TABLE 11–1

Partial chemical analyses (%) of nuclei and chromosomes (from Mazia 1952 after various investigators).

Material	DNA	RNA	—Protein— Basic	Residual	——Other—— (Lipid and Ash)
Mouse-liver nuclei	28	3.6	69 total		3.5
Rat-liver nuclei	1.84	0.64	20 total		—
Calf-thymus nuclei	31		35	14	1.43
Calf-thymus chromosomes	48	1.2	40	8.5	—
Calf-liver chromosomes	25	2.4	20	50	—

It cannot yet be stated how these molecules are arranged to form a chromosome capable of carrying out its cellular and genetic function. The nature of the gene also remains unknown in a chemical sense, and it is therefore impossible to state with certainty its functional relation to the character that it determines.

THE TECHNIQUES

Staining reactions. The usefulness of a stain as a means of identifying, qualitatively and quantitatively, the components of the cell is dependent upon the specificity of the dye for certain chemical groupings, and upon the degree to which the dye can be bound (Novikoff 1955) (Table 11–2). Both acid and basic dyes have been used. Although use of them as intracellular probes has been greatly refined, extreme care must be employed in interpretation of the data, largely because slight variations in technique introduce rather marked differences (Swift 1953). This appears to apply particularly to the localization of chemical substances within the cell, as well as to qualitative and quantitative measurements.

TABLE 11–2

Relative amounts of basic dye bound by mouse nuclei as compared with the Feulgen reaction (after Swift 1953).

Basic dye and tissue	Relative amounts per nucleus	Ratio to liver parenchyma
Methyl green		
Liver parenchyma	11.2	1.0
embryonic cells	16.7	1.5
Small intestine interphase	12.2	1.1
metaphase	30.2	2.7
Azure B (after ribonuclease)		
Liver parenchyma	13.1	1.0
embryonic cells	20.8	1.6
Testis spermatogonia	40.0	3.0
primary spermatocytes	37.4	2.8
spermatids	8.6	0.7
Feulgen reaction		
Liver parenchyma	15.5	1.0
embryonic cells	16.6	1.1
Small intestine interphase	16.1	1.0
metaphase	31.5	2.0
Testis spermatogonia	30.0	1.9
primary spermatocytes	31.4	2.0
spermatids	8.4	0.5

The Feulgen reaction has proved to be particularly useful because of its specificity for DNA. The method consists chiefly of an acid hydrolysis followed by treatment with Schiff's reagent (basic fuchsin that has been bleached with sulfurous acid to form a leucobase). The hydrolysis frees aldehyde bases in the purines (adenine and guanine) of the DNA molecule, and these then react with the leucofuchsin to form a purple-colored compound. RNA does not react with basic fuchsin. When the Feulgen reaction is used for a quantitative determination of DNA, the variables that affect the dye intensity must be understood and considered (Mirsky and Ris 1949; Kurnick 1955), but under properly controlled conditions the amounts of DNA determined by the Feulgen reaction and by biochemical extraction methods agree very well. In such instances the amount of bound basic fuchsin is determined photometrically, the peak of absorption of the colored compound being at 540 mμ (Di Stefano 1948). Swift (1953), however, reports two peaks at 570 mμ and at 555 mμ following acetic alcohol fixation, and only the 570 mμ peak after chromic acid fixation.

Methyl green also exhibits a specificity for DNA (Kurnick 1950, 1955), although the amount of bound dye is dependent upon the method of handling of cells, and on the state of the associated proteins (Swift 1953). It appears to be useful in distinguishing between polymerized and depolymerized DNA (Pollister and Leuchtenberger 1949). It is therefore more variable than the basic fuchsin in binding power, but in conjunction with photometric methods it has been widely used for quantitative determinations of DNA. Methyl green absorbs heavily in the 630 mµ region of the visible spectrum. Some evidence indicates that the methyl green staining of onion roottip cells is lost if preceded by ribonuclease digestion, at the same time that the Feulgen reaction is unimpaired (Kaufmann, McDonald, and Gay 1951), suggesting two very different types of dye binding.

Proteins have been studied in stained tissues mostly by the Millon reaction, which results in the formation of a colored compound when the phenolic groups of tyrosine and trypotophane combine with mercuric ions and nitrite in acid solution. The tyrosine-mercurial complex has two maxima at 350 and 500 mµ, while the tryptophane-mercurial complex absorbs at about 400 mµ, thus making possible the identification of two of the constituent amino acids. The histones are soluble in sulfuric acid, thus permitting a determination of the total non-histone protein, while the total protein content can be obtained by using trichloracetic acid instead of sulfuric acid as a means of protein extraction. Much protein is generally lost through the handling of tissues prior to staining, so that care and standardization of technique becomes very necessary. Other staining techniques have also been employed, but their standardization has not been perfected (Pollister and Ris 1947).

Photometric procedures. Organic molecules have a characteristic absorption in the ultraviolet, visible, and/or infrared regions of the spectrum. This fact, plus the additional knowledge that the degree of absorption is a linear function of the concentration of the absorbing material, has permitted both qualitative and quantitative studies to be made of intact cells (Pollister and Ornstein 1955). Even minute parts of cells one-half micron in diameter may be so examined. Developed to a high degree of perfection by the Swedish school of cytochemists (Caspersson 1950), quantitative measurements to within an accuracy of a few percent are possible. The difficulty, however, lies in adequately determining the degree to which light scattering (due to inhomogeneities within the cell, or to differences in molecular orientation), stray light, and the distribution of absorbing materials influence the measurements made (Commoner 1949; Commoner and Lipkin 1949). When all the variables are taken into account, the values for photometric measurements often vary considerably from those obtained from the Feulgen staining reaction. The data obtained are most reliable when used in conjunction with other testing devices.

The use of visible light for measuring the amount of bound dye has al-

ready been mentioned. Ultraviolet light, on the other hand, is characteristically absorbed in both the nucleic acids and the proteins. Figure 11–1

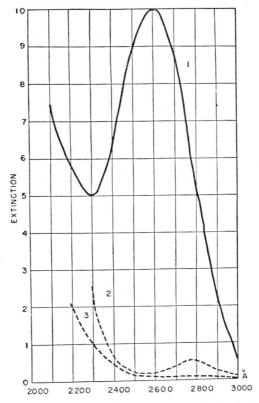

Fig. 11–1. Absorption spectra of nucleic acid and typical proteins at similar con-
centrations and at the same thickness of layer. Curve 1, 0.5% solution of thymus
DNA; 2, 0.5% solution of serum albumen; 3, 5.0% solution of protamine sulfate
(Caspersson and Schultz 1951).

illustrates the absorption curve for DNA, the absorption being due to the
presence of purine and pyrimidine bases. For this reason it is impossible
to distinguish between DNA and RNA, although one or the other can be
preferentially eliminated from the cell by specific enzymatic action. When
the photometric methods are used in conjunction with the Feulgen reaction,
they complement each other, since RNA absorbs in the ultraviolet but
does not react with basic fuchsin.

Protein molecules give a maximum absorption at 280 mμ, in contrast
to the 260 mμ peak for the nucleic acids. When the two types of molecules
are together, for example, in the form of a nucleohistone, it is often impossible to distinguish the protein absorption component; it is obscured
by the greater total absorption by the nucleic acids. Other methods must
then be used to make a further distinction.

Photometric devices generally consist of a light source, a monochromator or a set of filters for obtaining distinct regions or bands of spectral light, a microscope, and a means of measuring light absorption (Fig. 1–5). If ultraviolet is being used, a mercury arc for obtaining the sharply defined mercury reasonance bands, a quartz monochromator with a narrow slit aperture, and a microscope with quartz or reflecting lens are necessary since the short ultraviolet (between 200–300 mμ) will not past through the usual glass lenses. Measurements can be made either with photographic plates, in which the degree of darkening serves as a measure of transmission (the reverse of absorption), or with a photoelectric cell.

The use of ultraviolet light, while reasonably satisfactory for the qualitative study of cells, has its limitations. On living cells, radiation of this type is quite damaging and may lead to much distortion at the same time that movement of particulate matter within the cell makes measurements difficult to obtain. Despite these objections, however, cytospectrophotometry has become an extremely useful and necessary tool as cytology advances into one of its most fascinating and productive analytical phases.

Enzyme digestion. Two groups of enzymes—proteases and nucleases—have been successfully used both for demonstrating the presence and distribution of certain molecular structures in the chromosome and nucleus, and for ascertaining to what extent these molecules are of importance in maintaining the structural integrity of the chromosome. A necessary first step in the use of enzymes for specific digestion of chromatin is their purification; contaminants, however slight, can lead to erroneous conclusions, and as Kaufmann (1950; Kaufmann, McDonald, and Gay 1951) points out, crystallization of an enzyme is not by itself a sufficient guarantee of purity. Other variables that determine the enzyme's activity must also be taken into account. So far, fixed tissues provide the most suitable material with which to work.

Of the proteases, both trypsin and pepsin have been employed. The former does not lead to disintegration of the chromosome, but does transform the chromosome, in the presence of electrolytes, into a gel-like structure capable of swelling or shrinking as water enters or leaves the nucleus (Kaufmann 1952, 1953; Kaufmann, Pennoyer, and Rowan 1953). Presumably this is due to the hydrolysis of the nucleoproteins as an intact molecular species since removal of the nucleic acids inhibits the swelling. Trypsin attacks peptide bonds, and leads to a degree of degradation, but complete dissolution of the chromosome is prevented presumably by the presence of other bonds that tend to preserve it, although nucleic acids are released in the process. Pepsin causes a distinct shrinkage of the chromosome, possibly by the removal of certain proteins having acidic properties (Mazia, Hayashi, and Yudowitch 1947), but swelling can be brought about by washing with water.

The nucleases, both DNA-ase and RNA-ase, act to remove the respective nucleic acids from the chromosome, nucleus, and cell (RNA being in the cytoplasm as well as in the nucleus). The proteins remaining can then be stained with appropriate dyes. DNA-ase renders the chromosome Feulgen negative. Although RNA does not stain with basic fuchsin, RNA-ase reduces the stainability of the chromosome, cytoplasm, and nucleoli with such dyes as pyronin or toluidine blue. The enzymatic methods of analysis have therefore proven most useful when combined with critical staining procedures.

Direct chemical analysis. A mass analysis of nuclei or chromosomes is dependent upon the isolation of them in a relatively pure state and in sufficient amounts to be handled conveniently. Fish sperm and pus cells were used earlier, but newer methods of cell fractionation by differential centrifugation have eased the problems of separation (Claude 1946). Cells are mechanically broken and the structural components can be sedimented in layers in a centrifuge. Entire nuclei can be obtained in this way by washing macerated cells in a citric acid, which frees them from the cytoplasm. Isolated chromosomes are said to be obtained in much the same way (leukemic cells, Claude and Potter 1943; blood cells, Mirsky and Ris 1947), although Lamb (1950) has questioned the chromosomal nature of the isolated strands. Since these are isolated from resting cells, they are not visible in the nuclei prior to isolation; reasonable criteria for such structures are not known, although Mirsky and Ris (1951) have described morphologically characterized strands that appear similar to somewhat extended metaphase chromosomes. Since these workers have also demonstrated that the interphase chromosome can be changed into a metaphase-like appearance by varying the degree of hydration, their claim seems valid enough. At least it can be safely assumed that the material is chromatin, and that the analyses made from such material can be applied directly to the interphase chromosome.

CHEMICAL CONSTITUENTS OF CHROMOSOMES

The major chemical components of the chromosome are DNA, RNA, histones, and non-histone proteins. There is, in addition, calcium, which seems to be associated with the DNA (Barton 1951; Mazia 1954a), but how these components fit together to form the fabric of the chromosome is problematical. Mazia has shown that a chelating agent, versene, which binds calcium, causes the chromosomes to fragment into pieces of minute size, suggesting that calcium is important in binding sections of the chromosomes together. This is supported by the studies of Steffensen (1955), who demonstrated that the spontaneous rate of breakage is greatly increased when the nutrient conditions are calcium-deficient.

The association of the nucleic acids and proteins into a nucleoprotein complex is known largely from extraction methods, but to what extent these complexes correspond to their natural state in the intact cell remains a perplexing question. Apparently no one component can be considered more important than any other, for the emerging structural picture of the chromosome seems to be that of a fabric in which each of the several nucleic acids and proteins has a vital position and presumably an equally vital function.

Desoxyribose nucleic acid. DNA is a polymer of some complexity and variability. It was assumed at one time that it was composed of regularly repeated units of unvaried composition, but this view is giving way to a point of view that considers DNA to be capable of as much internal variation as are the proteins.

Structurally, the basic DNA unit is made up of a sugar, d-2-desoxypentose, to which are attached nitrogenous bases of the purine and pyrimidine types. The most widely occurring of these are the purines, adenine and guanine, and the pyrimidines, cytosine and thymine. An additional pyrimidine, 5-methylcytosine, has been found in DNA from both higher plants and animals although not in that from the bacteria and the viruses (Zamenhof 1952). Linkage of the base-sugar complexes is by means of phosphoric acids, and conventionally the structural formula can be depicted as in Figure 11–2. The relative amounts of bases appear to be fixed in

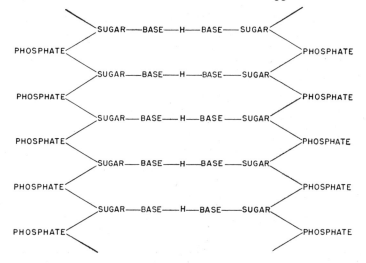

Fig. 11–2. Schematic arrangement of phosphates, sugars, and bases in DNA, with the right and left portions of the molecule held together by hydrogen bonds. It is uncertain whether the double structure, which in the case of DNA forms a double helix, is also characteristic of RNA as well; present evidence on base ratios would indicate that it is not.

the DNA from a given species, no matter from what organ the DNA was extracted, but the proportions differ among different species. DNA extractions from a wide variety of sources indicate that the adenine:thymine and the guanine:cytosine ratios closely approximate unity, but that the cross ratios, i.e., adenine:guanine and thymine:cytosine, vary appreciably (Table 11–3). The variations indicate that DNA, once supposed to be a most uniform and regular structure, is probably of great complexity simply by a variation in the proportion of the bases present and in their structural relations to each other.

TABLE 11–3

Composition of DNA preparations from various sources (after Zamenhof 1952).

Source	adenine thymine	guanine cytosine	adenine guanine	thymine cytosine
Man (sperm)	0.92	0.97	1.6	1.7
(thymus)	1.00	1.19	1.47	1.75
Ox (sperm)	1.05	1.01	1.29	1.31
(thymus)	1.04	1.00	1.29	1.43
Turtle (erythrocytes)	1.03	1.03	1.31	1.31
E. coli	1.06	0.97	1.04	0.95
Gypsy-moth virus	1.06	1.07	0.72	0.72
Wheat (germ)	1.00	0.97	1.22	1.62

Such complexity, suggested also by the fact that DNA's from various species differ in their rates of acid depolymerization as well as in ease of extraction, provides DNA with the diversity judged necessary if, as is generally supposed, DNA is the basis of genetic differences. From one cell to another within a tissue, and from one tissue to another within a species, the amount of DNA per nucleus is remarkably constant (Table 11–4), as one would suppose on *a priori* grounds the hereditary substances of the cell would have to be. The sperm, of course, have approximately one-half the content of a diploid cell.

TABLE 11–4

DNA content, in micrograms $\times$ 10^{-6} per nucleus, in various tissues of beef [from Mazia 1952, after Vendrely and Vendrely (1948) and Mirsky and Ris (1947)].

Tissue	V. and V.	M. and R.
Sperm	3.3	2.82
Thymus	6.4	7.15
Liver	6.4	6.22 (calf)
	—	8.4 (adult)
Kidney	5.9	6.25 (calf)
	—	6.81 (adult)
Pancreas	6.9	——

Differences in amounts of DNA per nucleus have been found when species comparisons are made (Table 11–5), and as Mirsky and Ris

(1951) point out, there is a strong suggestion of an evolutionary trend, with the amount of DNA per cell decreasing in the more recently evolved forms of animals. Where differences have been noted within a single species, it has been shown that the differences have a set ratio to each other, and follow a 1:2:4 relationship. Since tissues are known to have varying degrees of polyploidy, particularly if they are not in an active state of division, the increase in chromosome number should be reflected in an increase in DNA content, as found. This is strikingly illustrated when diploid (scutellar) and triploid (endosperm) tissues of maize are compared. In the scutellum the relative amounts per cell follow a 2:4:8:16 series while those in the endosperm follow a 3:6:12:24 series (Swift 1953). Where a range of variability in amounts of DNA per nucleus has been found in the same tissue, as is true for several mouse tumors, this can often be ascribed to aneuploidy or to misdivision of nuclear materials (Klein 1951; Hauschka and Levan 1953).

TABLE 11–5

DNA content, in micrograms $\times 10^{-6}$ per nucleus, in various species [after Mazia (1952) from Mirsky and Ris (1949)].

	Tissue		
Source	Erythrocyte	Hepatic cell	Sperm
Domestic fowl	2.34	2.30	1.26
Shad	1.97	2.01	0.91
Carp	3.49	3.33	1.64
Trout	5.79	—	2.67
Frog	15.0	15.7	—
Toad	7.33	—	3.70
Turtle	5.27	5.12	—

The constancy of DNA per nucleus finds reflection also in the chemical stability of the molecule. Overturn of phosphorus and nitrogen, based on the use of radioactive $P^{32}O_4$ and N^{15}-adenine, is very low, and occurs possibly only during the synthesis of chromatin, although N^{15}-glycine, C^{14}-formate and $C^{14}O_2$ show high overturn rates. As Swift (1953) suggests, it may be that parts of the molecule have high overturn rates, other parts relatively low rates.

The state of DNA in the cell is not known. Various molecular weights, running up to 10^7, suggest a long, thin molecule about 20 A wide and possibly 1000 times longer than thick, but the molecular weight varies with the method of extraction. DNA and histone, added separately in aqueous solution, readily combined with each other to form a viscous complex, but this provides only a suggestive clue as to how they are combined in the cell.

On the basis of the constancy of the amount of DNA per nucleus, the purity of the DNA transforming principle that can be transferred from one bacterium to another as heritable genetic information, and the injection of nearly pure viral DNA by a bacteriophage into a bacterium to be replicated in the formation of new viral progeny, there is good reason for assuming that the critical genetic portion of a nucleus is to be found in the DNA molecule. The structure of this molecule is, therefore, of immense importance if we are to understand the physical and chemical basis of inheritance (Watson and Crick 1953a, b; Crick 1954).

The DNA molecule exists in only one isomeric form; the shape of the molecule is consequently of importance. A second factor is the 1:1 adenine-thymine and guanine-cytosine ratios as indicated in Table 11–3, while a

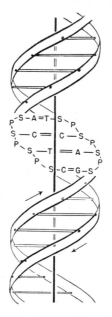

Fig. 11–3. Schematic representation of the Watson-Crick model of the DNA molecule. P, phosphate; S, sugar; A, adenine; T, thymine; G, guanine; C, cytosine. Horizontal parallel lines represent hydrogen bonds between the companion A-T and G-C bases (Beadle 1955, after Watson and Crick 1953).

third factor is the x-ray diffraction patterns of fibrous DNA, which indicate that the molecule exists as a double helix. From these pieces of information Watson and Crick have proposed a model which visualizes the DNA molecules as consisting of two complementary helices wound around a central axis (Fig. 11–3). The phosphate and sugar groups are on the outside of the helices, the bases inside, and the latter connect with each other by hydrogen bonds in such a way as to bind the two helices into a compound structure. The bases, therefore, are in pairs, and to account for the ratios indicated in Table 11–3 it is proposed that a pair consists of a purine and a pyrimidine grouping, and further that the only pairs chemically possible are adenine-thymine and guanine-cytosine. Any specific pair can be followed by any other pair to give diversity to the entire molecule.

Spatially, it is the phosphate-sugar chains that provide for a helical arrangement; the bases lie on flat planes between the complementary strands to bind them into a long but fairly rigid form. A base occurs every 3.4 A along the helix, and a complete turn in the helix takes in 10 base-pairs, or a 34 A distance. It should be emphasized that the structure proposed is only a working model which has not been unambiguously proved (see also Dekker and Schachman 1954). However, the Watson-Crick model accounts for many of the experimental facts known about DNA, it provides for the diversity of structure apparently necessary for its diversity of genetic function, it is stereochemically possible, and it offers a ready means for the replication of DNA, which, previously, has been an awkward problem. If one assumes, as has been proposed, that the helix can be split longitudinally and unwind, each of the halves can then form a new structure complementary to itself to complete two double helices. This could be done by drawing from a pool of cellular materials those molecular fragments necessary to complete a complementary structure. Precise and unequivocal experiments, probably by means of radioactive labelling and through the use of radioautographs of dividing chromosomes, will be necessary before it can be decided that the method of replication is as proposed by Watson and Crick, or whether the DNA molecule remains intact to act as a template.

Attractive as the Watson-Crick model is, it does not provide any information concerning the genetic activity of DNA except so far as the model provides for chemical diversity. The possible arrangements of the four nucleotides do provide a biological "alphabet" which can convey a large number of coded pieces of information much as the arrangements of amino acids of proteins account for their specificity of action. This, however, remains a problem for the future, although Schwartz (1955), Gamow (1954, 1955;) Gamow and Yčas (1955) and Lockingen and De Busk (1955) suggest possible mechanisms by which the coded information in the nucleic acid molecule can be transferred, with retained specificity, to proteins.

Ribose nucleic acid. Structurally, RNA differs from DNA in that the sugar is ribose and that the pyrimidine thymine is replaced by uracil. Whether the presumed structural variability of DNA finds a counterpart in RNA remains to be determined, although such diversity is suggested by the conclusion that nuclear RNA and cytoplasmic RNA are not identical in sea urchin eggs (Elson and Chargaff 1952).

Unlike DNA, RNA is found relatively abundantly in the particulate fractions of the cytoplasm. In the nucleus it appears to be part of the chromosome fabric where it is associated primarily with histone-like proteins, and in addition is found in the nucleolus where it is associated with tryptophane-containing proteins (Kaufmann, Gay, and McDonald 1951). The DNA-RNA ratios in the nucleus vary rather widely, Mirsky (1947) having obtained a 40:1 ratio from thymus chromosomes and a 10:1 ratio from liver chromosomes (Table 11–1). In the kidney the nuclear DNA-RNA ratio was about 10:1, while about 11 percent of the total cellular RNA was nuclear, the remainder being cytoplasmic. In the nuclei of Paramecium, rat pancreas, and onion epidermis, ratios from 0.6:1 to 3:1 have been found. Other ratios have been found, suggesting either marked variations in different tissues or marked differences due to extraction methods. Usually the amount of DNA is so much greater in the chromosome that RNA is stained and recognized only with difficulty, but after enzymatic removal of DNA by desoxyribonuclease the RNA stains well with Azure B. It is not known to what extent the amount of nuclear RNA is correlated with the phases of cell division, although a high overturn rate of P^{32} suggests more chemical change than that found for DNA. The variability in amount of RNA further indicates that it does not possess the constancy required of a substance having genic properties, but this supposition may be more illusory than real.

A seemingly important discovery is that the RNA content of the nuclei of tumor cells is much higher than that of more normal tissues. Ascites tumor cells contain five times as much RNA as normal cells, and leukemic cells show the same trend, suggestively pointing to a profound difference between normal and malignant tissues. On the other hand, RNA is more prevalent in active than in quiescent cells, but the amount may be simply a reflection of metabolic activity rather than a characteristic that would distinguish between normal and malignant cells.

RNA appears to be necessary for protein synthesis; it is found wherever these molecules are being formed within the cell (Swift 1953). In the chromosome it is not certain that RNA is an integral part of the chromosomal complex, but the belief has been expressed by many that the RNA is derived from, or made by, DNA for transport to the cytoplasm where it functions in protein synthesis. Hämmerling (1953) believes the nucleolar RNA to be synthesized in the nucleolus itself. When living amoebae are freed of RNA through the use of ribonuclease, the reappearance of RNA is in the nucleus first. It is also likely that RNA is dumped into the cytoplasm from the nucleus at the time of breakdown of the nuclear membrane, but the entire status of RNA, as to formation, structure, and function, is considerably less certain than that of DNA.

Proteins. The basic proteins, histone and protamine, have a molecular weight of about 2000, with protamine being the less complex of the two. Protamine has been found only in the spermatozoa of some fishes where it appears to have replaced histone; histone, on the other hand, is found in practically all the types of nuclei that have been studied. That there is more than one type of histone is indicated by electrophoretic analysis and by the fact that histones from mammalian sperm are not easily extracted with salt solutions. Nitrogen determinations show arginine and lysine to be conspicuous amino acids going into the structure of histone with but little tryptophane or tyrosine. Protamine has 90 percent arginine and no tryptophane or tyrosine. The basic character of the histones and protamines is derived therefore from the prevalent diamino acids.

The histones are readily extractable from the chromosome. A highly viscous complex of DNA and histone is removed from the chromosome by NaCl (concentration of one mol/liter), and the DNA-histone ratio of the removed complex is about 1.2:1 to 1.6:1. Dilute acids can also be used to free the DNA-histone complex, but not as completely as by the salt method. In such isolated complexes, a salt linkage bridges the DNA and histone molecules, but it is not yet certain that such a linkage is a natural one in the untreated cell.

The non-histone, or residual, protein remains in the chromosome after DNA and histones have been removed. It is insoluble in concentrated salt solutions and in the sulfuric acid-mercuric sulfate solution, both of which readily remove histones. The diamino acid arginine is present only in low concentrations (about 9 percent in cod sperm), while a great deal more tryptophane is found than in histones. The residual protein (*chromosin* of Mirsky and Pollister 1946) is probably to be equated with the *chromosomin* of Stedman and Stedman (1947), and both groups of investigators have considered this fraction to be the fundamental structure of the chromosome which remains after the DNA and histone have been removed. This hypothesis was advanced prior to the Watson-Crick studies, however, and seems no longer tenable. Both DNA and RNA seem to be associated with the residual protein, for the degradation of residual chromosomes by nucleases leads to their complete disintegration.

Other protein fractions have been isolated from nuclei, and it is safe to state that our knowledge of the protein structure of the nucleus is still far from complete. Certainly it appears that while DNA is a fairly reliable constant from cell to cell, the amount of protein can vary widely. This is illustrated by the data of Schrader and Leuchtenberger (1950) on spermatocytes and spermatids in the bug Arvelius. Small, medium, and large spermatocytes have nuclear volume ratios of 1:2:8, and yet each develops into a similar sized sperm. The amounts of DNA are the same in all the cells, regardless of size, but the total protein content is in direct proportion to cellular volume.

Radioisotope studies with N^{15}-glycine indicate that histone turnover is slow as it is for DNA, and residual protein turnover rapid in the cell, suggesting that the residual protein fraction of the nucleus, together with RNA, is actively involved in the immediate metabolism of the cell. The amount of residual protein also varies widely in different tissues (Mirsky and Ris 1949, 1951), but it is not certain whether the variation in amount is correlated with physiological activity (Swift 1953). On the basis of isotope studies, Hämmerling (1953) suggests that the nucleolus, which is rich in RNA, is also the site of synthesis of the proteins of the nucleus. It is not certain whether this includes both histone and non-histone types.

THE CHROMOSOME IN CELL DIVISION

The cytochemistry of the chromosome and nucleus is admittedly fragmentary, but studies of the past decade or so have lifted the nucleo-proteins from a position of comparative obscurity to one of great importance in both the long- and short-range activity of the cell. The DNA and RNA fractions of the nucleus and cell have been well characterized, the protein fractions less satisfactorily, but the problem remains as to how these components fit together in the nucleus to form a chromosomal fabric which at the same time can govern the immediate activity of the cell, control the transmission of hereditary influence, and duplicate itself with a very narrow margin of error once in each cell generation. Somewhere in this fabric —in its structure and function—lie the answers that are fundamental to our understanding of the cell.

In interphase. Various complexes, or sub-complexes, of nucleic acid and protein have been considered to be the all-important element in maintaining the integrity of the chromosome. Pollister (1952) estimates the average composition of the actively metabolic interphase nucleus to be about 9 percent DNA, 1 percent RNA, 11 percent histone, 14 percent residual protein. The percentage composition of the chromosome, based on an analysis of isolated chromosomes according to the methods of Mirsky and Ris (1947), is as follows:

1. DNA-histone salt-extractable complex (90–92%) $\Big\langle\begin{array}{l}\text{DNA } (45\%)\\\text{histone } (55\%)\end{array}$

2. Residual chromosome (8–10%) $\Big\langle\begin{array}{l}\text{RNA } (12–14\%)\\\text{DNA } (2–3\%)\\\text{non-histone protein } (83–86\%)\end{array}$

Lamb (1950) has criticized this work vigorously, insisting that the so-called "isolated chromosomes" are not chromosomes at all. But, even though isolated from lymphocytes in interphase, the structures are apparently chromosomal in nature inasmuch as "chromosomes" carrying the nucleolar organizer and the nucleolus have been identified.

Mirsky and Ris (1947) consider the backbone of the chromosome to be a protein framework, which may be the genetic structure or simply a structure to which the genetic portion of the chromosome is attached. Removal of the DNA-histone complex by NaCl solutions does not destroy the integrity of the chromosome, and they therefore consider the residual chromosome to be the basic unit. Kaufmann (1950), on the other hand, on the basis of degradation of the chromosome with highly purified enzymes, takes a more conservative point of view, according to which the chromosome is an integrated molecular fabric in which no particular protein or nucleic acid may be regarded as the primary and indispensable structural feature. It may well be, however, that this fabric has a dual and complementary chemical organization, one part being the DNA-histone fraction and one the residual fraction containing insoluble non-histone proteins and RNA (Mazia 1952). Both fractions are demonstrable by staining and by extraction methods.

The role of the interphase nucleus in the physiology of the cell poses a difficult problem (Mazia 1952). The assumption that it is the oxidative center must be modified since the oxidative enzymes are almost wholly concentrated in the cytoplasmic granules. In fact, the nucleus appears to exist in a definitely anaerobic environment (Stern 1955), although the more recent studies of Allfrey, Mirsky, and Osawa (1955) strongly support the view that calf thymus nuclei, at least, are capable of active oxidative metabolism. Nor is it, insofar as short-term activities are concerned, a coordinating center, for the cytoplasm can exist and metabolize for a while without a nucleus. Enucleation experiments (Danielli 1952, 1953; Mazia 1952) suggest that the nucleus is a replacement center, governing the activities of the cell but on a long- rather than a short-term basis. This occurs probably through its synthetic abilities, since DNA, RNA, and protein are believed to be formed in the nucleus.

The proteins and possibly RNA may actually be of a cytoplasmic origin, diffusing into the nucleus through the nuclear membrane; the fact that RNA turns over faster in the nucleus than in the cytoplasm, that it reappears first in the nucleus after depletion, and that it is rapidly depleted from enucleated cells, suggest however, that it, like DNA, has a nuclear origin, possibly through a transformation from DNA or by some as yet unknown synthetic process.

In mitosis. It is generally agreed that doubling of the DNA content of the interphase nucleus takes place in interphase prior to the initiation of cell division, although there appear to exist minor variations. In division, therefore, it would be expected that little or no synthesis of DNA occurs, and this is indicated by the findings of several workers, using both photometric and radioisotope methods of detection. Figure 11–4 illustrates diagrammatically the levels of DNA in the cell during successive divisions, and indicates that the total DNA is halved at anaphase when separation of the chromosomes takes place, and that re-synthesis is confined to interphase or early prophase stages. In Vicia roottip cells, the period of synthesis in meristematic tissue is about six hours in duration and at a time about eight hours prior to prophase (Howard and Pelc 1953).

In meiotic tissues, synthesis seems not to be complete until zygonema (Tradescantia) or pachynema (Trillium). The values remain constant through the pollen mother cell stage, are halved in the second meiotic division, and are quartered in the newly formed microspores. Synthesis begins anew in late interphase of the microspore, is halved again with the formation of tube and generative nuclei, and then apparently ceases in the tube nucleus but is doubled in mid-interphase in the generative nucleus which is preparing for division into two sperm cells in the pollen tube (Moses and Taylor 1955).

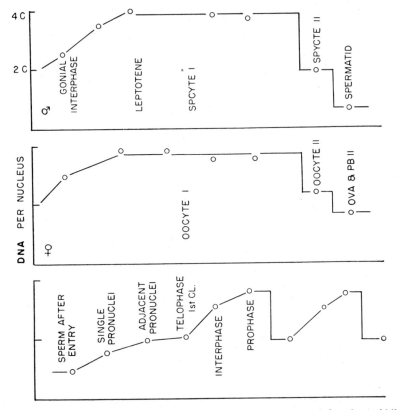

Fig. 11–4. Changes in amount of DNA during male (top) and female (middle) gametogenesis, and early cleavage stages (bottom) of the grasshopper, *Melanopus differentialis*. The abscissa represents time in relative values (Swift 1953).

The situation is much the same in spermatocytes and oöcytes of the grasshopper (Fig. 11–4). An interesting observation (Swift and Kleinfeld 1953) is that in the oögonial nuclei of the grasshopper, the chromosomes appear split both before and after DNA doubling, thus making obscure the relation between amount of DNA and the number of chromatin strands. This is contrasted with the salivary gland chromosomes of Drosophila, which contain about 500 times the diploid value of DNA (Kurnick and Herskowitz 1952). It is natural to consider that DNA synthesis and chromosome replication are coincident and interrelated events, but it may well be that replication is actually the joining together of chromosomal substance that had been earlier synthesized (Schwartz 1954).

The protein changes in the cell during division are imperfectly known. Caspersson (1947, 1950) has indicated that the nucleic acid:protein ratio changes from 1:20 in prophase to 1:3 in metaphase, suggesting a marked disappearance of nuclear proteins during early division stages; but Swift (1953) suggests that condensation into a nucleoprotein state rather than a disappearance may account for the ultraviolet absorption changes found by Caspersson. The loss of proteins for spindle formation may also account for part of the changing ratio.

The possible protein changes in division make the observations of Ris and Mirsky (1949) particularly pertinent. Since the amount of DNA cannot account for the chromosome changes of prophase (i.e., coiling, and so on), the shortened metaphase chromosomes and the extended ones of telophase and interphase must owe their differences either to an increased protein content, which is contrary to the few observations made, or to a change in state of the nucleoproteins of the chromosome. Studies on isolated nuclei show that in a non-electrolyte such as sucrose the interphase chromosomes are extended, but that salts added to the medium induce a considerable condensation. Removal of the DNA-histone complex prevents this condensation, while lampbrush chromosomes of frog oöcytes, having but little DNA, cannot be condensed by added salts. It would appear, therefore, that condensation of the DNA-histone complex is responsible for the observed changes in the chromosome, but as yet no answer is available in chemical terms as to what is involved in condensation.

In development. A number of cytochemical studies have been made on embryos to determine the pattern of chemical change in nuclei as a function of development. While the usual doubling of DNA during interphase can be detected, interphase embryonic nuclei in the mouse, grasshopper, and lily show a greater range of variability in the amount of DNA than do cells where the stage of division can be more accurately determined (Alfert 1950; Swift and Kleinfeld 1953). The values, however, fall between two and four times the haploid value as would be expected, and the variation can possibly be ascribed to a non-synchronously dividing tissue (Swift 1953). Egg nuclei have been found to contain a much greater total amount of DNA than do sperm nuclei of the same species; the problem, however, is complicated by the greater possibilities of contamination from egg cytoplasm which may have reserve DNA in degraded form dumped into it from degenerating nurse cells. In later stages of development in the sea urchin, i.e., from gastrula to pluteus, a DNA constancy per cell is maintained (Mazia 1952).

An assessment of our present knowledge of the chemistry of the chromosome and its relation to the cell as a whole has been made by Mazia (1952) and Swift (1953). The chromosome is a dual structure made up of a DNA-basic protein (histone or protamine) portion and an RNA-protein (containing tryptophane and tyrosine) portion. The former appears more likely to fulfill the role of the genetic material of the cell, and in this capacity its function is a long-range one. The RNA-protein portion, with its high overturn, its considerably greater variability in amount, and its location in both nucleus and cytoplasm has a short-term role in that it governs the more immediate activities of the cell. So far, both nucleic acid and protein synthesis have been demonstrated in the nucleus, but there is a relative paucity of the usual enzymes that govern the physiological functions of the cell as a whole (Dounce 1954). The nucleus is consequently parasitic on the cytoplasm for its energy supply. However, the cytoplasm is also dependent upon the nucleus, and Mazia suggests that the nucleus functions by continuously replacing cytoplasmic mechanisms, possibly through RNA formed in the nucleus and passed on to the cytoplasm. The porous nature of the nuclear membrane is such as to permit the ready passage of materials across the membrane in either direction (Watson 1955).

In terms of differentiation, no ready answers are provided by the cytochemical data as to how one cell comes to be different from another. The observations of Beermann (1952a, b) on the changing appearance of chromosomes in different tissues suggest that different segments of the chromosome may come into functional activity at a specific time and place to play a role in differentiation, but it is premature to speculate on the general significance of these data at present. The studies of King and Briggs (1955), however, reveal that the nucleus may differentiate in the same sense that cells and tissues do. By transplanting nuceli from chordamesoderm and presumptive medullary-plate cells into enucleated frog eggs, they demonstrated that these nuclei are capable of further division, but that the cells derived from them do not differentiate into the three germ layers to form normal embryos. From this they conclude that nuclei from differentiated areas are themselves differentiated.

It would appear, therefore, that differentiation is both cytoplasmic and nuclear in character and possibly in origin, a conclusion also supported by the interspecific nuclear transplantation studies of Danielli (1952) in amoebae, and those of Hämmerling (1953) who has shown in Acetabularia that the nuclei are clearly responsible for morphogenetic effects. We are still a long way, however, from any interpretation that permits a correlation of the chemistry of the chromosome and nucleus with morphological events as expressed during the process of differentiation.

CHAPTER 12

Chromosomes and Genes

Chemical analysis reveals that the chromosome is for the most part constructed of nucleic acids and proteins, with possibly still-to-be-discovered other components as minor constituents, i.e., minor in amount although not necessarily in essentiality. This is indicated by the studies of Mazia (1954a) and Steffensen (1953, 1955), which point to the importance of divalent ions in maintaining the structural integrity of the chromosome.

How the various components are joined together to form a chromosome is not known; still less certainty exists as to what part of this fabric constitutes the gene, although the great likelihood of DNA possessing a major genic role has been discussed. The gene is of concern at this point, however, not only because the physical and chemical nature of the gene has been of paramount importance since the beginning of genetics but because of the very real difficulty of distinguishing between gene mutations and chromosomal aberrations (Stadler 1954; Muller 1954a, b). This difficulty has not yet been resolved, but realization of the existence of the problem has raised questions as to whether the gene is the well-defined, particulate, and measurable structure it was once thought to be. It has, in fact, been proposed that rigid limits as to dimensions of genes are no longer considered necessary (Goldschmidt 1946, 1951). As we shall see, the gene may be defined variously, and the definition proposed tends to set an approximate limit to gene size. To what extent these dimensions correspond to reality remains to be determined, and any considerations of gene size at this time must therefore be provisional.

DEFINITION OF A GENE

The concept of the gene is a logical extension of the hereditary character it determines, for the existence of a gene can be recognized only when its mutated form can be compared, in a variety of ways, with the normal, or wild type, gene from which it presumably arose. The Chromosome Theory of Inheritance owes much of its validity to the fact that a discernible character, inherited in predictable fashion, can be traced backward to a determining gene that resides in the nucleus in a particular chromosome. By crossing over, the gene can be referred to a particular region of a chromosome.

The first definition of the gene, therefore, is that it is the *ultimate unit of recombination.* Or, to phrase it otherwise, genes are those parts of the chromosome between, but not within, which crossing over can take place. The chromosome thus has a linear organization, the parts of which are concerned with the determination of different features of the organism. Delineation of a character, however, may depend upon only one gene, or, more likely, on the cooperation of many genes. At a cytological level, reinforcement of this concept is provided by the observed linear differentiation of meiotic chromosomes and by the detailed banding of dipteran salivary gland chromosomes. Indeed, many cytogeneticists have expressed the belief that there is a 1:1 correspondence between gene and band, e.g., the $3C_7$ band of the X-chromosome is thought to be the site of the gene *facet.* It has been claimed by some that there is more than one gene per band, but there is no positive and critical evidence, other than circumstantial, that the site of the gene in the chromosome is in the banded or inter-band region.

Recombination, useful though it has been in establishing the existence of a linear organization in the chromosome, has its limitations. With the higher organisms crossover rates of one in 10^4 to one in 10^6 are possible to detect (Pontecorvo 1952; Stadler 1954), while in some micro-organisms one in 10^{11} is feasible (Demerec 1955). Once the crossover rate approaches the mutation rate of the genes in question, however, the results become equivocal. When large numbers of organisms are used, and minute areas of chromosomes under study are properly flanked by marker genes, many supposedly single genes having numerous alleles are found to consist of two or three separate loci having similar or identical effects, e.g., the *white, forked, lozenge,* and *vermilion* loci in the X-chromosome of *D. melanogaster* (Lewis 1952; Green 1953, 1954, 1955a, b), the *Beadex* and *Starasteroid* loci in the autosomes (Lewis 1950, 1951, 1955), and the clustered mutants in Salmonella (Demerec, Blemstrand, and Demerec 1955) and bacteriophage (Benzer 1955). It was once believed that recombination provided a critical means for the separation of two genes that were non-allelic, and this concept remains valid so far as the studies in Drosophila and maize indicate, but the recent work in Salmonella and bacteriophage suggest that recombination can occur among the alleles of a given locus.

Benzer (1955, 1956) has studied a group of phenotypically similar *r* mutants belonging to Group II in the T4 bacteriophage; these are mutants that lyse some strains of *E. coli,* but not others. The mutants are clustered within a very limited segment of the linkage map, and their allelism to each other can be tested by special techniques of mixed infection. By such tests, Group II was shown to consist of two functionally independent segments, A and B (Fig. 12–1), and the mutants in segment A, while behaving as if allelic to each other in that mixed infection does not give extensive lysis, are non-allelic to those in segment B. Crossing over between mutants can be detected both within and between segments by the production of wild

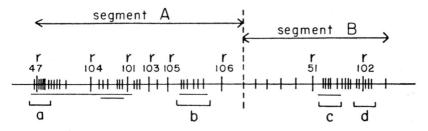

Fig. 12–1. Preliminary location of various rII mutants in the T4 bacteriophage, with the two primary segments A and B and the tested microclusters (a-d) indicated. Mutants in segment A are non-allelic to those in segment B, while those within a segment are non-identical alleles of each other. Horizontal lines represent mutants which show no recombination with other mutants within their span, and may be aberrations of some kind (Benzer 1955).

type after mixed infection (Fig. 12–2), but of particular interest is the recombination between mutants in the microclusters within a segment (these are designated by the letters *a* to *d* in Figure 12–1).

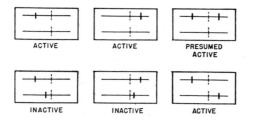

Fig. 12–2. Summary of the means whereby rII mutants are located within the linkage group and their "pseudoallelic" relations determined. The rII phenotype fails to lyse strain K of *E. coli*, but a "diploid heterozygote" condition can be created by doubly infecting the bacteria with two independently obtained mutants. When the mutants (position indicated by vertical solid lines) are in different segments (separated by the vertical dotted lines) extensive lysis (active) occurs, since these mutants are functionally independent; when both mutants are in the same segment, failure to lyse (inactive) is observed. Actually some lysis does occur in the inactive cultures, but in these cases it would be due to recombination between the non-identical alleles, and the frequency would be a measure of their distance apart within the segment (Benzer 1955).

The mutants in the microclusters are allelic to each other, as stated above, yet recombination between them can be demonstrated. Figure 12–3 indicates the degree of recombination occurring in microcluster A. Mutant *r 47* fails to show recombination with *r 312, r 295* and *r 168*, yet *r 312* and *r 295* undergo recombination with *r 168*. Benzer explains these results by proposing that a mutant locus extends over a certain length of the linkage map (designated by the length of the bars in Figure 12–3), and that recombination takes place in the space between these lengths. This postulate necessitates the assumption that mutants overlap each other, i.e., *r 47* overlaps other alleles in the microcluster, but it may well be that aberrations of some sort can account for the suggested overlapping.

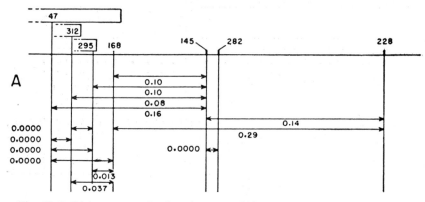

Fig. 12–3. Linkage map of microcluster *a* within segment A of T4 bacteriphage. The frequency of recombination between these non-identical alleles is indicated; where no recombination is found, the mutants are presumed to be identical (Benzer 1955).

Figure 12–4 illustrates the progressive dissection of a portion of the linkage map into particular alleles. It must be recognized, however, that the term "allele" does not have the meaning in Drosophila and maize genetics that it does in the bacteriophage. In the higher organisms an allele is indivisible by recombination so far as is known; this is the classical definition of an allele. In bacteriophage, however, the alleles in, say segment A, are strung in linear fashion along the linkage map and are separable through recombination. According to the classical definition these would be considered non-allelic to each other since they are separable, yet in a functional sense they are allelic in that they are phenotypically similar in their effect, and in that mixed infection of a bacterium by two particles having mutants in the same microcluster does not cause extensive lysis. Benzer (1955) proposes that recombination can take place within a gene "simply because functional genetic units are composed of smaller recombinational and mutational elements," but this concept does not agree with the Drosophila studies, where the functional, recombinational, and mutational unit is one and the same physical unit (Green 1955a). It is not likely that the genetic units differ greatly in the different forms studied since DNA seems to be the common denominator of heredity, but it may be that the recombinational process in bacteriophages is radically different from that in higher organisms, and that this determines the degree to which the gene can be segmented into its parts.

Translation of the bacteriophage results into specific chemical distances is also possible. As Figure 12–1 indicates, the recombination distances are reasonably large even though the linkage maps, physically, must be extremely small. This must mean that the recombination rate is higher per unit of hereditary material than it is in higher organisms. It has been

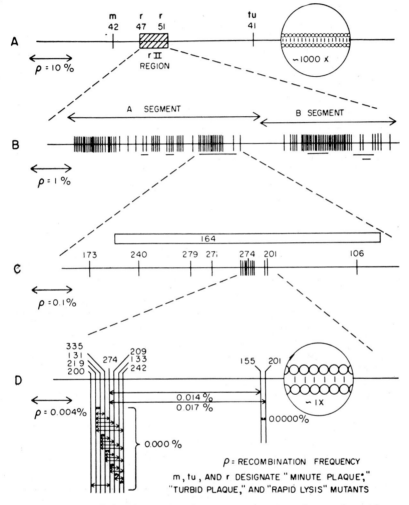

Fig. 12–4. Linkage maps of T4 bacteriophage. A, location of rII region with respect to other mutants. The circled inset represents nucleotide pairs according to the Watson-Crick model of the DNA molecule, and based on the assumption that the bacteriophage chromosome is a DNA fiber. B, segments A and B of the rII region. C, selected group of mutants on a larger scale. D, further magnification (Benzer 1956).

further estimated that the number of nucleotides per bacteriophage particle is about 4×10^5 (Hershey, Dixon, and Chase 1953). If the Watson-Crick model for the DNA molecule is provisionaly accepted, this means 2×10^5 nucleotide pairs. If it is assumed that the length of the T4 genetic map, consisting of three linkage groups, is double its present length of 100 units, then recombination per nucleotide pair is 10^{-3} percent. To state it otherwise, if two mutants were situated the distance of one nucleotide from each, then one in 10^5 progeny should be a recombinant type. As Benzer points out, these calculations are very rough, but they do indicate that the units of recombination are not larger than 10 to 12 nucleotide pairs, or 34 to 40 A in length (Fig. 12–4). Such recombination distances are several orders of magnitude smaller than those in higher organisms.

A somewhat similar situation exists in Salmonella (Demerec, Blemstrand, and Demerec 1955). Of 42 cystine-requiring mutants, eight fall into Group A, 20 into Group B, and 14 into Group C. Similar groupings were obtained with other nutritional mutants. The mutants in any group have a higher degree of similarity to each other than to mutants in different groups. There are, as in bacteriophage, indications of allelism within, but not between, groups of mutants, yet recombination takes place among mutants within a group. It has been suggested that "all mutants belonging to the same class (group) are non-identical alleles of the same gene locus." This definition coincides, therefore, with that proposed by Benzer, and a genetic locus includes a segment of the linkage map. Changes occurring within different regions of this segment give rise to different alleles. Transduction can lead to the incorporation of an allele from donor to recipient cell, and on the basis discussed above, the transduced piece would be smaller than a locus but as large as or larger than an allele.

The gene has also been defined as the *ultimate unit of mutation*. This definition assumes identity between the gene and the smallest segment of the chromosome capable of a change that is reflected in the form of a detectable phenotypic character. Under most circumstances, no difficulty is encountered in equating this definition with that based on the gene (or allele, as used above) as the unit of recombination. The studies in bacteriophages and Salmonella, described above, leave no doubt but that recombination can resolve genes that lie 100 A or less apart, and this order of magnitude for the unit of recombination does not differ appreciably from that calculated by Lea (1955) from radiation mutation studies for the size of the gene (see next section).

A third definition is that the gene is a unit of *physiological activity*. At a qualitative level, it is relatively easy to distinguish between a gene that controls one phenotype and another that controls a different and distinguishable phenotype, but the distinctions become blurred as the criteria become more quantitative or as the phenotypes overlap. The *r* mutants in bacteriophages and the pseudoalleles in other organisms emphasize these inherent difficulties. The *r* mutants of Group II, and the cystine-requiring mutants of any single group in Salmonella are phenotypically similar, and this similarity extends to the biochemical level of synthesis in the case of Salmonella, so that the conclusion is forced that the functional unit of the chromosome is considerably larger than the recombinational or mutational unit (Pontecorvo 1952). The unit of physiological activity can therefore be subdivided by recombination and mutation, and it seems advisable to follow Demerec (1955; Demerec, Blemstrand, and Demerec 1955) in referring to this unit as a *locus* rather than as a gene or an allele. A locus, then, is a section of a chromosome that has a unitary function, and any mutation occurring within its boundaries produces an impairment of this function. All mutations, so localized, will be phenotypically similar even though separable by recombination, and segmentable by mutations. The one-gene-one-function hypothesis (Horowitz and Urs 1951) may be provided, consequently, with a more exact physical basis if the physiological rather than the recombinational or mutational unit is used.

On the other hand, it should be emphasized that functional identity of adjacent parts of the chromosome, however large or small, is not an easy point to establish, particularly when adjacent, and functionally cooperative, loci such as pseudoalleles are involved, and both Green (1955a) and Lewis (1955) argue for an identity between spatial, functional, recombinational, and mutational genes. As Stephens (1955) points out, a common denominator of agreement still remains to be found that will permit a unification of the present divergent views, but a definition of the gene, acceptable to all, may well rest on no single criterion of function, behavior, or size.

Pontecorvo (1952) adds a fourth definition of the gene, namely, that it is the *ultimate unit of self-reproduction,* but as he further emphasizes, this definition has little meaning until one recognizes what is being self-reproduced. If the Belling hypothesis of crossing over, and the partial-replica ideas of Levinthal and Visconti (1953) and Doermann, Chase, and Stahl (1955) have any valid basis, it may well be that size of the self-reproducing unit can ultimately be calculated. Studies with bacteriophage, the pneumococcal transforming principle, and transduction in Salmonella seem to offer the greatest present hope, but the current lack of knowledge of genic structure and, indeed, of any self-reproducing body, makes the solution of this problem a formidable one.

It must be quite obvious that the four definitions of a gene given are inconsistent with each other to varying degrees, and that each definition is meaningful only within the limits of the techniques used in studying the gene. Stadler (1954), in fact, makes the point that a clear distinction must be made between the *hypothetical gene* of classical genetics, which was early visualized as a corpuscular and discrete particle inherited in Mendelian fashion, and the *operational gene,* which "can be defined only as the smallest segment of the gene-string that can be shown to be consistently associated with the occurrence of a specific genetic effect." This definition recognizes merely that a gene has properties, and the definition given is approached most closely when the gene is considered to be a unit of physiological activity. If so, microbial genetic studies inform us that it is further subdivisible into recombinational and mutational elements, but whether a gene or its subunits are separated from neighboring genes by definite boundaries remains to be proved. The banded structure of salivary gland chromosomes would suggest that this is so, but it remains a suggestion only.

With the gene being so difficult of precise definition, a similar difficulty is encountered for any definition of a gene mutation. A definition of the latter presupposes a definition of the former, since the existence of a gene can only be recognized through its mutated form. A type of circular reasoning is obviously involved here. Experimentally, it is known that mutations comprise a mixed assemblage of heritable changes. Some are obviously chromosomal, some are expression-mutations (i.e., position effects), while others give no evidence of being associated with extragenic phenomena. Whether the latter group is due to intragenic changes (transmutations or point mutations) or not will remain a point of dispute so long as discriminatory tests are lacking.

SIZE OF THE GENE

Any considerations of the size dimensions of a gene imply that the gene has finite limits. In the absence of critical data as to the chemical nature of the gene, together with inconsistencies encountered in defining a gene, determinations of gene size become little more than mental exercises, particularly since the classical concept of the corpuscular gene is gradually giving way to a more loosely conceived notion which admits, on the one hand, of recombining and independently mutating subunits, and, on the other, of the co-action of neighboring genes. The gene, therefore, at the present time is more a concept of function and behavior than it is of structure.

However, certain crossing over and radiation studies have tended to set maximal limits as to gene "size." The values are of importance only if considered within the frame of reference of the techniques that yielded them, and difficulties are apparent when the values are extended more broadly. In terms of crossing over, genes that are spaced 100 A apart can be separated if the technique permits the detection of one crossover in 10^5 organisms (Pontecorvo 1952). Benzer (1955), as mentioned, has pushed the size of the unit of recombination to even lower limits. If it is assumed that the gene occupies most of the 100-A-or-less limit, the estimate of size is in reasonable agreement with independent calculations made by Timofeeff-Ressovsky, Zimmer, and Delbrück (1935) and Lea (1955) from radiation "target volume" experiments, but it is lower by several orders of magnitude from other estimates. Muller (1947), on the basis of four genes located in a limited length of salivary gland chromosome, concluded that these genes had a mean length of 1250 A, while Pontecorvo considers 4500 A to be an approximation of gene size in *Aspergillus nidulans*. Lea argues that the radiation target volume (based on inactivation measurements) and the gene volume can be equated, and is from 0.003–0.005 cubic millimicrons (i.e., a sphere 20 to 60 A in diameter), while Delbrück's estimate indicates gene size to be that approximated by an amount equal to 1000 atoms. These calculations assume that an alteration within this volume leads to mutation, but since conditions other than the radiation employed can alter the mutation rate, gene size would correspondingly fluctuate. The target method of calculating size is therefore questionable (Muller 1954a).

If it is assumed that the maximum length of a gene is of the order of thousands, hundreds, or even tens of Angstroms, it must, on the basis of a DNA molecule, encompass numerous nucleotides within its dimensions, plus other molecular species that might go into its makeup. Present chemical knowledge of the chromosome is too fragmentary to permit any precise meaning to be attached to the above implications, and indeed the genetical knowledge is sufficiently vague and conflicting to lead Goldschmidt (1946, 1951) to propose that the gene, as a particulate structure, does not exist. According to his theory, mutations are simply rearrangements of parts of the chromosome—at sub-microscopic as well as at microscopic levels of visibility; and spatial relationships within the chromosome, with the chromosome acting as a functional continuum, determine the hereditary potential of chromatin. Goldschmidt's ideas to a considerable extent are based on an extension of position-effect data, to be described later in this chapter, but in defense of the operational gene it should be emphasized that this concept simply proposes that the chromosome is linearly differentiated into units having different functional and, consequently, phenotypic potentials. Crossing over has adequately demonstrated that this is true (Sturtevant 1951a). The gene, as a particulate entity, therefore has blurred boundaries, and until much more is known about its physico-chemical nature, it can be considered only in functional terms without straining the available cytogenetic evidence.

STABILITY OF THE GENE

It has been pointed out that the chromosome is an extremely stable, though dynamic, structure, appearing in unchanged form, cell generation after cell generation. In the Tradescantia study done by Giles (1940, 1941), a measure of this stability can be made on a chromosomal basis. Since the frequency of spontaneously arising visible aberrations in roottip cells ranged from 0.27 to 0.48 percent per cell, it can be stated that in Tradescantia one chromosome out of every 5,000 will undergo breakage every cell generation. This assumes, of course, that all chromosomes in the roottip cell are equally unstable, which remains to be proved.

In microspores, the number of chromosomes in the nucleus, or at least in the preceding pollen mother cell, determines, in part, the degree of stability. Thus in haploid microspores the rate of broken chromosomes was one in 1700; in diploid microspores from $4n$ pollen mother cells, one in 1000; in those derived from triploid pollen mother cells, one in 70. Hybridity and polyploidy consequently decrease stability. Nichols (1941) further showed that aging increases instability in the chromosomes of onion seed, with the degree of increase controlled by the genotype.

The stability of the gene can be similarly studied. This can be done in terms of the half-life of a gene, i.e., the time elapsing for a 50 percent probability that a particular gene will mutate, or conversely, the time in which 50 percent of the genes would be expected to mutate. Mutation rates can also be calculated in terms of cell or organism generations. Muller (1950a) has calculated that in Drosophila a gene, on the average, has a half-life of 10^3 to 10^4 years, while in man, approximately 10^6 years. The difference can be attributed to a faster generation time in Drosophila. In *D. virilis,* a group of mutable genes change at a rate of 3–14 percent per generation (Demerec 1941).

The differences are perhaps more understandable when considered on a cell, or gamete, basis. In maize, the R gene mutates at a rate of 492, the I gene 106, the S gene one in every 10^6 gametes, and Wx not at all in 1.5×10^6 gametes (Stadler 1942). The rate of sex-linked lethals in *D. melanogaster* depends upon the stock in question, the Florida stock having a rate of 1.09 percent and grading down to 0.07 percent in the Oregon-R stock (Plough 1941). These rates, however, are very misleading in terms of over-all mutation rate, for they are calculated on the basis of mutations that are readily detectable. It is known from Drosophila studies that in comparison to sex-linked lethals visible mutations are five to ten times as infrequent, dominant lethals slightly less frequent, and detrimental mutations (invisibles affecting viability) about five times more frequent. Muller (1950) has calculated on the basis of 5,000–10,000 genes present in Drosophila that one gamete out of 20 has a new mutation, a figure startlingly high. In man, one out of every 10 gametes would have a new mutation. An evaluation of all genic studies places the average mutation rate per gene at one in 10^6 per cell generation for higher organisms.

The stability of genes, as determined by their rates of spontaneous mutation, can be more accurately assessed in micro-organisms because of the large numbers of cells that can be handled. The usual practice is to plate a stock possessing a gene-determined nutritional deficiency on a medium that will not support growth, with the mutation rate being determined by the number of cells that have mutated to a nutritionally independent state. There is some hazard involved in that all reversions are not mutations of the particular gene in question, e.g., they may be suppressor-mutations at another locus which permit nutritional independence (Giles 1951; Giles, de Serres, and Partridge 1955).

The results (Tables 12–1 and 12–2), however, permit a comparison of different genes as well as of different alleles of a single locus but independently obtained. The inositolless mutants in Neurospora show variable

TABLE 12–1

Frequency of spontaneous and ultraviolet-induced reversions of various inositol-requiring mutants of Neurospora crassa (after Giles 1951).

Mutant #	——Reversions per 10^6 viable conidia——	
	spontaneous	UV-induced
37401	0.013	10.0
37102	0.0	3.7
64001	0.10	0.9
46316	0.025	0.3
89601	0.0	0.1
46802	0.0	0.0

TABLE 12–2

Frequency of spontaneous reversion obtained in different experiments for four nutritional mutants in E. coli (after Demerec 1955).

Experiment	——————————Mutants per 10^9——————————			
	leu-1	ar-2	leu-6	try-6
1	0.08	0.34	0.83	4.50
2	0.12	0.20	1.59	7.35
3	0.05	0.34	1.52	7.00
4	0.08	0.40	1.74	7.52
5	0.04	0.22	1.09	4.66
6	0.08	0.50	2.17	4.12
7	0.06	0.44	1.67	5.30
8	0.06	0.53	1.53	4.45
9	0.06	——	0.68	5.61
Average	0.07	0.37	1.42	5.61

spontaneous rates, and their response to a mutagenic dose of ultraviolet is also different. Mutant #46802 shows no spontaneous or induced reversions, although chromosomal abnormalities seem to be ruled out by crossover studies. The mutants of *E. coli* (Table 12–2) are highly stable, yet the mutability of each strain is characteristic. When a number of different mutants are tested for reversion by mutagenic agents (Table 12–3), it is clear not only that they differ among themselves but also that their response to various agents follows no consistent pattern. Each mutation has its own characteristic response to any particular set of conditions. Demerec (1955) postulates that mutagenic agents bring about a change in the cell to which the genes respond by mutating, and that different genes react differently to the cellular disturbances caused by mutagens. The cellular changes may be spontaneous as well as induced, and thus account for the spontaneous rates of mutation.

The above data inform us only that genes react differently one from another under any given set of circumstances. Why this is so is difficult to explain. This problem has been discussed in terms of the thermodynamics

TABLE 12–3

Frequency of reversion of nine nutritional mutants in E. coli arranged in increasing order of mutabilty on exposure to MnCl$_2$, UV, and x-rays (Demerec 1955).

| | —MnCl$_2$— | | —UV— | | —x-rays— |
Gene	Mutations/10^8	Gene	Mutations/10^8	Gene	Mutations/10^8
phe-1	11	hi-1	22	leu-2	12
leu-2	24	phe-1	100	hi-1	34
ar-3	63	ar-2	440	ar-2	54
hi-1	121	leu-2	1,200	try-3	113
try-2	448	try-3	1,800	ar-3	468
leu-3	1,050	try-5	3,110	try-2	1,160
ar-2	1,720	ar-3	4,600	leu-3	1,380
try-3	10,200	leu-3	6,300	try-5	1,563
try-5	14,000	try-2	10,700	phe-1	2,460

of chemical change (McElroy and Swanson 1951; Blum 1955), but until the structure of the gene is known, explanatory remarks can be no more than speculative.

It is interesting to note, however, that the many bacteriophage *r* mutants (Benzer 1955) are non-allelic in that recombination between them can occur, indicating that a locus may have many sites at which a mutation can occur, each presumably with its own inherent spontaneous and induced rate of change. Among higher forms, the only example of such a wealth of alleles at supposedly single loci are the sterility factors known in such forms as Nicotiana, Tradescantia, clover, and Oenothera. Over 200 phenotypically different alleles have been estimated to exist in a single variety of clover (Bateman 1949), and the number may be considerably larger. Such loci must be complex indeed, but it would suggest that minor chemical changes lie at the basis of mutability.

The stability of the gene can, of course, be influenced by various radiations and chemicals, as Table 12–3 indicates. The staggering amount of research carried out in this field and recently reviewed by Muller (1954a, b), Russell (1954), Lea (1955), Swanson and Stadler (1955), Zelle and Hollaender (1955) and others, can only be touched upon briefly. With ionizing radiations, the rate of mutation varies linearly with dose (Fig. 12–5), and little quantitative difference is found with radiations of different ion density. When departures from linearity are found, as for sex-linked lethals from *D. melanogaster* males irradiated 7–9 days earlier (Muller, Herskowitz, Abrahamson and Oster 1954), the discrepancies can usually be accounted for on the basis of some selective process that is operative. As a result, the linear relationships have been interpreted to

mean that each mutation is caused by a single "hit" event, i.e., the passage
of a single path of ionization through some sensitive portion of the chromosome. The mutations, most of which are unanalyzed as to origin, consti-

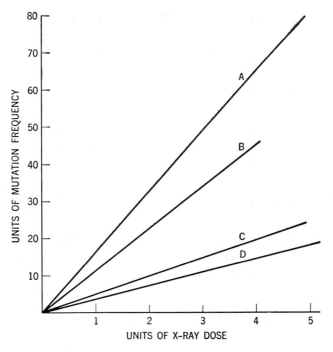

Fig. 12–5. Relation of mutantion frequency to dose of x-rays. A, morphological
mutants in *Aspergillus terreus*; frequency in per cent mutants among survivors, dose
unit 34,000 *r* (Swanson, Hollaender and Kaufmann 1948). B and C, reverse-mutations
in two inositolless strains (B, #37401; C, #89601) of *Neurospora crassa*; frequency
in number of mutations per 10° survivors, dose unit 10,000 *r* (Giles 1951). D, sex-
linked lethal mutations in *D. melanogaster* at 27°C; frequency of per cent mutations
in offspring from irradiated males, dose unit 1,000 *r* (Baker and Sgourakis 1950).

tute a mixture of extra- and intragenic types, and consequently yield little
information referable directly to the effect of radiation on genic stability.
Muller (1954a) argues strongly in favor of the idea that radiations markedly alter intragenic stability; Stadler (1954) takes the opposite point of
view that no conclusive evidence points to an experimental modification
of the frequency of mutations in the narrow sense of intragenic alteration.

The mutation rate with ultraviolet (λ 2537 A is generally employed for
this purpose) follows a relationship that generally departs greatly from a
linear relationship (Fig. 12–6). The exponential rise of the curve at low
doses, the power of which varies with the organism, the mutation in question, and various adjunctive treatments (Zelle and Hollaender 1955;
Pomper and Atwood 1955), suggests that for a mutation to occur several

photons of ultraviolet must be absorbed within a sensitive site. The drop in the curve at higher doses is difficult to explain, since it could mean a heterogeneity of cells of varying sensitiveness either to survival or to mu-

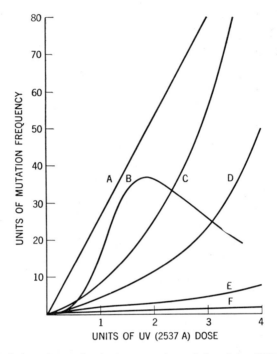

Fig. 12–6. Relation of mutation frequency to dose of ultraviolet (2537 A) radiation. A, mutation rate of streptomycin susceptibility to streptomycin resistance in strain B/Sd-4 of *E. coli*; frequency in number of mutants per 0.25 X 10^{11} survivors, dose unit 1,000 ergs/mm² (Demerec 1951). B, rate of morphological mutations in *Aspergillus terreus*; frequency in per cent mutants among survivors, dose unit 390 ergs/mm² (Swanson 1952). C. to F, rates of reverse-mutations of four inositolless strains (C, #37401; D, #37102; E, #64001; F, #89601) of *Neurospora crassa*; frequency in number of mutations per 10^6 survivors, dose unit 500 ergs/mm² (Giles 1951).

tation. Cells that were mutated at lower doses may well be less capable of surviving additional exposure than non-mutated cells, thus effectively lowering the mutation rate among the survivors. Markert (1953) has demonstrated that differential pigmentation of cells, serving to screen out the effective radiation, can produce the same results. When ultraviolet is used on higher organisms, the problems of penetration and differential absorption are such as to make the results of questionable quantitative significance (Swanson and Stadler 1955).

Chemicals of various kinds can also effect genic stability (Auerbach 1951; Demerec and Hanson 1951; Jensen, Kirk, Kolmark, and Westergaard 1951). The effective chemicals are of varying kinds, and there is no hint in their structure or mode and degree of reactivity to indicate why they in particular are mutagenic while others are not. They include such diverse compounds as urethane, phenol, mustard gas, peroxides of various kinds, and manganous chloride. The hope that a specific chemical will induce a specific heritable mutation has not yet been realized. As might be imagined, the quantitative aspects of chemical mutagenesis, in terms of time, concentration, and temperature, are less well known than they are for radiations, but Table 12–4 gives some indication of how these three parameters affect the induction of morphological mutations by nitrogen mustard in the fungus, *Aspergillus terreus*. The higher the temperature the higher is the frequency, but the relations to time of exposure and to concentration are not so clear-cut.

TABLE 12–4

Effect of nitrogen mustard [bis-(beta-chloroethyl)-amine ·HCl] on the frequency of morphological mutations in Aspergillus terreus when concentration of mutagen, time of exposure, and temperature are varied. Approximately 300 isolates per treatment.

Time of exposure in hours	Concentration in percent	Frequency of mutations (%) among survivors			
		13 C	22° C	40° C	50° C
1		0.43	0.46	2.90	16.73
2	0.1	0.00	2.02	8.52	18.22
3		0.52	3.51	8.33	23.38
6		—	—	—	28.40
1		1.34	2.87	9.69	8.74
2	0.01	2.48	4.23	9.09	18.90
3		2.49	4.81	12.18	16.82
6		—	—	—	11.41
1		1.32	5.78	18.18	17.60
2	0.001	2.13	3.51	14.60	22.71
3		1.44	4.35	7.04	21.08
6		—	—	—	21.91

A last point to be made in terms of induced mutations is that not all are immediately realized, but some may be delayed in their appearance. The delay may involve a few or many cell generations. This can best be demonstrated in micro-organisms (Demerec 1946, 1953, 1955), but it was clearly demonstrated first in Drosophila following exposure to mustard gas (Auerbach 1951). These results have been interpreted as an indication that the gene, following exposure to a mutagenic agent, can exist in a metastable or activated state, and that some further event must take place to return it either to is normal state or to move it over into a recognizable mutated state. This problem has been discussed by McElroy and Swanson (1951), and it is paralleled by similar findings as regards chromosomal aberrations following exposure to infrared and x-rays (Swanson and Yost 1951). The nature of genic or chromosomal metastable states is unknown, however.

GENE MUTATIONS AND CHROMOSOME ABERRATIONS

The parallelism between chromosomal and genic stability, as reflected in breakage and mutation rates, poses the problem therefore of whether mutations and aberrations have any causal relation. In many instances they obviously do; in other instances uncertainty exists.

As pointed out earlier, Goldschmidt has taken the positive stand that mutations are rearrangements of chromatin, with breakage being invariably involved. Most geneticists, on the other hand, consider that the point mutation, defined as an intramolecular change in the gene without rearrangement of chromatin, is a valid category of genetic change. Many, however, have emphasized that point mutations constitute a residue of genetic change in which no visible change can be detected in the chromosome (Stadler 1954); here the resolving powers of the microscope set an arbitrary limit between point mutations on the one hand and chromosomal mutations on the other, although alterations in linkage and crossover patterns provide additional criteria for distinguishing between the two. But as Stadler points out, no test can identify an intramolecular change within a gene with certainty. The strongest piece of evidence in favor of point mutations is their reversibility, the argument being that what is knocked out of the chromosome in the form of submicroscopic chromatin is unlikely to be knocked back in when the mutation reverts to normal, but even this point of view lacks meaning when one considers that genic expression is a variable phenomenon (McClintock 1951, 1953).

In what follows, a parallel will be drawn between the induction of mutations and chromosomal aberrations, together with the discrepancies that have been noted. The list is by no means complete, and the parallelism is used merely to indicate the complexity of the problem rather than to further any particular point of view or to suggest that mutations are due to any single mechanism operative in the cell.

Temperature. A Q_{10} of 5 has been found for sex-linked lethals in *D. melanogaster* (Plough 1941). This would indicate that a mutation is not a simple chemical change obeying Van't Hoff's law. It is reasonable to assume that the heritable material of the cell is well buffered against chemical reactions which could more easily take place in an aqueous solution, and that mutations involve more complex reactions, mediated perhaps by cellular mutagens rather than by simple chemical kinetics. Plough has demonstrated that a temperature shock, using both high and low temperatures on larvae at the supposed time of crossing over, also causes an increased frequency of sex-linked lethals. Translocations, however, failed to show similar increases. In Tradescantia, Sax (1937) showed that high temperatures produce aberrations in much the same manner as do x-rays.

Aging. Seed and pollen that have been aged for some time show higher mutation rates than do unaged materials of similar genetic constitution

(Cartledge and Blakeslee 1934), an observation that parallels studies made on aberrations (Nichols 1942).

Ultraviolet radiation. Both mutation rates and aberrations show a similar wavelength dependence (Swanson and Stadler 1955; Kirby-Smith and Craig 1955), but while aberrations show a linear relationship to dose (Swanson 1942c) mutations almost invariably exhibit a non-linear relationship (Hollaender and Emmons 1941; Pomper and Atwood 1955).

X-rays. Mutations of many kinds and in a wide variety of organisms are linear with dose and independent of intensity (Muller 1954), and where a departure from linearity is found (Muller, Herskowitz, Abrahamson, and Oster 1954) a selective mechanism appears to be responsible for the deviation. Chromosome breaks are presumed to be linear with dose and independent of intensity, but aberrations show a departure from linearity on the basis of their one- or two-hit character; i.e., simple chromatid deletions, being one-hit events, show a linear relationship, while translocations involving two breaks do not (Lea 1955; Kaufmann 1954; Giles 1954). Mutation frequencies appear to be independent of the ion density of radiations between x-rays and gamma rays (Muller 1940, 1954), but aberrations clearly are not (Kirby-Smith and Daniels 1953; Swanson 1955).

Neutrons. Mutations and aberrations are both linear with dose (Giles 1940b, 1943), but the relative biological efficiency of neutrons as compared to x-rays, calculated on a *rep* basis, appears to differ for mutations as compared to aberrations. Although the quantitative aspects of the problem are still clouded because of inherent difficulties of neutron dosimetry, neutrons appear to have a higher relative efficiency than x-rays for aberrations (Conger 1954a, b; Conger and Giles 1950; Lewis 1954; Kirby-Smith and Swanson 1954) than for mutations (Mickey 1954; Muller 1954a; Baker and Von Halle 1954; Atwood and Mukai 1954). However, since these mutations, for the most part, remain unanalyzed as to constitution, doubt must be attached to the significance of the differences observed.

Combined radiations. When x-rays are combined with near-infrared radiation, increases in aberrations are readily achieved (Kaufmann, Hollaender and Gay 1946; Kaufmann 1954; Swanson 1949; Yost 1951). Sex-linked and dominant lethals are not increased in D. *melanogaster,* however, by the combined treatments, although morphological mutations are in *Aspergillus terreus* (Swanson, Kaufmann and Hollaender 1949). Decreases in aberration frequency are obtained when ultraviolet (2537 A) is combined with x-rays (Swanson 1944; Kaufmann and Hollaender 1946), while both increases (Swanson 1952) and decreases (Newcombe and McGregor 1954) have been reported for mutations. The effect of oxygen and various chemicals in combination with x-rays indicate that oxidative systems govern, in part, the production of both aberrations and mutations without, however, any pronounced selectiveness between the two.

Chemicals. In general, those chemical mutagens that induce aberrations also induce mutations, although there is a good deal of specificity involved as to the effectiveness of any chemical on a particular species. X-rays, however, induce many more aberrations than do the mustard, diepoxide, and triazine compounds when the frequency of sex-linked lethals is used as a basis of comparison (Auerbach 1951; Fahmy and Bird 1953). The very slight lethal effect of $MnCl_2$ in contrast to its efficiency as a mutagen in *E. coli* would suggest that it would produce few, if any, aberrations (Demerec and Hansen 1951; Demerec 1955).

Genic modifiers. The *sticky* gene in maize increases both aberrations and mutations (Beadle 1932), and in a somewhat different sense this is also true for the *Ac-Ds* complex in the same species (McClintock 1951, 1953). In fact, a graded series of *Ac-Ds* systems are known, some of which affect a rise in mutation frequency with little influence on the aberration frequency, while others affect both. Specific modifiers such as the *Dt* locus in maize, which increases the mutability of the a_1 locus (Rhoades 1941a), have no known effect on aberration frequency.

The above compilation, partial though it is, indicates that most agents that cause an increase in aberrations also do so for mutations. There remains, however, enough discrepancy still to be accounted for to suggest that many mutations are not necesarily associated with chromosomal aberrations, and may be of an intragenic variety.

Sex-linked lethals, for example, are of heterogeneous origin, even when obtained spontaneously, some being associated with visible rearrangements, other not (Muller 1954). Like visible mutations, they show a linear relation to dose, and are independent of the intensity, fractionation, and wavelength of radiation between gamma rays and soft x-rays. Of 87 lethals induced by 3000 r in Drosophila, Lea (1955; Lea and Catcheside 1945) estimates that 30 are associated with gross structural changes, 18 with minute deficiencies, and 39 with no detectable cytological change. Of the last 39, Lea further calculates that 28 are the result of damage caused by breaks which, however, were restituted without visible alteration of structure, while the remaining 11 can be considered minute inversions that would pass undetected even in salivary gland chromosomes. On this basis, all sex-linked lethals are associated with breaks. This is supported by Demerec (1937) who found 90 percent of such lethals to be located close to or at the breakage point of rearrangements, while others have been unable to separate lethals from rearrangements by crossing over (Herskowitz 1946, 1951). Herskowitz (1951), however, on the basis of further calculations, concludes that 0.6 lethals unassociated with breakage are produced by 1000 r in contrast to 2.3 lethals associated with breakage in one form or another.

A group of induced mutations at the A_2 locus in maize have also been critically analyzed, and it appears that while those induced by ultraviolet behaved as point or intragenic changes, those induced by x-rays always were associated with chlorophyll modifications and were, in addition, cell lethal in a homozygous state (Stadler and Roman 1948). Further, the great majority of gross rearrangements in Drosophila are lethal when homozygous, indicating damage or loss of genic material at the point of breakage. The question of the relation between mutations and breaks must therefore still be considered an open one, although the reversibility of biochemical mutations in haploid cells of fungal or bacterial species argues strongly in favor of true intragenic change, despite the fact that position-effect mutations can be reversed when the rearrangement of chromatin is changed back to normal.

POSITION EFFECT

Early concepts of the gene, especially those relating to its particulate nature, were derived from crossing over data and from radiation studies. But a greater appreciation of the gene as a functional unit of inheritance, and of the chromosome as an organized structure, has come from an analysis of position effects. Discovery of this phenomenon by Sturtevant (1925) has been followed by numerous analyses in Drosophila (Lewis 1950, 1951, 1952, 1955; Green and Green 1949; Green 1954, 1955a, b), Oenothera (Catcheside 1947), and maize (McClintock 1951, 1953), and it is becoming increasingly evident that the genetically determined phenotype is not only dependent upon the gene itself but upon the nature of the chromatin adjacent to it. The gene, therefore, even if it is of a particulate nature, is not an isolated unit operating simply in conjunction with other genes; it is actively influenced by them.

Two general types of position effects are known (Lewis 1950). The first is the stable or S-type, and is illustrated by the action of the *Bar* locus. The *Bar* effect is known to be associated with a duplication of the 16A region of the X-chromosome in *D. melanogaster*. Through unequal crossing over chromosomes can be obtained that have the 16A region in triplicate, thus permitting a comparison of the effects of four *Bar* loci in two different combinations. If the 16A region in the normal chromosome is designated as *B* and *Bar* as *BB,* then females of *BB/BB* can be compared with *BBB/B*. It is found that the latter flies have a more extreme *Bar* effect (reduced number of ommatidia in the compound eye) than the former.

In another instance the two supposedly equivalent *Star-asteroid* genotypes in *D. melanogaster*—S $ast/ + ast^4/$ and S $ast^4/ + ast$—produce different phenotypes, with the former producing a larger eye than the latter. The same phenomenon is encountered when a comparison is made between S $ast/ ++$ and S $+/+ ast$. This has been termed "position pseudoallelism" and is based not only on the fact that the adjacent loci have a close functional relationship but that the "cis" type $(ab/++)$ can be distinguished from the "trans" type $(a+/+b)$ phenotypically. Genic expression is therefore a function not only of a gene itself but of the neighboring chromatin.

The S-type of position effect is a stable one, simulating that produced by a genuine mutation. Furthermore, analysis of the chromosomal condition shows that this type is invariably confined to the euchromatic regions of the chromosome. The V-type, or variegation, position effect appears to be invariably associated with the heterochromatic regions of the chromosome. The effect is such that stable euchromatic genes display a phenotypic instability when placed close to or within heterochromatin. The instability is variable in expression, appears not to be restricted to any particular type of gene, results in a type of somatic mosaicism, and, in contrast to the S-type, which is confined to single phenotypic expressions, has a spreading effect such that a number of genes can simultaneously exhibit variegation. The fact that euchromatic genes must be brought into contact with heterochromatin means that they are usually involved in some type of aberration that can bring about genic displacements.

The *white-mottled-4* (w^{m4}) effect in *D. melanogaster* is typical of the V-type position effect. Since a rearrangement is involved, the altered X-chromosome with a normal gene (w^+) is designated $R(w^+)$. A heterozygote between $R(w^+)$ and a chromosome bearing the mutant white allele (w) has a variegated eye color, i.e., a mosaic of red and white patches. On the other hand, $R(w^+)/+$ heterozygotes have normal red eyes, the normal $+$ gene dominating the phenotype. The $R(w^+)$ X-chromosome also leads to mosaicism when unpaired, as it would be in the male fly.

That such variegation is not due to mutation but rather to a genic expression that varies from cell to cell is indicated by the fact that removal of the gene from the vicinity of the heterochromatin, i.e., an insertion back into euchromatin, restores to the gene its normal function and stability, provided no heterochromatin accompanies it. Under certain circumstances, this can be accomplished through crossing over, as shown for the *hairy* (*h*) wing mosaicism in *D. melanogaster* (Dubinin and Sidorov 1935), and the *P*-locus position effect in *Oenothera blandina* (Catcheside 1947). In the latter case, the *P*-locus, which is concerned with pigment patterns in the sepals, is involved in a translocation in such a manner that, through crossing over, it can be moved out of the translocation into a normal chromosome, or vice versa. Some 58 transfers of the *P*-locus in or out of the translocation were made, and without exception, when in the rearrangement, variability in sepal pattern was evident, when out, stability was regained. The gene, therefore, was unchanged; its position determined its reactivity.

V-type position effects exhibit other interesting characteristics. First, the effect can include neighboring genes as well as that one immediately adjacent to heterochromatin. In one extreme case, that of an inversion, five genes showed variegation, one of them being about 50 bands of salivary chromosome length from the rearrangement break point. Second, the degree of variegation may be greatly modified either by depression of the effect or by its enhancement. The addition of Y-chromosomes, which are totally heterochromatic, tends to suppress variegation; temperature increases produce a similar trend; while deficiencies of euchromatin or heterochromatin may enhance. Y-chromosomes, on the other hand, seem to have no effect on S-type position effects. Interestingly enough, mosaicism of genes normally situated in heterochromatin occurs when they are placed in euchromatin; additional heterochromatin in the form of Y-chromosomes enhances rather than suppresses the degree of mosaicism.

Two hypotheses have been advanced to explain position effects. The *structural hypothesis* (Ephrussi and Sutton 1944) assumes that the gene has been altered in such a way as to change its functional activity and consequently its phenotypic expression, but that this alteration is a readily reversible one. The changed gene is supposed to be altered geometrically by the forces of somatic pairing, which are prevalent in Drosophila, but it is hardly likely to serve as an explanation for the situation in Oenothera or in maize where somatic pairing does not occur.

The *kinetic hypothesis* (Sturtevant 1925, Lewis 1951, 1955) considers that the effects produced are the result of an interaction of neighboring genes at the level of immediate gene products. The *S-ast* position effect illustrates the point. These two genes, believed to be located in the two halves of a doublet, and hence to be duplications, are considered once to have had a similar function, but now to have diverged slightly in their genic activity. If it is assumed that genes, in determining phenotypic expressions, do so through the process of gene products, then a substrate (X) is necessary. If both S and *ast* utilize X, then two reactions are possible:

$$A \xleftarrow{\quad S \quad} X \xrightarrow{\quad ast \quad} B$$

$$or$$

$$X \xrightarrow{\quad S \quad} A \xrightarrow{\quad ast \quad} B$$

The first is a competition action, the second a sequential one, but since S and *ast* must be on the same chromosome in order to have the reaction proceed, the second seems the more feasible on the basis of diffusibility of products in the neighborhood of adjacent genes, but not between unlinked genes or homologous chromosomes. The "cis" reaction,

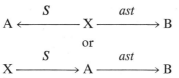

$$X \xrightarrow{\quad S \quad} A \xrightarrow{\quad ast \quad} B,$$ must therefore be different from the "trans"

reaction, $X \xrightarrow{\quad S \quad} A \xrightarrow{\quad + \quad} B.$ Lewis (1955) concludes, therefore, on the basis of the *S-ast* case as well as the more complex *bithorax* series (described in Chapter 15), that position pseudoallelism can be interpreted as a chain of gene-controlled reactions in which each intermediate substance (X, A, B, etc.) has two roles: as substrate for the succeeding reaction and as a determiner for a specific physiological process. On this basis each gene has a separate and specific function and the physiological, recombinational, and mutational unit is one and the same.

A third type of position effect, related to the S-type, has also been described by Lewis (1954). It is concerned with the *bithorax* group of pseudoalleles, and it appears that structural heterozygosity for certain chromosomal rearrangements involving the right arm of Chromosome III between *bithorax* and the centromere (which includes about 500 bands), shifts the phenotypic expression of the "trans" type further from wild type, but has no effect on the "cis" type. If the rearrangement is designated as *R,* then the effect of the two "trans" types, $Ra_+/_+b$ and a_+/R_+b, can be compared with $a_+/_+b$. The rearrangement would tend to reduce somatic pairing and interfere with the diffusibility of substrates from one homologue to another, and thus modify the phenotype of the "trans" type but not of the "cis" type. This hypothesis is, in a sense, a combination of the structural and the kinetic, and supports further the concept of sequential reactions.

Ac-Ds POSITION EFFECTS IN MAIZE

The instability of genes in the V-type position-effect phenomenon in Drosophila obviously urges caution in interpreting mutations as intragenic changes. Clearly heterochromatin and, to a certain extent, the centromere are involved in determining in part gene function and phenotypic expression, and this in turn can be extrapolated backward to the level of differentiation, as shall be pointed out later. The validity of this point of view is tremendously strengthened by the remarkable studies of McClintock (1950, 1951, 1953) in maize.

In these studies, which were mentioned in an earlier chapter, McClintock has demonstrated that genic expression is intimately related to chromosomal organization. In a variable and mutable strain of maize, two loci have been shown to be in control of genic action in the course of development. One of the loci, *Activator* (*Ac*), appears to be a master locus in that the second locus, *Dissociation* (*Ds*), is unable to function in its absence. The presence of both in the same nucleus, however, gives rise to an increase in spontaneous chromosome breaks and unstable and mutable genic loci. The two phenomena, breakage and mutation, are causally related, and in fact may be viewed as two facets of a single basic phenomenon.

Historically, the *Ac-Ds* system arose out of a breakage-fusion-bridge cycle involving Chromosome 9. Although both *Ac* and *Ds* behave as genes in that they exhibit Mendelian inheritance, show crossing over with other genes, and are mutable, they have been referred to as "loci" rather than as genes, since evidence indicates that they are blocks of heterochromatin. Presumably there are no recessive *ac* or *ds* loci that are normal in behavior. Their properties may be indicated as follows:

1. *Ac* controls both the activity of *Ds* and the time in development when *Ds* acts. The latter is inactive when the former is absent.

2. *Ac* is unstable and can exist in a number of different states similar to the allelic states of ordinary euchromatic genes. These changes in state are detected by a change in the control of *Ds,* as well as in a change in the control of the type of mutability that it permits. Changes in state of *Ac* are presumed to be due to alterations in the block of heterochromatin forming the *Ac* locus.

3. *Ds* is unstable in the presence of *Ac,* and can exist in a number of different states. Its instability is presumably also a reflection of altered heterochromatin, and the state of *Ds* will determine the relative frequency of events occurring at *Ds*.

4. Both *Ac* and *Ds* are capable of movement (transposition) within and among chromosomes of the complement. It is believed that this occurs through breakage at these loci, and their removal and subsequent re-insertion at other points. Changed positions can be initially detected by their activity, and confirmed by linkage data. Since *Ds* affects genes adjacent to it (see below), while *Ac* acts only to influence *Ds, Ds* is more readily mapped than is *Ac*.

5. *Ds* has a dual action in the presence of *Ac*. First, it is the site of high breakability. A simple break at *Ds* would lead to the loss of all chromatin distal to it, and this can be detected, as to time and place, by the loss of known genes affecting plant or endosperm. However, many other aberrations occur, with one break always at the *Ds* locus. Second, *Ds* affects genes lying adjacent to it. Thus, if *Ds* lies adjacent to the Waxy (*Wx*) gene in Chromosome 9, the *Wx* gene behaves as if it had mutated to recessive condition, or as if it were completely inactive or absent. The unchanged condition of *Wx* can, however, be demonstrated; removal of *Ds* from its neighborhood returns *Wx* to its normal active state. *Ds* therefore governs the functioning of *Wx* without permanently altering its inherent structure. The relation between mutability and breakage is consequently a function of the *Ds* locus, and both phenomena are *Ac*-controlled. However, various combinations of states of *Ac* and *Ds* can be obtained that give a large spectrum of events ranging from many breaks and aberrations and few mutations, to few breaks and many mutations. Mutations and breakage must, as a result, be determined by the nature of the locus, and no clear line of demarcation can be drawn between those events that lead to detectable chromosomal breakage and those that give rise to mutations unaccompanied by chromosomal alteration.

6. Certain loci have been discovered that remain mutable, but that no

longer require the presence of *Ac*. McClintock has postulated that the activity of a locus as regards its mutability is primarily a function of the type of chromatin material present at the locus, and does not involve changes in the gene itself. Rather, she believes it is the type of chromatin that functions to control how the genic material may operate in the nuclear system, but at this level it would have been manifestly impossible to separate her postulated system from that of the conventional gene were it not for the known activity of *Ac* and *Ds* under other conditions.

7. Genes affected by *Ac* and *Ds* are many and varied in their phenotypic expression, and the direction of mutability can be toward lowered or enhanced degrees of expressivity, or it can be toward recessiveness or dominance.

8. In triploid endosperm, 0 to 6 doses of *Ac* may be obtained. The larger the number of *Ac's* present, the later in the development of endosperm is the action of *Ds*. *Ac* thus influences the timing as well as the activity of *Ds*.

In many respects *Ac* is very similar to the *Dt* locus, which alters the mutability of the a_1 gene in maize (Rhoades 1941), but that it is not identical is indicated by the failure of *Ac* to increase the mutability of a_1. However, McClintock has been able to reconstruct a *Dt-like* action on a_1 by modification of the heterochromatic knob of Chromosome 9 through the breakage-fusion-bridge cycle, thus strongly supporting the contention that their origins are identical even if their actions are now somewhat dissimilar. Two additional loci in maize also exhibit some of the characteristics of the *Ac-Ds* system, but these are single instead of dual systems and like *Dt* are more restricted in their action. These are the *Modulator* (*Mp*) element, which affects the *P* locus (Brink and Nilan 1952, Brink 1954), and the *Enhancer* (*En*) element, which alters the phenotypic expression of the *pg* locus (Peterson 1953). Both *Mp* and *En* are separable by recombination from the loci they affect, but while *Mp* is closely linked to *P,* the position of *En* is variable in the genome. *Mp* is similar to *Ac* in that increasing doses of *Mp* lead to a later and later time of influence, as well as a greater reduction in the intensity of the *P* (*pericarp*) phenotype.

The action of the *Ac-Ds* system can more properly be visualized if the origin of the c^{m-1} locus is considered. This is a mutable locus, and is an "allele" of the dominant *C* gene, which is concerned with the production of colored aleurone in the endosperm. In a particular cross the male parent contributed a Chromosome 9 marked with *Yg, C, Sh, wx,* and *Ds* (with *Yg* distal and *Ds* in its first-discovered and so-called standard position) as well as one *Ac* in an unlinked position; the female contributed a Chromosome 9 carrying the stable recessives *yg, c, sh* and *wx,* and without *Ds* or *Ac* present. One-half of the kernels should be *C Sh wx* and unvariegated since *Ac* was present in only one-half of the pollen grains; the other half should be variegated as the result of *Ds,* in the presence of *Ac,* initiating a breakage-fusion-bridge cycle with consequential and occasional loss of *C*. Sectors showing *c* and *sh* should be present due to loss (*Yg* losses will not be detected in the endosperm). A single kernel, however, was quite the reverse, being largely colorless but with small colored sectors showing through. It thus appeared as if recessive *c* had mutated back to a dominant *C*. This could only occur in the Chromosome 9 contributed by the male parent.

Subsequent linkage studies showed that *Ds* had now been transposed from its position to the right of *wx* to the position of *C*, and that in this position *Ds* caused the dominant *C* to function as a recessive *c* giving a colorless kernel. The colored sectors arose when *Ds* was lost through breakage, and when lost, *C* regained its dominant expression. Further, all *Ds* breakage events now occurred at the *C* locus rather than to the right of *wx* where *Ds* had been previously. And, lastly, the mutations to *C* and the *Ds*-type breakage ceased when *Ac* was removed from the nucleus through crossing. Reintroduction of *Ac* would resume the mutation-breakage events. Also the mutations to *C* were now stable, as would be assumed if the change were the result of removal of *Ds* from its neighborhood.

It is difficult to avoid the conclusion, therefore, that c^{m-1} arose from *C* because *Ds* was transposed to its vicinity, that *Ds* inhibited the action of *C* to give a recessive *c* phenotype, and that the dominant *C* phenotype was restored when *Ds* was again removed. A number of other loci have been similarly studied, and they yield to the same interpretation.

These studies are of obvious importance to the problem of differentiation. They strongly suggest that nuclear factors can control the time and the place of certain events in the nucleus which, at a higher level of organization, appear as acts of differentiation. The process of differentiation is a sequential one, and the steps involved during development lead to definitive cell types aggregated into organ systems. These steps have their origin in a mechanism set into action within certain cells, and it is known from embryology as well as from genetics that sister cells of presumably identical gentic content can have different fates. Something sets one or more cells apart from others by leading them into different pathways of reaction and morphology. The state of events described by McClintock provides a mechanism for such a segregation, and although that described is at a more readily observable level, the gradations found point to the possibility of existence of such segregations at a much more refined and subtle level. Evolution would of course tend to keep these under refined control. It is known that certain genes act only at certain times in development; a mechanism for setting genes into action is therefore needed, and this may be in the nature of an "uncovering," much as the disappearance of *Ds* from the neighborhood of a gene "uncovers" it and allows it to function properly.

In this sense, McClintock (1951) considers that "the nucleus is organized into definite units of action, and that the potentials for types of genic action in any one kind of cell differ from the potentials in another kind of cell." Nuclei are therefore of different functional capacities, and their different fates are simply an expression of this "non-equivalence." This, of course, assumes either a somatic segregation of controlling components or differential mitoses that permit alterations of chromatin that in turn permit genes to become active. The variegations arising in maize endosperm under the influence of the *Ac-Ds* and other similar systems are of course abnormal; it is not expected that such are to be found in well regulated developmental patterns. However, the fact that at one extreme of the *Ac-Ds* system mutations without aberrations can be produced suggests that this type of differentiation is the one most likely to be found in nature, since natural selection would have screened out the aberration-producing types. In any event, the preferential segregations found in many organisms indicate that more subtle ones are likely to be normally prevalent but undetected by our present methods of investigation.

A striking cytological parallel to McClintock's concept of different nuclear capacities is found in the studies of Balbiani rings in the salivary-gland-type chromosomes of certain Diptera (Bauer 1952; Bauer and Beermann 1952; Beermann 1952a, b; Mechelke 1953). These rings are modifications of the chromosome structure, and are derived from, and presumably can regress to, the normal banded regions of the chromosome (Figs. 5–21, 5–22). However, in any single tissue the rings are restricted to certain loci, and involve a single band or localized region at a time. Further, they appear at a predictable time in larval development. It would appear that the Balbiani rings are an expression of particular genic activity at specified times and in specified tissues. It would be difficult to detect such events in chromosomes other than those of the salivary-gland-type, and it may well be that McClintock's *Ac-Ds* system is a mechanism of differentiation which, for unknown reasons, has gotten out of normal control.

Nuclear differentiation of a more permanent sort is suggested by the transplantation studies of King and Briggs (1955). The problem under investigation was whether nuclei from a variety of differentiated tissues retained their capacity to cause the uninhibited development of enucleated eggs after transplantation. By transplanting nuclei from progressively more differentiated cells of the frog embryo (mainly from chorda-mesoderm and the neural crest) to undivided but enucleated eggs, it was found that the nucleus gradually loses its capacity to evoke and control complete development. Thus, nuclei from blastulae and gastrulae caused development to progress normally, but nuclei from more differentiated and older embryos lacked the capacity to serve as a complete replacement for the normal egg nucleus. The nature of nuclear differentiation is not known, but it would appear that both nucleus and cytoplasm are capable of permanent change during development.

GENETIC EFFECT OF HETEROCHROMATIN

From what has been discussed earlier in this chapter, it is evident that heterochromatin can no longer be regarded as the genetically inert chromatin it once was considered to be. Position-effect studies have demonstrated that heterochromatin exerts a profound effect on the functioning of euchromatic genes placed, through rearrangement, in its vicinity. The influence of the heterochromatic Y-chromosome in suppressing position-effect variegation in Drosophila also argues a genetic role for heterochromatin, as does the *Ac-Ds* system, which is conisdered to be of a heterochromatin nature. The role of heterochromatin is difficult to define, however, and indeed its distinction from euchromatin, while clear at the cytological level (allocycly, generalized pairing, and heteropycnosis), is at the genetical level vague and ill-defined.

The genetic inertness of heterochromatin was postulated on the basis of the fact that the Y-chromosome and much of the centric heterochromatin of the X-chromosome in Drosophila were not necessary for viability or phenotypic expression of other genes (Goldschmidt 1949; Hannah 1951). Position-effect variegation, however, has changed this, although how heterochromatin exerts its influence remains unknown.

Schultz (1947) has postulated that heterochromatin is concerned with nucleic acid metabolism of bands placed near it, a postulate that gains in credence because of the fact that variegation as well as nucleination of the bands is less affected the farther away from the juncture the particular locus is. The chemical activity of heterochromatin, particularly the nucleolar organizer type, as contrasted to euchromatin, is stressed by Caspersson (1947). He considers that this type of chromatin forms a nucleolus rich in di-amino acid proteins and ribose nucleic acid, and that through the nuclear membrane these substances react with, or pass into, the cytoplasm, where again protein and nucleic acid synthesis is stimulated.

From the variety of seemingly unrelated data bearing on the role of heterochromatin there has arisen a growing conviction that the role of heterochromatin in heredity is different from that of euchromatin, and that its primary influence is generalized, quantitative, and largely concerned with cell division, cellular growth, and embryonic differentiation, rather than being circumscribed and qualitative as is true for most euchromatic genes. This belief, championed by Mather (1943) and Goldschmidt (1949) in particular, considers that heterochromatin consists of a repetitive series of genes having small, similar, and supplementary effects because their products are not highly differentiated and their action is not elaborate. These genes consequently are supposed to govern a type of continuous quantitative variation rather than one that is sharply defined and qualitative. Mather has called these "polygenes," and his suppositions are based on a study of continuous variation in Drosophila chateae or bristles, which could be selected for, and which were modified by, various Y-chromosomes of different origin. The influence of *Ac-Ds* in maize on the induction of a tremendous variability at supposedly individual loci is in keeping with this concept if, as McClintock (1950b) infers, the *Ac-Ds* loci consist essentially of heterochromatin.

The influence of heterochromatin on cell division, growth, and differentiation is largely inferential rather than direct, and the basis for this impression is derived from observations on the preferred segregation of chromatin. As mentioned in Chapter 9 preferential segregation in Ascaris and Sciara, and of the accessory chromosomes of maize and rye, involve elements that, so far as is known, are heterochromatic. In Sciara, it is known that the part of the chromatin responsible for determining these events resides in or near the centromere of the X-chromosome (Crouse 1943). This could mean that such eliminations of heterochromatin, accurate as they are in time and place of development, are part and parcel of differentiation, while in organisms such as nematodes, which have a constant number of somatic cells, heterochromatin is retained only in sex cells which continue to divide. That extra amounts of heterochromatin may stimulate cell division is indicated by the supernumerary divisions that occur in the pollen grains of Sorghum when accessory chromosomes of a heterochromatic nature are included in the nucleus (Darlington and Thomas 1941).

The influence of heterochromatin is also considered by Goldschmidt (1949, 1950) to be shown in the expression of *podoptera,* a genetic condition that transforms wings into leg-like appendages in Drosophila, and in the determination of sex in Lymantria. Both cases are examples of differentiation involving a time element, a dosage effect, and a balance in achieving final expression. Considered in the light of the *Ac-Ds* data, the parallel is obvious even if the details are lacking and an understanding obscure.

EVOLUTION OF THE GENE

The preceding discussion makes it apparent that there is no definition of a gene that satisfies all experimental situations. It is equally apparent that a positive distinction between an intragenic mutation and submicroscopic rearrangement of chromatin is virtually impossible at the present time. The studies of McClintock in maize show that a gene can have its phenotypic expression modified by the action of the *Ds* locus (presumably heterochromatin) lying adjacent to it, a phenomenon that recalls the V-type position effect in Drosophila; the gene, however, remains structurally unchanged since it can return to its former state with the departure of the *Ds* locus from its vicinity. This points to the fact that the properties of a gene are not totally inherent in itself, but are, to a greater or lesser extent, dependent upon the type of, and degree of nearness to, neighboring genes. Such spatial relationships had emerged from the earlier studies on position effect, and on the *cis-trans* system operative in Drosophila, and are reinforced by position effects described by Catcheside in Oenothera, and others.

The role of duplication is indicated in the development of pseudoallelic systems. How extensive the role is in terms of the evolution of genetic systems can only be judged from the examples given, but continued divergence of once similar but duplicated genes could provide for the origin of genes having properties different from the ancestral type. Once fully diverged in a functional sense, and no longer recognizable as being mutually related in origin to neighboring genes, pseudoallelism would no longer be detectable. It is very possible, therefore, that it is only during the intermediate stages of evolution from complete similarity to total dissimilarity that pseudoallelism can be recognized and studied. If this is true, it would be expected that a graded series of genic differentiations, as well as a graded series of amounts of duplication, would be found, and that the differences exhibited by various pseudoallelic systems are but a reflection of the direction and degree of evolutionary divergence.

This implies, of course, that the gene itself is capable of evolving new properties. How this can be accomplished cannot be known until reference to a chemical model of gene action can be made (Schwartz 1955), but there is no immediate reason for believing that the properties of the gene in terms of physiology, mutation, recombination, and reproduction need to evolve in the same direction and at the same rate. The studies of Green and Lewis in Drosophila, and of Laughnan in maize, support the concept that the spatial gene is one and the same with the gene of function, mutation, and recombination, but this is clearly not the case in bacteriophage and Salmonella where the physiological gene appears to be physically larger than the gene of recombination and mutation. The former is a unitary structure, the latter a composite of sub-parts. It can be suggested that the differences are merely those of evolution, and that both types of genes are evolutionary possibilities. It is premature, however, at the present time to do more than speculate.

CHAPTER 13

Evolution of the Karyotype

The *karyotype* is defined as the basic chromosome set of a species, and is further characterized as to form and size of chromosomes as well as to their number. When represented in diagrammatic fashion, as in Figure 13–1, the karyotype is usually referred to as an *idiogram*.

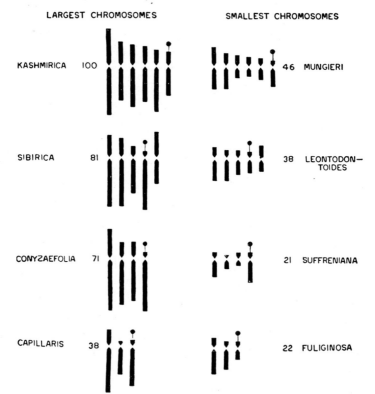

Fig. 13–1. Idiograms of the haploid chromosomes of eight species of Crepis showing reduction in number, total length, and symmetry. Using 100 as the arbitrary length of the chromosomes of *C. kashmirica*, the relative lengths of the other species are as indicated. *Kashmirica, sibirica, conyzaefolia, mungieri* are perennials with woody rhizomes; *leontodontoides* is a perennial or a biennial with a woody stem; *capillaris* is a biennial or an annual; *suffreniana* and *fuliginosa* are annual herbs (Babcock, Stebbins, and Jenkins 1942).

The karyotype was early recognized as a definite species character, the morphology of the chromosomes among individuals of the same species being reasonably constant, with departures from the species pattern being attributed largely to recognizable aberrations. Cytology became an accepted and exceedingly useful science in the hands of the taxonomist who was interested in something more than simple morphological criteria for defining species relationships. In fact, relationships within natural groups of species can scarcely be considered complete in an evolutionary sense without good cytotaxonomic data to reinforce conclusions based on morphological criteria.

Like all systematic characters, however, the karyotype is subject to variation. In general, a particular karyotype can be designated as representative of the species, and in some instances even of the genus. In certain genera of the Liliaceae and in the North American species of Tradescantia, the same karyotype is employed as representative of an assemblage of species, while in Crepis, Drosophila, the lizards, and the grasshoppers, the number, form and size of chromosomes vary widely from species to species. It is from a close study of related species—using hybridization where possible, salivary gland chromosome and genetic analysis in dipterous forms, and metaphase comparisons—that the evolution of the karyotype has been to a limited extent unravelled. The usefulness of a comparative cytological approach should, in the future, be greatly enhanced by cytochemical techniques, with DNA and protein comparisons forming the bases of evolutionary criteria (Mirsky and Ris 1951a). It is apparent, however, that criteria from all levels—morphological, cytogenetic, and cytochemical—must be integrated, for any one set of data can be misleading.

Since chromosomes spontaneously undergo breakage and recombination to form inversions, translocations, and the like, it is logical that karyological differences between related species have come about by a gradual series of changes that have altered the visible appearance of the chromosomes. The importance of these changes in evolution has only recently been appreciated. The significance of position effect as a genic phenomenon emphasizes the fact that a reshuffling of the genic content does not leave the hereditary potential unaffected, as was earlier believed, but creates new chromosomes whose total genotypic influence is different from what it was prior to reshuffling.

It is true, of course, that chromosomal rearrangements can occur without altering visibly the external appearance of the chromosome, just as a changed karyotype does not necessarily have a significant genotypic impact on the individual. In general, however, an altered karyotype is indicative of more profound changes at a submicroscopic level, and the difficulty, if not impossibility, of separating genic and chromosomal changes means that the earlier and cruder belief that the chromosome is a string of entirely independent genes is being replaced by one that looks upon the chromosome as a definite structure whose separate as well as total functions depend, in part at least, on the spatial relationships of the segments of the chromosome. Changes in sequence of genes, which gradually bring about altered karyotypes, are consequently an important evolutionary feature even though at the present time it is not possible to appraise the significance of every chromosomal change that has occurred.

In discussing the evolution of the karyotype, consideration will be given to alterations in (1) basic chromosome number, (2) form and size of chromosomes and (3) amount and distribution of heterochromatin.

CHANGES IN BASIC NUMBER

One can assume, in diploid species, that a series of haploid numbers, varying by steps of one, have evolved from some particular ancestral number. Determination of the ancestral number, however, is not always an easy matter, for the base number can increase or decrease, and unsuspected aneuploidy and polyploidy may confuse the picture. The genus Carex in the Cyperaceae is a classic example of cytotaxonomic confusion for the haploid numbers range from $n = 6$ to $n = 56$, with every number between 12 and 43 reported for one or more species (Heilborn 1939).

Undoubtedly aneuploidy and polyploidy have played a large role, but Carex is by no means unique in its cytological variability. A like situation is found in the genera Scirpus and Eleocharis in the Gramineae, Draba and Brassica (Cruciferae), Viola (Violaceae), Euphorbia (Euphorbiaceae), and Nicotiana (Solanaceae) (Stebbins 1950). In the animal kingdom, where polploidy is presumed to have played an insignificant part in speciation, variation is nonetheless equally prevalent, both within genera and within the larger groups (White 1954, Matthey 1949). In Drosophila the base number varies from 3 to 7, and there is good proof (Patterson and Stone 1952) that polyploidy has not been involved in any way. The grasshoppers, which because of their large chromosomes have been extensively investigated (White 1951, 1954), present a similar picture with the diploid number in males (XO type) ranging from 13 to 57. The lizards (Lacertilia) vary almost continuously in haploid numbers from 12 to 26 (Matthey 1949). Genera showing widely different haploid numbers among related species are Cyclops (Crustacea) 3–11; Isagorus (Phasmatoidea) 14–24; Liturgousa (Mantoidea) 9–17; Lethocerus (Heteroptera) 2–15; Nemobius (Orthoptera) 6–10; Limnophilus (Trichoptera) 6–30; Erebia (Lepidoptera) 8–40; and Meriones (Rodentia) 22 and 30 (White 1954). In addition to variations in number there are also variations in form and size of chromosomes.

Before considering the mechanism of karyotype evolution, it will be well to inquire into the relation of basic number to other features of taxonomic or evolutionary significance. So far as can be determined there is no direct connection in either the plant or the animal kingdom between basic number and phylogenetic position. To be sure, there are differences between phyletic groups, but no obvious trends can be correlated with primitiveness or with specialization unless such correlations are made within the much narrower limits of family or genus. At this level a general tendency toward reduction in basic number parallels specialization (see later), but more striking is the correlation of basic number with growth habit in plants (Stebbins 1938).

The woody plants are presumed, on good phylogenetic evidence, to be ancestral to their herbaceous relatives. Cytologically the woody groups have higher basic numbers than herbaceous types, with $n = 12$–13 as an average. Since the woody gymnosperms have basic numbers of 11 and 12, and the pteridophytes as high or higher numbers, there is the suggestion that the living woody angiosperms were derived from them or from similar ancestral types with little change in basic number. A too-rigorous application of this hypothesis should not be made, however, for certain woody members of the Leguminosae have basic numbers of 6, 7, and 8 (Senn 1938), suggesting a polyploid derivation of some woody forms, but Stebbins' survey make it quite clear that the woody forms have, in general, a higher basic number than herbaceous types, which average about $n = 8$–9.

In addition, a greater stability of basic numbers among woody genera is indicated by the fact that of 51 woody genera studied, 49 have only one basic number. This can be contrasted with the herbaceous forms (151 genera) where 55 percent have one basic number, 28 percent have two, and 17 percent have three or more. Such stability on the part of woody genera, as contrasted to herbaceous types, may stem from their more constant growth rhythm and habit, but the need for more extensive data, particularly from genera in tropical regions, indicates that the conclusions derived must be regarded only as tentative at the moment.

On the other hand, there is little doubt that evolution within families and genera, giving rise to a variety of growth habits, is accompanied by greater cytological change than is the chromosomal evolution that differentiates new families or orders. This would suggest that the families and orders of angiosperms were differentiated soon after their origin in the early Tertiary period, and that the principal evolutionary changes have been within groups of lesser taxonomic rank. No similar survey has been carried out in the animal kingdom so it is not possible to say whether any particular characteristic of animals, phylogenetic or otherwise, is correlated with cytological stability or instability.

When only changes in basic number are involved, and polyploidy can be definitely excluded, the major problem is one of determining the mechanisms leading to such change. A theoretical means of accomplishing this end was suggested by Darlington (1937a). The scheme proposed that gain or loss of chromosomes from a basic set involves gain or loss of centromeres, and that the success of such change depends upon whether the chromatin adjacent to the centromere is inert (heterochromatin) or active (euchromatin). As Figure 13–2 indicates, reciprocal translocations, with at least one of the breakage points being in inert regions, can transfer euchromatin to a centromere carrying only inert chromatin (a B-type chromosome such as that found in maize would serve this purpose) to give an added chromosome, or can transfer all of the euchromatin from one chromosome to another, with loss of the depleted and now inert chromosome, to reduce the number.

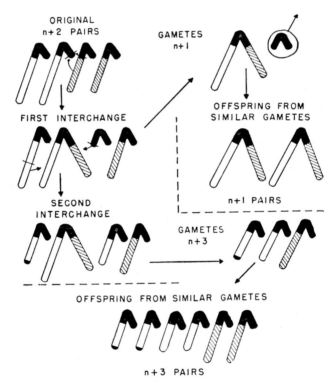

Fig. 13–2. Diagram to illustrate how, by means of reciprocal translocation of unequal chromosomal segments, the basic number of chromosomes can be increased or decreased. The black portions are heterochromatin, the white portions euchromatin (Stebbins 1950, after Darlington 1937).

The essential correctness of Darlington's hypothesis has been confirmed in Crepis, and studies of Drosophila, grasshopper, and lizard species have supported it. In Crepis, the evolutionary trend has been toward a reduction in chromosome numbers. The species that from a taxonomic point of view are primitive have high basic numbers ($n = 6$) while the more specialized forms have base numbers of 5, 4, and 3. Tobgy (1943) has demonstrated that *C. fuliginosa* ($n = 3$) was derived from the closely related *C. neglecta* ($n = 4$), or some similar ancestor, by reciprocal translocations (Fig.

13–3). The chromosomes of *C. neglecta* are designated A_N, B_N, C_N, and D_N, with C_N being largely heterochromatic, while those of *C. fuliginosa* are A_F, B_F and D_F, the C element having been lost. The F_1 species hybrid shows

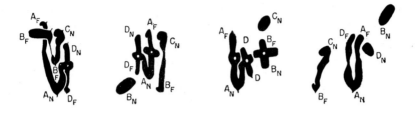

Fig. 13–3. Metaphase I configurations in the F_1 species hybrid of *Crepis fuliginosa* X *C. neglecta*. Chromosomes are labelled as to origin and type (Tobgy 1943).

that at meiosis two groups of chromosomes are formed, and those complexes have been identified as $A_F A_N D_F N_N$ and $B_N B_F C_N$, recognition of each element being simplified by the fact that size differences are retained in the hybrid at metaphase. Interestingly enough, complete pairing at pachytene indicates an almost intact homology between the two sets despite the difference in numbers. The A- and D-chromosomes of the two species are essentially intact although a portion of the short arm of A_N has been transferred to the long arm of D_F, giving a translocation complex in meiosis of the hybrid. C_N has been lost in *C. fuliginosa,* although enough of the tip of C_N has been transferred to the B_N element to permit pairing in the hybrid to give the $B_N B_F C_N$ complex.

In a similar analysis, it has been shown that *C. kotschyana* ($n = 4$) has been derived by reduction from *C. foetida* ($n = 5$) or some closely related form (Sherman 1946). Other evidence indicates that in Youngia and Ixeris, two genera related to Crepis, a like process has gone on, for the more primitive forms have higher numbers than the more specialized derived species. The precise details in these genera, however, have not been worked out.

It is presumed that it would be relatively easier for a species to increase the basic number than to decrease it in those species having accessory and genetically inert chromosomes. The transfer of euchromatin to these inert elements would, at one step, convert them from unessential to essential members of the complement. The process of fixation of the new complement would obviously be facilitated by self-fertilization. No clear analytical evidence has been obtained to show that such a process has gone on in nature, but in Allium of the Liliaceae and in Dorstenia of the Moraceae the more primitive species exhibit lower numbers than the more advanced forms. Aneuploidy, followed by a transfer of parts of the duplicated chromatin to other non-homologous chromosomes, could be responsible, but in the absence of genetic data uncertainty exists as to the manner of increase.

Stebbins (1950) indicates, however, that known or suspected increases in number (6) are far fewer than similarly detected decreases (25), and he further suggests that, since many of the low-chromosome, specialized forms are annuals, the reduced number leads to increased linkage and consequently to a greater degree of genetic constancy of population for short time periods. A consideration of this topic, with its evolutionary implications, will be reserved for a later chapter on polyploidy.

Changes in the basic number of Drosophila have been extensively investigated (Patterson and Stone 1952), and the pattern of change indicates that reductions in number are frequent (128 of the cytologically known 215 species and forms) while increases are rare, only one being known in *D. trispina.* The basic primitive number is 6, comprising five rods with subterminal centromeres and a dot chromosome. This configuration is represented in such species as *virilis, funebris, repleta,* and *tripunctata.* The great majority of species, however, show a modified complement, and the variations arise through centric fusions, pericentric inversions, translocations, and losses or gains in amount of heterochromatin. Figure 13–4 represents relationships within the genus from both a taxonomic and a cytological point of view, but does not on the other hand reveal the precise steps through which such variations occur. Presumably many of the intermediate configurations have been lost or are not yet discovered, and the stepwise formation in many cases can only be surmised.

In the *virilis* group, however, an indication of how this is achieved can be seen in Figure 13–5. This is a group of closely related species or subspecies, and it can be seen that in addition to inversions which produce an intrachromosomal scrambling of genes, as well as a pericentric inversion in Chromosome 2 of *primitive III, montana,* and *laciola,* which converts a rod into a small V-shaped element, the principal changes have been a centric fusion of Chromosomes 2 and 3 to produce a large V in *texana* and *americana* and a similar fusion in *americana* between the X and Chromosome 4. In *americana* this latter fusion brings about an alteration in the sex-chromosome mechanism (to be discussed in the next chapter). *D. littoralis,* also a member of this group, shows a different centric fusion, namely between Chromosomes 3 and 4, as well as a pericentric inversion in the Y to convert this into a J-shaped element. Such analyses are possible because the species can hybridize to permit a salivary gland chromosome analysis of pairing and band sequence, a type of study quite impossible in plants.

The centric fusions are simply a special type of translocation involving the entire euchromatic arms of rod chromosomes, and appear to be peculiar to the animal kingdom, being prevalent as well as in the Orthoptera (White 1954) and the Lacertilia lizards (Matthey 1949). Translocations involving only a part of an arm are very rare in Drosophila, only one, in *D. ananassae,* having become established as a fixed part of the chromosome complement

(Kaufmann 1937). It involves an X-4 chromosome exchange, and led to a shift of the nucleolar organizer and the *bobbed* locus from the X to Chromosome 4. Since this region is also present in the Y-chromosome, the case

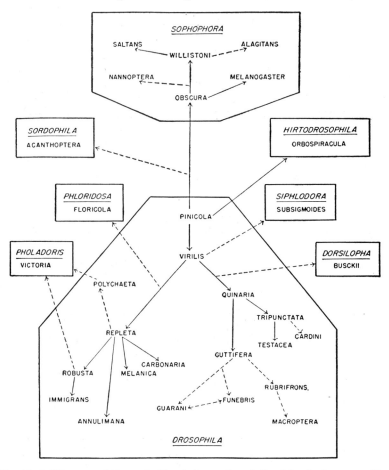

Fig. 13–4. Diagram of the probable phylogenetic relationships in the genus Drosophila. Only the major species and species groups are represented. (From Patterson and Stone, *Evolution in the Genus Drosophila,* copyright 1952 by The Macmillan Company, and used with their permission.)

is also an instance of hyperploidy becoming established; this region is represented three times in the male, but only twice in females.

Centric fusions, however, are possible as well as more likely in Drosophila than other kinds of translocations because of the large blocks of centric heterochromatin. Loss of a centromere plus adjacent heterochromatin produces no marked effect on viability, and can consequently be more readily withstood than the loss of euchromatin. The more pronounced breakability of heterochromatin as contrasted to euchromatin would tend to favor centric fusions, even though this cannot be too valid an argument since centric heterochromatin is present in many plants although centric fusions appear not to be.

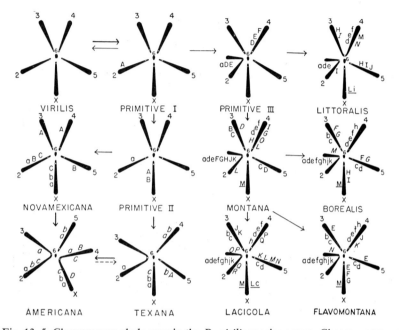

Fig. 13–5. Chromosome phylogeny in the *D. virilis* species group. Chromosomes are identified by numbers except for the X; inversions are identified by capital letters in the species in which they first occurred, by a small letter thereafter; centric fusions (translocations) can be recognized by the union of two chromosome (e.g., the 3-4 fusion in *littoralis*). A pericentric inversion in chromosome 2 occurs in the six species to the right of the diagram. (From Patterson and Stone, *Evolution in the Genus Drosophila*, copyright 1952 by The Macmillan Company, and used with their permission.)

Centric fusions have likewise altered the basic number in the Orthoptera. This is particularly true in the short-horned grasshoppers (Acrididae) where the number of arms is quite constant, but not necessarily the number of chromosomes. Thus in the Cryptosacci, a sub-group of the Acrididae, $2n = 23$ in the males of most species, with all chromosomes being rod shaped. V-shaped chromosomes appear in numbers up to three, involving autosome-autosome or autosome-X fusions, thereby reducing the basic number, while in other species a real loss of arms has occurred. Both processes are apparently involved in the chromosome sets of species of Nemobius (Fig. 13–6), where differences in numbers of V's and rods, as well as in total number of arms, are found. Where meiotic pairing in species hybrids, or a salivary gland chromosome type of analysis, is impossible, it cannot be stated with certainty that V-shaped chromosomes arise by fusion or by pericentric inversions unless the lengths of the arms in the V-elements can be used to distinguish between the two types of aberrations. The relative absence of inversions in the grasshoppers, on the other hand, would tend to favor fusion as the basic cause of reduction and change in form, a conclusion also drawn by Matthey (1949) for the lizards.

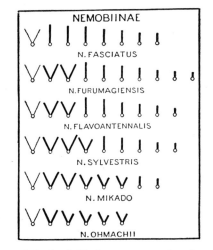

Fig. 13–6. Idiograms of the haploid chromosomes of various species of the cricket genus, Nemobius. The X chromosome is to the left in all cases. (From White, *Animal Cytology and Evolution,* copyright 1954 by the Cambridge University Press.)

Other changes in basic number involve loss or gain of "dot" or microchromosomes. Their minute size, and the difficulty in distinguishing heterochromatic accessory chromosomes from euchromatic necessary ones, make for uncertainty in their disposition if lost, or origin, if gained. In *Drosophila trispina,* the only species in the genus known with seven haploid chromosomes, the extra one is a small chromosome, somewhat larger than the usual dot-like element present in many species. Patterson and Stone (1952) suggest that it may have arisen as the "free" centromere released from a centric fusion of two rod elements, with the V-chromosome being lost while the "free" centromere with some attached chromatin was retained. Presumably the inert Y-chromosome could serve as a source for an extra centromere, but to date no case is known for certain where this avenue of change has been utilized. When the dot chromosome is lost, as it has been from a number of Drosophila species, it is uncertain whether it has been totally lost without an effect on viability or whether its essential parts have been transfered to other chromosomes through translocation.

CHANGES IN FORM AND RELATIVE SIZE OF CHROMOSOMES

From what has been stated earlier, it is clear that changes in form of chromosomes take place through translocations and pericentric inversions. Duplications and deletions would further alter form, but paracentric inversions merely shift gene order within arms. In animals the centric-fusion type of translocation appears to be a particularly prevalent mode of chromosomal change, but in plants most well analyzed translocations involve a part of, rather than a whole, arm. There is no clearly compelling evidence that would suggest why such a difference should exist. Changes in form also occur when a V-shaped chromosome breaks to form two rod chromosomes, and there are indications in animals that this happens, but it is not known whether the necessary extra centromere is actually a "new" one, derived possibly from an accessory chromosome, or whether the original centromere was fragmented to give two smaller but still functional centromeres. As Rhoades (1940) has shown, terminal centromeres are unstable, at least in maize, but it may be that stability can eventually be achieved.

Centric fusions, of course, convert two distinctly asymmetrical chromosomes into a single symmetrical one, there being a tendency, according to White (1954), for arms of equal length to be involved. If it is assumed, as Figure 13–5 would indicate, that species having rod-shaped chromosomes are primitive, evolution would seem to be, at least in Drosophila, in the direction of symmetry (i.e., toward V-shaped chromosomes), but Matthey's (1949) study of lizards, and White's (1954) in Orthoptera, while supporting such a hypothesis, would permit no such generalization to hold for all animal groups. In plants, however, asymmetry rather than symmetry of chromosomes seems to go hand-in-hand with specialization, the more primitive forms having symmetrical types, the specialized forms, asymmetrical (rod- or J-shaped) types (Stebbins 1950). This is evident from the Crepis studies (Babcock 1947), in which asymmetry is correlated with not only reduction in number but specialization of floral and vegetative parts.

The trend is not absolute, but enough instances are known to suggest that it is not without significance. Thus in Vicia (Leguminosae) perennial species have symmetrical genotypes, annual ones asymmetrical; in the Liliaceae, Lilium, Kniphofia, and Allium are generally symmetrical and primitive while Yucca, Agave, Haworthia, and Northoscordum are specialized and asymmetrical. If, as appears to be the case, centric fusions in animals are the rule while unequal translocations are more frequent in plants, this could account for the trends toward symmetry and asymmetry of animal and plant karyotypes, respectively.

The form of somatic metaphase chromosomes also depends upon the presence or absence, and the location, of constrictions. The primary constriction, of course, is that produced by the centromere, and separating the two arms. The secondary constriction, however, is related to nucleolar formation and leads to the development of a satellite or trabant of varying length. A shift in the nucleolar organizer region through translocation, as has happened in *Drosophila ananassae,* leads to an altered karyotype. Furthermore, nucleolar formation can be suppressed or enhanced by the degrees of strength of the involved regions, as Navaschin (1934) has demonstrated, or the region can be fragmented with both parts functional, as demonstrated by McClintock (1934). Both phenomena would alter metaphase chromosome shape.

The terms, symmetry and asymmetry of karyotype forms, have been employed differently by White (1954) to indicate differences in relative size of chromosomes in the same karyotype. Apart from accessory chromosomes, which are generally, although not necessarily, smaller than the usual chromosomes, microchromosomes are found throughout the plant and animal kingdom (Fig. 13–7). Agave and Yucca of the Liliaceae, both

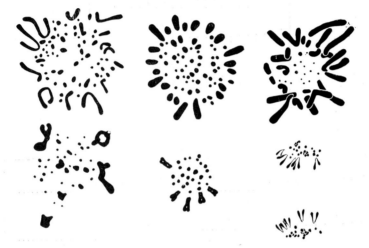

Fig. 13–7. Micro- and machrochromosomes of bird and plant species at meiosis I illustrating the manner by which the microchromosomes tend to congregate in the center of the spindle. Top left, *Oceanodroma leucorroa* (Procellariidae); top middle, *Melopsittacus undulatus* (Psittacidae); top right, *Cuculus canorus* (Cuculidae); bottom left, *Anas platyrhyncha* (Anatidae); bottom middle and right, metaphase I and anaphase I in *Yucca flaccida* (Liliaceae) (Matthey 1949 and O'Mara 1932).

specialized forms, have five large chromosomes and 25 much smaller ones. The "dot" chromosome of many Drosophila species falls into the category of a microchromosome, while many of the vertebrates show both macro- and microchromosomes (Matthey 1949). In the lizards, for example, two distinct karyotypes are evident: (1) in the Geckonidae, Eublepharidae, Scincidae, and Lacertidae, there exist a graded series of chromosomes from large to small, while in other groups such as the Iguanidae, Zonuridae, and Gerrhosauridae the karyotypes are of large often V-shaped chromosomes with many micro elements (Figs. 13–8, 13–9). It is almost as if the majority of chromatin were transformed to the large elements, leaving the microchromosomes with little more than centromeres.

Whether there is an evolutionary trend here is not certain, and even if one existed the selective advantages would not be immediately obvious. Clearly the chromosomes have a mechanical limitation as to maximum size, but there is no apparent limit as to minimum size except that it be consistent with maneuverability on the spindle. Where chromosomes of different sizes exist, the small ones usually cluster in the center of the spindle, the larger

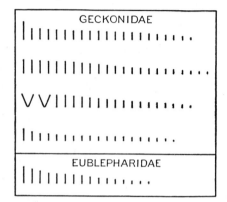

Fig. 13–8. Idiograms of the haploid chromosomes of two groups of lizards. (After Matthey, from M. J. D. White, *Animal Cytology and Evolution,* copyright 1954 by the Cambridge University Press.)

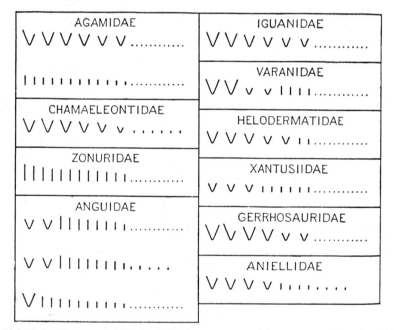

Fig. 13–9. Idiograms of the haploid chromosomes of ten groups of lizards. (After Matthey, from M. J. D. White, *Animal Cytology and Evolution,* copyright 1954 by the Cambridge University Press.)

ones at the periphery, this arrangement presumably reflecting a satisfactory mechanical arrangement on the metaphase plate.

Differences in absolute size of chromosomes have been mentioned in Chapter 5, and here we need only consider possible evolutionary implications. There is no evident reason, for example, why the chromosomes are large in the Orthoptera and Amphibia and small in the vertebrates; large in the monocots, small in the dicots, and minute in the fungi and bacteria. Size of cell is obviously related directly to number and size of chromosome and to the amount of DNA per nucleus (Mirsky and Ris 1951a), but what is the primary cause and what the secondary effect is not known. Stebbins (1938, 1950), however, has shown that certain trends may be observed phylogenetically, particularly within families, and, to a minor extent, within genera.

Nutritional conditions (Pierce 1937), degree of polyploidy (Manton 1952; Walker 1938), and genetic conditions (Thomas 1936) can influence chromosome size. Indeed, in the hybrid *Crepis neglecta* $\times$ *C. fuliginosa,* Tobgy (1943) has shown that determination of size must reside within the chromosome itself rather than being of a more general nuclear origin. In certain groups, however, increases or decreases can occur.

In a very general way, primitiveness in a phylogenetic sense is more closely correlated with larger-sized chromosomes than is specialization. This has already been indicated in Crepis (Fig. 13–1) where annuals have smaller chromosomes than perennials, and this is true for other composite genera related to Crepis, for Dianthus in the Caryophyllaceae, and for a number of genera in the Gramineae and the Commelinaceae. The same trend occurs in the ferns (Manton 1952), the primitive Osmundaceae having the largest chromosomes, the somewhat more advanced Polypodiaceae those of intermediate size, and the specialized Salviniaceae the smallest. On the other hand, phylogenetic increases in size of chromosomes may also accompany specialization, as for instance in certain members of the Polygonaceae, Cruciferae, Leguminoseae, and Onagraceae.

When the growth habits of plants are compared, it is found that woody species have smaller chromosomes than their herbaceous relatives. Stebbins considers that this trend relates to wood morphology, the cambial initials that produce fiber cells having small transverse dimensions, and hence requiring small chromosomes if only because of mechanical considerations. The relative constancy of the nucleocytoplasm ratio would seem to demand this, and there would be a selection for small size. In support of this is the fact that the Coniferales, which lack fibers and have cambial initials of relatively large and constant size, have both symmetrical as well as rather large chromosomes. Also the most primitive woody angiosperms, e.g., those in the Magnoliaceae, have larger chromosomes than the more specialized forms having an extensive fiber cell system in the xylem.

Stebbins (1938) also points out that among the woody angiosperms there is a far greater degree of stability of chromosomes than that evident among herbaceous types. This stability extends to basic number, which tends to be somewhat higher in general than in related herbaceous species, and to size and form as well. Internal stability, i.e., uniformity in genic pattern, is also evident from the fact that species hybrids often show regular meiotic behavior and high fertility. Thus, in the genus Platanus, a hybrid between *P. occidentalis* and *P. orientalis,* two species native to eastern North America and western Europe, respectively, and separated from each other since the Tertiary, show a regular meiotic pairing and high fertility, indicating an extraordinary chromosomal stability. The Rhododendrons of eastern Asia and eastern North America show a similar stability despite widely separate habitats and long separation periods.

Another type of change that introduces karyotype variations is the gain or loss of heterochromatin. Where considerable amounts of heterochromatin are found in the karyotype, alterations in form, size, and number of chromosomes can be accomplished without sacrifice of euchromatic portions. As pointed out above, centric fusions in animals, which probably involve only heterochromatic regions, as well as loss or gain of centromeres with adjacent heterochromatin, are without drastic effect on the individual. In this sense, a certain amount of heterochromatin is evolutionarily desirable as a safety factor, permitting a greater degree of karyotype variability than an inflexible system composed of euchromatin alone. It may well be that the North American species of Tradescantia, which have no detectable heterochromatin, together with a symmetrical and almost unvarying karyotype, lack the flexibility necessary for karyotype change except that gained through the medium of inversions. These latter aberrations are very widespread throughout the genus (Anderson and Sax 1936; Darlington 1937; Swanson 1940), but other types of aberrations are relatively infrequently encountered in nature although they are formed spontaneously at rather high rates (Giles 1940, 1941). On the other hand, other more specialized members of the Commelinaceae, such as Callisia, Campelia, Commelina, Cyanotis, and others, have asymmetrical and often very small chromosomes, suggesting the capacity for change exists in the family. Rhoeo, another genus related to Tradescantia, is a well known translocation heterozygote.

In both the Drosophila and grasshopper groups of species, gain or loss of heterochromatin has varied chromosome morphology considerably. Seven different types of Y-chromosomes, entirely heterochromatic, have been recognized in *D. pseudoobscura* (Dobzhansky 1935). These vary in their geographical distribution, with three being widespread, and the remaining four occupying limited localities. In the *repleta* group of species, *D. melanopalpa* has three heterochromatic arms in somatic metaphase configurations, *D. repleta* none, yet salivary-gland chromosome analysis reveals only a single major inversion separating them. Where the added *melanopalpa* heterochromatin was derived from is uncertain, but the fact that Patterson and Stone (1952) list 28 examples of added heterochromatin in this genus indicates that it is not an uncommon evolutionary feature of karyotype variation. Instability of heterochromatic elements is also indicated by the variability found in the B-chromosome of maize and in the accessory chromosome in rye.

In the Orthoptera, heteromorphic homologues (unequal bivalents) in meiosis of many grasshoppers are indicative of considerable chromosomal polymorphism (White 1954). Such variation is found both within and between species, and the logical assumption is that heterochromatin is involved. Presumably polymorphism of this sort has an adaptive significance —if it had none or was deleterious, it would presumably be eliminated from the population—and in the genus Trimesopteris there is a suggestion that it is of recent origin. In the more primitive section of the genus all the chromosomes are acrocentric (i.e., have their centromeres near the end of a chromosome), while in the more advanced species centric shifts and chromosomal polymorphism is strongly evident. Variation within a species indicates that the phenomenon has not yet become fixed, although the degree of variation differs between species and from population to population with a species.

From what has been said above, it is convincingly clear that the chromosome has an evolution of its own, apart from yet related to genic change. Certain phylogenetic trends are accompanied by chromosomal change, but it is too early to state whether these are fortuitously or causally related. Studies such as those made of Drosophila and Crepis species are needed if the changing patterns of karyotype morphology are to be fully understood from an evolutionary point of view, while surveys such as that made by Stebbins (1938) in the plant kingdom need to be undertaken in zoological groups. A very obvious gap, for example, exists in our knowledge of primate cytology, despite a wealth of material and species hybrids in our zoological gardens. The data already accumulated, however, indicate the usefulness of the approach through comparative cytology, and together with genetics and cytochemistry, it should reveal in greater detail the flexibility as well as the limitations of the hereditary materials of the cell.

CHAPTER 14

Evolution of Sex-Determining Mechanisms

The sex- or X-chromosome is a special element of the karyotype, and in some form or another it is found in most if not all of the higher animals and in many plant species. Allen (1940) lists 70 species of angiosperms, spread throughout 25 families, in which recognizable sex-chromosomes have been reported, while 46 cytologically investigated dioecious species have no such recognizable elements (5000 or more dioecious species of angiosperms are known).

The Y-chromosome, usually a pairing partner with the X, may or may not be present. Only rarely, as in Melandrium, does the Y function positively in sex determination, and the rather frequent occurrence of XO types in widely separated groups indicates that it has been repeatedly lost in the course of evolution. Its complete or partial heterochromatic nature together with its extreme variability in form and size even within a single species, e.g., *D. pseudoobscura,* implies a certain degree of dispensability, and retention of the Y would be necessary only when the X requires a pairing partner for normal segregation in meiosis or when the Y still possesses genetic functions of an essential nature.

Both the X- and the Y-chromosomes have passed through an evolutionary process in attaining their distinctive characteristics. As yet no positive sequence of steps in a closely related group of organisms is known to reveal the manner by which an undifferentiated autosome becomes a highly differentiated X- or Y-chromosome, but enough examples of varying degrees of differentiation have been recognized to permit the elaboration of a plausible scheme of events that would lead to such an end result.

The experimental induction of a bisexual state from a previous one of hermaphroditism, as has been done several times in maize (Emerson 1924; Jones 1939), and the shifting of sex determination in the fish, Lebistes, from one chromosome pair to another (Winge 1932), emphasize the fact that separation of the sexes, while almost invariable in the higher animals, is nonetheless relatively easy of attainment from a hermaphroditic state, at least under experimental conditions. Conversely, the return to hermaphroditism from a state of bisexuality by certain species of coelenterates, nematodes, and echinoderms (these phyla being largely characterized by bisexuality) indicates that the development of a chromosomal mechanism for sex determination does not insure an absolute and permanent separation of the two sexes. This is particularly true in plants where dioecism seems to be readily subject to reversion to hermaphroditism through mutation or environmental influence (Loehwing 1938; Allen 1940).

The existence of separate sexes, however, is by no means an indication of a chromosomal or a genetic basis for sex determination. In hermaphrodites, of course, the formation of eggs and sperm is clearly a matter of histological differentiation. Gametophytes of the moss Funaria, for example, produce antheridia and sperm on apical branches, the lateral branches forming oögonia and eggs, and sexual differentiation is apparently determined at the time of branching. The diploid sporophyte in this genus is neuter. The alga, Codium, presents a variable picture. *C. discorticatum* has both male and female structures on the same diploid plant, individuals of *C. tomentosum* are either male or female, and *C. elongatum* resembles *C. discorticatum* in having both male and female structures on the same plant during part of the year, but with the approach of autumn a seasonal variation sets in, the newly produced individuals being either male or female. Among animal species many invertebrate groups are entirely or largely hermaphroditic. Even in bisexual animals, histological differentiation can be the mode of sex determination. The marine worm Dinophilus is an example, the female producing large and small eggs in the same ovary, and these, whether fertilized or not, develop into females and males, respectively.

An environmental determination of sexuality is known in the worm Bonellia and in the horsetail Equisetum. The eggs of Bonellia are potentially alike, but free living forms develop into females, attached ones into structurally degenerate males which take up a parasitic existence within the sexual organs of females. Equisetum, grown in strong sunlight and with ample nutrition, exhibits marked female tendencies, with opposite conditions leading to maleness. Whether there is a subtle and unrecognized genetic basis for sex in these, and similar, organisms is not known.

Each sex, therefore, seems to have the potentialities of the opposite sex. This can be most clearly demonstrated in those species where a strong genetic mechanism is lacking; but even where a clear-cut chromosomal mechanism is involved a bipotentiality can be shown to exist. Hormones, of course, reinforce or blur the separation of sexes by their influence on secondary sexual features, but these need not be considered here.

The bipotentiality of the sexes, however, is implicit in Bridges' (1932) balance theory, as well as in Goldschmidt's (1934) hypothesis based on Lymantria intersexuality. Bridges' theory considers that, in the Drosophila XX-XY determined system, femaleness and maleness are a reflection of a balanced influence between X-chromosomes and autosomes. The former influence development toward femaleness, the latter toward maleness; and the system is so balanced that a ratio of one X to one set of autosomes gives femaleness, while one X to two sets of autosomes gives maleness. The Y-chromosome in this system is without sex influence.

The correctness of the balance theory is borne out by a study of triploid females. When crossed to diploid males, variable chromosome numbers in the offspring are possible, but only certain combinations are viable. The combination 3X:3A is a triploid female, varying only from the normal 2X:2A female by features brought on by polyploidy. The combination 1X:3A gives a male with exaggerated maleness, while 2X:3A leads to the formation of intersexes (Table 14–1).

A search for female-determining genes in the X-chromosome (Dobzhansky and Schultz 1934; Pipkin 1940b) and for male-determining genes in the autosomes (Pipkin 1947) has revealed no special sex-determining regions. This could mean one of two things: either there are multiple genes, all with small but similar effects, operating in the direction of femaleness in the X-chromosome and of maleness in the autosomes, or there are no such genes in the classical sense but rather a different sort of balance in which whole chromosomes rather than individual, Mendelizing genes set the developmental pattern. In Lymantria, where the female is the heterogametic sex, and the sex determiners vary in potency, Goldschmidt (1950) has likened the situation to the *Ac-Ds* system in maize, with heterochromatin playing a possible vital role. A complete explanation of sex determination in Lymantria still remains to be given.

Determination of sex, however, by individual genes, or by specific regions of chromosomes, is known. The mating types of many microorganisms—Neurospora, for example—are governed by genes in the usual Mendelian sense of the term, although it is more correct in these instances to speak of compatibility reactions than of sex determination with its usual connotations. The wasp Habrobracon, in which males are generally haploid and females diploid, has, however, a sex-determination mechanism based on a series of at least nine alleles (or non-alleles localized in a block of chromatin within which crossing over does not occur). When these genes are heterozygous in the diploid state, femaleness results, but when hemizygous (haploid) or homozygous (diploid), maleness is expressed. The mode of operation of such a system is difficult to comprehend.

XX-XY MECHANISM

The types of bisexuality that are dependent upon an established chromosomal basis arose in all probability from a state of hermaphroditism (in plants, possibly, hermaphroditism to monoecism to dioecism), or from a non-genetically determined bisexuality. If this is a valid point of view, it becomes necessary, therefore, to account evolutionarily for the establishment of a highly differentiated sex chromosome from an essentially un-

TABLE 14-1

Chromosome constitution and sex in Drosophila and Melandrium (after Warmke 1946). A = set of autosomes.

Drosophila

Chromosome Constitution	Sex	X/A Ratio
2 A XXX	superfemale	1.5
2 A XXX 2 A XXY 3 A XXX 4 A XXXX	female	1.0
3 A XX 3 A XXY	intersex	0.67
4 A XXX	intersex	0.75
2 A X 2 A XY 2 A XYY 4 A XX	male	0.50
3 A X	supermale	0.33

Melandrium

Chromosome Constitution	Sex	X/Y Ratio
2 A XX	female	0.00
2 A XYY	male	0.5
2 A XY 3 A XY 4 A XY 4 A XXYY	male	1.0
4 A XXXYY	male	1.5
2 A XXY 3 A XXY 4 A XXY 4 A XXXXYY	male (occasional blossom) ♂+	2.0
3 A XXXY 4 A XXXY	male (occasional blossom) ♂+	3.0
4 A XXXXXY	hermaphrodite (occasional blossom) ♂	4.0

differentiated autosome-like chromosome. Since this sex chromosome must have, at least initially, a pairing partner, the Y, it too must have an evolution, but one quite different apparently from that of the X. A consideration of the structure of the X- and Y-chromosomes in *D. melanogaster,* or that of the X in the XO male grasshoppers, indicates that changes of some magnitude have occurred in the past history of these forms.

It is not to be expected, in some closely related group of organisms, that all transitional stages of development of such a chromosomal mechanism will be available for study. Sexual differentiation has without doubt arisen independently in many different plant and animal groups; and, while the existence of sex chromosomes may seem to provide a common basis of origin, the fact that quite diverse genic complexes often determine similar phenotypes (parallel or convergent evolution), cautions against the proposing of any unitary theory of sex determination even at a chromosomal level. Within the framework of these limitations, however, the uncovering of certain steps in the sequence of events leading to chromosomal differentiation permits at least a partial understanding of sex chromosomes. How broadly these can be applied to the evolution of all forms of sex chromosomes remains undetermined.

The widespread existence of cross-fertile, self-sterile species among hermaphrodites is an indication of the evolutionary value of genetic recombination. Separation of the sexes represents a positive reinforcement of this system. In maize this can be accomplished by two mutational steps. *Tassel-seed* (*ts*), a recessive gene, converts the terminal male inflorescence into a pistillate structure, while *silkless* (*sk*), another recessive, causes ovule abortion. *Tassel-seed* is epistatic to *silkless,* so that a plant homozygous for both mutants (*ts ts sk sk*) has a normal lateral inflorescence bearing ovules, while the terminal staminate inflorescence is modified to a pistillate condition. Plants that are *Ts ts sk sk* are totally staminate, the terminal inflorescence being normal, and the lateral ear bearing only aborted ovules. A cross between these two genotypes produces only female (*ts ts sk sk*) and male (*Ts ts sk sk*) plants, with the male being the heterogametic sex. These genes are not linked, and the pair of chromosomes bearing *ts* and *Ts* become the equivalent of X- and Y-chromosomes, respectively. Dependence upon the *sk* genes for maintenance of the system, however, is evident. The separation of sexes can be maintained indefinitely, and Jones (1939) has shown that through selection modifying genes can be accumulated that influence fixation of maleness and femaleness. In addition, there are 40 or more known genes that affect maleness or femaleness in maize in a variety of ways, each of which could presumably strengthen an incipient system once it was formed.

In the experimentally produced dioecious strain of maize described above the "X" and "Y" chromosomes are alike in structure, i.e., they do not possess the distinctive characteristics of many sex chromosomes observed in both plants and animals. From what is known of other X- and Y-chromosomes, the attainment of a distinctiveness that sets these chromosomes apart from other elements of the karyotype as well as from each other involves a number of related steps: (1) accumulation, in the X-chromosome, of factors governing the development of that sex which is homogametic; (2) concomitant accumulation, in the Y-chromosome or in the autosomes, of factors governing the development of the opposite heterogametic sex; and (3) isolation of the X from the Y by a reduction in crossing over in order to preserve gene combinations favoring sexual separation.

The first two steps could proceed slowly or rapidly, depending on mutation and selection pressures, and the rigidity of the two systems will be a reflection of the efficacy of these pressures. In Drosophila it would appear that a stabilized state has developed, while a relatively flexible one still exists in Lebistes. Isolation of the X from the Y proceeds very likely from an initial localized chiasma formation, a step that could be fostered genetically or cytologically, i.e., by aberrations. Once a region is isolated from crossing over there would be little or no natural selection to prevent the functional degeneration of most of the genes through mutation; in fact, mutation pressure theoretically should produce precisely this condition (Muller and Painter 1932). The genic inertness of the Y in Drosophila is, therefore, a direct result of its isolation from the X; and the genic function it once is presumed to have had, has been either transferred to the autosomes or compensated for by other mutations in other chromosomes. It also seems reasonable to assume that the genic inertness of centric regions or other chromosomes in Drosophila, as well as in many other organisms, arises out of a failure to cross over regularly, although homology of certain parts of the inert region of the X with the Y in *D. melanogaster* may mean that translocations as well have been involved in their origin once inertness was established (Muller and Painter 1932).

Genic inertness, in a Mendelian sense, and heterochromatin are recognized generally as being the genetical and cytological expressions, respectively, of the same state in the chromosome. In essence, this proposes that heterochromatin is formed from euchromatin by a process of genic degeneration, with a parallel, or possibly later, development of allocycly which permits cytological recognition of heterochromatin. The end point of such an evolutionary trend, which introduces a "permanent structural hybridity" into a normally functioning system (Darlington 1937a), would be heterochromatinization of the entire Y, as seen in Drosophila. Being inert, such chromosomes are subject to loss or variation in both form and size. Loss has occurred in many groups to give XO type males, while diversity of morphology in Y-chromosomes can be found in *D. pseudoobscura* in which seven forms of the Y have been recognized (Dobzhansky 1935).

Loss of the Y leads to isolation of the X in XO individuals. This would suggest that the X would similarly become heterochromatinized; and this appears to be true, for example, in the XO males of grasshoppers, where the X has no apparent or striking genetic function other than that of sex determination (Nabours and Stebbins 1950). It should be pointed out, however, that the correlation between heterochromatin and genic inertness is by no means complete, since heterochromatinization may be evident in one type of cell but not in another, even in the same individual (White 1950). On the other hand, evidence that heterochromatin can be derived from euchromatin, and that reduction in crossing over plays a role in the transformation process, is indicated by the heterochromatinization of autosomal euchromatin when transferred to the Y in the neo-XY mechanisms in certain crickets, grasshoppers, and tenebrionid beetles (Smith 1952; White 1954).

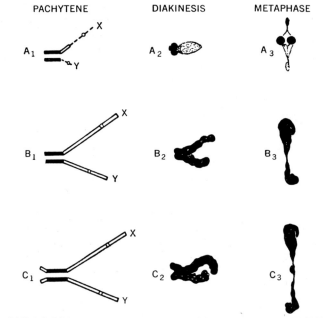

Fig. 14–1. Diagrammatic representations of the structure of the sex chromosomes in five genera of marsupials, and at several stages of meiosis I. A, structures typical of the X and Y in Dasyurus, Sarcophilus and Phascolarctus; B, Trichosurus; C, Pseudochirus (Koller 1936).

The X-chromosomes depicted in Figure 14–1 may be presumed to represent intermediate stages of differentiation between the incipient "X" chromosomes of dioecious strains of maize and the entirely heterochromatic X-chromosomes of the grasshopper. These possess both a pairing and a differential segment. If the basic sex genes possess a "trigger" action in determining the direction of development toward femaleness or maleness, selective forces would tend to protect them from exposure to normal segregation. The evolution of a differential segment containing the sex genes accomplishes this end, and the widespread occurrence of differential and pairing segments (the permanent structural hybridity of Darlington) points to this as a fundamental step in the formation of differentiated sex chromosomes.

Evolution of the potential Y-chromosome must follow that of the X, but in a different direction. Its differential segment may or may not contain sex genes. If it does, these must influence development of the opposite sex; if it does not possess such genes, the autosomes must take over this function, and the fate of the Y evolutionarily depends upon which circumstance prevails. In Drosophila, where the major portion of the Y has no homology with the X, these steps seem to have been accomplished, only secondary sex functions (i.e., fertility genes) having been retained. Further genic inertness on the part of the Y would set the stage for its permanent loss.

The situation in *Melandrium album* (Warmke 1946, Westergaard 1948) may be examined in detail to illustrate the points made. This species can be presumed to occupy an intermediate position in sex determination between the incipient stage in maize and the reinforced system known in *D. melanogaster,* or the even more terminal state reached in XO organisms in which the Y has been dispensed with. Figure 14–2 illustrates the nature of the X- and Y-chromosomes of *M. album.* Only Region IV is similar in

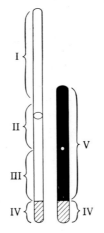

Fig. 14–2. Diagram of the X (right) and Y (left) chromosomes of Melandrium. I, female suppressor region in the Y which when absent leads to bisexual development; II, essential male promoting region which when absent leads to female development; III, essential male fertility region which when absent causes anthers to abort; IV, pairing region in both X and Y chromosomes (length in diagram somewhat arbitrary); V, differential portion of the X (redrawn from Westergaard 1948).

both chromosomes, and pairing and crossing over are confined to this segment in each chromosome. Regions I, II, and III constitute the differential portion of the Y, Region V the differential segment of the X. In the Y-chromosome, Region I exerts a female suppressor action; when absent from the chromosome, a plant with complete flowers results. Region II possesses a male promoting action, since its absence results in a female plant. Region III has a secondary sex function, in that its presence is necessary for male fertility but not necessary for either the formation of male organs or the suppression of female ones. Region V in the X contains the basic sex genes for femaleness. The Y-chromosome, therefore, has a positive male influence necessitating its retention, but this influence is exerted both by female suppression as well as by male promotion.

The balancing effect of X- and Y-chromosomes can be see in Table 14–1, where it is contrasted with the situation in *D. melanogaster.* The absence of the Y leads to the absence of males, but where Y's are present either males or intersexes (hermaphrodites) appear. A single Y is clearly stronger than a single X; but, where polyploidy or aneuploidy of autosomes exists, the distinction can be blurred, since there is evidence that weaker male- and female-determining tendencies can be exerted by the autosomes.

VARIATIONS IN THE CHROMOSOMAL DETERMINATION OF SEX

When the determination of sex is dependent upon a chromosomal mechanism, it is easiest to assume that the XX-XY condition is a primitive one, not only because of its prevalence throughout the plant and animal world but because all other types are derivable from it. There are XY states known now to be derived from an earlier XO type, but it is also logical to assume that the ancestral XO type had a previous origin from a more primitive XY condition.

Even with the XY types, there is a bewildering variation both in size of the two elements and in their manner of segregation during meiosis (White 1954, Schrader 1928). This seems to be particularly true in the insects, and possibly not without reason, for the vast reproductive potential of this phylum could present for selection innumerable changes, most of which would be disadvantageous but some of which could, and have, survived. It is expected that the X and Y, and particularly the latter, would be subject to change as they became more and more concerned with sex determination to the exclusion of other genetic functions.

As pointed out in *D. pseudoobscura,* many species possess a variety of Y-chromosomes, their genetic inertness permitting a diversity of form and chromatin content without impairment of viability to the individual. Total loss of the Y, as has occurred in several species of Drosophila, could result from its total genetic inactivity or by a transfer of its essential parts to autosomes. The X, under such circumstances, must accommodate itself for independent movement on the spindle. A prelude to this sort of inherent behavior may be seen in the Heteroptera where in most species the X and Y rarely form true bivalents in meiosis I, while in others the X and Y do not pair at all, but divide equationally (Hughes-Schrader 1948b). A temporary association occurs at metaphase of meiosis II between the X and Y, this presumably facilitating segregation. XO species of the same group follow a similar pattern but the X segregates to one pole at the second division independently.

XO conditions, by translocations with autosomes, can give rise to two different neo-chromosomal mechanisms, depending on whether the X is rod- or V-shaped. The latter situation is illustrated in Figure 14–3, and

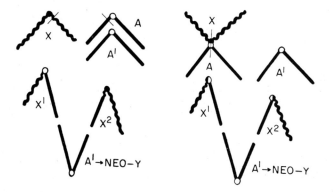

Fig. 14–3. Diagrammatic representation of the origin of an X^1X^2Y mechanism from an original XO type of male. Fine lines indicate the position of breaks; solid outline, euchromatin of autosomes; wavy outline, heterochromatin of original X chromosome (Hughes-Schrader 1950, after White and Oguma).

the translocation will give rise to a neo-X_1X_2Y condition. Centric fusion of an X-chromosome and an autosome to give a neo-XY condition transforms an autosome into a Y-chromosome and confines it to the male line. This has occurred independently in 14 not-too-closely-related genera in the grasshopper group (Helwig 1941, 1942), and in three instances there is good evidence that the neo-Y, now heterochromatinized, is no longer homologous with its supposedly former homologue in the neo-X.

The species *Hesperotettix viridis* is interesting in this respect. In the subspecies *H. v. brevipennis* an XO condition prevails, while a neo-XY is present in *H. v. protensis*. *H. v. viridis* has both conditions, and in this instance the Y and its homologous arm of the X are both euchromatic and capable of pairing. It would appear that the neo-XY is of such recent origin that it has not yet become fixed in the population and that the Y has not yet achieved a heterochromatic state. A neo-XY derived from an XO condition has also been shown to have occurred in the phasmid *Isagorus schraderi* (Hughes-Schrader 1947) and in the tenebrionid beetle

Tribolium confusum (Smith 1952). In both cases heterochromatinization of the neo-Y has taken place.

In Drosophila, 12 species reveal that X-autosome fusions have occurred, although they may not all be of independent origin (Patterson and Stone 1952). These, however, although XY at the present time, are presumed to have arisen from an original XY to give an XY_1Y_2 condition, with subsequent loss of the original Y either through total loss or through transfer of essential parts to other chromosomes.

That such a change can occur has been demonstrated by Smith (1949) in *Agrilus anxius,* a buprestid beetle. Composed actually of two species, one feeding on poplar and the other on birch, the former (Species A) has a $2n$ formula of 18 A + XY (the Y being large), while the latter (Species B) is 20 A + Xy (y being small). Analysis of the chromosomes indicates that Species A has been derived from Species B by chromatin loss and translocation, the loss involving the y element and the translocation being between the original X and an autosome. The following mode of origin is indicated: 10 AA + Xy $\longrightarrow$ 9 AA + $\widehat{AAXy}$ $\longrightarrow$ 9 AA + $\widehat{AXA}$, with the solitary A becoming the large Y in Species A.

Neo-X_1X_2Y derivations from an XO condition characterize a number of subfamilies of the mantids (Orthoptera) (Hughes-Schrader 1950). Females of these species would be $X_1X_1X_2X_2$. Interestingly enough, there is strong evidence that these subfamilies have their origin from a single ancestral species, the neo-X_1X_2Y being very likely of monophyletic origin. Its presence or absence, therefore, provides an excellent tool for revealing taxonomic relationships which may have become obscured by various morphological specializations.

The Y-chromosome in these mantids, being confined to males alone, has undergone change in form as well as in degree of heterochromatinization. As Hughes-Schrader points out, the only limits to variation in the Y are the retention of sufficient homology for proper pairing and segregation from both X's, plus the retention of whatever genetic requirements are demanded of it for viability or fertility. Assuming that the length of the original neo-Y was equal to the arms of the two X's with which it pairs— a ratio retained by some genera—an extreme in variation is reached in the genus Melliera, where the ratio is about 0.07 (Figure 14–4). It would appear in this case that the neo-Y can serve little function other than that of a pairing device.

A similar situation to that in the mantids has been encountered in the grasshopper *Paratylotropidia brunneri* (King and Beams 1938), although in this case two pairs of rod autosomes have become involved to produce an X_1X_2Y mechanism in which one X is now a V-shaped $\widehat{XA_1}$, the other X is A_2, and the Y is $\widehat{A_1A_2}$ (A_1 and A_2 being the original autosomes) (White 1954). *P. morsei* possesses the same mechanism as that in *P.*

brunneri, but *P. beutenmulleri* has a neo-XY resulting from an X-autosome fusion.

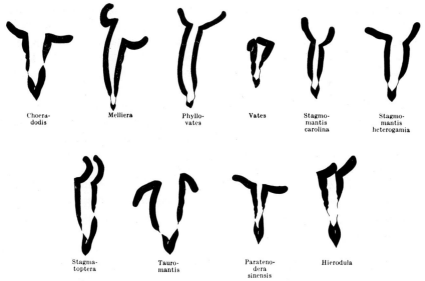

Fig. 14–4. Sex trivalents of 10 species of X^1X^2Y mantids at metaphase I, showing the variable size of the Y chromosome (located at the bottom of each trivalent). Some variation in the pairing and the lengths of the free arms of the X chromosomes is also evident, and can be presumed to be the result of evolutionary modification, since the X^1X^2Y mantids appear to have a monophyletic origin (Hughes-Schrader 1950).

At meiosis such an X_1X_2Y combination forms a trivalent, and gametes possessing a full complement of genes will result only if X_1 and X_2 go to the same pole, the Y to the other. The same type of trivalent would be formed if an autosome were translocated to an already existent Y. This has taken place in the evolution of the karyotype of *Drosophila miranda* (MacKnight and Cooper 1944, Cooper 1946), the translocation involving Chromosome 3 and a V-shaped Y. The unchanged X is V-shaped, while the remainder of Chromosome 3 becomes a rod neo-X. In *D. americana americana* the dot Chromosome 4 has fused centrally with the X, thus forcing the homologous Chromosome 4 into the male line as a neo-Y_2. Since this arrangement is not present in *D. a. texana* it is assumed to be of relatively recent origin (Patterson and Stone 1952).

In general, therefore, it can be stated that any fusion or translocation of autosomal chromatin with the X- or Y-chromosomes will, if viable, lead to the formation of an altered chromosomal mechanism for sex determination. The evolution of this system proceeds apparently in the direction of increased heterochromatinization of the introduced euchromatin, followed by possible loss or variation in size and form of the heterochromatic elements.

Not all multiple sex-chromosome mechanisms have their origin in X or Y fusions with autosomes. In the Heteroptera, where diffuse centromeres exist, simple fragmentation of the X-chromosome would lead to an increase in the number of sex chromosomes. A range from XO and XY up to $X_1X_2X_3X_4X_5Y$ has been found, the X's dividing equationally in the first meiotic division, and segregating from the Y (when present) as a group in the second division. White (1954) does not believe that this process alone can produce these types, since fragmentation would complicate the situation through sister reunion of broken ends; but, since fragments from chromosomes with diffuse centromeres produced by x-rays are not lost during cell division, but behave as if they were simply smaller editions of the chromosomes from which they were derived (Hughes-Schrader and Ris 1941), his argument that these are duplicated sex-chromosome fragments loses its cogency. This is also supported by the transmissibility of x-ray induced fragments in the presumed polycentric chromosomes of the Brazilian scorpion *Tityus bahiensis* (Rhoades and Kerr 1949).

A variation in numbers of sex chromosomes in the Heteroptera is found within a single species of bedbug (*Cimex lectularius*), the number varying from 2 to 15. There is no certainty, however, that these are true sex chromosomes exerting a sex determining influence, for as White suggests they may be simply derivatives of former X-chromosomes carrying only homologous but inert chromatin. Other strange mechanisms are found in the beetle Blaps, where a range is encountered from X_1X_2Y to the somewhat ridiculous situation found in the species *B. polychresta,* the male having 18 autosomes, 12 X's, and six Y's. In certain nematodes a whole series of numbers based on an XO type have been found, the highest being $X_1X_2X_3X_4X_5X_6O$, while a corresponding variation in the number of Y-chromosomes is encountered in the coreid bugs of the genus Acanthocephala (Metapodius) (Wilson 1925). These extremes have not been found in any group of plants; but it is quite apparent that the specialized nature of sex chromosomes provides for the possibility of an enormous range of variability in form, size, and number, a situation not encountered, or at least not recognized, among autosomes.

CHAPTER 15

Role of Aberrations in Evolution

Two preceding chapters have indicated that evolution of the karyotype is accomplished through the medium of aberrations. Breakage of the chromosomes, followed by recombination of the broken ends and often accompanied by gain or loss of parts, leads to reconstituted karyotypes that may distinguish one species from another closely related form.

The extent to which related species differ in karyological characters provides a measure of the extent to which chromosomal rearrangements have contributed to, or at least have paralleled, speciation. The comparison made between the karyotypes of *Crepis fuliginosa* and *C. neglecta,* as well as those between chromosomal sex-determining mechanisms in various species of animals, are, however, relatively gross and reveal only that in these cases certain species are distinguished by karyotypes that are related in the sense that the derivation of one from the other can be postulated with some degree of certainty.

Translocations of one sort or another provide the most easily recognized type of aberration, but it must be remembered that aberrations alone are unlikely to have any immediate effect on the species. At most, an aberration may bring about a detectable position effect, and may lead to a certain degree of sterility as the result of meiotic disturbance; but no chromosomal aberration, however complex, is known that could result in the immediate formation of a new species. This is indicated by the considerable chromosomal polymorphism—the presence of many inversions, translocations, and so on, in natural populations of a single species—found in a wide variety of species, and is supported by the immense number of aberrations artificially induced by x-rays which in no way lead to the formation of new species. Once these aberrations become established in a species, the possibility of a variation in the karyotype will depend upon the extent to which this visibly affects the form and size of chromosomes.

Furthermore, the fact that related species may have similar karyotypes indicates that aberrations *per se* are not a necessary accompaniment to speciation. Thus, two species of Platanus, *occidentalis* and *orientalis,* occurring respectively in eastern United States and in southeastern Europe, hybridize easily and the F_1 hybrid, called *P. acerifolia,* is highly fertile, meiosis giving no indication of aberrations (Sax 1933). Here speciation is due entirely to gene mutations, with geographical space providing the barrier between them to prevent crossing.

On the other hand, similar karyotypes as seen in mitotically dividing cells may mask a wealth of hidden aberrations. In dipteran species having salivary gland chromosomes capable of band analysis, such minute aberrations can be brought to light. *Drosophila pseudoobscura* and its near relatives may be used as examples. The only chromosomal differences between *D. pseudoobscura* and *D. persimilis* which are always found in species hybrids are two paracentric inversions, one in the second and the other in the left arm of the X-chromosome. Other inversions are known in these two species, but they may or may not be present in any particular individual (Dobzhansky and Epling 1944). A comparison between *D. pseudoobscura* and *D. miranda,* the latter being more distantly related than *D. persimilis* but nevertheless capable of producing hybrids with *D. pseudoobscura* in the laboratory, reveals very numerous structural changes which would require at least 49 and possibly 100 or more breaks to have produced the rearrangements observed (Dobzhansky and Tan 1936). A somewhat fewer number of aberrations separates *D. melanogaster* from the closely related *D. simulans,* and many of these are quite minute in size (Horton 1939). Were the salivary gland type of chromosome absent these would escape detection; consequently, in plants and other animals only the grosser aberrations can be identified with certainty.

From what has been said it is clear that aberrations are not themselves alone responsible for the evolution of species; good evidence has been provided, however, as to the possible role they can play. This can best be done by considering their action within rather than between species.

The evolutionary change in species is dependent in the long run upon a constantly produced series of random gene mutations—using the term "mutation" rather broadly—which are being as constantly subjected to environmental selection. The species is, therefore, a dynamic rather than a static entity, flowing, as it were, through time, and modified as mutation and selection pressures permit. Selection, however, operates not on single genes but on organisms, and it is therefore the genotype as a whole that is selected for or against by the environment in which it finds itself. In any randomly breeding population, where the recombination of genes through crossing over is uninhibited, analyzed species have been shown to be extremely heterozygous genetically. The genotype under these conditions presents a fluid rather than a fixed pattern, with the environment determining the limits beyond which genotypic variation cannot transgress.

Diversity enters the picture through the medium of gene and chromosomal mutations. In a very general sense, deficiencies and duplications can be considered chromosomal mutations on a par with gene mutations, while translocations and inversions serve as mechanisms for the isolation and maintenance of blocks of genes. These blocks, being relatively undisturbed by crossing over and diverging from each other by randomly occurring mutations within them, become in essence units of evolution at a higher level of complexity from that of single genes. In this sense, chromosomal aberrations can be legitimately discussed as to their role in the evolution of species.

DEFICIENCIES

There is little reason for believing that deficiencies can contribute in any substantial manner to the evolution of organisms. To be sure, deficiencies are responsible for many so-called mutations in Drosophila and maize, and what evidence is available indicates that species differ from one another by a great many mutations; but since most deficiency mutations are homozygous lethal the likelihood of this particular class of chromosomal mutations contributing to speciation is vanishingly small, and can generally be ruled out of serious consideration.

On the other hand, a reduction in chromosome number, as has occurred during speciation in the genus Crepis, for example, involves not only a loss of centromeres but, presumably, of some chromatin adjacent to it. This material is, however, heterochromatic, and, whether or not it contains polygenes, its loss is better withstood by the organism than is the same amount of euchromatin. Such losses, although they may accompany speciation, are not likely to contribute directly to it. The loss of a centromere and its adjacent heterochromatin can, under these circumstances, be viewed as a cast-off by-product of an event that translocates the euchromatin to other chromosomes, and consequently reshuffles the linkage groups, but until more is known of the function of heterochromatin it is somewhat difficult to appraise its loss or gain in evolutionary terms.

Another class of loss, which has already been mentioned, may again be considered here although the change is not, in the true sense of the word, a deficiency. Here reference is being made to the progressive loss of euchromatin that occurs through heterochromatinization of autosomal material that, by chance, becomes part of a neo-sex chromosomal mechanism, e.g., in the phasmids as described by Hughes-Schrader (1947), and in the tenebrionid beetles as suggested by Smith (1952).

In these two cases, as well as in certain species of grasshoppers having the neo-XY mechanisms, loss of the euchromatic genetic functions must be accompanied by one of two possible changes: (1) other autosomal regions take over the genetic function of the chromatin that is being neutralized through heterochromatinization, or (2) *dosage compensation* sets in. This term, proposed by Muller (1950), is used to describe the existence of a mechanism that permits a single dose of genes in the X-chromosome of the heterogametic sex to produce the same degree of effect as two doses of the same gene in the XX homogametic sex. It may be presumed that dosage compensation operates in species such as Drosophila where the sexes are basically similar as to form and function, but too little is known of the mechanism of origin of either dosage compensation or heterochromatinization to do other than to point out that they are evolutionary steps associated with either abrupt or progressive loss of euchromatin.

DUPLICATIONS

There is a widespread belief among geneticists that genes do not arise *de novo* in organisms today, although the first gene or genes must have had some such origin in the primeval past. On the other hand, presumably all organisms do not have the same number of genes, so that the differences in number must arise through either gain or loss. In the case of abrupt loss through deficiency, reasons have been given to consider this an unlikely evolutionary event. Duplications, however, do not possess such evolutionary limitations, and in fact the duplication of loci would appear to provide a feasible method for the acquisition of new genes.

Inherent in this hypothesis is the further assumption that two genes, identical as to origin and function, can diverge through mutation to such an extent that they, at a later stage in evolution, control entirely different and separate functions. Mutations in general lead to the loss or impairment of function, and are consequently likely to be weeded out from a population because of their undesirability. Should the mutated gene be present as a duplication along with the normally functioning gene, the possibilities of its retention and continued mutation, possibly in new directions, become considerably enhanced (Lewis 1951).

In order to prove that such an event is anything more than a theoretical possibility, three criteria must be satisfied (Stephens 1951): (1) the existence of two or more separable units must be demonstrated; (2) the duplicate origin of these loci from an original single locus must be proved; and (3) the qualitatively different functions governed by these once similar but now diverged loci must be established. If these criteria are met, the stage is then set for an increase in the pool of heritable diversities which an organism must have in order to exploit new environments or to retain its status quo in a changing environment.

The role of duplications in evolution can be approached, therefore, by considering the data that bear on the three points made by Stephens.

In the first place, there is a considerable body of evidence, both cytological and genetical, that points to the establishment of duplications in natural populations. The most frequent type appears to be that which involves adjacent gene repetitions, called *repeats*. As Bridges (1935) early suggested, the "doublet" or "capsule" structure of the bands in salivary gland chromosomes is best interpreted as repeated band duplications, often in inverted order but not necessarily so. These may be seen in Bridges' (1935) salivary map, and confirmatory genetical evidence has come from a study of crossing over and aberrations involving doublets. Thus, the two doublets in 89E of the right arm of Chromosome 3 include the *bithorax* series of pseudoalleles (Lewis 1951). The pseudoalleles of the sex-linked *vermilion* locus are apparently located in the $10A_{1-2}$ double, with v^1 in the left half and v^{36f} in the right (Green 1954). The *Beadex* locus, with its dominant and recessive alleles, is associated with duplications in the 17A-E region of the X-chromosome (Green 1953). Such repeat sections, common to the genus Drosophila, have also been found in the fungus gnat, Sciara (Fig. 15–1), but they would not be cytologically detectable in any other type of chromosome.

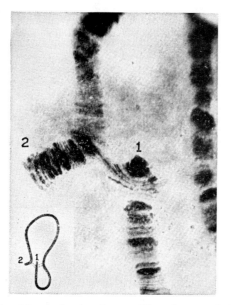

Fig. 15–1. Repeat pairing, reflecting the possible existence of duplications, as observed in the salivary gland chromosomes of Sciara. That such pairing may also reflect the existence of intercalary heterochromatin has not been disproved (Metz 1947).

A further cytological indication of duplicated regions in Drosophila is provided by what Slizynski (1945) has called "ectopic pairing," which means simply the vestiges of previous pairing that remain after the flattening out of salivary gland preparations (Fig. 15–2). These regions, if they are true duplications, are not of the tandem or inverted type, and since pairing of them with the chromocentral area is frequent there is reason for supposing that they are heterochromatic regions exhibiting a non-specific type of association. In general, however, it is the doublet type of structure, such as found at $1E_{3-4}$, $3C_{5-6}$, $11A_{8-9}$, and so on, that shows ectopic pairing, and Slizynski hypothesizes that these are duplications in which part of the doublet has become heterochromatic because the presence of duplicate loci permits one part, as it were, to degenerate through disuse. It may well be that this mechanism provides for a source of intercalary heterochromatin, but the studies of Green and Lewis indicate that the loci studied by

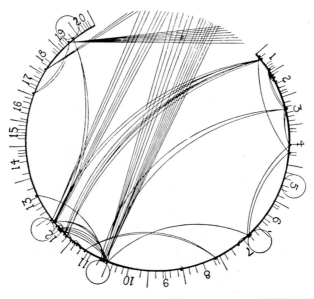

Fig. 15–2. Diagrammatic representation of the frequency and distribution of ectopic pairing in the X-chromosome of *D. melanogaster*. The subdivisions are numbered according to Bridges' (1938) map. Each connecting line represents one observed case of pairing, and the small circles indicate regions where nucleolar-like formations occur. Beyond the 20th division is the proximal heterochromatin, in which pairing is quite frequent (Slizynski 1945).

them are composed of functional parts rather than being regions differentiated into genetically active and inert sections.

The genetical evidence for gene duplications is rather extensive in Drosophila although by no means limited to this genus. The evidence is based upon the functional similarity of neighboring genes as well as upon the fact that these may be separated from each other by crossing over. The *Star-asteroid, Stubble-stubbloid,* and the *bithorax-bithoraxoid* loci are examples of these repeated sequences (Lewis 1951). The first two sequences are duplicated, while the latter is of a triplicated nature, similar to the triplicated *lozenge* loci described by Green and Green (1949). The *scute-acheate* region as well as the *white* locus in the X-chromosome of Drosophila is also known to be a duplicated gene sequence. Examples of supposed tandem repeats in other organisms involve the several tail mutants in the mouse (Dunn and Caspari 1945), the Q locus in Neurospora which is concerned with steps in nicotinic acid synthesis (Bonner 1951), the *biotin* loci in *Aspergillus nidulans* (Pontecorvo 1953), and the chlorophyll mutants in maize (McClintock 1944). The *r* bacteriophage mutants

(Benzer 1955) and the nutritional deficient mutants in Salmonella (Demerec, Blomstrand and Demerec 1955) also fall into this category.

Most of these mutant genes were first classified as examples of multiple allelism until crossing over between them or their independent loss established their separateness, and in some instances each of the separate genes can be shown to have its own group of true alleles, similar to and paralleling the action of, the alleles of the neighbor gene. The action of suppressor genes, which affect one part of a duplicate locus but not the other, also supports the concept of their separate and distinct nature (Green 1954). On the basis that the gene cannot, because of its molecular structure, provide an unlimited source of variation, such parallelism of alleles is expected and understandable. Their similar patterns of mutation, together with their association with doublet structures, strongly support the conclusion that the duplicate or triplicate loci stemmed from an original single locus.

Satisfaction of the third criterion—that the duplicated locus can carry out a qualitatively different function, and thus provide a source of new genes and of additional variation—is somewhat more difficult of proof. If the duplicated genes are assumed to have diverged so greatly from each other in function as to be no longer recognizable, proof would be difficult indeed, since it would be impossible to tell these from two unrelated genes lying adjacent to each other. It becomes necessary therefore to catch the genes, as it were, in a transitional state, with lingering evidence of their true origin from a former single locus and yet with sufficient diversity of action to justify the assumption that further divergence would qualify them as having totally different modes of action. Two approaches to the problem are presently available.

The first is that of Lewis (1951, 1954, 1955), and it can be illustrated by the *Star-asteroid* case described earlier as well as by his analysis of the mode of action of the three loci in the *bithorax-bithoraxoid* complex. If the initial assumption is made that genes act through the substrate of the cell to impress a detectable change in an organism, then one of two actions can occur:

(1) if the genes have not diverged in action, then their utilization of the substrate will be qualitatively similar and the phenotypic effect will be likewise similar, although to varying degrees depending upon the efficiency of the three loci concerned. Since the *bx* and *bxd* phenotypes are dissimilar, and the *Bxl* heterozygote (which is homozygous lethal) produces a phenotype like that of the double *bx bxd* homozygote, it can be assumed that divergence of action has taken place. Duplicate genes, however, giving a 15:1 dihybrid ratio in an F_2 population, can be considered to have similar action. However, since these genes often do not lie adjacent to one another, and indeed, must be located in different chromosomes in order to yield 15:1 ratios, it is impossible to prove their origin from a single original locus.

(2) If pseudoalleles have diverged in action, the reactions involved can be either competitive or sequential in nature. Reasons were given in Chapter 12 for believing that the sequential type of reaction explains the situation in Drosophila. Such sequential steps have been shown, by the techniques of biochemical genetics, to be genically controlled, but in no single instance has the common origin of the genes involved been demonstrated. The Q locus in Neurospora and the biotin synthesizing complex in Aspergillus, however, are suggestive of such a situation. Lewis believes that the *bithorax-bithoraxoid* complex satisfies the situation. The three loci, *bx, Bxl,* and *bxd,* in that order, lie 0.02 and 0.01 map units, respectively, from each other. The genes *bx* and *bxd* control thoracic development in such a manner as to suggest that they control steps that, embryologically, differ in time and structure. *Bxl* behaves as does the double mutant *bx bxd,* but in certain genotypic combinations it produces a *bx* phenotype, in others a *bxd* phenotype, and in still others a combined *bx* and *bxd* phenotype. In all of these cases the position-effect phenomenon is displayed since not only is the total genotype important, but so is the order of the genes in relation to each other. From evidence of a very complicated nature, Lewis has shown the *bx-Bxl-bxd* complex does control a sequential series of reactions; and this evidence, together with that which points to their origin from a former single loci, either by duplication or partition (which is not the same structurally but which leads to the same end result genetically), strongly suggests that duplication is one of the important methods by which the number of genes can be increased in number.

Stephens (1951) has approached the problem from a different point of view. The cultivated American cotton, *Gossypium hirsutum,* is an allotetraploid derived from two species, one of which contributed an A set of 13 chromosomes, the other a D set of a like number. Anthocyanin production is controlled by an *R* gene in both sets, and this gene is closely linked in both cases to a *Cl* gene, which governs the branching pattern. These genes are apparently homologous, so that the allotetraploid carries two sets of each. Since the A and D sets of chromosomes have been separated for long periods of time—being of American and Asiatic origin, respectively, and only brought together to form the cultivated cotton in pre-Columbian times—it is reasonable to inquire as to their possible divergence of action through mutation. If they are strictly similar in action, one would expect to obtain duplicate factor ratios in the F_2, i.e., 15:1 ratios with only the double recessives phenotypically different. The *R* alleles are different, however, and give 9:3:3:1 ratios, and it appears that the *Cl* alleles give a similar inheritance. It is difficult to explain the inability of a normal allele of either gene to mask the recessive allele of its respective duplicate locus unless divergence has occurred. On the other hand, duplicate and triplicate ratios (15:1 and 63:1) are found in polyploid wheats, suggesting divergence need not occur despite long periods of separation.

In conclusion, the evidence available strongly supports the idea that duplications, arising in diploid organisms through replicated sections of chromatin and in allopolyploids through the doubling of homologous (or near-homologous) chromosomes, provide the means for the origin of genes "new" in the sense that their original function has been altered to give rise to qualitatively different phenotypic expressions. At present there is little evidence to suggest how widespread the phenomenon is, or indeed how important it is in evolution. The cases studied are scattered, but it is also clear that the stringent proofs to be met in the positive establishment of such genic divergence greatly restricts the possibilities for investigation. Only the most favorable examples are likely to yield anything more than suggestive results.

INVERSIONS

Paracentric inversions are by far the most common type of aberration found in natural populations, and the indications are that they can be expected to turn up in any large natural population. The distribution, however, is not entirely random.

In Drosophila, only *virilis* and *hydei* appear to lack inversions, while other species vary rather widely as to their prevalence. *D. willistoni* probably exhibits the greatest degree of this type of chromosome polymorphism, some 40 different inversions having been identified in the various chromosomes. A variation is found in *D. pseudoobscura* and *D. persimilis* where the inversions are nearly as numerous, yet largely confined to the third chromosome. Many plant genera are also known to possess inversions, but, except for dipteran genera, relatively little is known about their frequency in animals except that in the grasshoppers they appear to be almost entirely absent (White 1954).

Evolutionary interest in inversions centers largely around the paracentric type. Pericentric inversions are, of course, instrumental in shifting the position of the centromere, and can thus be responsible for variations in the karyotype. Crossing over within them leads to duplication and deficiency in the resultant gametes, and they do, as a consequence, serve to lower fertility, as well as to reduce recombination of genes within their limits (Alexander 1952; Patterson and Stone 1952). Their relative infrequency would, on the other hand, suggest that they play a minor evolutionary role, although they may be shielded from immediate elimination, and eventually preserved in a population, if they are associated with paracentric inversions that reduce crossing over.

The paracentric inversion may not reduce crossing over within its limits, but the gene complex is preserved as an intact block since the inversion bridge, in animals at least, is cast out in the polar body. In plants, considerable zygote mortality may result from the inclusion of deficient-duplicated chromosomes in the functional egg nucleus (Rhoades and Dempsey 1953). In general, however, inversions are well tolerated in a natural population, and each block of chromatin, so isolated, will tend to become different from other similarly isolated blocks through random mutations. Since selection operates not on single genes alone but on a complex of genes carried by an organism, these gene pools, which vary in size according to the length of the inversion, have a more immediately expressed evolutionary potential than do gene pools that are being constantly reshuffled through genetic recombination. Recombination within an inversion can take place only through double crossing over, and since the frequency of doubles increases with the length of the inversion it can be assumed that evolution will tend to preserve inversions of an optimal size. The studies of Dobzhansky (1951) and his co-workers have done much to illustrate the manner by which inversions provide the variation necessary for the operation of selective mechanisms.

Prior to a consideration of the genetic role played by inversions, it should be pointed out that it is possible to construct a family tree of those inversions that, in time, are related to each other. This can be done only for overlapping inversions, and the work has been largely confined to the ubiquitous *D. pseudoobscura* and *D. persimilis*. The family tree of inversions in the third chromosome of these two species is diagrammed in Figure 15–3.

The method of reasoning behind this construction is as follows: three chromosomes, by two successive inversions that overlap, have come to differ from each other in the following way (break points indicated):

I	A	B	C	D	E	F	G	H	I	J	K
II	A	B	F	E	D	C	G	H	I	J	K
III	A	B	F	E	I	H	G	C	D	J	K

Sequentially their order of origin must be I⟶II⟶III, or III⟶II⟶I, or I⟵II⟶III. I cannot give rise to III directly, or the reverse, unless four separate breaks are present at the same time and recombination of the proper sort takes place. Since the 27 different inversions in *pseudoobscura* and *persimilis* can be shown to be related to each other by overlapping boundaries it seems logical to consider that the relationships are as indicated in Figure 15–3. The *Standard* (ST) arrangement is the only one common to both species, while *Hypothetical* has not been found although reasons will be given later to indicate that it existed once but has been selectively eliminated from natural populations today.

D. pseudoobscura and *D. persimilis* inhabit the western part of North America from lower Canada well into Mexico. No one of the inversion types occurs over the whole of the distribution range. As many as eight different inversions have been found in a single population, but when the distribution of inversions is plotted on a regional or a seasonal basis it is

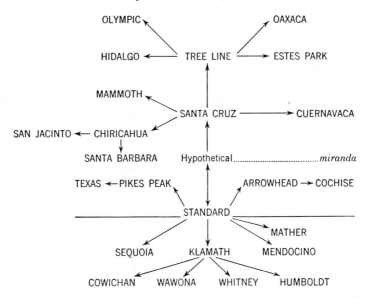

Fig. 15–3. Phylogenetic chart of the various gene sequences found in the third chromosomes of *D. pseudoobscura* and *D. persimilis*. The relationships have been established through the use of overlapping inversions, and sequences connected by a single arrow differ by a single paracentric inversion. Those above *Standard* occur only in *D. pseudoobscura*; those below, only in *D. persimilis*, with *Standard* being common to both species. (After Dobzhansky 1951, from M. J. D. White, *Animal Cytology and Evolution,* copyright 1954 by the Cambridge University Press.)

found that certain patterns of frequency are found (Dobzhansky and Epling 1944; Dobzhansky 1948a). Differences in pattern may be found within a few miles of each other; yet it is quite clear that certain inversions, or inversion combinations, are adapted to particular ecological niches. This is illustrated in Figure 15–4 for three gene arrangements. ST (Standard) is obviously more frequent at lower altitudes in the Sierra Nevada Mountains than is AR (Arrowhead), but a reversal of dominance of type takes place as the altitude increases. CH (Chiricuaha) shows less change with change of altitude than do the other two. At Mount San Jacinto, also in California, a similar but nearly opposite relationship is found. ST, as in the Sierras, is most common at low and least common at high altitudes. The complementary replacement of dominance is, however, with CH, it being infrequent at low and frequent at high altitudes, while AR shows little variation.

If it is considered that altitude provides a temperature gradient, then it is to be expected that ST would, at any particular locality, be at its highest population density during the hot summer months (June through August) while on Mount San Jacinto, for example, CH would be in ascendency during the cooler period (March to June). Figure 15–5 indicates that this expectation is realized, with the AR arrangement being relatively unresponsive in this respect.

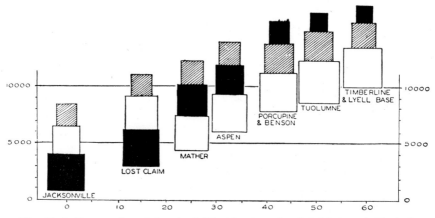

Fig. 15–4. Frequencies of *Standard* (black), *Arrowhead* (white) and *Chiricahua* (hatched) chromosomes in *D. pseudoobscura* at different elevations in the Sierra Nevada Mountains. Vertical distances in feet, horizontal distances in miles (Dobzhansky 1948a).

The situation existing in natural populations can be subjected to experimental tests. A population of *D. pseudoobscura* consisting of 11 percent ST and 89 percent CH chromosomes was placed in a breeding cage (Dobzhansky 1948b, 1949, 1951). At a temperature of 25° C, the population shifted slowly until in about nine months a population equilibrium was reached that consisted of 70 percent ST and 30 percent CH (Fig. 15–5, Curve D); at 16° C. there was no marked shift in the population status. Figure 15–6 illustrates this point over a shorter period of time. The situation in *D. persimilis,* however, is almost the reverse, with different karyotypes having different adaptive values at 16° C., but tending toward equality at 25° C. (Spiess 1950).

These observations point to certain conclusions. First, it is clear that the inversion complexes have definite selective values; second, that the selective differentials are sufficiently great that the population is in a constant state of flux because of the changing character of the local environment; third, that the heterozygotes (ST/CH) possess a greater selective advantage than the two homozygotes (CH/CH or ST/ST). In other words, the population structure at any time and place is a function of the particular environment, and each such population can be considered in the nature of an ecotype fluctuating about a norm.

Certain questions can be raised at this point. What is the nature of the genetic mechanism that allows the constant delicate population adjustments to be made as the environment changes? Why is it that certain inversions persist in a population rather than being eliminated? Why is it that certain inversions, related to those present in a population, appeared to be excluded?

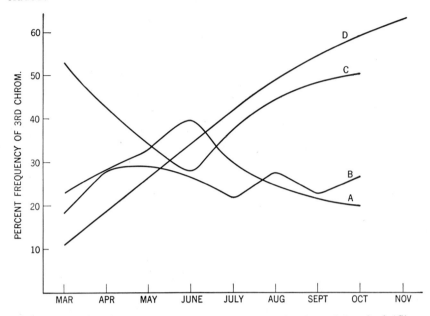

Fig. 15–5. Frequency of *Chiricahua* (A), *Arrowhead* (B), and *Standard* (C) sequences in *D. pseudoobscura* as a function of seasonal changes in the Mount San Jacinto region of California. Curve D represents the seasonal change in an experimental population of the *Standard* rearrangement when the initial population in March consisted of 11% *Standard* and 89% *Chiricahua* (redrawn from Dobzhansky 1951).

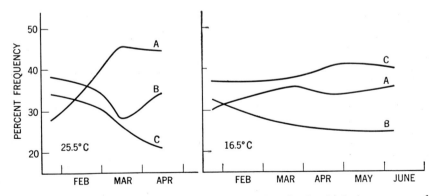

Fig. 15–6. Changes in frequency of three inversions in the third chromosome of *D. pseudoobscura* when raised under laboratory conditions at 25.5°C (left) and 16.5°C (right). A, *Standard*; B, *Chiricahua*; C, *Arrowhead* (after Wright and Dobzhansky 1946).

The answers to these questions are related to the nature of inversions and their effect on the genetic structure of a population. The presence of an inversion in a heterozygous condition removes a portion of the chromosome, along with its included genes, from effective recombination through crossing over. The shorter the inversion the less likely the prospects of double crossing over, and consequently the more intact will be that segment of genes. Through random mutation, the undisturbed segments will tend to diverge from each other, and the stage will be set for the establishment of a system that favors the existence of inversion heterozygosity. Since most mutations are both deleterious and at random, homozygosity will be selected against, and heterozygosity favored, because of the heterosis (hybrid vigor) effects. If selection is for heterozygosity rather than for a single gene block, neither inversion will be eliminated from the population. However, since the single gene blocks have adaptive values that differ for different environments, the changing environment will determine, at any particular time period, the proper ratio of homozygotes and heterozygotes that is best adapted to it. Thus the ST as compared to the AR or CH arrangement can be said to have a superior adaptive value at low altitudes and higher temperatures, but the presence of AR and CH provides both the hybrid vigor contributed by heterozygotes as well as the flexibility necessary to survive a change in temperature. On the other hand, the superiority of heterozygotes is not a function only of the genes which lie within the inverted section, but also of an interaction with other karyotypes in the same population (Levene, Pavlovsky and Dobzhansky 1954). A balanced polymorphism, sensitive as it obviously is, is therefore responsive to a combination of physical, nutritional, and genetic environments, each of which exerts its own effects (Dobzhansky and Spassky 1954).

The situation described above is characteristic of a versatile species such as *D. pseudoobscura*. The same is true for *D. persimilis,* its close relative, and for *D. willistoni,* which is very prevalent in South America. It has some 40 known inversions, most of them short in length, and it is able to occupy a very wide variety of ecological habitats. It seems reasonable to ascribe this versatility to the inversion systems it carries.

D. prosaltans, however, is also a southern species, but, unlike *D. willistoni* and *D. pseudoobscura,* it occupies very specialized ecological niches and does not reach high population densities (Dobzhansky and Spassky 1954). Breeding experiments indicate that it does not depend for adaptiveness upon the inversion heterozygosity system with its attendant heterosis, but rather on the high selective value of its chromosomal and genetic structure in a homozygous state. Thus inbreeding is not so deleterious to *D. prosaltans* as it is to other species. Its third chromosome, for example, contains in natural populations only about 9–10 percent lethals and semilethals, while *willistoni, pseudoobscura,* and *persimilis* reveal 25–32 percent, 21–33 percent, and 25 percent, respectively.

The opposite situation from that in *D. prosaltans* occurs in several European species, e.g., *D. ambigua* and *D. obscuroides*. These are almost never found in a homozygous state, and inversion heterozygosity may actually be obligatory (White 1954). It is not certain, however, in these species whether an enforced heterosis is required for preservation or whether the structural homozygotes are lethal.

The exclusion of certain inversions from a population has been discussed by Wallace (1953a, b). From what has been said, it would seem that the principal evolutionary role of inversions is to suppress recombination and thus keep intact a segment of the chromosome that has a selective value in a particular environment. Yet there are population patterns of association that suggest that certain inversion combinations are regionally suitable while others are not. As Figure 15–7 indicates, AR and PP (Pikes Peak) are the principal southwestern arrangements, AR, ST, and CH the principal western ones.

Because of their prevalence, the gene blocks isolated by these arrangements must be of an optimal size. The AR-PP complex isolates about 60 percent of the length of the third chromosome, AR-ST 35 percent, and CH-ST about 55 percent. The AR-PP and CH-ST combinations are complex in that they are separated by two or more steps (Fig. 15–3), and crossing over does not break up the gene block despite its length. AR differs from ST, however, only by a single inversion, and the isolated block is considerably shorter than the other two, indicating that optimal length is governed by the degree of complexity of the heterozygous combination. A further comparison of existing inversion combinations indicates that those that are longer or shorter than optimal length, although present in the population, never make up a large proprotion of the population in terms of numbers of individuals, although they may in numbers of localities found. This appears to be because longer ones are broken up by recombination, thus losing the adaptive value of the isolated gene block, while the shorter ones will not have a sufficiently long gene segment in which to accumulate the necessary mutations for selective forces to act upon.

Another point of interest is that three arrangements, related in simple sequence to each other, rarely occupy the same territory. Thus ST and AR and AR and PP are coadapted systems, but a population containing the AR-PP-ST triad combination, with all three in frequent proportions, does not exist. Either PP is rare and AR and ST frequent, or ST is rare with AR and PP frequent. Wallace believes that the third arrangement in these populations—i.e., either PP or ST, whichever is rare—is essentially excluded because its presence serves to break up the adaptive complexes through recombination. The AR-ST-CH combination would not do this, and it may be the reason for loss of the *Hypothetical* arrangement indicated in Figure 15–3. This hypothesis points even more strongly to the fact that inversions are very significant factors in ecological adaptation, and that the balanced polymorphism created by them is most delicately adjusted.

The question of whether inversions serve as foci for the evolution of species remains to be answered. A comparison of related species—e.g.,

Fig. 15–7. Main associations of third chromosome inversions in *D. pseudoobscura* in the western United States (Wallace 1953).

pseudoobscura with *persimilis* and *miranda*—reveals the presence of a number of distinguishing inversions, yet a female of *D. willistoni* has been found that was heterozygous for 16 inversions. It is clear that inversions in themselves cannot be the source of variation, but the genes within them may diverge sufficiently to develop a barrier to cross-breeding, and thus set up the initial steps for eventual separation. If the pressures forcing the maintenance of coadapted systems are strong enough, the possibilities are present for the development of a highly selected system, and possibly for a new species to evolve. Certainly the inversion studies in Drosophila point in this direction and emphasize the efficacy, the importance, and often the rapidity of natural selection.

TRANSLOCATIONS

An experimental assessment of the role of translocations in evolution is more difficult than it is for inversions, largely because organisms possessing translocations as an aberration type in a balanced polymorphic system are longer-lived than the ephemeral-generationed Drosophila, and it may well be that the length of the generation will determine which type of aberration comes to play the dominant role. This remains to be proved, but the fact is that inversions are known to be of major adaptive importance only in Drosophila—although this may be only because they can be successfully studied in this genus—while translocations tend to characterize the longer-lived forms such as plants, grasshoppers, etc. Despite these limitations, however, the situation in plants permits an appraisal of the evolutionary significance of translocations.

A survey of the animal kingdom (White 1954) indicates that the centric-fusion type of translocation has been important in reforming karyotypes and in altering sex-determination mechanisms. Often heterochromatinization of autosomal material has followed its incorporation into the sex-determining mechanism, but it is difficult to appraise the evolutionary meaning of such an alteration since it is only found as an established rather than as a transitional condition. The same is true for centric fusions involving autosomes exclusively; these in general characterize species rather than provide chromosomal polymorphism within a species, although exceptions are known. The unequal bivalents peculiar, yet common, to certain groups of grasshoppers may represent translocations, but if so they are of a special type since it is largely heterochromatin rather than euchromatin that appears to be involved. It is only in the Brazilian scorpions Tityus and Isometrus that translocation complexes similar to those in plants seem to exist. Numerous translocations have been found in the same populations. White makes the point that, since these genera possess polycentric centromeres, have no chiasma formation in the male, and often show rings with odd instead of even numbers of chromosomes, there is something relatively peculiar to the system since there appears to be no logical reason for adaptive significance to any translocation where crossing over does not occur. The situation remains unexplained at present.

In plants structural hybridity in the form of translocations has played an important role in evolution, and in certain groups is a dominant mechanism. The situation can best be examined in the genus Oenothera where translocation complexes are the rule rather than the exception. However, a rather large number of unrelated plant genera possess similar, though not so extensive, structural features (Stebbins 1950), indicating the independent origin of like situations on numerous occasions.

In order to appreciate the chromosomal situation in Oenothera it is necessary to understand the nature of the "Renner complex" and the "Renner effect," so named after their discoverer (Renner 1917, 1921). Oenothera has a haploid complement of seven chromosomes and 14 pairing ends. If it is assumed that any particular end can be reciprocally translocated to any other end, then 91 different end combinations are possible (1–2, 1–3, 1–4, 1–5, 1–6, 1–7; 2–3 . . . 2–7; . . . 6–7). Most of these have been found in natural populations (Cleland 1949; Cleland, Preer, and Geckler 1950), a finding that in itself gives indication either that there is a strong propensity for Oenothera chromosomes to undergo translocation, or that this is a structural alteration possessing considerable survival value.

Of the known end combinations, seven in particular obviously outnumber the others in frequency and distribution, and for a variety of reasons these seven chromosomes are believed to constitute the ancestral arrangement from which others arose. A single translocation would give rise to a ring of four chromosomes in meiosis; a translocation between a member of the ring and another chromosome would produce a ring of six. By successive translocations rings of 14 are built up. These would be unstable, however, in a population, for structural homozygosity would result, and individuals with variable sized rings and numbers of bivalents would be expected. Structural heterozygosity becomes enforced only when lethal genes are included in the ring of chromosomes, and the end point is a ring of 14 chromosomes with different lethals in each of the two haploid sets of seven. Since only alternate segregation from the ring leads to the formation of viable gametes, each group of seven chromosomes becomes, in essence, a single large linkage group with recombination confined to the pairing ends of each chromosome. These linkage groups, consisting of seven separate but collectively inherited chromosomes, are called "Renner complexes," and each individual possessing balanced rings of 14 is actually a dual entity, since each contains two complexes that, because of mutations and lack of proximal recombination, may differ appreciably from each other. For example, in *O. lamarchiana* the two complexes, called *gaudens* and *valens,* yield two very different species hybrids when outcrossed to other forms. The individual plants of *O. lamarchiana,* which are generally self-pollinated, breed true, however, since the incorporated lethals prevent the existence of homozygotes and the breakdown of the complex.

The "Renner effect" is a further refinement of the system. It is achieved when one of the Renner complexes is transmitted only through the egg, the opposite complex only through the sperm. Such separation can be accomplished by the establishment of either gametic or zygotic lethals, and, as Figure 15–8 indicates, *O. lamarchiana* makes use of one method, *O. muricata* the other.

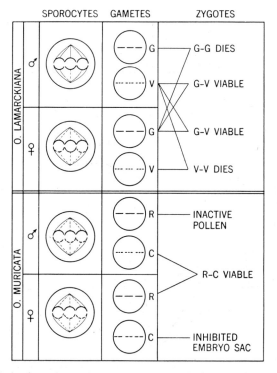

Fig. 15–8. Behavior of translocation complexes in *Oenothera Lamarckiana* and *O. muricata*. Above, maintenance of the translocation heterozygote in *Lamarckiana* is through the differential survival of zygotes, with the *gaudens-gaudens* (G-G) and *valens-valens* (V-V) complexes lethal and only the *gaudens-valens* complex viable. Below, maintenance of the translocation heterozygote in *O. muricata* is through the differential viability of gametophytes (the Renner effect), with the *rigens* (R) pollen inactive and the *curvans* (C) embryo sacs inhibited. Only the *curvans* pollen and the *rigens* embryo sacs are functional to give the *rigens-curvans* complex. Only three of the seven pairs of chromosomes are represented.

Alternate segregation from a ring of 14 is highly regular in Oenothera, and non-disjunction of chromosomes is not frequent enough to markedly affect fertility or to lead to aneuploidy. Regularity of segregation can be attributed to the fact that all of the chromosomes, despite many transloca-tions, have median centromeres, a feature that permits mobility of chromo-somes on the metaphase plate. This means that the surviving translocations have been not only reciprocal but also approximately equal in length.

The North American Oenotheras provide an over-all picture of the man-ner by which evolution has proceeded via the translocation-complex route. The advantages as well as the limitations of both the methods and the goal are fairly evident (Cleland 1936, 1950); indeed, it might be said that the Oenotheras have achieved their present evolutionary position and diversity by means of a unique evolutionary unorthodoxy.

The *O. hookeri* complex of California and contiguous areas represents the ancestral condition in North America. Bivalent formation and crossing over is normal, and the plants are large-flowered and open-pollinated. To the eastward (Fig. 15–9) is a transitional zone in which structural hetero-

HOOKERIS
TRANSITIONAL
STRIGOSAS
BIENNIS GROUP 1
BIENNIS GROUP 2
BIENNIS GROUP 3
PARVIFLORAS
GRANDIFLORAS
UNDETERMINED

Fig. 15–9. Distribution of different Oenothera species and types in the United States (Cleland 1950). See text for explanation.

zygosity is frequent, and individuals possessing rings of four, six, or eight chromosomes are encountered. Some of these rings are present in a balanced lethal condition; in most, however, lethals are absent. Where lethals are present, structural heterozygosity becomes more or less enforced; when no lethals are present, the ring structure is impermanent and the translocations are "floating" rather than "fixed" in the population. This transitional zone makes up a loose alliance, the *irrigua* group, similar to *O. hookeri* in being large-flowered and open-pollinated but representing a gradual change from the typical *hookeri* condition in both a phenotypic and a cytological sense.

From the Rocky Mountains east to the Mississippi Valley is found the *strigosa* group, characterized by rings of 14, balanced lethals, small flowers, self-pollination, and thick grayish leaves. The two haploid sets of chromosomes, the *alpha* and *beta* Renner complexes, are contributed by egg and sperm, respectively, and are quite dissimilar to each other, although neither is far removed from the ancestral *hookeri* condition. Apparently the *strigosa* group possesses a permanent hybrid nature, being the offshoot from two divergent populations, one coming in from the northwestern area of the United States, the other moving northward from Mexico and eastward of the continental divide. These overlapped and crossed to produce the surviving permanent hybrid. Both *alpha* and *beta* complexes, when outcrossed to another species, yield *strigosa*-like offspring, suggesting similar genotypes within dissimilar haploid karyotypes.

The *biennis* group, cytogenetically similar to *strigosa,* but morphologically distinct, consists of three distinct races covering jointly a very wide geographical area in the eastern United States, but with each race occupying a more or less distinct territory. Race 1 is located west of the Allegheny Mountains and somewhat to the middle south and reaches the Atlantic Ocean only in North Carolina and Virginia. It has broad, thin, crinkly leaves, a phenotype that is determined by its *alpha* (egg) complex. The *beta* (sperm) complex, on outcrossing, yields a typical *strigosa* phenotype. Race 2, phenotypically indistinguishable from Race 1, extends from Wisconsin eastward to the Atlantic Ocean in Canada and southward along the coastal plain to North Carolina. Its cytogenetic picture is the reverse of that in Race 1 in that its *alpha* complex, contributed by the egg, yields a *strigosa* phenotype on outcrossing while the *beta* complex possesses the *biennis* phenotype potentiality. Race 3, localized in North Carolina and Virginia, is apparently a product of the other two races, both of its complexes producing *biennis* phenotypes on outcrossing. Consequently, the *biennis* leaf character is somewhat exaggerated, making it morphologically distinct from Races 1 and 2. Presumably its *alpha* complex came from Race 1 and its *beta* from Race 2.

The range of the *parviflora* group coincides roughly with that of *biennis* Race 2, and its distinctive morphology depends upon its *beta* complexes. Its *alpha* complexes are two types, one producing a *strigosa*-like effect, the other *biennis*-like effect. The origin of the *beta* complex is unknown for certain, but there are taxonomic resemblances to Raimannia, a subgenus of Oenothera, which in turn is linked to the South American Oenotheras.

The *grandiflora* group is Southeastern in distribution and possesses individuals showing seven pairs of bivalents and no lethals while others have the typical ring of 14, both with and without lethals. Being large-flowered and open-pollinated, it relates to the ancestral *hookeri,* and those individuals with rings of 14 differ primarily in their *beta* complex, the origin of which is so far uncertain.

The evoultionary pattern, then, is the initial formation of small rings that increase in size until all 14 of the chromosomes are incorporated in a single ring at meiosis. The system, therefore, is an evolutionary funnel with increasingly narrow limits of flexibility. Small rings are at a disadvantage, since segregation from them is not as regular as from larger rings. Once a translocation is formed, therefore, there is a further tendency to enlarge the ring, the selection in this direction being favored by the heterosis resulting from the different gene combinations (the situation here is similar initially to that in the inversion complexes in Drosophila). Structural heterozygosity, with its accompanying heterotic effects, will be reinforced by the incorporation of lethals into the system.

The Oenotheras have, consequently, utilized a number of essentially retrograde genetic devices, each deleterious to a certain degree, and have combined them into a single system that functions very well. These devices are as follows: (1) reciprocal translocations which because of non-disjunction lead to a reduction in fertility, and which because of the linkage system established drastically reduce crossing over; (2) accumulation of lethals and other deleterious mutations; and (3) self-pollination, which in itself favors inbreeding and lack of vigor. Any one of these three is, in open-pollinated species, disadvantageous genetically, yet the translocations lead to the development of diverse linkage groups (the complexes), the lethals enforce structural heterozygosity with its accompanying heterotic effects, and self-pollination prevents outcrossing which tends to break the complex up. On this basis, the progress of evolution in the Oenotheras is the formation of ring complexes, followed by the incorporation of lethals and then by the establishment of self-pollination. It is only in this order of occurrence that the system makes evolutionary sense.

The system, however, is not without its disadvantages. While large rings, balanced lethals, and self-pollination have, in combination, a high survival value—the Oenotheras are numerous and successful, covering a wide territory, and occupying a variety of ecological habitats—the system has effectively prevented polyploidy from becoming the important evolutionary factor it is in other plant groups. Polyploidy (see next chapter), thrown in on top of the structural heterozygosity present, would lead to high sterility because of the complex and irregular pairing possibilities available during meiosis. Polyploidy is known in certain of the Oenotheras, but where it accompanies structural heterozygosity it has no survival value.

Two factors favor the formation of many races, and present to the environment a variety of forms for selection. One is the occasional outcrossing that occurs. Through this device the bringing together of independently evolved complexes can occur, and, as can be seen in experimental crosses, F_1 and F_2 individuals with rings of various sizes, together with paired bivalents, arise. Segregation of genes can occur between the paired homologues, and from this comes a burst of biotypes upon which natural selection can act. The selection will be toward the ring of 14 again, but the possibility of new races with different gene combinations arising is good. The fact that numerous races abound in nature, making the taxonomy of the group exceedingly difficult, indicates that outcrossing occurs frequently enough to provide a wide variation of types for selection.

The second source of variation results from crossing over between homologous segments in the ring of 14. Because of the somewhat haphazard manner of origin of the translocation complexes, segments of chromatin located proximally may occasionally cross over with other segments homologous with them. When proximal chiasmata are formed, a figure-of-8 instead of a ring is observed in meiosis, and the complexes are broken up because such crossing over also involves the interchange of ends as well. Out of such events, many of the combinations will be inviable, but other rare ones may be balanced, and the gene content and arrangement will be different from the ones from which they arose, again providing variation.

Structural heterozygosity through the formation of translocations is found in other plants (Stebbins 1950). *Rhoeo discolor,* a monotypic genus, is known only as a form having rings of 14. No interstitial chiasmata are ever formed, and even in a tetraploid form bivalent formation is very low (Walters and Gerstel 1948). *Paeonia californica, P. brownii* and *Godetia whitneyi* have many individuals with varying sizes of rings, but none have reached the stabilized condition of the Oenotheras, and it may be assumed that such translocations have not yet been fixed and will remain floating until the formation of lethals enforces heterozygosity.

In Datura, translocations have been involved in the formation of many homozygous but cytologically different races. In *D. stramonium,* these have been recognized by selecting one strain as standard, and crossing other races to this standard. The translocations can be recognized as being present by the formation of a ring of 4 in the interracial hybrid, and each of these has been called a *prime type*. Ninety-six of these have been identified in some 700 racial crosses (Blakeslee 1940), but in no case has a ring become established as a balanced lethal system. A comparative study of the ends of the chromosomes in *D. inoxia, D. meteloides,* and *D. metel,* as contrasted to those in prime type I (Standard) of *D. stramonium,* revealed the presence of many translocations that had become established in a homozygous state in nature, but Satina (1953) has concluded that there is no direct correlation between translocations and speciation.

CHAPTER 16

Polyploidy and Evolution

The types of polyploidy, together with their genetic and cytological behavior characteristics, were described in Chapter 6. These characteristics, which have a profound effect on the reproductive potential of the individual and on the genetic variability of the offspring, must obviously influence the role polyploidy can play in evolution. But such knowledge does not provide a complete answer to the successful exploitation of polyploidy by plants, and it is necessary to consider the effect of polyploidy on the structure and function of the individual as well.

The greater portion of our knowledge of polyploidy, as an evolutionary mechanism, comes from the comparison of natural polyploids with their supposed diploid relatives, but of late it has been possible to test conclusions drawn from earlier investigations by parallel studies of artificially produced polyploids. In several instances the resynthesis of polyploid species in the laboratory from the suspected diploid parents has been successfully accomplished, thus providing critical proof of the hypothesis that hybridization between species, followed by chromosome doubling, has taken place time and again in nature to contribute to the formation of new species.

The result has been that polyploidy, as a factor in evolution, is probably the best understood of all mechanisms that contribute to species formation. Its prevalence in the plant kingdom as compared to its relative paucity among animals is still not fully explained, but there can be no doubt as to its far-reaching importance on the flora of the world, particularly among the pteridophytes and angiosperms, and mainly through allo- rather than autopolyploidy.

EFFECTS OF POLYPLOIDY ON STRUCTURE AND FUNCTION

The success of a newly formed polyploid individual will depend upon its reproductive potential and its ability to find an ecological niche for itself. The accidents of successful innovation and ecological opportunity must coincide.

The reproductive potential is, of course, dependent upon its chromosomal mechanism and for this reason the allopolyploids (including the segmental types) have a greater chance for survival; it is also dependent upon genetic compatibility of the associated genomes. It was formerly believed that the sterility of autopolyploids could be traced to the abnormalities of segregation arising out of multivalent formation, but studies on autotetraploid maize, lettuce, snapdragon, and other species point as much to genetic disharmonies as to chromosomal irregularities as the basis of poor seed set. Self-compatibility or incompatibility may also be affected by polyploidy, but the general conclusion seems to be that the situation existing at the diploid level is simply reinforced rather than drastically altered at the polyploid level. In only Tulipa and Hyacinthus is there indication that diploids are self-incompatible and tetraploids self-compatible (Lewis and Modlibowska 1942).

The effect of polyploidy on the physiology and morphology of the individual will, in large measure, determine its ability to establish itself. Allopolyploids will generally exhibit a mingling of the parental characteristics, with the degree of resemblance shifted toward one or the other of the parents if dominance intervenes, but it is difficult to determine to what extent quantitative and qualitative differences are a reflection of the genetic mechanism or of polyploidy *per se*. Artificially induced autotetraploids, however, permit an evaluation of the effects of polyploidy in an essentially similar genetic background. Gigantism often occurs, but not universally so. Tetraploid cells are, in general, larger than diploid ones, but an increase in over-all size of individuals depends also on the number of cells and the degree of cell elongation (Fig. 16–1). Giant tetraploid snapdragons (*Antirrhinum majus*) and marigolds are available commercially, and the autotetraploid *Cuthbertia graminea* is readily distinguished by its size and vigor from its diploid progenitor (Giles 1942). On the other hand, $2n$ and $4n$ Tradescantias are indistinguishable from each other externally, while studies of artificially doubled moss gametophytes from a segregating population revealed that cell-volume increases in the diploid as compared to the haploid were very much dependent on the genotype; some showed large increases with doubling, others small or none at all (Tobler 1931).

The other important changes induced by polyploidy can be summarized as follows (Stebbins 1940; 1950):

1. The water content is generally increased along with cell size, and this has a tendency to make autotetraploids less resistant to frost than the diploids, because of a lowered osmotic pressure of the cell sap. This is, of course, contrary to the generally accepted belief that polyploids are more tolerant than diploids of ecological conditions, but although this situation may be true for allotetraploids it is not necessarily so for autotetraploids.

2. The growth rate of polyploids appears to be slower, although the evidence is conflicting. Physiological development is slower, but this may relate to a slower rate of cell division, a proportionately decreased auxin supply, or a lower rate of respiration (Noggle 1946). Catalase, diastase, and dehydrogenase activities show a relative depression per unit of weight in $4n$ as compared to $2n$ plants, while Vitamin C content is higher in polyploids.

The relation of these factors to rate of growth, however, is difficult of assay.

3. Certain organs of the plant are usually increased or altered in size, particularly those floral parts or seeds that have a determinate type of

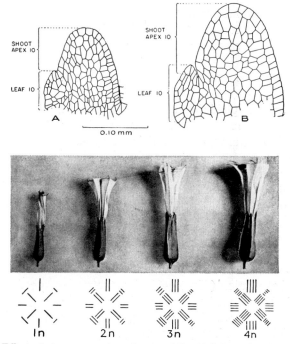

Fig. 16–1. Effect of chromosome number on cell and flower size. Above, apices and primordia of the tenth leaf in diploid (A) and tetraploid (B) maize; below, increase in flower size in haploid, diploid, triploid, and tetraploid Datura (Randolph 1941, and Blakeslee).

growth. This aspect of growth takes the form of thickened leaves in some species such as maize, whereas tomato fruits may even decrease in size. Other parts may be shorter and broader, as the leaves of certain solanaceous species and the fruits of Datura. The effects of polyploidy are not progressive, however, for higher degrees of doubling eventually lead to marked dwarfing, presumably when some point of incompatibility or disharmony is reached.

4. The time of blooming is delayed and often prolonged. This is presumably related to a slower rate of growth, which in turn reflects a less rapid metabolic rate. For those species that bloom in the spring, a longer reproductive season is possible, but such may prove to be disadvantageous to late-summer and fall-blooming species that can have their reproduction impaired by early frosts.

On the other hand, it is misleading to take a positive stand that the effect of polyploidy on structure and function is of evolutionary significance.

These studies have been carried out principally on artificially produced autotetraploids, and Stebbins (1950) and Clausen, Keck, and Hiesey (1945) have given good reason for believing that, in evolution, autopolyploid has played a relatively minor role compared to that of allopolyploidy. Granted that the line between autopolyploidy and segmental polyploidy is poorly delineated so far as the chromosomal mechanism is concerned, the heterosis effects in segmental types may mean that they constitute quite a different class genetically.

DISTRIBUTION OF POLYPLOIDS

With exception of the lower plants, polyploidy (to mean allopolyploidy except where stated otherwise) is found throughout the plant kingdom.

Among the bacteria and the fungi nothing is known cytologically as to the possible existence of polyploidy, and tetraploidy has been induced only in certain strains of baker's yeast (*Sacchromyces ceriviseae*) (by treatment with camphor). Tischler (1950) lists a number of the algae as possessing polyploidy to varying degrees, and the same holds true for the bryophytes. Polyploidy can be induced in the latter by regenerating diploid gametophytes from the cut-off end of the stalk of the spore capsule.

Among the vascular plants, only the gymnosperms have failed to utilize polyploidy to any marked degree as a convenient evolutionary mechanism. The Equisetales, Psilotales, and Lycopodiales are remnants of a once-extensive flora of earlier geological ages and their chromosome numbers indicate that they are relics of an ancient polyploidal system (Manton 1952). The Equisetums have a uniform 108 as a haploid number, while two species of Psilotum have about 100 and 200 chromosomes, respectively, and Tmesipteris over 400 chromosomes in diploid cells. Such high numbers cannot be regarded as anything other than a sign of antiquity, with the degree of polyploidy conferring on them a means of lingering survival in a world from which they have been largely displaced. Diploid numbers in Lycopodium range from 48, to 68, to at least 260; in Isoetes from 20 to over 100; but Selaginella, a genus of some 800 species, has a low and uniform haploid number of only 9.

The Filicales (Ferns) are divided into the Eusporangiatae and the Leptospangiatae, with the former believed to be the more ancient. The Ophioglossaceae are probably the most ancient of living ferns, and *O. vulgatum* has over 500 chromosomes as a diploid number. *O. lusitanicum* has 250–260. Botrychium, in the same family, has a mere 90. In the Hymenophyllaceae, diploid numbers of 26, 36, and 144 have been recorded. The Osmundaceae, which are believed to lie, phylogenetically, between the ancient and modern ferns, have a uniform diploid number of 44, and it is unlikely that they can be considered polyploids. The Polypodiaceae represents the largest family of the modern Leptosporangiate ferns, and polyploidy is widespread. Most of the numbers recorded are tetraploids with occasional hexaploids, octoploids, and decaploids. It is not always possible to ascertain the degree of polyploidy, however, for in many instances the base numbers are unknown (37 and 41 have been found, and being prime numbers they may represent aneuploidal tendencies or true base numbers). No certain case of natural autopolyploidy is known among the ferns, but hybridization is known or suspected to have played an important role.

Manton estimates that 53 percent of the British ferns are polyploid, while the island of Madeira has 42 percent polyploids among its fern population. The difference in percent is probably without significance, but there remains a marked difference in degree of polyploidy. The British ferns are predominantly tetraploid, and these are still in geographical contact with their diploid ancestors and are still evolving. Polyploidy of this sort can be considered of recent origin, and arising, according to Manton, when climatic upheavals brought together many species and set the stage for numerous hybridizations. The Madeira polyploid ferns, on the other hand, are of a high degree of polyploidy with the diploid species established as endemic forms. They must, therefore, be phylogenetically old and settled, and past the stage of active evolution.

Among the gymnosperms, polyploids are found among the Gnetales. In the conifers some species of Podocarpus, *Sequoia semperivens,* and *Juniperus chinesis* var. *pfitzeriana* are tetraploids, while *Pseudolarix amabilis* may be polyploid or, more simply, a case of chromosome increase through fragmentation, since of its 22 chromosomes 20 have subterminal and two have median centromeres. The 24 major arms correspond possibly to the 24 arms found in the majority of conifers ($n = 12$, and all chromosomes have median centromeres). Gingko and the cycads are without known polyploid forms.

Polyploids make up 30 to 35 percent of the angiosperms (Stebbins 1938, 1940, 1947, 1950; Tischler 1950; Darlington and Janaki-Ammal 1945); but it is quite apparent that the distribution, based largely on temperate zone studies, is very irregular among plant families. Nearly 75 percent of the Gramineae are polyploid, and a high frequency is found among the Rosaceae, Polygonaceae, Malveceae, Crassulaceae, Nymphaeaceae, and Arabaceae. In the monocot families, Cyperaceae, Juncaceae and Iridaceae, aneuploidy and polyploidy confuse the picture with non-multiple series of chromosomes. In other families, some genera are largely polyploid, others predominantly diploid. Salix in the Salicaceae shows much polyploidy, Populus none; Betula is the only genus of the Betulaceae exhibiting polyploidy; in certain genera such as Crepis and Solanum some sections are totally diploid, others a mixture. In the widespread families, Fagaceae, Moraceae, Cucuritaceae, and Polemoniaceae, polyploidy is unknown. It is difficult to see rhyme or reason in these distributions, but since hybridization and polyploidy go hand-in-hand, it is little wonder that particular groups of angiosperms, such as the Rosaceae, present such difficult taxonomic problems.

Stebbins (1938) has shown, however, that polyploidy among the angiosperms bears a degree of correlation with plant form. In a broad sense, the angiosperms can be grouped into woody, herbaceous perennial, and annual forms, and a compilation of available chromosome counts indicates that polyploidy is most prevalent in herbaceous perennials, and least among woody forms. The difference between the herbaceous perennials and annuals cannot be accounted for by assuming that polyploidy has transformed annual species into perennial forms, or that perennials were derived from annuals with lower chromosome numbers, as suggested by Müntzing (1936). The answer, most probably, lies in the fact that annuals have little chance of forming polyploids during their single year of existence, particularly if they are sterile species hybrids. Sterile perennial hybrids, however, if vigorous, and if possessed of a vegetative means of reproduction, have only to wait until chance provides the opportunity for doubling to produce a fertile allopolyploid.

The supposed relative infrequency of polyploids among woody species may be very misleading. As Stebbins (1938) points out, the base numbers of these forms (11–16) are higher than those for the herbaceous types (7, 8, and 9 are most characteristic), and a derived polyploidy might be suspected. This is now believed to be entirely possible, since base numbers of 7, 8, and 9 have been found in the tropical woody Anonaceae and numbers of 6 and 7 in the primitive Caesalpinoideae, a woody subfamily of the large and primitive Leguminoseae (Stebbins 1950).

The angiosperms, as a whole, appear then to have a form of evolution that can best be described as reticulate rather than dendridic. Hybridization has led to the sharing of gene combinations; polyploidy has fixed these and at the same time insured the reproductive potential by restoring fertility. A discussion of polyploidy as an evolutionary factor that extends beyond species limits will be reserved for a later section of the chapter, but it is apparent that the overlapping phylogenetic lines stand in sharp contrast to the relatively clean generic and familial patterns in the animal kingdom, where hybridization and polyploidy have not been rampant.

Any conclusions drawn as to the extensiveness and geographical distribution of polyploids as compared to diploids must be considered tentative at the present time, if only because so much of the available data is from temperate and north-temperate floras. Tropical and sub-tropical floras have been investigated only sporadically, yet the finding of low base numbers in the tropical Anonaceae and Leguminoseae may necessitate a revision of estimates as to the proportion of polyploids among woody species of more northern zones. Furthermore, the composition of a particular flora, whether predominantly woody, perennial or annual, may lend an unrecognized bias to patterns of polyploidy. Thus, Löve and Löve (1943) have demonstrated that from Schleswig-Holstein in Germany to Spitzbergen in the north there is a progressively greater proportion of polyploids encountered in the various floras, and the conclusion was drawn that this is proof of the fact that polyploids are more resistant to cold and consequently form a larger pare of northern as compared to southern floras. This hypothesis, however, has been criticized (Gustafson 1948), principally on the basis that northern regions have a typically herbaceous perennial flora abounding in members of the Gramineae, Cyperaceae and Rosaceae, whereas more southern zones have a greater proportion of woody and annual species. It is only when polyploids can be compared to the diploids from which they arose that legitimate deductions can be drawn as to distributional patterns.

Stebbins (1950) has done this for some 100 groups and it is clear that no broad generalizations can be formulated. Some 60 of the 100 have wider distributions for the polyploids than for the diploids, while in 33 groups polyploids occupy distinctly smaller areas. Thirty-three of the groups show the polyploids centrally located with the diploids around the periphery while 28 show the reverse; 27 show that the polyploids occupy a more northerly distribution than the diploids, and seven have reverse distributions.

One conclusion can, however, be drawn: the polyploids occupy a different habitat than their related diploids, and in general these habitats are ones that were newly opened to colonization by plants. This would suggest that the polyploids possess a wider range of tolerances, this permitting them to occupy ecological habitats unavailable to the diploids, but this will depend upon the wealth of variability the diploids have at their disposal for the formation of ecotypes. Certain diploid *Rosa* species, for example, possess such inherent variability, and they appear to migrate as widely and as rapidly as their related polyploids.

Several other examples can serve to illustrate the points made. *Iris versicolor* ($2n = 108$) is the common blue flag of the Northeast, and it is an allopolyploid derived from *I. virginica* var. *shrevei* ($2n = 72$) and *I. setosa* var. *interior* ($2n = 36$). The former is more Southeastern in distribution, the latter is isolated in interior Alaska (Fig. 16–2). *I. versicolor* is entirely within an area occupied by the Wisconsin ice sheet, and it appears probable that hybridization between *setosa* and *virginica* took place during the Pleistocene and at the advancing edge of the ice. Since then *setosa*, which probably had a wider distribution, has been lost in the intervening regions, *virginica* has retained its southern occupancy, while *versicolor* advanced into regions uncovered by the retreating ice. The allopolyploid, therefore, lies between its supposed parental types, but overlaps in distribution only with one of the two species.

The North American Tradescantias demonstrate the ability of certain polyploids to run rampant under disturbed ecological conditions (Anderson and Woodson 1935; Anderson and Sax 1936). *T. occidentalis* is extremely widespread through the midwestern region in part because it can success-

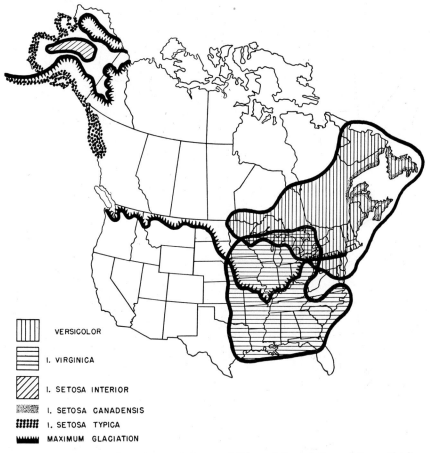

VERSICOLOR

I. VIRGINICA

I. SETOSA INTERIOR

I. SETOSA CANADENSIS

I. SETOSA TYPICA

MAXIMUM GLACIATION

Fig. 16–2. Distribution of several forms of Iris and the relation of these distributions to the maximum Pleistocene glaciation (Stebbins 1950, after Anderson).

fully colonize and spread along the railway embankments. *T. virginiana* is similarly widespread, *T. subaspera* somewhat less so, but their habitats differ from each other as well as from *T. occidentalis*. The diploid forms, however, are largely concentrated in the southern United States and in the plateau regions of Texas, and with the exception of *T. bracteata* have shown little ability to spread beyond these limits (Fig. 16–3).

Of the eight diploid species of Tradescantia, only *T. bracteata* has approached the status of a weedy species, and the average range of each is about 80,000 square miles. The nine tetraploid species occupy an average range of some 375,000 square miles, which, translated into spreading

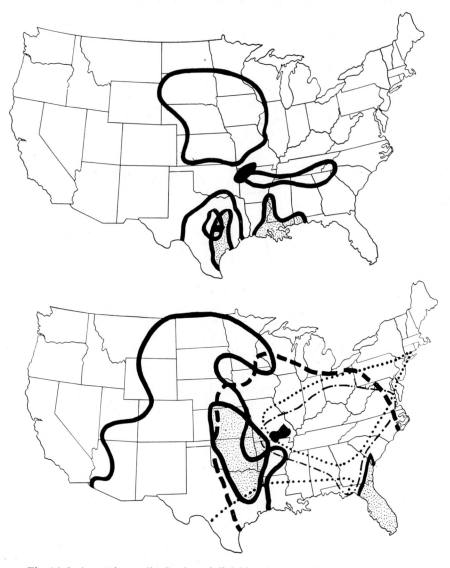

Fig. 16–3. Approximate distribution of diploid and tetraploid species of Tradescantia in the United States. Above, diploid species: solid lines, *T. bracteata* in the Middle West, *T. humilis* in Texas, *T. hirsuticaulis* in the southern states, and *T. gigantea* in central Texas; stippled areas, *T. paludosa* in the Mississippi delta and *T. subacaulis* in Texas; solid black areas, *T. ernestiana* in the Ozarks and *T. edwardsiana* in Texas. Below, tetraploid species: solid lines, *T. occidentalis*; dashes, *T. canaliculata*; dots, *T. virginiana* in the north and *T. hirsutiflora* on the gulf coast; dash and dot, *T. subaspera*; stippled areas, *T. tharpii* in the Middle West and *T. roseolens* in Florida; solid black area, *T. longipes* (Anderson and Sax 1936).

power, favors the tetraploids in a ratio of about 2 to 1. Where both diploid and tetraploid individuals of the same species exist, as is true for *T. occidentalis* and *T. canaliculata,* the diploids are very narrowly restricted in distribution as compared to the tetraploids.

Cuthbertia graminea, a xeric sandhill species closely related to the *T. virginiana* group, is of some interest since, unlike the others discussed, it appears to possess an autotetraploid form (Giles 1942). The diploids occupy a very restricted area in southern North Carolina that is geologically old (Cretaceous), and they can probably be considered the remnants of a population that has now reached a relic status (Fig. 16–4). The coastal area occupied by the tetraploids is much larger, extends principally to the east and south, and is geologically young (Pleistocene), being newly arisen as

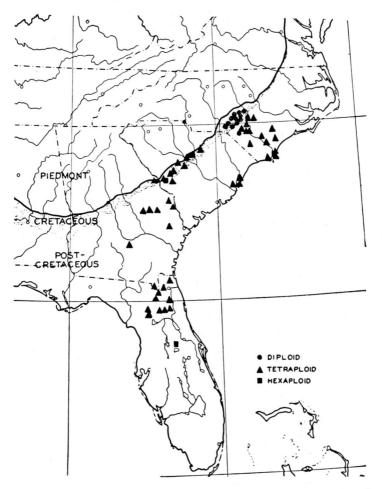

Fig. 16–4. Distribution of three cytological forms of *Cuthbertia graminea* in relation to the geology of the South Atlantic Coastal Plain (Giles 1942).

the sea retreated. Correlated with the spread of the tetraploids is their greater size, vigor and cytological variability, a marked contrast to the less vigorous uniform diploids. A related species to the south crosses with the tetraploid form, and from this union a hexaploid hybrid has arisen.

Although these are but a few of the examples that can be cited to indicate that polyploids often differ in habitat and distribution from their related diploids, there remain many polyploids that exist as isolated species, far removed in some cases from their taxonomically similar diploid relatives, or indeed, without diploid bases from which they stem. The ancient pteridophytes, Equisetum, Lycopodium, Psilotum, Tmesipteris, and Ophioglossum are of this latter type, and they probably owe their continued survival to the high degree of polyploidy they possess. Manton believes the polploid ferns of Madeira also stem from ancient stock, while the extensive polyploidy of the British Isles is more likely related to the disturbing influences of the Pleistocene.

In some instances the fossil record can yield information as to the earlier distribution of these types. In other instances, where both polyploids and diploids still exist, but widely separated from each other, it can be assumed that they once occupied the intervening areas. The New World tetraploid cotton, Gossypium hirsutum, is a synthetic species with both Asiatic and American diploid species contributing to its present genome. How these came together is still a matter of dispute, but the chromosome analysis leaves little room for doubt as to its parentage. The situation in Iris, earlier described, is an example of a once-continuous distribution that is now disrupted, and the same holds true for the Bromus species of North and South America (see later), the Paeonias of Europe and Asia, and the Oryzopsis species of North America and Europe (Stebbins 1950). The relationships detected through chromosomal studies are, therefore, an aid in unravelling the distribution patterns of earlier ages, and bolster the knowledge of disrupted distributions known formerly only from phytogeographical studies.

POLYPLOIDY AND SPECIATION

The implication of the preceding sections has been that polyploidy has played a particularly vital role in the success of the angiosperms as the dominant flora of the world, and that it has played a similar role among the leptosporangiate ferns. On the basis of high polyploid numbers in certain surviving but ancient pteridophytes, polyploidy would appear to have been an important factor in the past as well, although reconstruction of earlier events is no longer possible.

Fossil evidence reveals that the angiosperms have had four major outbursts of evolution—Cretaceous, middle and late Tertiary, Pleistocene, and Recent periods—and it is believed that such outbursts stem from climatic and edaphic changes that fostered hybridization and polyploidy. When only polyploid remnants exist in the flora, or when the polyploids and diploids of related ancestry have discontinuous distributions, it can be assumed that this polyploidy had an ancient origin; when the polyploids and diploids co-exist in the same area [e.g., *Madia citrigracilis* of the West coast (Clausen, Keck, and Hiesey 1945)] it is probable that such polyploidy is of more recent origin. The Iris complex earlier described is undoubtedly of Pleistocene origin; the woody Oryzopsis complex, now split between America and Europe, stems from Tertiary times (Stebbins 1949a).

It is only when the cytological picture is complete, however, that certainty can be attached to a particular evolutionary complex, and chromosome homology provides the critical basis for judgment. *Galeopsis tetrahit, Nicotiana tabacum,* and *Gossypium hirsutum,* among other polyploids, have been essentially resynthesized in the laboratory from their suspected diploid parents, but it will be well to examine in detail the detective studies that have unravelled the past history of certain groups, and have demonstrated the role of polyploidy in speciation.

Bromus is a large genus of the grass family, a family that contains 70 percent polyploids among its species. Bromus is widespread through both North and South America as well as through Eurasia, and it is with the American species, falling into three sections, that the phylogenetic studies have been concerned (Stebbins 1947, 1949b; Stebbins and Tobgy 1944; Stebbins, Tobgy, and Harlan 1944). As Figure 16–5 indicates, polyploidy figures prominently in phylogenetic relationships, a fact that can be tested by the study of hybrids between the sections. Of the diploids contributing genomes to the polyploid complexes, only *B. laevipes* of the section Bromopsis is known. It is found in western North America and its genome (LL) can be accurately traced because of the exceptional size of the chromosomes. Of the section Ceratochloa, the hexaploids (e.g., *B. catharticus*) contain the A, B, and C_1 genomes, and are concentrated in South America. The diploids contributing these genomes are unknown, being either lost or undiscovered. The octoploids (*carinatus, marginatus,* and *maritimus*) contain these genomes plus the L genome from a *laevipes*-like diploid, but are mainly of North American distribution. *B. Trinii,* a hexaploid of both Americas, possess a C_2 genome similar in homology to the C_1 of the South American hexaploids, plus D and E genomes of unknown origin. *B. arizonicus,* a 12-ploid species of North America, was once considered a variety of *B. carinatus,* but its cytology reveals the fact that it owes its origin only partly to *B. carinatus,* with the C_2, D, and E genomes coming from another ancestor comparable to *B. Trinii.*

It would appear therefore that the hexaploid North American members of the Bromus complex have disappeared; however, fossil evidence indicates that the hybridization necessary for the interrelationships took place in the Pliocene, with the hexaploids disappearing from the North American scene during the Pleistocene. This disappearance could be due to climatic conditions brought on by the ice, a suggestion made plausible because the South American hexaploids are adapted to a milder climate than that afforded now in North America, or because the octoploids displaced them through

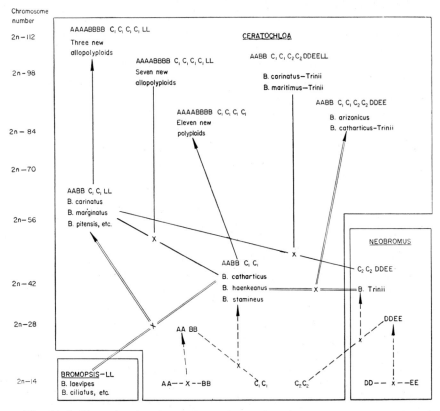

Fig. 16–5. Chart showing the phylogenetic relationships among known species of Bromus and the origin of new allopolyploids. Broken lines, supposed relations between presumed extinct or undiscovered species; double lines, experimentally verified relations between existing species; single lines, origin of newly synthesized polyploids (Stebbins 1949).

competition (Stebbins 1947). A number of artificially produced allopolyploids in this genus demonstrate very conclusively that the vigor and sterility of a newly formed polyploid cannot be predicted on the basis of known parental characteristics (Stebbins 1949), and it must be concluded that those surviving constitute only a minimum of the total number of such trials attempted in the past.

Such comparative methods of determining genome homologies and origins are not without attendant pitfalls. Loss of identity of genomes, leading in turn to loss of pairing, can take place in polyploids through translocations between member chromosomes of different genomes, while, conversely, pairing may take place between members of different genomes thus obscuring their differences of origin. In general, however, the concept of homology, as reflected in pairing relationships in meiosis, still provides the best cytological criterion of related ancestry.

Where the cytological findings can be correlated with genetical data, a more refined analysis of phylogenetic lines can be achieved. This has been done most successfully in the hexaploid vulgare bread wheat, *Triticum aestivum*. The three genomes making up this species have been designated A, B, and D (Sears 1948). There is general agreement that the D genome is derived from a different genus, *Aegilops squarrosa*, a small weedy form of the Near East. The A and B genomes are derived either from the tetraploid *T. dicoccoides*, a wild species, or from *T. dicoccum*, a cultivated form. These two genomes are somewhat related, with A coming probably from *T. monococcum* or *T. aegilopoides*, and B from some other as yet unknown diploid. A cross between *A. squarrosa* and *T. dicoccoides* produced a hybrid very similar to *T. spelta* from which *T. aestivum* is derived, and doubling of the chromosome number produced a fertile hexaploid which in turn was fertile when crossed to *T. spelta* (McFadden and Sears 1946). The characters that distinguish the hexaploid from the tetraploid wheats are consequently derived from a different genus. Additional studies suggest that the wheat grown by the Neolithic Lake Dwellers of Europe provided the tetraploid form that hybridized with *A. squarrosa*, indicating that the vulgare wheats arose after the birth of agriculture.

Extensive genetic studies have been made on the various wheats, and a comparison and a location of genes in the three genomes has pointed to their similarities and dissimilarities of homology. Such studies permit the unscrambling of the contributions of the three genomes to the total character of the vulgare wheats, and reemphasize the fact that separate lines of evolution carried on at the diploid level are often blurred by their combination and intermingling at the higher levels of polyploidy. It is often for this reason that the term "complex" is used taxonomically to cover a variable group of related forms.

The *Sanicula crassicaulis* complex is an example of the taxonomist's dilemma which may be resolved through cytological investigation (Bell 1954). A widespread and polymorphic species having a considerable ecological adaptiveness, it is composed of tetraploids, hexaploids, and octoploids. It is believed that the tetraploids are doubled hybrids from a cross between two diploid species, *S. laciniata* and *S. Hoffmannii*. The hexaploid probably arose from the union of a reduced and an unreduced gamete from the tetraploid form, while the octoploids are of several types. Some appear to be autoallooctoploids, while others, somewhat more morphologically distinct, stem from a cross between the hexaploid and a third diploid, *S. bipinnatifida*. Ecological preference seems to bear no relationship to the degree of polyploidy, and it must be assumed therefore to be more a function of genic variation than of polyploid *per se*. Despite the diverse origins of this complex, the various components comprise taxonomically a single species of wide variability. The cytological evidence, however, indicates how, through hybridization, this has arisen and how, through polyploidy, it has become fixed.

The above enumeration of various aspects of polyploidy leaves one evolutionary question to be answered. Can polyploidy lead to the formation of categories higher in the taxonomic scale than species? The direct evidence presently available seems to provide a negative answer, for the species derived through hybridization and polyploidy do not depart radically from their diploid ancestors either morphologically or ecologically. The general belief is that most of the hereditary changes leading to generic and familial differentiation originate at the diploid level, and that polyploidy is actually a conservative and, indeed, a deterrent factor in preventing the segregation necessary for the establishment of divergent lines. Gene variation and aneuploidy offer greater possibilities for such divergence, while polyploidy offers continued stability and survival to already established gene combinations.

Indirect evidence, however, would suggest that this is too narrow a point of view to adopt without reservation. As Stebbins (1950) indicates, many woody species, which now behave as diploids, undoubtedly had a polyploid origin in early times. Diploidization of a polyploid can presumably take place through aberrations which gradually reduce the homology between the sets of chromosomes present. This process of diploidization is, in itself, an evolutionary factor which in time tends to undo the stabilizing effects of polyploidy, and to permit gene variation and aneuploidy to operate again as they would at diploid levels. Coupled with the fact that polyploids are invaders of new habitats, the variation and isolation necessary for divergence is available.

The entire tribe Pomoideae of the family Rosaceae appears to have arisen through polyploidy. Having a base number of 17, it is quite likely on morphological as well as cytological grounds that the Pomoideae are ancient diploidized polyploids stemming from the Spiraeoideae ($n = 9$) on the one hand and the Prunoideae ($n = 8$) on the other (Sax 1931, 1932a). A similar origin can be postulated for many genera of the three subfamilies of the Leguminoseae (Senn 1938; Atchison 1947), but the ancient origin (probably Cretaceous) of these genera precludes any search for their putative ancestors.

It may well be, then, that the immediate success of polyploid derivatives resides in their stabilizing as well as their colonizing abilities, but that over long periods the reshuffling of separate genomes returns the polyploids to an essentially diploid condition, permitting therefore the re-entry of a polyploid state at a later stage in the continuous evolutionary cycle. This would become less and less likely the higher the degree of polyploidy, with tetraploidy the most advantageous level at which such a process could take place. The higher categories of polyploidy would place greater restrictions on progressive evolution, and in this sense polyploidy would permanently slow down and prevent the emergence of new forms. Psilotum, Tmesipteris, and Ophiglossum among the ferns and fern allies, and the high polyploids in such families as the Gramineae, can therefore be considered evolutionarily stagnant.

The sequence of evolution, where polyploidy has been an important factor, can probably be visualized as follows: gene mutation, aberrations, recombination, aneuploidy, and selection will provide the principal means for the production of favorable types at the diploid level, and out of this welter of ecotypes will come most of the divergent lines that lead to the formation of higher taxonomic categories. Autoploidy will have relatively little influence on this complex, for there is little evidence that autoploids will be appreciably different from the diploids giving rise to them. They may, however, facilitate hybridization and thus permit the intermingling of diverse genomes, which might otherwise be prevented by barriers at the diploid level. Hybridization and the doubling of chromosomes in species hybrids are both accidents of chance, but when these coincide, the entry of alloploidy at a tetraploid level leads almost immediately to the creation of a new species, provided, of course, that morphological distinctness and fertility accompany the change.

The breeding experiments of Clausen, Keck, and Heisey (1945) show, however, that not every sterile species hybrid is converted by polyploidy into a vigorous fertile form; probably the great majority of them are eliminated as unfit. The proper gene combination, therefore, goes hand-in-hand with hybridization and chromosome doubling if full advantage is to be taken of alloploidy. Varying degrees of polyploidy may be superimposed upon the tetraploid level to give complex polyploidy; these may prove successful—those in the Gramineae are an example of this—but in the long run further evolution is likely to be blocked since recombination is greatly reduced, and the dying out of related forms will leave them in "splendid isolation," as has happened to the high polyploid pteridophytes.

At the tetraploid level, diploidization may set the stage for another cycle of evolution comparable to that which took place at the diploid level. The limitations, however, are more strict here, and will be increasingly so as the degree of polyploidy increases. Consequently, the diploid and, to a lesser extent, the tetraploid levels appear to be the major sources of new genera and families; the higher levels contribute only to an increase in species.

POLYPLOIDY IN ANIMALS

The great prevalence of polyploidy among plants and its almost total absence among animals has never been satisfactorily explained. Polyploidy is known in various groups of animals—particularly in the Protozoa, Crustacea, Coleoptera, Lepidoptera, and Orthoptera—but it is almost invariably associated with parthenogenesis (Vandel 1938). Among sexually reproducing organisms it is almost entirely absent, despite the fact that the range of haploid numbers in some related groups is sufficiently wide to encompass several degrees of polyploidy. Thus cases of suspected polyploidy in the Salmonid fishes ($n = 29$ to 51), the hamster ($n = 11$ in two species of Cricetus and 22 in Mesocricetus), and the butterflies ($n = 11$ to 40 in the genus Erebia) are believed by White (1946) to be examples of chromosome fragmentation (accessory chromosomes could likewise contribute to the stepwise series of haploid numbers) rather than multiple series stemming from some particular base number. This point of view is also supported by the data of Schrader and Hughes-Schrader (1956) on the hemipter, *Thyanta calceata,* where the chromosome number is double that of related species, but the amount of DNA is the same.

Two instances are known of apparent tetraploidy even though the circumstances of reproduction are not entirely clear. The sawfly *Diprion simile,* having a haploid-diploid sex-determining mechanism, has 14 chromosomes in the male, 28 in the female (Smith 1941). Related species have seven and 14 chromosomes, respectively. In the *D. simile* male, the 14 chromosomes, behaving as univalents, pass to a single pole; 14 bivalents, however, form in the female and there is no indication of the presence of quadrivalents. This could indicate allotetraploidy, but the occurrence of parthenogenesis in both diploid and tetraploid forms places the status of polyploidy, as an evolutionary factor, in an uncertain position.

Schrader (1929) has also reported an anomalous case of polyploidy in the coccid *Gossyparia spuria.* Four sets of haploid chromosomes are present in the male, but two of them appear heteropycnotic, the other two normal. The situation is consequently out of the ordinary, and difficult to appraise.

The absence of polyploidy among sexual organisms was explained by Muller (1925) as due to the upset that polyploidy would cause in the segregation of sex factors. This apparently holds when sex is a matter of balance between the X-chromosomes and the autosomes. Thus, in *D. melanogaster,* triploids, or individuals trisomic for the X-chromosomes, were females or intersexes but never were functional males. Confirmation of this hypothesis has been obtained from dioecious mosses and some dioecious angiosperms.

The situation in *Melandrium dioicum* indicates, however, that dioecism and polyploidy are not incompatible provided that the Y as well as the X-chromosome functions in sex determination in such a manner that the Y is stronger in valence than the X. The XXXX tetraploids are female and XXXY, XXYY, and XYYY individuals are males (Warmke and Blakeslee 1940; Westergaard 1940). The XXXX and XXXY individuals, as parents, would regularly produce an equal number of both sexes; the XXYY and XYYY would have a preponderance of male offspring, provided that segregation of the four chromosomes was in pairs. Among animals, the axolotl is the only form known where the Y is functional in sex determination, making Muller's hypothesis generally applicable.

Another factor that may interfere with the formation of functional polyploids among animals has been found in amphibians, where polyploidy seriously interferes with the developmental pattern (Fankhauser 1945). Whether such restrictive influences of polyploidy are peculiar to amphibia, or whether a similar pattern is expressed generally among the vertebrates, has not been determined.

CHAPTER 17

Apomixis and Parthenogenesis

Evolution is one of the most characteristic features of the organic world, and its basis resides in the variability of its hereditary mechanism and the selectivity of the environment. The avenues of evolutionary change that can be successfully explored are consequently limited only by the physical environment in which the organism lives and by the variations of which the hereditary mechanism is capable. Gene mutations constitute the principal source of variation, with gene recombination, chromosomal aberrations, hybridization, aneuploidy, and polyploidy assisting in ways that have already been described.

There can be no doubt that sexual reproduction is an integral cog in the machinery of evolution, permitting, as it does, the union of gametes that are genetically dissimilar and thus presenting to the environment diverse genotypes to be acted upon by natural selection. The balanced polymorphism found in Drosophila species indicates the delicateness of the adjustment between genotype and environment. Many organisms, however, have forsaken, in part or entirely, sexual for asexual reproduction—this is not meant to include those forms that have never attained a state of sexual reproduction—and in doing so, they have sacrificed, as it were, the genetic plasticity necessary for further evolutionary change by withdrawing from the sexual pool and preserving intact certain genotypes that have immediate advantages for survival.

The various types of asexual reproduction that substitute for, and in many instances replace, sexual reproduction can be conveniently grouped under the term *apomixis. Parthenogenesis,* which is defined as the development of a new individual from an egg without fertilization, is but one phase of apomictic behavior. Both apomixis and parthenogenesis in the plant kingdom have been extensively discussed by Stebbins (1941, 1950), Fagerlind (1940), Gustafson (1946, 1947a, b, 1948), and Nygren (1954), and in the animal kingdom by White (1954) and Suomalainen (1950).

In normal sexual reproduction, reduction in chromosome number brought about by meiosis and resulting in the formation of haploid gametes is compensated for by the process of fertilization. Thus a haploid-diploid alternation of stages is a necessary aspect of sexual organisms. A functional apomictic or parthenogenetic cycle consequently must have a suitable substitute for both meiosis and fertilization, and these must be coordinated with each other. We can consider how this can be accomplished by examining the various processes in both plants and animals.

APOMIXIS IN PLANTS

The structure and development of plants is relatively simple as compared to that in animals, and the ability of a plant to produce an entire individual from one of its member parts—e.g., stem, root, and leaf cuttings for propagation—furnishes additional means for asexual reproduction not commonly available to any except the most primitive animals such as the Porifera, certain coelenterates, or some flatworms. Apomixis, therefore, is of two principal types: *vegetative reproduction* and *agamospermy* (Fig. 17–1).

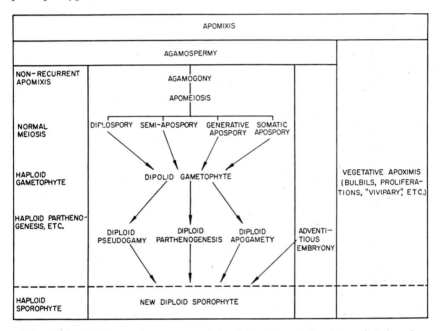

Fig. 17–1. Diagrammatic representation of the interrelationships of the various systems of apomixis (Stebbins 1950, after Gustafson).

Vegetative reproduction occurs as an accessory reproductive process in many plant species along with normal seed production through sexual means, but, as Stebbins points out, such asexual reproduction is not customarily considered to be a form of apomixis unless it is the *only* means of reproduction. Thus the strawberry cannot be classified as being apomictic simply because it produces new individuals through the development of runners, since meiosis, fertilization, and seed formation are still normal.

Elodea canadensis, however, is a facultative apomict in that in northern latitudes its only means of reproduction is asexual and vegetative, while under warmer conditions it flowers and fruits normally at the same time that it may also propagate vegetatively. Other vegetative apomicts, however, have had the flowering head converted into a source of *propagules,* these essentially replacing the flowers. Several wild species of Allium possess such a reproductive system, and their success as invaders can be largely attributed to a faculty for producing viviparous individuals in large numbers. Several of the grasses are viviparous, as well as a number of dicotyledenous species, but although some are complete or nearly complete obligate apomicts in that this is their only means of reproduction, others have occasional flowers that produce seed through normal processes.

Clausen (1954), however, considers that there are very few plant species that are obligate apomicts, and he emphasizes that the balance between apomixis and sexuality is a delicate one controlled by the genotype and the environment. The equilibrium is apparently maintained through a time differential which, under some circumstances, favors the early development of the apomictic embryo, and under other circumstances, the development of a sexual embryo.

Apomictic seed production occurs by a variety of devices, and is collectively referred to as *agamospermy.* In one type, *adventitious embryony,* the usual gametophytic stage in the cycle of development is omitted, and the embryo formed arises from some cell in the diploid sporophytic tissue of the ovule. This may be a cell of either the nucellus or the ovule integument, with the result that maternal inheritance is inevitable, since the offspring are of precisely the same chromosomal and genotypic pattern as the mother plant. The genus Citrus is an example of a form reproducing by this device, and Stebbins points out that, for reasons unknown, this phenomenon is more typical of species native to warm climates.

Most apomictic species have retained a semblance of the sporophyte-gametophyte-sporophyte alternation of generations, but with meiosis and fertilization eliminated as functional steps in the process of embryo formation. Referred to as *gametophytic apomixis,* since a gametophyte is formed, the process utilizes either somatic or archesporial cells, the latter being those that, under normal circumstances, undergo meiosis and a reduction division to form a haploid embryo sac. If somatic cells are involved (*apospory*), these are usually of nucellar or of integumental origin, and a diploid embryo sac is formed directly by a series of cell divisions. The nature of the stimulus causing their development is unknown. If the cells are of archesporial origin (*diplospory*), the meiotic processes are missing or abortive so that a gametophyte of diploid character is preserved.

The manner by which the consequences of meiosis are circumvented are quite various, but the results are essentially the same. Once the embryo sac is formed with its customary complement of nuclei, the embryo may develop by cell division from the egg cell (*parthenogenesis*) or from one of the remaining cells (*apogamety*). Parthenogenesis is by far the most common method of embryo formation in the angiosperms, but apogamety is more frequent in the ferns (here, however, one would be dealing with an archegonial cell rather than with a cell in an embryo sac). As a general rule, these apomicts are *pseudogamous* in that development of the embryo does not proceed unless pollination has taken place, but the role of pollination is different in different forms. In *Allium odorum,* for example, the egg cell may enter cell division prior to pollination, but endosperm formation will not follow unless union of the sperm and fusion nucleus takes place. A partial fertilization is consequently necessary. In some species of Ranunculus, on the other hand, fertilization of the endosperm is not a necessary feature, and the development of both embryo and endosperm may begin before the flower is open or the stigma is receptive to pollen.

The nature of meiotic disturbances in apomictic species is extremely varied, and may be found in microsporocytes as well as in megasporocytes. The sporogenous tissue may degenerate, the meiotic division may lack chromosomal pairing and approach a mitotic-like character, or there may be some other disturbance that interferes with the synchronization of the steps that, in toto, make up the process of meiosis. In some species, sexual and apomictic phenomena may take place side by side in the same ovary or in the same individual (*Festuca ovina*) (*facultative* rather than *obligate* apomicts). In others, microsporogenesis may be essentially normal and megasporogenesis abnormal (*Calamagrostis lapponica*), while in related species (*C. chalybaea*) the reverse is true (Nygren 1946). Table 17–1 provides a list of species showing various types of apomixis.

TABLE 17–1

Types of apomixis in angiosperms and pteridophytes with representative genera [after Stebbins (1941, 1950) and Manton (1952)].

Type of apomixis	Representative genera
1. Vegetative apomixis	*Festuca, Poa, Deschampsia, Allium, Polygonum, Saxifruga, Agave*
2. Adventitious embryony	*Citrus, Euphorbia, Ochna, Opuntia, Hosta, Allium, Spiranthes, Mangifera*
3. Somatic apospory	*Dryopteris, Cyrtomium, Pteris, Asplenium* and *Pellaea* among the ferns; *Potentilla, Rubus, Poa, Malus, Sorbus, Hieracium, Crepis*
4. Diplospory	*Hieracium, Taraxacum, Antennaria, Calamagrostis, Chondrilla, Erigeron*

A survey of apomictic species makes it clear that the great majority of apomicts have a hybrid origin and are polyploid. The available evidence, however, indicates that neither hybridization nor polyploidy can cause apomixis directly, although both may contribute to its expression in the sense that they may assist in producing circumstances that favor its appearance. Apomixis may, in fact, disappear in hybrids, only to reappear in later segregants (Gustafson 1942).

Breeding experiments point to a genetic basis for apomixis. A cross between the predominately apomictic *Allium carinatum,* in which flowers are replaced by bulbils, and the sexual species *A. pulchellum* reveals that a single dominant gene governs the expression of apomixis. This situation, on the other hand, appears to be an exception, for other extensive experiments with Parthenium, Poa, and Potentilla indicate that, in general, sexuality is dominant to apomixis, and that apomictic behavior is governed principally by a balance between a series of genetic factors. Thus, the hybrid offspring derived from a cross between a high-polyploid sexual form and a low-polyploid apomict are almost invariably sexual in reproductive behavior. A similar situation is found when diploid sexual and apomictic individuals are crossed. However, when high-polyploid apomicts are crossed to low-polyploid sexual forms, the offspring are generally apomictic. These results point to the existence of many recessive genes present in established apomicts, and their coordinated action is necessary for the full expression of apomixis.

The genetic circumstances present in guayule (*Parthenium argentatum*) illustrate this point (Powers 1945). Most of the polyploid forms of guayule are apomictic and the diploid individuals are sexual; occasional polyploids, on the other hand, are also sexual. Breeding experiments indicate that three pairs of genes determine the breeding behavior of individual plants. A recessive gene *a* in the homozygous condition leads to the formation of unreduced eggs; gene *b* prevents fertilization; gene *c* causes the eggs to develop without fertilization. Plants with the genetic constitution *aaBBCC* form unreduced eggs, but these cannot develop apomictically. Fertilization is necessary, and when it occurs a higher degree of polyploidy results. Plants with the genotype *AAbbCC* produce reduced eggs, but embryos are not formed since fertilization is prevented. Those with an *AABBcc* genotype have a normal sexual behavior; *cc* has no effect in the presence of *A* and *B* since the eggs are reduced and fertilization takes place. Only those plants with an *aabbcc* genetic constitution would be apomictic. In a population of mixed genotypes, therefore, segregation would occur, and fully sexual plants could give rise to apomictic offspring. Polyploidy, in increasing degrees, would serve to reinforce the genetic basis determining apomixis.

The genetic determination of apomixis in Poa and Potentilla seems to be more complicated than that in Parthenium since no distinct monofactorial segregation occurs. When it is realized that the complete expression of apomixis in an obligate form involves the coordinated action of several phenomena of not necessarily related origin—e.g., suppression of meiosis in anthers and/or ovaries, suppression of fertilization, stimulation of egg and/or endosperm development—it is not to be wondered at that apomixis has a recessive multifactorial basis except in the most simple cases. Furthermore, dominance of factors causing these effects would be deleterious unless all had arisen simultaneously to promote apomixis suddenly. If recessive, they could survive in the population without harm until the proper recessive genotype appeared.

The relation of hybridization and polyploidy to apomixis has been appraised by both Stebbins and Gustafson. Hybridization appears to favor apomixis indirectly in two ways. In the first place, it is the most satisfactory method for bringing together diverse genomes that by chance have the proper combination of factors to promote apomixis. This must be a chance formation, because numerous crosses of species closely related to other apomictic forms have never yielded hybrids that are apomictic, thus leaving little doubt that hybridization is only a means to an end, rather than a direct cause of apomixis. Stebbins also suggests that the heterotic effects often found in hybrids allow for a greater expansion in the range of ecological habits over that found in the parent species, and apomixis would tend to preserve such adapted genotypes through maternal inheritance. Facultative apomixis is consequently a device that, on one hand, permits the mass production of seeds of like genotype, and on the other, preserves a store of potential variability that may be later released through sexual seed production (Clausen 1954).

The knowledge that genera having both diploid and polyploid species may show the former to be sexual and the latter apomictic, suggests that polyploidy is directly responsible for apomixis. However, the entire spectrum of apomictic events is known among diploids as well as polyploids, indicating that polyploidy *per se* cannot be responsible; further, many polyploid series of plants, both naturally occurring and artificially produced, retain sexuality through all levels of polyploidy, and argue against such direct effects of polyploidy.

The great prevalence of polyploids among apomictic forms—this holds true for ferns as well as angiosperms (Manton 1952)—requires explanation. The most plausible conclusion is that put forth by Gustafson who argues that while apomixis can be induced at diploid levels by favorable gene combinations, there is a stronger action of these genes at the polyploid than at the diploid level. Support for this contention is derived from breeding experiments. In Potentilla and Poa, crosses between diploid species or those with low chromosome numbers that are preponderantly apomictic but which can still function sexually to a limited extent, yield progeny having a high proportion of sexual individuals. On the other hand, crosses between polyploid apomictic forms yield mostly apomictic progeny. There is danger, however, in applying Gustafson's principle too broadly for there are many polyploid series of both ferns and angiosperms that cannot be so interpreted.

It would appear, therefore, that hybridization and polyploidy are intimately associated, and run concurrently, with apomixis, but the relationships are not clearly revealed or understood. It may well be that poly-ploidy shifts the timing differential between the development of apomictic and sexual seed production in the direction of apomixis, but this remains to be proved.

From an evolutionary point of view, apomixis presents a complex and exceedingly difficult problem. With hybridization, polyploidy, and apomixis tending to confuse the clear-cut differences between species, the taxonomist is confronted with a problem that is well-nigh insoluble unless cytological data are at hand. This is particularly true since the apomicts, despite the prevalence of maternal inheritance, are highly polymorphic because of the occasional successful sexual reproductions. Many of the sexual offspring of apomicts are weak (Clausen 1954), but each little variant, despite its irregular genic or chromosomal background, possesses the potentiality for preservation, leading to what have been termed *agamic complexes.* These are found in such genera as Crepis, Taraxacum, Hieracium, Rubus, Poten-tilla, Poa, and Parthenium, and all are known as taxonomically difficult groups.

The structure and origin of the agamic complex can be examined best in the North American species of the genus Crepis (Babcock and Stebbins 1938; Stebbins and Babcock 1939; Babcock 1947; Stebbins 1950). These species, eight in number, have a base number of 11 chromosomes ($2n = 22$) and can be regarded as sexually reproducing forms, which probably had a more ancient origin as allotetraploids of Asiatic species having 4 and 7 as their base numbers. Their present behavior is that of normal sexually reproducing diploids, and, with the exception of *C. run-cinata,* they have given rise to a polyploid, apomictic series having $2n$ numbers of 33, 44, 55, up to 88. As indicated in Figure 17–2, the distri-bution of the seven diploids is, except for *C. acuminata* (area #1 in Fig. 17–2), quite restricted as compared to that of the polyploids. Furthermore, the diploids are morphologically and ecologically distinct from each other, no two species existing side by side in the same ecological habitat.

The polyploid apomicts, on the other hand, show all gradations of morphology and ecological preference, without possessing any new char-acters that set them apart from the diploids. It appears therefore that the polyploid complex is made up of individuals that combine the features of various diploids, a combination brought about by species hybridization and both auto- and allo-ploidy. Some of the polyploids appear to be simply larger editions of particular diploids, and autopolyploidy can be evoked to account for their origin. Others, however, clearly have arisen by hybridi-zation followed by polyploidy, and certain combinations of characters found in the diploids suggests that more than two of the diploids have con-tributed genes to some of the individuals. Some of the plants produce occasional offspring through sexual reproduction, thus providing a means for continued segregation and hybridization. These latter events continue to contribute to the polymorphism of the complex, while apomixis insures the perpetuation of any strain that is ecologically fit.

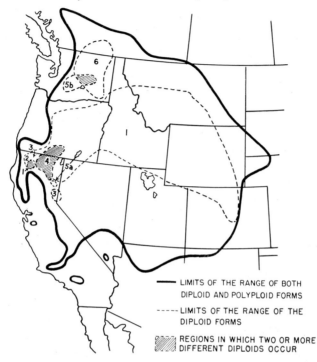

Fig. 17–2. Areas of distribution of diploid sexual forms of Crepis in western North America and of their polyploid apomitic derivatives (Babcock and Stebbins 1938).

In a structural sense, the agamic Crepis complex rests on seven pillars, these being the seven distinct diploid species. In terms of numbers of individuals, the seven species constitute but a small fraction of the total population. The vast and taxonomically nebulous superstructure owes its origin to hybridization and polyploidy, with apomixis permitting the continued propagation of both fertile as well as sterile forms, and occasional sexual seed set permitting the segregation and recombination of genes to further the extensive polymorphism. The polyploid apomicts, having wider ecological tolerance as a result of a combination of physiological characters in the diploids, have spread beyond the limited ranges of the diploids; yet each apomict tends to form its own colony of identical individuals, which are different from the individuals of adjacent colonies. New variability bursts forth when the occasional sexual forms cross with each other, and as a rule genetic heterozygosity is characteristic of the polyploid apomicts.

The pattern of evolution found in the agamic complex of Crepis is met with in other groups, although minor differences are evident. In Taraxacum, 12 or more diploid species form the base of the complex, and the same is true for Antennaria. Parthenium, however, has only two diploid species ($2n = 18$) contributing to a complex confined to a single desert area in the western United States, but the somatic numbers of the polyploids range as high as 144. Auto- rather than allo-ploidy seems to be important in this species, for the range of morphological characters forms two series grouped about the two diploid species. Further variations are encountered in Rubus, Potentilla, and Poa, and these differences will depend upon the number of sexual diploids contributing to the complex, the degree of polyploidy attained, the amount of hybridization between polyploids, and the amount of facultative as opposed to obligate apomixis present in the complex.

It is quite clear that the species concept cannot be rigorously applied to these apomicts, and yet it would be equally absurd to consider them a single species. The terms *agamospecies* or "circle microspecies" have been applied to these groups, with the species designation being restricted to the morphologically distinct, sexually reproducing diploid forms, but it is only when the interrelationships are known that such a taxonomically difficult group can be comprehended as an evolutionary unit.

A final word may be said regarding the agamic complexes and plant geography. The situation in Crepis, where the diploid species are known, and the derivation of the polyploid apomicts can be reasonably well determined, permits a determination of the centers of origin and the routes of dispersal. Where the diploid species are no longer living, as appears to be the case to a certain extent in Rubus, such appraisals become more difficult, but the presence of agamic complexes in arctic and subantarctic regions (Taraxacum and Antennaria) and their possible diploid ancestors in temperate and subarctic areas enables one to use apomicts as indicators of floral migration. The recent studies of apomicts makes this approach to plant geography a more feasible one.

PARTHENOGENESIS IN ANIMALS

The existence in plants of an alternation of diploid sporophyte with haploid gametophyte makes possible a far greater range of parthenogenetic behavior than can be evolved or exhibited by animals in which meiosis is immediately followed by fertilization. The same is true for vegetative apomixis as well, for every organ of a plant has, potentially, the possibilities of being transformed into a propagule of some sort. It is only among the very primitive animal groups that vegetative reproduction by cell groups is at all possible, but among sexually reproducing animals parthenogenesis is a widespread form of reproduction. It may take many forms, but except in certain groups it is of sporadic occurrence, being naturally absent only in the vertebrates and in the insect orders Odonata and Heteroptera (Suomalainen 1950; White 1954). It is unnecessary here to distinguish among all types of parthenogenesis, and consideration will be given to haploid parthenogenesis (*arrhenotoky,* according to White's terminology) and somatic parthenogenesis (*thelotoky*).

Haploid parthenogenesis is both a form of reproduction and a means of sex determination. Fertilized eggs develop into diploid females, unfertilized parthenogenetic ones into haploid males. So far as is known, haploid parthenogenesis has evolved independently six or seven times in the animal kingdom: in the Rotifera, Acarina (mites), and in four orders of insects, the Hymenoptera, Homoptera, Coleoptera, and Thysanoptera. The entire order of Hymenoptera exhibits arrhenotoky, among the Homoptera it is found in a few species of coccids and aleurodids, in the Coleoptera only a single species, *Micromalthus debilis,* has male haploidy, while in the Thysanoptera the phenomenon is believed to exist simply because virgin females produce haploid males. The most extensive studies, both cytological and genetic, have been done on various species of Hymenoptera, and the account below is based largely on these data.

Oögenesis in these forms is essentially normal in that synapsis, chiasma formation (and presumably crossing over as well), and reduction division are a regular part of the meiotic process. Since the males are haploid, however, spermatogenesis cannot follow a normal course of events; the reduction in chromosome number is eliminated. Several different types of spermatogenesis have been noted. In most of the Hymenoptera the first meiotic division is abortive. A first division spindle, which is often monopolar, is formed but the chromosomes do not divide. A non-nucleated cytoplasmic bud is pinched off and later degenerates, while the larger nucleated cell undergoes a mitotic division to produce two functional spermatids. This type of spermatogenesis is also found in the beetle, Micromalthus, and has been shown to occur even in the rare diploid males of the wasp, Habrobracon, where homologous chromosomes capable of pairing in meiosis are available. It is undoubtedly an ancient mechanism not governed by the number of chromosomes present in the nucleus.

In the scelionid wasp, *Telenomus fariai,* the first division in the spermatocytes is mitotic in character to give rise to two secondary spermatocytes. Each of these undergoes an abortive second division, but only a small non-nucleated bud is pinched off.

Even the pretense of a meiotic division is dispensed with in other forms, and spermatogenesis consists only of a mitotic-like, equational division (Acarina, the aleuronic Homoptera). In the coccid, *Icerya purchasi,* the spermatocyte chromosomes are distinguished from mitotic ones only by their somewhat greater degree of contraction.

It is of some interest to consider the possible origin as well as the evolutionary consequences of male haploidy. There is every reason to believe that male haploidy has arisen independently in each of the groups mentioned, and, in the Coleoptera and Homoptera, at least, from ancestors having X-chromosomes. In Habrobracon and in the honey bee, sex determination depends upon a series of multiple alleles in such a manner that hemizygosity or homozygosity results in maleness, and heterozygosity in femaleness (Whiting 1943, 1945). To be derived from an ancestral XO-XX mechanism, male haploidy must depend either upon the elimination or transformation of sex chromosomes and the construction of a new sex system based upon genetic factors (as in Habrobracon), or on the elimination of the autosomes and the retention only of sex chromosomes. The former is believed to have taken place in the attainment of haploidy by the males of Icerya (Hughes-Schrader 1948b), and an evolutionary trend in various coccid species reveals that a progressive series of changes in diploid males brings on asynapsis first, followed by an asynchrony in the functioning of the two haploid sets of chromosomes, a permanent hetero-pycnosis of one set, and a suppression of sperm formation in the cell bearing this set. The result is that the male coccid breeds as a physiological haploid. Elimination of the pycnotic set, as well as removal of the block to development of an unfertilized egg, would culminate in a male that was cytologically haploid as well.

White (1954), on the other hand, suggests that elimination of the autosomes would produce a genetic system with a multiple X but no Y or autosomes. However, neither system is capable of proof at the present time, so that the origin of male haploidy is still uncertain.

In an evolutionary sense, the presence of haploid males means that every mutation is immediately exposed to natural selection, and one might expect that natural populations of these organisms would show a greater degree of homozygosity and far fewer lethals than would similar populations of diploid species. In fact, one can compare the X-chromosome of Drosophila species with the entire set of chromosomes in a haploid male since both are exposed to natural selection in an unprotected state, and while genetic studies of natural populations of haploid males have not been made, the X-chromosomes of Drosophila species do not contain the degree of variability in the form of recessive mutations found in the autosomes, which are always in a paired state in both males and females.

Unlike haploid parthenogenesis, which leads to the development of haploid males, somatic parthenogenesis produces only diploid females from unfertilized eggs. Two general types may be distinguished: *obligatory,* or complete, parthenogenesis where this is the only form of reproduction and where the population consists exclusively of females (an occasional male may be found, but its presence is not a necessary feature in the continuation of the species), and incomplete or *cyclical* parthenogenesis where a sexual generation intervenes after one or more parthenogenetic generations. The genetic consequences of thes two types are obviously quite different.

Obligate parthenogenesis, when an unreduced egg undergoes development, represents a closed genetic system. Meiosis and the recombination of genes has been abolished, and except for occasional mutations which may have an effect, evolutionary change is blocked. Such a group of organisms represents, in essence, a clonal line of unvarying genotype, and is consequently at the mercy of a changing environment. The fact that most forms exhibiting obligatory parthenogenesis are polyploid suggests that those organisms are provided with a better buffered genotype and wider ecological tolerance than that possessed by their sexual diploid progenitors, but if violent ecological changes occur within its range, they do not have a reservoir of variability in the form of recessive genes which, through recombination, can yield offspring capable of adapting to new conditions. Certain obligatory forms, however, undergo a regular meiosis, with the somatic number of chromosomes being restored by fusion with one of the polar bodies, or by a fusion of cleavage nuclei, and these have a greater possibility for phenotypic and genotypic variation. Even so, the entire range of variability is limited by the degree of heterozygosity of the mother and once homozygosity is established for any gene it must remain so except for mutations. It is not surprising, therefore, that obligatory parthenogenesis is of sporadic occurrence in the animal kingdom, and does not characterize any entire group.

Cyclical parthenogenesis, on the other hand, utilizes the advantages of both parthenogenetic and sexual reproduction. Since parthenogenesis makes mating unnecessary, the entire energies of adult life are turned to feeding and reproduction, and such organisms, as for example the aphids, are notoriously prolific during the warm seasons of the year. Every individual, being female, is a potential producer of offspring. When environmental circumstances are unfavorable, such as the advent of cold weather, a sexual generation intervenes, with the cycle being repeated as conditions permit.

Polyploidy and obligatory ameiotic parthenogenesis go hand-in-hand, although a number of diploid parthenogenetic forms are known. Where meiosis is abolished, any degree of polyploidy, and indeed any type of aberration, that does not interfere with mitosis and does not affect viability, can become established. Agamic complexes such as are found in plants seem not to have been established in animals, except possibly in certain earthworms and weevils, although, as White proposes, it may be that existing obligatory parthenogenesis is of relatively recent origin.

Although parthenogenesis in one form or another occurs in most animal phyla, a consideration of details can be confined to *Artemia salina* (Crustacea, *Trichoniscus elizabethae* (Isopoda), *Solenobia triquetrella* (Lepidoptera), and the cynipid wasps and aphids.

The brine shrimp, *A. salina,* has a wide but discontinuous distribution in both the New and the Old Worlds, being ecologically restricted to waters of high salinity such as are found in inland salt lakes and salt pans. The separation of strains, presumably for very long periods of time, has permitted some morpohological differentiation to take place, but systematists agree generally in considering the strains as belonging to a single species. The most widespread of the strains is the diploid ($2n = 42$) sexual form. Its eggs do not develop unless fertilized. A sexual tetraploid strain has been reported, but diploid, triploid, tetraploid, pentaploid, octaploid, and decaploid parthenogenetic races consisting mostly of females are known, with the most intensive work being done on those in the region of Palestine.

Cytological behavior in the parthenogenetic strains shows some variation. The diploid parthenogenetic race has a normal first meiotic division taking place in the egg, 21 bivalents being formed regularly. The second division, however, is irregular and even abortive, but by the time of cleavage the diploid number is restored. Either the polar body fuses with the reduced egg nucleus, or the second division is prevented and the chromosomes simply divide in an endomitotic fashion. In the tetraploid race, the first division shows no bivalent formation, and a single mitotic-like division of 84 univalents leads to the formation of the egg. Maturation behavior in the other polyploid races is not known, although the occurrence of aneuploidy in some strains from Palestine suggests meiotic irregularities. It is difficult to account for the origin of the odd-numbered parthenogenetic races except through chromosome loss during an abortive meiotic division, but once initiated, parthenogenesis permits the continued existence of these cytologically aberrant types.

Trichoniscus elizabethae is a diploid ($2n = 16$) sexual sowbug restricted to the moist mountainous regions of southern France. A variety *coelebs,* however, is both triploid and parthenogenetic, with a single mitotic-like division leading to egg formation. It does not co-exist with the diploid strain, but rather is found in isolated drier regions of the Mediterranean, which would be ecologically unsuitable for the diploid. It also ranges as far north as southern Sweden and Finland. Triploid males occur in a frequency of 1–2 percent, but their origin is unknown. White believes that parthenogenesis preceded triploidy in Trichoniscus, but if a diploid parthenogenetic form existed it has either not been discovered or has died out. This suggestion gains credence with the knowledge that diploid parthenogenetic races exist in Artemia and in Solenobia as well as in certain weevils, earthworms, water fleas, and cockroaches.

Solenobia triquetrella is a psychid moth having three European races: a diploid ($2n = 62$) sexual race, and two parthenogenetic races, one diploid and the other tetraploid and presumably of autoploid origin. The parthenogenetic races have normal meiotic behavior to produce reduced eggs which commence development without fertilization. After four cleavage nuclei are formed, these unite in pairs to restore the somatic number of chromosomes. Sexual diploid males can mate with parthenogenetic females to produce progeny. These are mostly females when the mother is a diploid parthenogenetic form, but triploid intersexes if the mother is tetraploid since the sperm unites with the reduced egg prior to the usual cleavage fusion. Intersexuality apparently stems from the fact that the females in the Lepidoptera are heterogametic and the triploid would be XXY balanced against three sets of autosomes.

The distribution of *S. triquetrella* is of some interest. The diploid sexual race is narrowly restricted to areas of Alpine Switzerland and nearby Germany that were not glaciated during the Würm Ice Age. The diploid parthenogenetic race co-exists in these areas, but in addition has extended its range somewhat to take in neighboring glaciated regions. The tetraploid parthenogenetic race is more extensively distributed, extending northward into southern Sweden and covering Central Europe generally, with its eastern limits in Roumania.

As pointed out earlier, cyclical parthenogenesis takes advantage of the rapidity of development and the prolificity characteristic of parthenogenetic organisms in general, and yet retains the genetic advantages of sexual reproduction. The cycles are often complicated, and the factors involved in the determination of each step are not understood in any physiological sense. However, low and high temperatures favor the production of males in the crustacean, Cladocera, while nutrition, crowding, humidity, and illumination are known to influence parthenogenesis in the gall wasps.

The aphids exhibit cyclical parthenogenesis as a group, and *Tetraneura ulmi* can serve as an example (White 1954). The fertilized eggs winter over, and in the spring the female nymph forms a leaf gall on the European elm. Within the gall, adult development of a wingless form is attained, followed by the parthenogenetic production of about 40 winged offspring. The gall-making wingless mother is called a stem mother, or *fundatrices;* the winged offspring, also parthenogenetic, migrate to a summer food plant (in the case of *T. ulmi,* grasses are the summer host). These are the *emigrantes,* and on the grasses may produce a succession of generations (the *exules*), the last of which, coinciding with the approach of cold weather, includes winged sexual males and parthenogenetic females. These, the *sexuparae,* return to the elm, their winter host, where winged sexual females are produced, and these, together with the winged males of the previous generation, form the *sexuales.* The males and the females (with which they will mate to produce the fertilized eggs for wintering-over) are therefore the products of different generations.

Cytologically, the sexual males have a $2n$ number of 13 chromosomes, the females 14, indicating the existence of an XO:XX sex mechanism. The parthenogenetic forms—the fundatrices, emigrantes, and exules—have 14 chromosomes, and only a single maturation division takes place in the egg. The sexuparae produce two kinds of oöcytes, in one of which a single maturation division gives rise to a female-producing egg, while in the other the single division is modified to the extent that only the two X-chromosomes pair and are reduced to give an XO egg which develops into a male.

Spermatogenesis in the males is also anomalous. The reduction division is normal except for the X-chromosome, which, after being hung between the poles in a stretched condition, passes undivided into a secondary spermatocyte much larger than the one that receives no X. Only the X-bearing secondary spermatocyte divides, producing two X-bearing sperm, and these, uniting with reduced X-bearing eggs, produce only eggs that will give rise to female fundatrices the following spring.

In other aphid species the cycle of generations may be profoundly modified. In *Phylloxera caryaecaulis,* for example, there are only three generations per year, and the emigrantes and exules are missing as parts of the cycle. The stem-mother produces sexuparae, but these are either male- or female-producing. Lines of maleness and femaleness are thus separated in terms of parental origin. The cynipid wasps have only two yearly generations. The bisexual generation produces eggs in the fall, from all of which hatch parthenogenetic females; these produce both males and females for the sexual generation. It can be assumed that these insects have not developed the complicated system evolved by the aphids, for the more primitive species have a single yearly bisexual generation.

CHAPTER 18

Concluding Statement

It would be presumptuous and, indeed, a grave error to assume that the preceding chapters have done much more than introduce the student to the general science of cytology, indicate the relation of this science to the physiology, inheritance and evolution of organisms, and point out the areas of experimental study which seem particularly pertinent to our understanding of the cell as a basic unit of organization. In organizing this information, an attempt has been made to delineate the *certain* from the *uncertain,* the *hypothesis* from the *proven observation,* the *causal relationship* from the *disconnected fact.* An attempt, implicit rather than explicit, has also been made to convey to the student something of the philosophy of cytology as a descriptive and an experimental science, and to lay down for him, without being dogmatic, the basic tenets of the cytologist.

The cytologist, for example, has confidence, even faith, in the validity of the Cell Theory, the Theory of Cell Lineage, the Chromosomal Theory of Inheritance, and the Evolution Theory. These are "theories" in name only; they are the cornerstones not only of cytology but also of modern biology itself. Implicit in them are two fundamental principles: that of *inorganic and organic continuity,* and that of *random chance* rather than *predetermined purpose.* The Evolution Theory, which, in a sense, embraces within its scope the other theories, forces us to accept these principles as rational working bases. Only man, in the more recent stages of his evolution, possesses the capacity of replacing chance with *choice,* and of determining and directing his own evolution in a purposeful manner.

The cytologist, in keeping with his fellow scientists, has an even greater confidence in his methods and point of view: observation on repeated observation, experiment and repeated confirmation. His hypotheses and theories mean little if they are not in accord with his recorded data.

When we look beyond these basic tenets we are made painfully aware of our ignorance of the "whys" and "wherefores" of the biological world. Our knowledge is fragmentary in almost every respect, and many structures and processes once thought to be simple are now known to be deceptively complex. Through use of the electron microscope and the techniques of the biochemist and biophysicist, we see the "empty vessels" of Robert Hooke through new eyes, and their fine structure and spatial organization beg for an integrative interpretation in terms of the equally important findings of the cellular physiologist.

A number of questions were raised in the preface, and an attempt was made to answer them in the text. They concerned, in particular, the structure, function, behavior, and evolution of the chromosomes and the nucleus. These seemed legitimate questions, for heredity as we know it is largely centralized in these bodies. We can now extend this generalization and safely state that the key to resolution of the basic questions of cytology lies in the interrelations of three kinds of macromolecules: RNA, DNA, and proteins. We may speak, therefore, of the *chemical basis of inheritance and evolution,* for within this framework of thought are being sought the answers to questions concerning the nature of biologically specific syntheses, the nature of the gene and of gene action, the structure and activity of euchromatin and heterochromatin, mutation rates and direction, and the recombination of genes. The bacteria and viruses have proved to be exciting objects of study in this search for answers. They appear to be simpler in structure and function than higher organisms, and they are more amenable to physical and chemical study. We find, too, that they have new modes of inheritance which were previously unknown in the organic world. While these pathways of inheritance are difficult to understand and evaluate, a knowledge of them is contributing to our understanding of more conventional organisms.

The same problems are encountered when we attempt to unravel the principles operating in evolution. Here, however, the element of competition is actively encountered, and where survival is involved, one genetic system is pitted against another. As White (1954) points out, comparative evolution studies must take into account many things: modes of reproduction, population dynamics, chromosome cycles as seen in meiosis, recombination frequencies, and degrees and kinds of genetic and chromosomal polymorphism. Each species flows, as it were, through time, and these factors will determine its chance of survival, its capacity for change, and its value as a focal point for further radiating evolution.

We recognize that our knowledge of the structure and function of the cell, and of the interlocking role of the cell in growth and development, and in heredity and variation, is far greater than it ever was, but we are still confronted with ambiguities and uncertainties. These have been mentioned in the text, but they should be no cause for concern. As Wilson (1925) has so clearly pointed out, evolutionary theory originally grew out of the study of natural history and took definite shape long before the structure of living things was known. Its convergence with cytology and genetics is of more recent origin, yet it is now possible to describe the "grand pattern of evolution" largely in terms of particulate inheritance and natural selection (White 1954).

The same can be said of cytology. It emerged as a science because of a distinterested curiosity in the structure of living things and because the invention of the microscope permitted the study of structures of small dimensions. It merged first with anatomy, histology and embryology, and then later with genetics, and its more recent union with physics and chemistry should make it possible, within the not too distant future, to view the "grand pattern of the cell" in a much more intimate way.

References

Adams, M. H., 1955. Genetic recombination in bacteria. Science *122:*278.

Alexander, M. L., 1952. The effect of two pericentric inversions upon crossing over in *Drosophila melanogaster.* Univ. Texas Publ. *5204:*219–226.

Alfert, M., 1950. A cytochemical study of oögenesis and cleavage in the mouse. Jour. Cell. Comp. Physiol. *36:*381–409.

————, 1954. Composition and structure of giant chromosomes. Intern. Rev. Cytology *3:*131–176.

Allen, C. E., 1940. The genotypic basis of sex expression in angiosperms. Bot. Rev. *6:*227–300.

Allfrey, V. G., A. E. Mirsky, and S. Osawa, 1955. Protein synthesis in isolated cell nuclei. Nature *176:*1042–1049.

Altenberg, E., 1928. The limit of radiation frequency effective in producing mutations. Amer. Nat. *62:*540–545.

Anderson, E., and L. B. Abbe, 1933. A comparative anatomical study of a mutant Aquilegia. Amer. Nat. *62:*380–384.

————, and K. Sax, 1936. A cytological monograph of the American species of Tradescantia. Bot. Gaz. *97:*433–476.

————, and R. E. Woodson, 1935. The species of Tradescantia indigenous to the United States. Contrib. Arnold Arboretum, No. 9.

Anderson, E. G., 1925. Crossing over in a case of attached-X chromosomes in *Drosophila melanogaster.* Genetics *10:*403–417.

Anonymous, 1951. Atomic microscope. Scient. Amer. *185:*56.

Atchison, E., 1947. Studies in the Leguminosae. I. Chromosome numbers in Erythrina L. Amer. Jour. Bot. *34:*407–414.

Atwood, K. C., and F. Mukai, 1954. Survival and mutations in Neurospora exposed at nuclear detonations. Amer. Nat. *88:*295–314.

Auerbach, C., 1950. Differences between effects of chemical and physical mutagens. Publ. staz. zool. Napoli *22 (Suppl.):*1–23.

————, 1951. Problems in chemical mutagenesis. Cold Spring Harbor Symp. Quant. Biol. *16:*199–214.

————, and J. M. Robeson, 1947. Tests of chemical substances for mutagenic action. Proc. Roy. Soc. Edinburgh, B. *62:*284–291.

Babcock, E. B., 1947. The Genus Crepis, I and II, Univ. Calif. Publ. Bot. *21, 22:*1,030 pp.

————, and G. L. Stebbins, Jr., 1938. The American species of Crepis: their relationships and distribution as affected by polyploidy and apomixis. Carnegie Inst. Wash. Publ. *504:*200 pp.

Bacq, Z. M., and P. Alexander, 1955. Fundamentals of radiobiology, Academic Press, N. Y.: 389 pp.

Bailey, I. W., 1939. The microfibrillar and microcapillary structure of the cell wall. Bull. Torrey Bot. Club 66:201–213.

Baker, W. K., 1949. The production of chromosome interchanges in Drosophila virilis. Genetics 34:167–193.

———, and E. Sgourakis, 1950. The effect of oxygen concentration on the rate of x-ray induced mutations in Drosophila. Proc. Nat. Acad. Sci. 36:176–184.

———, and E. S. Von Halle, 1954. The production of dominant lethals in Drosophila by fast neutrons from cyclotron irradiation and nuclear detonations. Science 119:46–49.

———, and E. S. Von Halle, 1955. Evidence on the mechanism of the oxygen effect by use of a ring chromosome. Jour. Cell. Comp. Physiol. 45(2): 299–307.

Baldwin, J. T., Jr., 1941. Galax: the genus and its chromosomes. Jour. Heredity 32:249–254.

Barber, H. N., 1939. The rate of movement of chromosomes on the spindle. Chromosoma 1:33–50.

Barer, R., 1955. Phase-contrast, interference contrast, and polarizing microscopy. In Analytical Cytology, McGraw, N. Y.: 3/1–3/94.

Barratt, R. W., D. Newmeyer, D. D. Perkins, and L. Garnjobst, 1954. Map construction in Neurospora crassa. Adv. Genetics 6:1–93.

Barton, D. W., 1954. Comparative effects of x-ray and ultraviolet radiation on the differentiated chromosomes of the tomato. Cytologia 19:157–175.

Barton, J., 1951. Quantitative analysis of the results of the enzymatic digestion of nuclei. Thesis, Univ. Missouri, Columbia, Mo.

Bateman, A. J., 1949. Number of S-alleles in a population. Nature 160:337.

Bauer, H., 1938. Die polyploide Natur der Riesenchromosomen. Naturwiss. 26:77.

———, 1952. Die Chromosomen in Soma der Metazoen. Deutsch. Zool. Gesellsch., Freiburg, 252–268.

———, and W. Beermann, 1952. Chromosomale Soma-Keimbahn-Differenzierung bei Chironomiden. Naturwiss. 39:22–23.

Beadle, G. W., 1930. Genetical and cytological studies of Mendelian asynapsis in Zea Mays. Cornell Univ. Exp. Sta. Mem. 129:1–23.

———, 1931. A gene in maize for supernumerary cell divisions following meiosis. Cornell Univ. Exp. Sta. Mem. 135:1–12.

———, 1932a. The relation of crossing-over to chromosome association in Zea-Euchlaena hybrids. Genetics 17:481–501.

———, 1932b. A possible influence of the spindle fibre on crossing over in Drosophila. Proc. Nat. Acad. Sci. 18:160–165.

———, 1932c. A gene for sticky chromosomes in Zea Mays. Zeitschr. ind. Abstam. Vererbungsl. 63:195–217.

———, 1933a. Polymitotic maize and the precocity hypothesis of chromosome conjugation. Cytologia 5:118–121.

———, 1933b. Further studies in asynaptic maize. Cytologia 4:269–287.

————, 1934. Crossing over in attached-X triploids in *Drosophila melanogaster*. Jour. Genetics *29:*277–309.

————, 1935. Crossing over near the spindle attachment of the X-chromosome in attached-X triploids of *Drosophila melanogaster*. Genetics *20:*179–191.

————, 1945. Genetics and metabolism in Neurospora. Physiol. Rev. *25:*643–663.

————, 1955. Gene structure and gene function. Univ. Missouri Res. Bull. *588:*10–38.

————, and S. Emerson, 1935. Further studies of crossing over in attached-X chromosomes of *Drosophila melanogaster*. Genetics *20:*192–206.

Beasley, J. O., 1938. Nuclear size in relation to meiosis. Bot. Gaz. *99:*865–871.

————, 1940. The origin of the American tetraploid Gossypium species. Amer. Nat. *74:*285–286.

Beatty, A. V., and J. W. Beatty, 1954. Immediate effects of 200 *r* and 400 *r* of X-radiation on the microspores of *Tradescantia paludosa*. Amer. Jour. Bot. *41:*242–250.

Beermann, W., 1952a. Chromosomenstruktur und Zelldifferenzierung in der Speicheldrüse von *Trichocladius vitripennis*. Zeitsch. Naturforschg. *7b:*227–342.

————, 1952b. Chromosomenkonstanz und spezifische Modifikationen der Chromosomenstruktur in der Entwicklung and Organdifferenzierung von *Chironomus tentans*. Chromosoma *5:*139–198.

Belar, K., 1926. Der Formwechsel der Protistenkerne. Erg. Fortschr. Zool. *6:*235–652.

————, 1929. Beiträge zur Kausalanalyse der Mitose: II. Untersuchungen an den Spermatocyten von *Chorthippus* (*Stenobothrus*) *lineatus*. Panz. Arch. Entwm. *118:*359–484.

Bell, C. R., 1954. The *Sanicula crassicaulis* complex (Umbelliferae). A study of variation and polyploidy. Univ. Calif. Publ. Bot. *27:*133–230.

Belling, J., 1928. The ultimate chromomeres of Lilium and Aloe with regard to the number of genes. Univ. Calif. Publ. Bot. *14:*307–318.

————, 1931a. Chromomeres of liliaceous plants. Univ. Calif. Publ. Bot. *16:*153–170.

————, 1931b. Chiasmas in flowering plants. Univ. Calif. Publ. Bot. *16(8):* 311–338.

————, 1933. Crossing over and gene rearrangement in flowering plants. Genetics *18:*388–413.

Bennett, A. H., H. Osterberg, H. Jupnik, and O. W. Richards, 1951. Phase microscopy: principles and applications, Wiley, N. Y.: 320 pp.

Benzer, S., 1955. Fine structure of a genetic region in bacteriophage. Proc. Nat. Acad. Sci. *41:*344–354.

————, 1956. Genetic fine structure and its relation to the DNA molecule. Brookhaven Symp. Biol. *8:*3–5.

Berger, C. A., 1938. Multiplication and reduction of somatic chromosome groups as a regular developmental process in the mosquito, *Culex pipiens*. Carnegie Inst. Wash. Publ. *476:*209–232.

————, 1941. Multiple chromosome complexes in animals and polysomaty in plants. Cold Spring Harbor Symp. Quant. Biol. *9:*19–21.

————, R. M. McMahon, and E. R. Witkus, 1955. The cytology of *Xanthisma texanum*, D.C. III. Differential somatic reduction. Bull. Torrey Bot. Club *82:*377–382.

Bergner, A. D., 1928. The effect of prolongation of each stage of the life-cycle on crossing over in the second and third chromosomes of *Drosophila melanogaster*. Jour. Exp. Zool. *50:*107–163.

————, J. L. Cartledge, and A. F. Blakeslee, 1934. Chromosome behavior due to a gene which prevents metaphase pairing in Datura. Cytologia. *6:*19–37.

Berry, R. O., 1941. Chromosome behaviour in the germ cells and development of the gonads in *Sciara ocellaris*. Jour. Morph. *68:*547–583.

Bisset, K. A., 1951. Genetical implications of bacterial cytology. Cold Spring Harbor Symp. Quant. Biol. *16:*376–380.

————, 1952. Bacterial cytology. Intern. Rev. Cytology *1:*93–106.

————, 1955. The cytology and life-history of bacteria, 2nd ed., Williams & Wilkins, Baltimore: 164 pp.

Blakeslee, A. F., 1930. Extra chromosomes, a source of variations in the Jimson weed. Smithsonian Report, 431–450.

————, 1940. Annual report. Carnegie Inst. Wash. Publ.: 203–211.

Blum, H. F., 1955. Time's arrow and evolution, 2nd ed., Princeton Univ. Press, Princeton, N. J.: 217 pp.

Bonner, D. M., 1951. Gene-enzyme relationships in Neurospora. Cold Spring Harbor Symp. Quant. Biol. *16:*143–157.

Böök, J. A., 1940. Triploidy in *Triton taeniatus* Laur. Hereditas *26:*107–114.

Bourne, G. H., 1951. Mitochondria and the Golgi complex. In Cytology and cell physiology, Clarendon Press, Oxford: 232–286.

Braver, G., and J. L. Blount, 1950. Somatic elimination of ring chromosomes in *Drosophila melanogaster*. Genetics *35:*90.

Breuer, M. F., and C. Pavan, 1955. Behavior of polytene chromosomes of *Rhyncosciara angelae* in different stages of development. Chromosoma *7:*275–280.

Bridges, C. B., 1915. A linkage variation in Drosophila. Jour. Exp. Zool. *19:*1–21.

————, 1916. Non-disjunction as a proof of the chromosome theory of heredity. Genetics *1:*1–52, 107–163.

————, 1925. Elimination of chromosomes due to a mutant (*minute-n*) in *Drosophila melanogaster*. Proc. Nat. Acad. Sci. *11:*701–706.

————, 1927. The relation of the age of the female to crossing over in the third chromosome of *Drosophila melanogaster*. Jour. Gen. Physiol. *8:*698–700.

————, 1932. The genetics of sex in Drosophila. In Sex and internal secretion, Baillière, London: 53–93.

————, 1935. Salivary chromosome maps. Jour. Heredity *26:*60–64.

————, 1937. Correspondence between linkage maps and salivary chromosome structure, as illustrated in the tip of chromosome 2R of *Drosophila melanogaster*. Cytologia Fujii Jub. Vol.: 745–755.

————, 1938. A revised map of the salivary gland X-chromosome of *Drosophila melanogaster*. Jour. Heredity *29:*11–13.

————, and E. G. Anderson, 1925. Crossing over in the X-chromosome of triploid females of *Drosophila melanogaster*. Genetics *10:*418–441.

————, E. N. Skoog, and J-C. Li, 1936. Genetical and cytological studies of a deficiency (*Notopleural*) in the second chromosome of *Drosophila melanogaster*. Genetics *21:*788–795.

Bridges, P. N., 1942. A new map of the salivary gland III chromosome of *Drosophila melanogaster*. Jour. Heredity *33:*403–408.

Brink, R. A., 1954. Very light variegated pericarp in maize. Genetics *39:*724–740.

————, and R. A. Nilan, 1952. The relation between light variegated and medium variegated pericarp in maize. Genetics *37:*519–544.

Brown, M. S., 1940. The relation between chiasma formation and disjunction. Univ. Texas Publ. *4032:*11–64.

————, 1943. Haploid plants in sorghum. Jour. Heredity *34:*163–166.

Brown, S. W., 1949. The structure and meiotic behavior of the differentiated chromosomes of tomato. Genetics *34:*437–461.

————, 1954. Mitosis and meiosis in *Luzula campestris* Dc. Univ. Calif. Publ. Bot. *27:*231–278.

————, and A. Hannah, 1952. An induced maternal effect on the stability of the ring-X-chromosome of *Drosophila melanogaster*. Proc. Nat. Acad. Sci. *38:*687–693.

————, and W. Welshons, 1955. Maternal aging and somatic crossing over of attached-X chromosomes. Proc. Nat. Acad. Sci. *41:*209–215.

————, and D. Zohary, 1955. The relationship of chiasmata and crossing over in *Lilium formosanum*. Genetics *40:*850–873.

Brumfield, R. T., 1943a. Effect of colchicine pretreatment on the frequency of chromosomal aberrations induced by x-irradiation. Proc. Nat. Acad. Sci. *29:*190–193.

————, 1943b. Cell-lineage studies in root meristems by means of chromosome rearrangements induced by x-rays. Amer. Jour. Bot. *30:*101–110.

Buck, J. B., 1937. Growth and development of the salivary gland chromosomes in Sciara. Proc. Nat. Acad. Sci. *23:*423–428.

Burnet, F. M., 1955. Principles of animal virology, Academic Press, N. Y.: 486 pp.

Burnham, C. R., 1934. Cytogenetic studies of an interchange between chromosomes 8 and 9 in maize. Genetics *19:*430–447.

————, 1949. Chromosome segregation in maize translocations in relation to crossing over in interstitial segments. Proc. Nat. Acad. Sci. *35:*349–356.

Butler, J. A. V., and B. E. Conway, 1950. The action of ionizing radiations and of radiomimetic substances on deoxyribonucleic acid. II. The effect of oxygen on the degradation of nucleic acids by x-rays. Jour. Chem. Soc.: 3418–3421.

Callan, H. G., 1942. Heterochromatin in Triton. Proc. Roy. Soc. London, B. *130:*324–335.

Carlson, J. G., 1938. Some effects of x-radiation on the neuroblast chromosomes of the grasshopper, *Chortophaga viridifasciata*. Genetics *23:*596–609.

————, 1941. Effect of x-radiation on grasshopper chromosomes. Cold Spring Harbor Symp. Quant. Biol. *9:*104–112.

————, 1946. Protoplasmic viscosity changes in different regions of the grasshopper neuroblast during mitosis. Biol. Bull. *90:*109–121.

————, 1950. The effect of radiation on mitosis. Jour. Cell. Comp. Physiol. *35 (1):*89–102.

————, 1954. Immediate effects on division, morphology, and viability of the cell. In Radiation biology, McGraw, N. Y., *1(2):*763–824.

————, and A. Hollaender, 1944. Immediate effects of low doses of ultraviolet radiation of wavelength 2537 A on mitosis in the grasshopper neuroblast. Jour. Cell. Comp. Physiol. *23:*157–169.

————, and A. Hollaender, 1948. Mitotic effects of ultraviolet radiation of the 2250 A region with special reference to the spindle and cleavage. Jour. Cell. Comp. Physiol. *31:*147–157.

Carothers, E. E., 1917. The segregation and recombination of homologous chromosomes as found in two genera of Acrididae (Orthoptera). Jour. Morph. *28:*445–520.

————, 1921. Genetical behavior of heteromorphic homologous chromosomes of Circotettix (Orthoptera). Jour. Morph. *35:*457–483.

Carson, H. L., 1946. The selective elimination of inversion dicentric chromatids during meiosis in the eggs of *Sciara impatiens*. Genetics *31:*95–113.

Cartledge, J. L., and A. F. Blakeslee, 1934. Mutation rate increased by aging seeds as shown by pollen abortion. Proc. Nat. Acad. Sci. *20:*103–110.

Caspari, E., 1948. Cytoplasmic inheritance. Adv. Genetics *2:*1–66.

Caspersson, T., 1947. The relations between nucleic acid and protein synthesis. Symp. Soc. Exp. Biol. *1:*127–151.

————, 1950. Cell growth and cell function. Norton, N. Y.: 185 pp.

————, and J. Schultz, 1951. Cytochemical measurements in the study of the gene. In Genetics in the 20th Century, Macmillan, N. Y.: 155–172.

Castle, W. E., 1925. A sex difference in linkage in rats and mice. Genetics *10:*580–582.

Catcheside, D. C., 1947. The P-locus position effect in Oenothera. Jour. Genetics *48:*31–42.

————, 1948. Genetic effects of radiation. Adv. Genetics *2:*271–358.

————, and D. E. Lea, 1943. Effect of ionization distribution on chromosome breakage by x-rays. Jour. Genetics *45:*186–196.

————, D. E. Lea, and J. M. Thoday, 1946. The production of chromosome structural changes in Tradescantia microspores in relation to dosage, intensity, and temperature. Jour. Genetics *47:*137–149.

Cavalli, L. L., J. Lederberg, and E. M. Lederberg, 1953. An infective factor controlling sex compatibility in *Bacterium coli*. Jour. Gen. Microbiol. *8:*89–103.

Charles, D. R., 1938. The spatial distribution of crossovers in X-chromosome tetrads of *Drosophila melanogaster*. Jour. Genetics *36:*103–126.

Chase, S. S., 1949. Monoploid frequencies in a commercial double cross hybrid maize, and in its component single cross hybrids and inbred lines. Genetics *34:*328–332.

Chittenden, R. J., 1927. Vegetative segregation. Biblio. Genetica *3:*355–439.

Christensen, H. M., and R. Bamford, 1943. Haploids in twin seedlings of pepper. Jour. Heredity *34:*98–104.

Clark, F. J., 1940. Cytogenetic studies of divergent meiotic spindle formation in *Zea Mays*. Amer. Jour. Bot. *27:*547–559.

———, and F. C. Copeland, 1940. Chromosome aberrations in the endosperm of maize. Amer. Jour. Bot. *27:*247–251.

Claude, A., 1941. Particulate components of cytoplasm. Cold Spring Harbor Symp. Quant. Biol. *9:*263–271.

———, 1946. Fractionation of mammalian liver cells by differential centrifugation. I and II. Jour. Exp. Med. *84:*51–69.

———, 1949. Proteins, lipids and nucleic acids in cell structures and functions. Adv. Protein Chem. *5:*423–440.

———, 1951. Studies on cell morphology and functions. Ann. N. Y. Acad. Sci. *50:*854–860.

———, 1956. Fine structure of cytoplasm. In Fine structure of cells, P. Noordhoff, Groningen, 307–315.

———, and J. S. Potter, 1943. Isolation of chromatin threads from the resting nucleus of leukemic cells. Jour. Exp. Med. *77:*345–354.

Clausen, J., 1954. Partial apomixis as an equilibrium system in evolution. Caryologia *1:*469–479.

———, D. D. Keck, and W. M. Hiesey, 1945. Experimental studies on the nature of species. II. Plant evolution through amphiploidy and autoploidy, with examples from the Madiinae. Carnegie Inst. Wash. Publ. *564:*1–174.

Clausen, R. E., 1941. Polyploidy in Nicotiana. Amer. Nat. *75:*291–306.

Cleland, R. E., 1936. Some aspects of the cytogenetics of Oenothera. Bot. Rev. *2:*316–348.

———, ed., 1950. Studies in Oenothera cytogenetics and phylogeny. Indiana Univ. Publ., Science Series No. 16: 1–348.

———, and F. Oehlkers, 1930. Erblichkeit und Zytologie verschiedener Oenotheren und ihrer Kreuzungen. Jahrb. Wiss. Bot. *73:*1–124.

———, L. B. Preer, and B-B. H. Geckler, 1950. The nature and relationships of taxonomic entities in the North American Euoenotheras. Indiana Univ. Publ., Science Series No. 16: 218–254.

Cleveland, L. R., 1934. The wood-feeding roach Cryptocercus, its protozoa, and the symbiosis between protozoa and roach. Mem. Amer. Acad. Sci. *17:*182–342.

———, 1938. Origin and development of the achromatic figure. Biol. Bull. *74:*41–55.

———, 1949. The whole life cycle of chromosomes and their coiling systems. Trans. Amer. Phil. Soc. *39:*1–100.

Coleman, L. C., 1943. Chromosome structure in the Acrididae with special reference to the X-chromosome. Genetics *28:*2–8.

———, and B. B. Hillary, 1941. The minor coil in meiotic chromosomes and associated phenomena as revealed by the Feulgen technique. Amer. Jour. Bot. *28:*464–469.

Commoner, B., 1948. Quantitative determination of the pigment content of single cells by means of a new microspectrophotometer. Ann. Missouri Bot. Gard. *35:*239–254.

———, 1949. On the interpretation of the absorption of ultraviolet light by cellular nucleic acids. Science *110:*31–41.

———, and D. Lipkin. The application of the Beer-Lambert law to optically anisotropic systems. Science *110:*41–43.

Conger, A. D., 1940. Chromosome deficiencies in microspores of Tradescantia. Jour. Heredity *31:*339–341.

———, 1948. The cytogenetic effect of sonic energy applied simultaneously with x-rays. Proc. Nat. Acad. Sci. *34:*470–474.

———, 1953. The effect of boron enrichment on slow neutron-irradiated tissues. Genetics *38:*128–133.

———, 1954a. Radiobiological studies with Tradescantia at nuclear test detonations. Amer. Nat. *88:*215–224.

———, 1954b. The relative biological effectiveness of radiation from a nuclear detonation on Tradescantia chromosomes. Science *119:*36–42.

———, and L. M. Fairchild, 1952. The induction of chromosomal aberrations by oxygen. Proc. Nat. Acad. Sci. *38:*289–299.

———, and N. H. Giles, Jr., 1950. The cytogenetic effects of slow neutrons. Genetics *35:*397–419.

Conklin, E. G., 1939a. Predecessors of Schleiden and Schwann. Amer. Nat. *73:*538–546.

———, 1939b. Cell and protoplasm concepts: historical account. A.A.A.S., Publ. *14:*6–19.

Cooper, K. W., 1938. Concerning the origin of the polytene chromosomes of the Diptera. Proc. Nat. Acad. Sci. *24:*452–458.

———, 1941. Bivalent structure in the fly *Melophagus ovinus* L. (Pupipara, Hippoboscidae). Proc. Nat. Acad. Sci. *27:*109–114.

———, 1944. Analysis of meiotic pairing in Olfersia and consideration of the reciprocal chiasma hypothesis of sex chromosome conjugation in male Drosophila. Genetics *29:*537–568.

———, 1945. Normal segregation without chiasmata in female *Drosophila melanogaster*. Genetics *30:*472–484.

———, 1946a. The mechanism of non-random segregation of sex chromosomes in male *Drosophila miranda*. Genetics *31:*181–194.

———, 1946b. Detachment frequency of attached-X chromosomes in autosomal structural heterozygotes of *Drosophila melanogaster*. Proc. Nat. Acad. Sci. *32:*273–275.

———, 1948a. A new theory of secondary non-disjunction in female *Drosophila melanogaster*. Proc. Nat. Acad. Sci. *34:*179–187.

———, 1948b. The evidence for long range specific attractive forces during the somatic pairing of dipteran chromosomes. Jour. Exp. Zool. *108:*327–336.

———, 1949. The cytogenetics of meiosis in Drosophila. Mitotic and meiotic autosomal chiasmata without crossing over in the male. Jour. Morph. *84:*81–122.

———, S. Zimmering, and J. Krivshenko, 1955. Interchromosomal effects and segregation. Proc. Nat. Acad. Sci. *41:*911–914.

Cramer, P. J. S., 1954. Chimeras. Biblio. Genetica *16:*193–381.

Creighton, H. B., 1934. Three cases of deficiency in chromosome 9 in *Zea Mays*. Proc. Nat. Acad. Sci. *20:*111–115.

———, and B. McClintock, 1931. A correlation of cytological and genetical crossing-over in *Zea Mays*. Proc. Nat. Acad. Sci. *17:*492–497.

Cretschmar, M., 1928. Das Verhalten der Chromosomen bei der Spermatogenese von *Orgyia thyellina* Btl. und *antiqua* L. sowie eines ihrer Bastarde. Zeitschr. Zellforsch. *7:*290–399.

Crick, F. H. C., 1954. The structure of the hereditary material. Sci. Amer. *191:*54–61.

Crouse, H. C., 1943. Translocations in Sciara: their bearing on chromosome behavior and sex determination. Univ. Missouri Agr. Exp. Sta. Res. Bull. *379:*1–75.

——, 1950. The differential response of male and female germ cells of *Sciara coprophila* (Diptera) to irradiation. Amer. Nat. *84:*195–202.

——, 1954. X-ray breakage of lily chromosomes at first meiotic metaphase. Science *119:*485–487.

D'Amato, F., 1950. The quantitative study of mitotic poisons by the *Allium cepa* test: data and problems. Protoplasma *39:*423–433.

D'Angelo, E. G., 1946. Micrurgical studies on Chironomus salivary gland chromosomes. Biol. Bull. *90:*71–87.

——, 1950. Salivary gland chromosomes. Ann. N. Y. Acad. Sci. *50 (8):*910–919.

Danielli, J. F., 1952. On transplanting nuclei. Sci. Amer. *186:*58–64.

——, 1953. Cytochemistry: a critical approach, Wiley, N. Y.: 139 pp.

Darlington, C. D., 1929a. Meiosis in polyploids. II. Aneuploid hyacinths. Jour. Genetics *21:*17–56.

——, 1929b. Chromosome behavior and structural hybridity in the Tradescantiae. Jour. Genetics *21:*207–286.

——, 1930. A cytological demonstration of genetic crossing over. Proc. Roy. Sco., London, B, *107:*50–59.

——, 1934a. Anomalous chromosome pairing in the male *Drosophila pseudoobscura*. Genetics *19:*95–118.

——, 1934b. The origin and behavior of chiasmata. VII. *Zea Mays*. Zeitschr. ind. Abstam. Vererbungsl. *67:*96–114.

——, 1935. The internal mechanics of the chromosomes. I, II and III. Proc. Roy. Soc., London, B, *118:*33–96.

——, 1936. The internal mechanics of the chromosomes. V. Cytologia *7:*248–255.

——, 1937a. Recent advances in cytology, 2nd ed., Blakiston, Phila.: 671 pp.

——, 1937b. Chromosome behavior and structural hybridity in the Tradescantiae. II. Jour. Genetics *35:*259–280.

——, 1939. Misdivision and the genetics of the centromere. Jour. Genetics *37:*341–364.

——, 1940a. The origin of iso-chromosomes. Jour. Genetics *39:*351–361.

——, 1940b. The genetical and mechanical properties of the sex chromosomes. Jour. Genetics *39:*101–137.

——, 1940. The prime variables of meiosis. Biol. Rev. *15:*307–322.

——, ed., 1953. Symposium on chromosome breakage, Heredity 6 *(Suppl.):* 1–315.

——, and S. O. S. Dark, 1932. The origin and behavior of chiasmata. II. *Stenobothrus parallelus*. Cytologia *3:*169–185.

————, and T. Dobzhansky, 1942. Temperature and "sex ratio" in *Drosophila pseudoobscura*. Proc. Nat. Acad. Sci. *28*:45–47.

————, and E. K. Janaki-Ammal, 1945. Chromosome atlas of cultivated plants, G. Allen, London: 397 pp.

————, and L. La Cour, 1938. Differential reactivity of the chromosomes. Ann. Bot. *2*:615–625.

————, and L. La Cour, 1940. Nucleic acid starvation of chromosomes in Trillium. Jour. Genetics *40*:185–213.

————, and L. La Cour, 1941. The genetics of embryo-sac development. Ann Bot. *20*:547–562.

————, and L. La Cour, 1942. The handling of chromosomes, G. Allen, London: 165 pp.

————, and L. La Cour, 1945. X-ray breakage and the nucleic acid cycle. Jour. Genetics *46*:180–267.

————, and J. McLeish, 1951. Action of maleic hydrazide on the cell. Nature *167*:407–408.

————, and P. T. Thomas, 1941. Morbid mitosis and the activity of inert chromosomes in Sorghum. Proc. Roy. Soc., London, B, *130*:127–150.

————, and M. B. Upcott, 1941. Spontaneous chromosome change. Jour. Genetics *41*:297–338.

————, and A. P. Wylie, 1953. A dicentric cycle in Narcissus. Heredity *6 (Suppl.)*:197–214.

Dekker, C. A., and H. K. Schachman, 1954. On the macromoleclular structure of deoxyribonucleic acid: an interrupted two-strand model. Proc. Nat. Sci. *40*:894

DeLamater, E. D., 1951. A new cytological basis for bacterial genetics. Cold Spring Harbor Symp. Quant. Biol. *16*:381–412.

————, 1953. The mitotic mechanism in bacteria. Cold Spring Harbor Symp. Quant. Biol. *18*:99–100.

Delbrück, M., 1941. A theory of autocatalytic synthesis of polypeptides and its application to the problem of chromosome reproduction. Cold Spring Harbor Symp. Quant. Biol. *9*:122–126.

————, and W. T. Bailey, Jr., 1946. Induced mutations in bacterial viruses. Cold Spring Harbor Symp. Quant. Biol. *11*:33–37.

Demerec, M., 1937. The relationship between various chromosomal changes in *Drosophila melanogaster*. Cytologia Fujii Job. Vol.: 1125–1132.

————, 1941. Unstable genes in Drosophila. Cold Spring Harbor Symp. Quant. Biol. *9*:145–150.

————, 1946. Induced mutations and possible mechanisms of the transmission of heredity in *Escherischia coli*. Proc. Nat. Acad. Sci. *32*:36–46.

————, 1951. Studies of the streptomycin-resistance system of mutations in *E. coli*. Genetics *36*:585–597.

————, 1953. Reaction of genes of *Escherischia coli* to certain mutagens. Symp. Soc. Exp. Biol. *7*:43–54.

————, 1955. What is a gene?—Twenty years later. Amer. Nat. *89*:5–20.

————, I. Blomstrand, and Z. E. Demerec, 1955. Evidence of complex loci in Salmonella. Proc. Nat. Acad. Sci. *41*:359–364.

————, and J. Hanson, 1951. Mutagenic action of manganous chloride. Cold Spring Harbor Symp. Quant. Biol. *16:*215–228.

————, and M. E. Hoover, 1936. Three related X-chromosome deficiencies in Drosophila. Jour. Heredity *27:*207–212.

————, and M. G. Hoover, 1939. Hairy-wing—a duplication in *Drosophila melanogaster*. Genetics *24:*271–277.

Di Stefano, H. S., 1948. A cytochemical study of the Feulgen nuclear reaction. Chromosoma *3:*282–301.

Dobzhansky, T., 1931. The decrease in crossing-over observed in translocations and its probable explanation. Amer. Nat. *65:*214–232.

————, 1933. Studies on chromosome conjugation. II. The relation between crossing over and disjunction of chromosomes. Zeitschr. ind. Abstam. Vererbungls. *64:*269–309.

————, 1934. Studies on chromosome conjugation. III. Behavior of duplicating fragments. Zeitschr. ind. Abstam. Vererbungsl. *68:*134–162.

————, 1935. The Y-chromosomes of *Drosophila pseudoobscura*. Genetics *20:*366–367.

————, 1944. Distribution of heterochromatin in the chromosomes of *Drosophila pallidipennis*. Amer. Nat. *78:*193–213.

————, 1948a. Genetics of natural populations. XVI. Altitudinal and seasonal changes produced by natural selection in certain populations of *Drosophila pseudoobscura* and *Drosophila persimilis*. Genetics *33:*158–176.

————, 1948b. Genetics of natural populations. XVIII. Experiments on chromosomes of *Drosophila pseudoobscura* from different geographic regions. Genetics *33:*588–602.

————, 1951. Genetics and the origin of species, Columbia Univ. Press, N. Y.: 364 pp.

————, and C. Epling, 1944. Contributions to the genetics, taxonomy, and ecology of *Drosophila pseudoobscura* and its relatives. Carnegie Inst. Wash. Publ. *554:*1–183.

————, and J. Schultz, 1934. The distribution of sex factors in the X-chromosome of *Drosophila melanogaster*. Jour. Genetics *28:*349–386.

————, and B. Spassky, 1954. Environmental modification of heterosis in *Drosophila pseudoobscura*. Proc. Nat. Acad. Sci. *40:*407–415.

————, and C. C. Tan, 1936. Studies on hybrid sterility. III. A comparison of the gene arrangement in two species, *Drosophila pseudoobscura* and *Drosophila miranda*. Zeitschr. ind. Abstam. Vererbungsl. *72:*88–114.

Doermann, A. H., 1953. The vegetative state in the life cycle of bacteriophage: evidence for its occurrence and its genetic characterization. Cold Spring Harbor Symp. Quant. Biol. *18:*3–11.

————, M. Chase, and F. W. Stahl, 1955. Genetic recombination and replication in bacteriophage. Jour. Cell. Comp. Physiol. *45 (2):*51–74.

————, and M. B. Hill, 1953. Genetic structure of bacteriophage T4 as described by recombination studies of factors influencing plaque morphology. Genetics *38:*79–90.

Dounce, A. L., 1954. The significance of enzyme studies on isolated cell nuclei. Intern. Rev. Cytology *3:*199–224.

Dubinin, N. P., and B. N. Sidorov, 1935. The position effect of the *hairy* gene. Biol. Zh. *4:*555–568.

Dunn, L. C., 1920. Linkage in mice and rats. Genetics *5:*325–343.

——, and E. Caspari, 1945. A case of neighboring loci with similar effects. Genetics *30:*543–568.

Duryee, W. R., 1941. The chromosomes of the amphibian nucleus. Univ. Penn. Bicent. Conf. Cytology, Genetics Evol.: 129–141.

——, 1950. Chromosome physiology in relation to nuclear structure. Ann. N. Y. Acad. Sci. *50:*920–953.

Eames, A. J., and L. H. MacDaniels, 1947. An introduction to plant anatomy, McGraw, N. Y.: 427 pp.

Ebert, M., 1955. Hydrogen peroxide production under varying conditions of irradiation. In Radiobiology symposium (Liege), Academic Press, N. Y.: 30–38.

Einset, J., 1943. Chromosome length in relation to transmission frequency of maize trisomes. Genetics *28:*349–364.

——, 1947. Aneuploidy in relation to partial sterility in autotetraploid lettuce (*Lactuca sativa* L.). Amer. Jour. Bot. *31:*336–342.

Elson, D., and E. Chargaff, 1952. Observation on pentose nucleic acid composition in sea urchin embryos and in mammalian cell fractions. In Phosphorus Metabolism (2), Johns Hopkins Univ. Press, Baltimore: 329–334.

Emerson, R. A., 1924. A genetic view of sex expression in the flowering plants. Science *59:*176–182.

——, G. W. Beadle, and A. C. Fraser, 1935. A summary of linkage studies in maize. Cornell Univ. Exp. Sta. Mem. *180:*1–83.

Emerson, S. H., 1936. The trisomic derivatives of *Oenothera Lamarckiana*. Genetics *21:*200–224.

Emmerling, M. H., 1955. A comparison of x-ray and ultraviolet effects on chromosomes of *Zea mays*. Genetics *40:*697–714.

Emmons, C. W., and A. Hollaender, 1939. The action of ultraviolet radiation on dermatophytes. II. Mutations induced in cultures of dermatophytes by exposure of spores to monochromatic ultraviolet radiation. Amer. Jour. Bot. *26:*467–475.

Ephrussi, B., and H. Hottinguer, 1951. Cytoplasmic constituents of heredity. Cold Spring Harbor Symp. Quant. Biol. *16:*75–84.

——, and E. Sutton, 1944. A reconsideration of the mechanism of position effect. Proc. Nat. Acad. Sci. *30:*183–197.

Ephrussi-Taylor, H., 1951. Genetic aspects of transformations of pneumococci. Cold Spring Harbor Symp. Quant. Biol. *16:*445–456.

——, 1955. Current status of bacterial transformation. Adv. Virus Res. *3:*275–307.

Epling, C., 1947. Actual and potential gene flow in natural populations. Amer. Nat. *81:*104–113.

Esau, K., 1953. Plant anatomy, Wiley, N. Y.: 735 pp.

Fabergé, A. C., 1942. Homologous chromosome pairing: the physical problem. Jour. Genetics *43:*121–144.

548 REFERENCES

————, 1951. Ultraviolet induced chromosome aberrations in maize. Genetics 36:549–550.

————, 1956. The analysis of induced chromosome aberrations by maize endosperm phenotypes. Zeitsch. ind. Abstam. Verebungsl. 87:392–420.

Fagerlind, F., 1940. Die Terminologie der Apomixis-Prozesse. Hereditas 26:1–22.

Fahmy, O. G., and M. J. Bird, 1953. Chromosome breaks among recessive lethals induced by chemical mutagens in *Drosophila melanogaster*. Heredity 6 *(Suppl.)*:149–159.

Fankhauser, G., 1937. The sex of a haploid, metamorphosed salamander (*Triton taeniatus* Laur.). Genetics 22:192–193.

————, 1938. Triploidy in the newt, *Triturus viridescens*. Proc. Amer. Phil. Soc. 79:715–739.

————, 1939. Polyploidy in the salamander, *Eurycea bislineata*. Jour. Heredity 30:379–388.

————, 1945. The effect of changes in chromosome number on amphibian development. Quart. Rev. Biol. 20:20–78.

————, and R. B. Griffiths, 1939. Induction of triploidy and haploidy in the newt, *Triturus viridescens*, by cold treatment of unsegmented eggs. Proc. Nat. Acad. Sci. 25:233–238.

————, and R. R. Humphrey, 1950. Chromosome number and development of progeny of triploid axolotl females mated with diploid males. Jour. Exp. Zool. 115:207–250.

Fernandes, A., 1946. Sur le comportement des chromosomes surnuméraires hétérochromatiques pendant la méiose. Bol. Soc. Broteriana 20:93–155.

Fischer, A., 1946. Biology of tissue cells. Univ. Press, Cambridge: 345 pp.

Ford, C. E., 1949. Chromosome breakage in nitrogen mustard treated *Vicia faba* root tip cells. Proc. VIII Intern. Congr. Genetics (Hereditas, suppl.):570:571.

Fraenkel-Conrat, H., and R. C. Williams, 1955. Reconstruction of active tobacco mosaic virus from its inactive protein and nucleic acid components. Proc. Nat. Acad. Sci. 41:690–698.

Frankel, O. H., C. D. Darlington, and L. La Cour, 1940. The causal sequence of meiosis. I, II, and III. Jour. Genetics 41:9–64.

Frey-Wyssling, A., 1948. Submicroscopic morphology of protoplasm and its derivatives, Elsevier, N. Y.: 255 pp.

————, 1955. Plant cytology and the electron microscope. Endeavour 14:34–39.

Gabelman, W. H., 1949. Reproduction and distribution of the cytoplasmic factor for male sterility in maize. Proc. Nat. Acad. Sci. 35:634–640.

Gairdner, A. E., and C. D. Darlington, 1931. Ring-formation in diploid and polyploid *Campanula persicifolia*. Genetica 13:113–150.

Gall, J. G., 1952. The lampbrush chromosomes of *Triturus viridescens*. Exp. Cell Res. (Suppl. 2): 950102.

————, 1954. Lampbrush chromosomes from oöcyte nuclei of the newt. Jour. Morph. 94:283–352.

————, 1956. On the submicroscopic structure of chromosomes. Brookhaven Symp. Biol. 8:17–32.

Gamow, G., 1954. Possible mathematical relation between deoxyribonucleic acid and proteins. Kgl. Danske Videnskab. Selkab. Biol. Medd. *22:*1–13.

———, 1955. Topological properties of coiled helical systems. Proc. Nat. Acad. Sci. *41:*7–9.

———, and M. Yčas, 1955. Statistical correlation of protein and ribonucleic acid composition. Proc. Nat. Acad. Sci. *41:*1011–1019.

Gates, R. R., 1942. Nucleoli and related nuclear structures. Bot. Rev. *8:*337–409.

Gaulden, M. E., M. Nix, and J. Moshman, 1953. Effects of oxygen concentration on x-ray-induced mitotic inhibition in living Chortophaga neuroblasts. Jour. Cell. Comp. Physiol. *41:*451–470.

Geitler, L., 1937. Die Analyse der Kernbaus und der Kernteilung der Wasserläufer *Gerris lateralis* und *Gerris lacustris* (Hemiptera, Heteroptera) und die Somadifferenzierung. Zeitsch. Zellforsch. *26:*641–672.

———, 1939a. Die Entstehung der polyploiden Somakerne der Heteropteren durch Chromosomenteilung ohne Kernteilung. Chromosoma *1:*1–22.

———, 1939b. Das Heterochromatin der Geschlechtschromosomen bei Hemiptera. Chromosoma *1:*1970230.

———, 1941. Das Wachstum des Zellkerns in tierischen und pflanzlichen Geweben. Ergebn. Biol. *18:*1–54.

Gershenson, S., 1928. A new sex ratio abnormality in *Drosophila obscura.* Genetics *13:*488–507.

———, 1933. Studies on the genetically inert region of the X-chromosome of Drosophila. I. Behavior of an X-chromosome deficient for part of its inert region. Jour. Genetics *28:*297–313.

Giese, A. C., 1947. Radiations and cell division. Quart. Rev. Biol. *22:*253–282.

Giles, N. H., Jr., 1940a. Spontaneous chromosome aberrations in Tradescantia. Genetics *25:*69–87.

———, 1940b. The effect of fast neutrons on the chromosomes of Tradescantia. Proc. Nat. Acad. Sci. *26:*567–575.

———, 1941. Spontaneous chromosome aberrations in triploid Tradescantia hybrids. Genetics *26:*632–649.

———, 1942. Autopolyploidy and geographical distribution in *Cuthbertia graminea* Small. Amer. Jour. Bot. *29:*637–645.

———, 1943. Comparative studies of the cytogenetical effects of neutrons and x-rays. Genetics *28:*398–418.

———, 1951. Studies on the mechanism of reversion in biochemical mutants of *Neurospora crassa.* Cold Spring Harbor Symp. Quant. Biol. *16:*283–313.

———, 1954. Radiation-induced chromosome aberrations in Tradescantia. In Radiation biology, McGraw, N. Y.: *1 (2):*713–762.

———, 1955. The oxygen effect on radiation-induced chromosome aberrations: breakage-versus-recombination hypotheses. Jour. Cell. Comp. Physiol. *45 (2):*271–284.

———, A. V. Beatty, and H. P. Riley, 1952. The effect of oxygen on the production by fast neutrons of chromosomal aberrations in Tradescantia microspores. Genetics *37:*641–649.

———, and H. P. Riley, 1949. The effect of oxygen on the frequency of x-ray-induced chromosomal rearrangements in Tradescantia microspores. Proc. Nat. Acad. Sci. *35:*640–646.

————, and H. P. Riley, 1950. Studies on the mechanism of the oxygen effect on the radiosensitivity of Tradescantia microspores. Proc. Nat. Acad. Sci. *36*:337–344.

————, F. J. de Serres, and C. W. H. Partridge, 1955. Comparative studies of x-ray-induced forward and reverse mutations. Ann. N. Y. Acad. Sci. *59*:536–552.

————, and C. Tobias, 1954. Effect of linear energy transfer on radiation-induced chromosome aberrations in Tradescantia microspores. Science. *120*:993–994.

Glass, H. B., 1933. A study of dominant mosaic eye-color mutants in *Drosophila melanogaster*. II. Tests involving crossing-over and non-disjunction. Jour. Genetics *28*:69–112.

————, 1935. A study of factors influencing chromosomal segregation in translocations of *Drosophila melanogaster*. Univ. Missouri Agr. Exp. Sta. Res. Bull. *231*:1–28.

Goldschmidt, E., 1942. The pattern of salivary gland chromosomes in a hybrid in the genus Chironomus. Jour. Heredity *33*:265–272.

Goldschmidt, R. B., 1916. Theodore Boveri. Science *43*:263–270.

————, 1934. Lymantria. Biblio. Genetica *11*:1–186.

————, 1946. Position effect and the theory of the corpuscular gene. Experientia *2*:1–40.

————, 1949. Heterochromatic heredity. Proc. VIII Intern. Congr. Genetics (Hereditas suppl.): 244–255.

————, 1950. Marginalia to McClintock's work on mutable loci in maize. Amer. Nat. *84*:437–455.

————, 1951. Chromosomes and genes. Cold Spring Harbor Symp. Quant. Biol. *16*:1–12.

————, and K. Katsuki, 1927. Erblicher Gynandromorphismus und somatische Mosaicbildung bei *Bombyx mori* L. Biol. Zentralbl. *47*:45–55.

————, and K. Katsuki, 1928. Zweite Mitterlung über erblicher Gynandromorphismus bei *Bombyx mori* L. Biol. Zentralbl. *48*:39–43.

Gowen, J. W., 1928. On the mechanism of chromosome behavior in male and female Drosophila. Proc. Nat. Acad. Sci. *19*:122–126.

————, 1933. Meiosis as a genetic character in *Drosophila melanogaster*. Jour. Exp. Morph. *65*:83–106.

Graubard, M. A., 1932. Inversion in *Drosophila melanogaster*. Genetics *17*:81–105.

————, 1934. Temperature effect on interference and crossing over. Genetics *19*:83–94.

Gray, J., 1931. A text-book of experimental cytology, Univ. Press, Cambridge: 516 pp.

Gray, L. H., 1953a. Characteristics of chromosome breakage by different agents. Heredity *6 (Suppl.)*:311–315.

————, 1953b. The initiation and development of cellular damage by ionizing radiations. Brit. Jour. Radiol. *26*:609–618.

Green, M. M., 1953. The *Beadex* locus in *Drosophila melanogaster:* genetic analysis of the mutant Bx^{r49k}. Zeitschr. ind. Abstamm. Vererbungsl. *85*:435–449.

————, 1954. Pseudoallelism at the *vermilion* locus in *Drosophila melanogaster*. Proc. Nat. Acad. Sci. *40*:92–99.

————, 1955a. Pseudoallelism and the gene concept. Amer. Nat. *89:*65–74.

————, 1955b. Phenotypic variation and pseudoallelism at the *forked* locus in *Drosophila melanogaster*. Proc. Nat. Acad. Sci. *41:*375–379.

————, and K. C. Green, 1949. Crossing over between alleles at the *lozenge* locus in *Drosophila melanogaster*. Proc. Nat. Acad. Sci. *35:*586–591.

Gresson, R. A. R., 1948. Essentials of general cytology, University Press, Edinburgh: 184 pp.

Grell, S. M., 1946. Cytological studies in Culex. I. Somatic reduction divisions. II. Diploid and meiotic divisions. Genetics *31:*60–94.

Griffin, A. B., and W. S. Stone, 1940. The second arm of chromosome IV in *Drosophila melanogaster*. Univ. Texas Publ. *4032:*201–207.

Guilliermond, A., 1941. The cytoplasm of the plant cell. Chronica Botanica, Waltham: 247 pp.

Gustafson, A., 1944. The constitution of the *Rosa canina* complex. Hereditas *30:*405–428.

————, 1946. Apomixis in the higher plants. I. The mechanism of apomixis. Lunds Univ. Arsskr. N. F. Avd. 2, *42(3):*1–66.

————, 1947a. Apomixis in the higher plants. II. The causal aspects of apomixis. Lunds Univ. Arsskr. N. F. Avd. 2, *43(2):*71–178.

————, 1947b. Apomixis in the higher plants. III. Biotype and species formation. Lunds Univ. Arsskr. N. F. Avd. 2, *44(2):*183–370.

————, 1948. Polyploidy, life-form, and vegetative reproduction. Hereditas *34:*1–22.

Haas, F. L., E. Dudgeon, F. E. Clayton, and W. S. Stone, 1954. Measurement and control of some direct and indirect effects of x-radiation. Genetics *39:*453–471.

Hackett, D. P., 1955. Recent studies on plant mitochondria. Intern. Rev. Cytology *4:*143–196.

Haga, T., 1944. Meiosis in Paris. I. Mechanism of chiasma formation. Jour. Fac. Sci., Hokkaido Imp. Univ., Series V, Botany *5(3):*121–198.

————, 1953. Meiosis in Paris. II. Spontaneous breakage and fusion of chromosomes. Cytologia *18:*50–66.

Hakanson, A., 1945. Überzählige Chromosomen in einer Rasse von *Godetia mutans* Hiorth. Bot. Not. *1:*1–19.

Haldane, J. B. S., 1922. Sex ratio and unisexual sterility in hybrid animals. Jour. Genetics *12:*101–109.

————, 1930. Theoretical genetics of autopolyploids. Jour. Genetics *32:*359–372.

————, 1954. The biochemistry of genetics, G. Allen, London: 144 pp.

Hämmerling, J., 1953. Nucleo-cytoplasmic relationships in the development of Acetabularia. Intern. Rev. Cytology *2:*475–498.

Hannah, A., 1951. Localization and function of heterochromatin in *Drosophila melanogaster*. Adv. Genetics *4:*87–127.

Harvey, E. B., 1917. A review of the chromosome numbers in the Metazoa. I. Jour. Morph. *28:*1–63.

————, 1920. A review of the chromosome numbers of the Metazoa. II. Jour. Morph. *34:*1–67.

———, 1936. Parthenogenetic merogony or cleavage without nuclei in *Arbacia punctulata*. Biol. Bull. *71:*101–121.

Hauschka, T. S., and A. Levan, 1953. Inverse relationship between chromosome ploidy and host-specificity of sixteen transplantable tumors. Exp. Cell Res. *4:*457–467.

Hayes, W., 1953. The mechanism of genetic recombination in *Escherichia coli*. Cold Spring Harbor Symp. Quant. Biol. *18:*75–94.

Heilborn, O., 1939. Chromosome studies in Cyperaceae. III–IV. Hereditas *39:*224–240.

Heilbrunn, L. V., and W. L. Wilson, 1948. Protoplasmic viscosity changes during mitosis in the egg of Chaetopterus. Biol. Bull. *95:*57–68.

Heitz, E., 1928. Das Heterochromatin der Moose. I. Jahrb. wiss. Bot. *69:*762–818.

———, 1929. Heterochromatin, Chromocentren, Chromomeren. Der Deuts. Bot. Ges. *47:*274–284.

———, 1931. Nukleolen und Chromosomen in der Gattung Vicia. Planta *15:*495–505.

———, and H. Bauer, 1933. Beweise für die Chromosomen struktur der Kernschliefen in den Knäuelkernen von *Bibio hortulanus* L. (Cytologische Untersuchungen an Dipteran, I.). Zeitschr. Zellforsch. *17:*67–82.

Helwig, E. R., 1941. Multiple chromosomes in *Philocleon anomalus* (Orthoptera: Acrididae). Jour. Morph. *69:*317–327.

———, 1942. Unusual integrations of the chromatin in Machaerocera and other genera of the Acrididae (Orthoptera). Jour. Morph. *71:*1–33.

Hershey, A. D., 1946. Spontaneous mutations in bacterial viruses. Cold Spring Harbor Symp. Quant. Biol. *11:*67–77.

———, and M. Chase, 1951. Genetic recombination and heterozygosis in bacteriophage. Cold Spring Harbor Symp. Quant. Biol. *16:*471–479.

———, and M. Chase, 1952. Independent functions of viral protein and nucleic acid in growth of bacteriophage. Jour. Gen. Physiol. *36:*39–56.

———, J. Dixon, and M. Chase, 1953. Nucleic acid economy in bacteria infected with bacteriophage T2. I. Purine and pyrimidine composition. Jour. Gen. Physiol. *36:*777–789.

———, and R. Rotman, 1949. Genetic recombination between host-range and plaque-type mutants of bacteriophage in single bacterial cells. Genetics *34:*44–71.

Herskowitz, I. H., 1946. The relationship of x-ray induced recessive lethals to chromosomal breakage. Amer. Nat. *80:*588–592.

———, 1951. The genetic basis of x-ray induced recessive lethal mutations. Genetics *36:*356–363.

Hertwig, G., 1935. Die Vielwertigkeit der Speicheldrüsenkerne und Chromosomen bei *Drosophila melanogaster*. Zeitschr. ind. Abstamm. Verebungsl. *70:*496–501.

Hinton, T., 1942. A comparative study of certain heterochromatin regions in the mitotic and salivary gland chromosomes of *Drosophila melanogaster*. Genetics *27:*119–127.

———, 1945. A study of chromosome ends in salivary gland nuclei in Drosophila. Biol. Bull. *88:*144–165.

————, 1946. The structure of the bands of salivary-gland chromosomes. Jour. Heredity *37:*99–102.

————, and K. C. Atwood, 1941. Terminal adhesions of salivary gland chromosomes in Drosophila. Proc. Nat. Acad. Sci. *27:*491–496.

Hirschler, J., 1942. Osmiumschwärzung perichromosomaler Membranen in den Spermatocyten der Rhynchoten-Art *Palomena viridissima* Poder. Naturwiss. *30:*105–106.

Hollaender, A., ed., 1954. Radiation biology, McGraw, N. Y., *1(1,2):*1265 pp.

————, ed., 1955. Radiation biology, McGraw, N. Y., *2:*593 pp.

————, and C. W. Emmons, 1941. Wave-length dependence of mutation production in the ultraviolet with special emphasis on fungi. Cold Spring Harbor Symp. Quant. Biol. *9:*179–185.

Hollander, W. F., 1938. A sex difference in linkage intensity of three autosomal factors in the domestic pigeon. Genetics *23:*24–27.

Horton, I. H., 1939. A comparison of the salivary gland chromosomes of *Drosophila melanogaster* and *D. simulans.* Genetics *24:*234–243.

Horowitz, N. H., and L. Urs, 1951. Some recent studies bearing on the one gene - one enzyme hypothesis. Cold Spring Harbor Symp. Quant. Biol. *16:*65–74.

Hotchkiss, R. D., 1951. Transfer of penicillin resistance in pneumococci by the desoxyribonucleate derived from resistant cultures. Cold Spring Harbor Symp. Quant. Biol. *16:*457–460.

————, 1955. Bacterial transformation. Jour. Cell. Comp. Physiol. *45 (2):*1–22.

Houlahan, M. B., G. W. Beadle, and H. G. Calhoun, 1949. Linkage studies with biochemical mutants of *Neurospora crassa.* Genetics *34:*493–507.

Howard, A., and S. R. Pelc, 1953. Synthesis of desoxyribonucleic acid in normal and irradiated cells and its relation to chromosome breakage. Heredity *6 (Suppl.):*261–274.

Hsu, T. C., 1954a. Mammalian chromosomes in vitro. IV. Some human neoplasms. Jour. Nat. Cancer Inst. *14:*905–933.

————, 1954b. Cytological studies on HeLa, a strain of human cervical carcinoma. I. Observations on mitosis and chromosomes. Texas Reports Biol. Med. *12:*833–846.

Huettner, A. F., 1949. Fundamentals of comparative embryology of the vertebrates, Macmillan, N. Y.: 309 pp.

Hughes, A. F., and M. M. Swann, 1948. Anaphase movements in the living cell. Jour. Exp. Biol. *25:*45–70.

Hughes-Schrader, S., 1924. Reproduction in *Acroschismus wheeleri* Pierce. Jour. Morph. Physiol. *39:*157–205.

————, 1925. Cytology of hermaphroditism in *Icerya purchasi* (Coccoidae). Zeitschr. Zellforsch. *2:*264–292.

————, 1927. Origin and differentiation of the male and female germ cells in the hermaphrodite of *Icerya purchasi* (Coccoidae). Zeitschr. Zellforsch. *6:*509–540.

————, 1931. A study of the chromosome cycle and the meiotic division-figure in *Llaveia bouvari*—a promitive coccid. Zeitschr. Zellforsch. *13:*742–769.

————, 1935. The chromosome cycle of Phenacoccus (Coccoidae). Biol. Bull. *69:*462–468.

——, 1940. The meiotic chromosomes of the male *Llaveiella taenechnia* Morrison (Coccoidae) and the question of the tertiary split. Biol. Bull. *78*:312–337.

——, 1942. The chromosomes of *Nautococcus schraderae* Vays, and the meiotic division figure of the male llaveiine coccids. Jour. Morph. *70*:261–299.

——, 1943a. Meiosis without chiasmata in diploid and tetraploid spermatocytes of the mantid *Callimantis antillarum* Saussare. Jour. Morph. *73*:111–141.

——, 1943b. Polarization, kinetochore movements, and bivalent structure in the meiosis of male mantids. Biol. Bull. *85*:265–300.

——, 1944. A primitive coccid chromosome cycle in *Puto sp.* Biol. Bull. *87*:167–176.

——, 1947a. The "pre-metaphase stretch" and kinetochore orientation in phasmids. Chromosoma *3*:1–21.

——, 1947b. Reversion of XO to XY sex chromosome mechanism in a phasmid. Chromosoma *3*:52–65.

——, 1948a. Expulsion of the sex chromosome from the spindle in spermatocytes of a mantid. Chromosoma *3*:257–270.

——, 1948b. Cytology of coccids (Coccoidae, Homoptera). Adv. Genetics *2*:127–203.

——, 1950. The chromosomes of mantids (Orthoptera, Manteidae) in relation to taxonomy. Chromosoma *4*:1–55.

——, and H. Ris, 1941. The diffuse spindle attachment of coccids verified by the mitotic behavior of induced chromosome fragments. Jour. Exp. Zool. *87*:429–456.

Huskins, C. L., 1937. The internal structure of chromosomes—A statement of opinion. Cytologia, Fujii Jub. Vol.: 1015–1022.

——, 1941. The coiling of chromonemata. Cold Spring Harbor Symp. Quant. Biol. *9*:13–17.

——, 1946. Fatuoid, speltoid, and related mutations of oats and wheat. Bot. Rev. *12*:457–514.

——, 1947. The subdivisions of the chromosomes and their multiplication in non-dividing tissues: possible interpretations in terms of gene structure and gene action. Amer. Nat. *81*:401–434.

——, 1948. Segregation and reduction in somatic tissues. Jour. Heredity *39*:310–325.

——, and S. G. Smith, 1935. Meiotic chromosome structure in *Trillium erectum* L. Ann. Bot. *49*:119–150.

——, and L. N. Steinitz, 1948. The nucleus in differentiation and development. I and II. Jour. Heredity *39*:34–43, 66–77.

——, and G. B. Wilson, 1938. Probable causes of the changes in direction of the major spiral in *Trillium erectum* L. Ann. Bot. *2*:281–292.

Inoue, S., 1952. The effect of colchicine on the microscopic and sub-microscopic structure of the spindle. Exp. Cell Res. 2 (Suppl.): 305–311.

——, 1953. Polarization optical studies. I. Chromosoma *5*:487–500.

Ivanov, M. A., 1938. Experimental production of haploids in *Nicotiana rustica* L. Genetica *20*:295–397.

Iwata, J., 1940. Studies on chromosome structure. I and II. Jap. Jour. Bot. *10:*365–382.

Jacobj, W., 1925. Über das rythmische Wachstum der Zellen durch Verdoppelung ihres Volumens. Roux Arch. *106:*124–192.

Janssens, F. A., 1909. Spermatogénèse dans les Batraciens V., La Théorie de la Chiasmatypie, nouvelle interpretation des cinèses de maturation. La Cellule *25:*387–411.

——, 1924. La chiasmatypie dans les Insectes. La Cellule *34:*135–359.

Jensen, K. A., I. Kirk, G. Kølmark, and M. Westergaard, 1951. Chemically induced mutations in Neurospora. Cold Spring Harbor Symp. Quant. Biol. *16:*245–262.

Jones, D. F., 1937. Somatic segregation and its relation to atypical growth. Genetics *22:*484–522.

——, 1939. Sex intergrades in dioecious maize. Amer. Jour. Bot. *26:*412–415.

——, 1940. Nuclear changes affecting growth. Amer. Jour. Bot. *27:*149–155.

Jorgensen, C. A., 1928. The experimental formation of heteroploid plants in the genus Solanum. Jour. Genetics *19:*133–271.

Karpechenko, G. D., 1928. Polyploid hybrids of *Raphanus sativa* L. × *Brassica oleracea* L. Zeitschr. ind. Abstamm. Vererbungsl. *39:*1–7.

Kaufmann, B. P., 1933. Interchange between X- and Y-chromosomes in attached-X females of *Drosophila melanogaster*. Proc. Nat. Acad. Sci. *19:*830–838.

——, 1934. Somatic mitoses in *Drosophila melanogaster*. Jour. Morph. *56:*125–155.

——, 1937. Morphology of the chromosomes of *Drosophila ananassae*. Cytologia, Fujii Jub. Vol.: 1043–1055.

——, 1943. A complex induced rearrangement of Drosophila chromosomes and its bearing on the problem of chromosome recombination. Proc. Nat. Acad. Sci. *29:*8–12.

——, 1948. Chromosome structure in relation to the chromosome cycle. II. Bot. Rev. *14:*57–126.

——, 1950. An evaluation of the applicability in cytochemical studies of methods involving enzymatic hydrolysis of cellular materials. Port. Acta Biol., Goldschmidt Vol.: 813–830.

——, 1952. Cytochemical studies of the action of trypsin. I. Digestion of salivary-gland chromosomes. Proc. Nat. Acad. Sci. *38:*464–468.

——, 1953. Cytochemical studies of the action of trypsin. III. The course of deformation of salivary-gland chromosomes. Exp. Cell Res. *4:*408–425.

——, 1954. Chromosome aberrations induced in animal cells by ionizing radiations. In Radiation biology, McGraw, N. Y., *1(2):*627–711.

——, H. Gay, and M. R. McDonald, 1951. Enzymatic degradation of ribonucleoproteins. Amer. Jour. Bot. *38:*268–275.

——, and A. Hollaender, 1946. Modification of the frequency of chromosomal rearrangements induced by x-rays in Drosophila. II. Use of ultraviolet radiation. Genetics *31:*368–375.

——, A. Hollaender, and H. Gay, 1946. Modification of the frequency of chromosomal rearrangements induced by x-rays in Drosophila. I. Use of near infrared radiation. Genetics *31:*349–367.

——, M. R. McDonald, and H. Gay, 1951. The distribution and interrelation of nucleic acids in fixed cells as shown by enzymatic hydrolysis. Jour. Cell. Comp. Physiol. *38:*71–100.

——, J. M. Pennoyer, and M. E. Rowan, 1953. Cytochemical studies of the action of trypsin. II. Analysis of the swelling of salivary-gland cells. Jour. Cell. Comp. Physiol. *41:*79–102.

——, and K. Wilson, 1949. Modification of the frequency of chromosomal rearrangements induced by x-rays in Drosophila. IV. Posttreatment with near infrared radiation. Genetics *34:*425–436.

Keeffe, M. M., 1948. A reinvestigation of chromosome coiling in Trillium. Amer. Jour. Bot. *35:*434–440.

Kihlman, B., 1951. The permeability of the nuclear envelope and the mode of action of purine derivatives on chromosomes. Symb. Bot. Upsal. *11(2):*1–39.

——, 1952. Induction of chromosome changes with purine derivatives. Symb. Bot. Upsal. *11(4):*1–99.

——, 1954. Effect of oxygen on the frequency of chromosome aberrations produced by 8-ethoxycaffeine. Nature *174:*561.

——, 1955. Chromosome breakage in Allium by 8-ethoxycaffeine and x-rays. Exp. Cell Res. *8:*345–368.

——, 1956. Factors affecting the production of chromosome aberrations by chemicals. Jour. Biophy. Biochem. Cytology *2:*543–555.

Kikkawa, H., 1938. Studies on the genetics and cytology of *Drosophila ananassae*. Genetica *20:*458–516.

King, E. D., 1933. Chromosome behavior in a triploid Tradescantia. Jour. Heredity *24:*253–256.

——, and H. A. Schneiderman, 1952. The effects of carbon dioxide on the frequency of x-ray-induced chromosome aberrations in Tradescantia. Proc. Nat. Acad. Sci. *38:*809–812.

——, H. A. Schneiderman, and K. Sax, 1952. The effects of carbon monoxide and oxygen on the frequency of x-ray-induced chromosome aberrations in Tradescantia. Proc. Nat. Acad. Sci. *38:*34–43.

King, R. L., and H. W. Beams, 1938. The multiple chromosomes of *Paratylotropidia brunneri* Scudder (Orthoptera: Acrididae). Jour. Morph. *63:*289–300.

King, T. J., and R. Briggs, 1955. Changes in the nuclei of differentiating gastrula cells, as demonstrated by nuclear transplantation. Proc. Nat. Acad. Sci. *41:*321–325.

Kirby-Smith, J. S., and D. L. Craig, 1955. Some aspects of ultraviolet-induced chromosome aberrations in Tradescantia pollen. Rec. Gen. Soc. Amer. *24:*579.

——, and D. S. Daniels, 1953. The relative effects of x-rays, gamma rays, and beta rays on chromosomal breakage in Tradescantia. Genetics *38:*375–388.

——, and C. P. Swanson, 1954. The effects of fast neutrons from a nuclear detonation on chromosome breakage in Tradescantia. Science *119:*42–45.

Kirkpatrick, P., 1949. The x-ray microscope. Scient. Amer. *180:*44–47.

Klein, G., 1951. Comparative studies of mouse tumors with respect to their capacity for growth as "ascites tumors" and their average nucleic acid content per cell. Exp. Cell Res. *2:*518–573.

Kodani, M., 1942. The structure of salivary gland chromosomes of *D. melanogaster*. Jour. Heredity *33:*115–133.

———, 1947. Variations in the terminal bands of the salivary X-chromosome of *Drosophila melanogaster*. Genetics *32:*18–28.

———, and C. Stern, 1946. An "invisible" chromosome. Science 104: 620–621.

Koller, P. C., 1938. The genetical and mechanical properties of the sex chromosomes. IV. The golden hamster. Jour. Genetics *36:*177–195.

———, 1953. Dicentric chromosomes in a rat tumor induced by an aromatic nitrogen mustard. Heredity 6 *(Suppl.):*181–196.

Koshy, T. K., 1934. Chromosome studies in Allium. II. The meiotic chromosomes. Jour. Roy. Micr. Soc. *54:*104–120.

———, 1937. Number and behavior of chromosomes in *Aloe literalis*. Ann. Bot. *1:*43–58.

Kostoff, D., 1929. An androgenic Nicotiana haploid. Zeitschr. Zellforsch. *9:*640–642.

———, 1930. Discoid structure of the spireme. Jour. Heredity *21:*323–324.

Kotval, J. P., and L. H. Gray, 1947. Structural changes produced in microspores of Tradescantia by alpha radiation. Jour. Genetics *48:*135–154.

Kurnick, N. B., 1950. The quantitative estimation of desoxyribosenucleic acid based on methyl green staining. Exp. Cell Res. *1:*151–158.

———, 1955. Histochemistry of nucleic acids. Intern. Rev. Cytology *4:*221–268.

———, and I. H. Herskowitz, 1952. The estimation of polyteny in Drosophila salivary gland nuclei, based on determination of desoxyribonucleic acid content. Jour. Cell. Comp. Physiol. *38:*281–300.

Kuwada, Y., 1939. Chromosome structure. A critical review. Cytologia *10:*213–256.

La Cour, L., and A. Rautishauser, 1954. X-ray breakage experiments with endosperm. I. Sub-chromatid breakage. Chromosoma *6:*696–709.

Lamb, A. B., 1907. A new explanation of the mechanics of mitosis. Jour. Exp. Zool. *5:*27–33.

Lamb, W. G. P., 1950. The isolation of threads from interphase nuclei. Exp. Cell Res. *1:*571–581.

Lamm, R., 1936. Cytological studies on inbred rye. Hereditas *22:*217–240.

Lams, H., 1910. Recherches sur l'oeuf d'*Arion empiricorum* (Fér). Acad. roy. Belg., Classe de Sciences *2:*1–170.

Lane, G. R., 1951. X-ray fractionation and chromosome breakage. Heredity *5:*1–35.

Latarjet, R., and L. H. Gray, 1954. Definition of the terms "protection" and "restoration." Acta Radiol. *41:*61–62.

Laughnan, J. R., 1949. The action of allelic forms of the gene *A* in maize. II. The relation of crossing over to mutation of A^b. Proc. Nat. Acad. Sci. *35:*167–178.

———, 1955. Structural and functional bases for the action of the *A* alleles in maize. Amer. Nat. *84:*91–104.

Lea, D. E., 1955. Actions of radiations on living cells, 2nd ed., Cambridge Univ. Press, Cambridge: 416 pp.

———, and D. C. Catcheside, 1945. The relation between recessive lethals, dominant lethals, and chromosome aberrations in Drosophila. Jour. Genetics *47:*10–24.

LeClerc, G., 1946. Occurrence of mitotic crossing-over without meiotic crossing-over. Science *103:*553–554.

Lederberg, J., 1947. Gene recombination and linked segregation in *Escherichia coli.* Genetics *32:*505–525.

———, 1948. Problems in microbial genetics. Heredity *2:*145–198.

———, 1955a. Recombination mechanism in bacteria. Jour. Cell. Comp. Physiol. *45(2):*75–107.

———, 1955b. Genetic recombination in bacteria. Science *122:*920.

———, and P. R. Edwards, 1953. Serotypic recombination in Salmonella. Jour. Immunol. *71:*232–240.

———, E. M. Lederberg, N. D. Zinder, and E. R. Lively, 1951. Recombination analysis of bacterial heredity. Cold Spring Harbor Symp. Quant. Biol. *16:*413–443.

———, and E. L. Tatum, 1946. Gene recombination in *Escherichia coli.* Nature *158:*558.

———, and E. L. Tatum, 1954. Sex in bacteria: genetic studies, 1945–1952. Sex in Microorganisms, A.A.A.S., Washington: 12–28.

Lennox, E. S., 1955. Transduction of linked genetic characters of the host by bacteriophage P1. Virology *1:*190–206.

Lesley, J. W., and M. M. Lesley, 1939. Unfruitfulness in the tomato caused by male sterility. Jour. Agric. Res. *58:*621–630.

Lesley, M. M., and H. B. Frost, 1927. Mendelian inheritance of chromosome shape in Matthiola. Genetics *12:*449–460.

Levan, A., 1940. Meiosis of *Allium porrum,* a tetraploid species with chiasma localization. Hereditas *26:*454–462.

———, 1946. Heterochromaty in chromosomes during their contraction phase. Hereditas *32:*449–468.

———, 1951. Chemically induced chromosome reactions in *Allium cepa* and *Vicia faba.* Cold Spring Harbor Symp. Quant. Biol. *16:*233–244.

———, and T. S. Hauschka, 1953. Endomitotic reduplication mechanisms in ascites tumors of the mouse. Jour. Nat. Cancer Inst. *14:*1–43.

———, and T. Lotfy, 1950. Spontaneous chromosome fragmentation in seedlings of *Vicia faba.* Hereditas *36:*470–482.

Levene, H., O. Pavlovsky, and T. Dobzhansky, 1954. Interaction of the adaptive values in polymorphic experimental populations of *Drosophila pseudoobscura.* Evol. *8:*335–349.

Levine, R. P., and E. E. Levine, 1955. Variable crossing over arising in different strains of *Drosophila pseudoobscura.* Genetics *40:*399–405.

Levinthal, C., 1953. Recombination in phage: its relationship to heterozygosis and growth. Cold Spring Harbor Symp. Quant. Biol. *18:*13–14.

———, 1954. Recombination in phage T2: its relation to heterozygosis and growth. Genetics *39:*169–184.

————, and N. Visconti, 1953. Growth and recombination in bacterial viruses. Genetics *38:*500–511.

Lewis, D., and I. Modlibowska, 1942. Genetical studies in pears. IV. Pollen tube growth and incompatibility. Jour. Genetics *43:*211–222.

Lewis, E. B., 1945. The relation of repeats to position effects in *Drosophila melanogaster.* Genetics *30:*137–166.

————, 1950. The phenomenon of position effect. Adv. Genetics *3:*73–116.

————, 1951. Pseudoallelism and gene evolution. Cold Spring Harbor Symp. Quant. Biol. *16:*159–174.

————, 1952. The pseudoallelism of *white* and *apricot* in *Drosophila melanogaster.* Proc. Nat. Acad. Sci. *39:*953–961.

————, 1954. The theory and application of a new method of detecting chromosomal rearrangements in *Drosophila melanogaster.* Amer. Nat. *88:*225–239.

————, 1955. Some aspects of position pseudoallelism. Amer. Nat. *89:*73–90.

————, and W. Gengarella, 1952. *Claret* and non-disjunction in *Drosophila melanogaster.* Rec. Gen. Soc. Amer. *21:*44–45.

Lewis, H., 1951. The origin of supernumerary chromosomes in natural populations of *Clarkia elegans.* Evol. *5:*142–157.

Lewis, H., and C. Epling, 1946. Formation of a diploid species of Delphinium by hybridization. Amer. Jour. Bot. *33:*21s–22s.

Leyon, H., 1956. The structure of chloroplasts. Svensk Kemisk Tids. 68: 70–89.

————, and D. von Wettstein, 1954. Die Chromatophoren-Feinbau bei den Phaeophycean. Zeitschr. Naturforsch. *9b:*471–475.

Lima-de-Faria, A., 1949a. The structure of the centromere of the chromosomes of rye. Hereditas *35:*77–85.

————, 1949b. Genetics, origin, and evolution of kinetochores. Hereditas *35:*422–444.

————, 1954. Chromosome gradient and chromosome field in Agapanthus. Chromosoma *6:*330–370.

Lindegren, C. C., and G. Lindegren, 1937. Non-random crossing-over in Neurospora. Jour. Heredity *28:*105–113.

————, and G. Lindegren, 1939. Non-random crossing over in the second chromosome of *Neurospora crassa.* Genetics *24:*1–7.

————, and G. Lindegren, 1942. Locally specific patterns of chromatid and chromosome interference in Neurospora. Genetics *27:*1–24.

Lindsley, D. L., 1955. Spermatogonial exchange between the X- and Y-chromosomes of *Drosophila melanogaster.* Genetics *40:*24–44.

Lindstrom, E. W., 1936. Genetics of polyploidy. Bot. Rev. *2:*193–215.

Little, T. A., 1945. Gene segregation in autotetraploids. Bot. Rev. *11:*60–85.

Lockingen, L. S., and A. G. DeBusk, 1955. A model for intracellular transfer of DNA (gene) specificity. Proc. Nat. Acad. Sci. *41:*925–934.

Loehwing, W. F., 1938. Physiological aspects of sex in angiosperms. Bot. Rev. *4:*581–625.

Longley, A. E., 1938. Chromosomes of maize from North American Indians. Jour. Agric. Res. *56:*177–196.

————, 1945. Abnormal segregation during megasporogenesis in maize. Genetics *30:*100–113.

Löve, A., and D. Löve, 1943. The significance of differences in the distribution of diploids and polyploids. Hereditas *29*:145–163.

Loveless, A., 1953. Chemical and biochemical problems arising from the study of chromosome breakage by alkylating agents and heterocyclic compounds. Heredity *6(Suppl.)*:293–298.

————, and S. Revell, 1949. New evidence on the mode of action of "mitotic poisons." Nature *164*:938–955.

McClintock, B., 1929. A cytological and genetical study of triploid maize. Genetics *14*:180–222.

————, 1932. A correlation of ring-shaped chromosomes with variegation in *Zea Mays*. Proc. Nat. Acad. Sci. *18*:677–681.

————, 1933. The association of non-homologous parts of chromosomes in the mid-prophase of *Zea Mays*. Zeitschr. Zellf. u. Mikr. Anat. *19*:191–237.

————, 1934. The relation of a particular chromosomal element to the development of the nucleoli in *Zea Mays*. Zeitschr. Zellf. u. Mikr. Anat. *21*:294–328.

————, 1938a. The fusion of broken ends of sister half-chromatids following chromatid breakage at meiotic anaphases. Missouri Agric. Exp. Sta. Res. Bull. *290*:48 pp.

————, 1938b. The production of homozygous deficient tissues with mutant characteristics by means of the aberrant mitotic behavior of ring-shaped chromosomes. Genetics *23*:315–376.

————, 1941a. The association of mutants with homozygous deficiencies in *Zea Mays*. Genetics *26*:542–571.

————, 1941b. Spontaneous alterations in chromosome size and form in *Zea Mays*. Cold Spring Harbor Symp. Quant. Biol. *9*:72–81.

————, 1941c. The stability of broken ends of chromosomes in *Zea Mays*. Genetics *26*:234–282.

————, 1942. The fusion of broken ends of chromosomes following nuclear fusion. Proc. Nat. Acad. Sci. *28*:458–463.

————, 1943. Maize genetics. Carnegie Inst. Wash. Yearbook *42*:148–152.

————, 1944. The relation of homozygous deficiencies to mutations and allelic series in maize. Genetics *29*:478–502.

————, 1945. Neurospora. I. Preliminary observations of the chromosomes of *Neurospora crassa*. Amer. Jour. Bot. *32*:671–678.

————, 1950a. The origin and behavior of mutable loci in maize. Proc. Nat. Acad. Sci. *36*:344–355.

————, 1950b. Mutable loci in maize. Carnegie Inst. Wash. Yearbook *49*:157–167.

————, 1951. Chromosome organization and genic expression. Cold Spring Harbor Symp. Quant. Biol. *16*:13–47.

————, 1953. Induction of instability at selected loci in maize. Genetics *38*:579–599.

McElroy, W. D., and C. P. Swanson, 1951. The theory of rate processes and gene mutation. Quart. Rev. Biol. *26*:349–363.

McFadden, E. S., and E. R. Sears, 1946. The origin of *Triticum spelta* and its free-threshing hexaploid relatives. Jour. Heredity *37*:81–89; 107–116.

McLeish, J., 1953. The action of maleic hydrazide in Vicia. Heredity *6* *(Suppl.):*125–148.

———, 1955. Radiation sensitivity and the mitotic cycle in *Vicia faba.* Nature *175:*890.

Mackensen, O., 1935. Locating genes on salivary chromosomes. Jour. Heredity *26:*163–174.

MacKnight, R. H., 1937. Crossing-over in the sex chromosome of racial hybrids of *Drosophila pseudoobscura.* Genetics *22:*249–256.

———, and K. W. Cooper, 1944. The synapsis of the sex chromosomes of *Drosophila miranda* in relation to their directed segregation. Proc. Nat. Acad. Sci. *30:*384–387.

Maheshwari, P., 1950. An introduction to the embryology of angiosperms, McGraw, N. Y.: 453 pp.

Makino, S., 1936. The spiral structure of chromosomes in the meiotic divisions of Podisma (Orthoptera). Jour, Fac. Sci., Hokkaido Imp. Univ., Ser. VI *(1):*29–40.

———, 1938. A morphological study of the nucleus in various kinds of somatic cells of *Drosophila virilis.* Cytologia *9:*272–282.

———, 1951. An atlas of the chromosome numbers in animals, Iowa State College Press, Ames: 290 pp.

Malheiros, N., D. de Castro, and A. Camara, 1947. Chromosomas sem centrómero localizado. O caso de *Luzula purpurea* Link. Agron. Lusitana *9:*51–71.

Maly, R., and A. Wild, 1956. Ein cytologischer Beitrag zur "Entmischungstheorie" verschiedener Plastidensorten. Zeitschr. ind. Abstam. Vererbungsl. *87:*493–496.

Manton, I., 1939. Evidence on spiral structure and chromosome pairing in *Osmunda regalis* L. Phil. Trans. Royal Soc. London, B, *230:*179–216.

———, 1945. New evidence on the telophase split in *Todea barbara.* Amer. Jour. Bot. *32:*342–348.

———, 1950. The spiral structure of chromosomes. Biol. Rev. *25:*486–508.

———, 1952. Problems of cytology and evolution in the Pteridophyta. Univ. Press, Cambridge: 316 pp.

Marengo, N. P., 1949. A study of the cytoplasmic inclusions during sporogenesis in *Onoclea sensibilis.* Amer. Jour. Bot. *36:*603–613.

Markert, C. L., 1953. Lethal and mutagenic effects of ultraviolet radiation on Glomerella conidia. Exp. Cell Res. *5:*427–435.

Marquardt, H., 1938. Die Röntgenpathologie der Mitose, I und II. Zeitschr. Bot. *32:*401–482.

———, 1948. Das verhalten röntgeninduzierter Viererringe mit grossen interstitiellen Segmenten bei *Oenothera hookeri.* Zeitschr. ind. Abstam. Vererbungsl. *82:*415–429.

———, 1952. Über die spontanen Aberrationen in der Anaphase der Meiosis von *Paeonia tenuifolia.* Chromosoma *5:*81–112.

Mather, K., 1936. The determination of position in crossing over. I. *Drosophila melanogaster.* Jour. Genetics *33:*207–235.

———, 1938. Crossing over. Biol. Rev. *13:*252–292.

———, 1939. Crossing over and heterochromatin in the X-chromosome in *Drosophila melanogaster.* Genetics *24:*413–435.

562　　　REFERENCES

——, 1943. Polygenic inheritance and natural selection. Biol. Rev. *18*:32–64.

——, 1944. The genetical activity of heterochromatin. Proc. Roy. Soc. London, B, *132*:308–332.

Matsuura, H., 1940. Chromosome studies in *Trillium kamtschaticum* Pall. XII. The mechanism of crossing over. Cytologia *10*:390–405.

——, 1950. Chromosome studies on *Trillium kamtschaticum* Pall and its allies. XIX. Chromatid breakage and reunion at chiasmata. Cytologia *16*:48–57.

Matthey, R., 1933. Nouvelle contribution a l'étude des chromosomes chez les sauriens. Rev. suisse Zool. *40*:281–318.

——, 1949. Les chromosomes des Vertébrés, Lausanne, Rouge: 363 pp.

Mazia, D., 1952. Physiology of the cell nucleus. In Modern trends in physiology and biochemistry (E. G. Barron, Ed.), Academic Press, N. Y.: 77–122.

——, 1954a. The particulate organization of the chromosome. Proc. Nat. Acad. Sci. *40*:521–527.

——, 1954b. Sh and Growth. In Glutathione, Academic Press, N. Y.: 209–223.

——, 1955. The organization of the mitotic apparatus. Symp. Soc. Exp. Biol. *9*:335–357.

——, and K. Dan, 1952. The isolation and biochemical characterization of the mitotic apparatus of dividing cells. Proc. Nat. Acad. Sci. *38*:826–838.

——, T. Hayashi, and K. Yudovitch, 1947. Fiber structure in chromosomes. Cold Spring Harbor Symp. Quant. Biol. *12*:122–130.

——, and L. Jaeger, 1939. Nuclease action, protease action, and histochemical tests on salivary chromosomes of Drosophila. Proc. Nat. Acad. Sci. *25*:456–461.

Mechelke, F., 1953. Reversible Strukturmodifikationen der Speicheldrüsenchromosomen von *Acricotopus lucidus*. Chromosoma *5*:511–543.

Melander, Y., 1950. Accessory chromosomes in animals, especially in *Polycelis tennis*. Hereditas *36*:19–37.

Melland, A. M., 1942. Types of development of polytene chromosomes. Proc. Roy. Soc. Edinburgh, B, *61*:316–372.

Mellors, R., 1955. Analytical cytology, McGraw, N. Y.

Metz, C. W., 1916. Chromosome studies on the Diptera. II. The paired association of chromosomes in the Diptera and its significance. Jour. Exp. Zool. *21*:213–262.

——, 1941. Structure of salivary gland chromosomes. Cold Spring Harbor Symp. Quant. Biol. *9*:23–39.

——, 1947. Duplication of chromosome parts as a factor in evolution. Amer. Nat. *81*:81–103.

——, and E. G. Lawrence, 1938. Preliminary observations on Sciara hybrids. Jour. Heredity *29*:179–186.

Mickey, G. H., 1946. The presence of multiple strands in chromosomes of Romalea (Orthoptera). Amer. Nat. *80*:446–452.

——, 1947. Division cycle in grasshopper chromosomes. Louisiana Acad. Sci. *10*:49–66.

——, 1954. Visible and lethal mutations in Drosophila. Amer. Nat. *88*:241–256.

Mirsky, A. E., 1947. Chemical properties of isolated chromosomes. Cold Spring Harbor Symp. Quant. Biol. *12:*143–146.

————, and A. W. Pollister, 1946. Chromosin, a desoxyribose nucleoprotein complex of the cell nucleus. Jour. Gen. Physiol. *30:*117–148.

————, and H. Ris, 1947. Isolated chromosomes. The chemical composition of isolated chromosomes. Jour. Gen. Physiol. *31:*1–18.

————, and H. Ris, 1949. Variable and constant components of chromosomes. Nature *163:*666–667.

————, and H. Ris, 1951a. The desoxyribonucleic acid content of animal cells and its evolutionary significance. Jour. Gen. Physiol. *34:*451–462.

————, and H. Ris, 1951b. The composition and structure of isolated chromosomes. Jour. Gen. Physiol. *34:*472–492.

Moffett, A. A., 1932. Chromosome studies in Anemone. I. A new type of chiasma behaviour. Cytologia *4:*26–37.

Morgan, L. V., 1922. Non-criss-cross inheritance in *Drosophila melanogaster.* Biol. Bull. *42:*267–274.

————, 1933. A closed X-chromosome in *Drosophila melanogaster.* Genetics *18:*250–283.

Morgan, T. H., C. B. Bridges, and J. Schultz, 1932. Constitution of the germinal material in relation to heredity. Carnegie Inst. Wash. Yearbook *31:*303–307.

————, C. B. Bridges, and J. Schultz, 1933. Constitution of the germinal material in relation to heredity. Carnegie Inst. Wash. Yearbook *32:*298–302.

————, C. B. Bridges, and J. Schultz, 1935. Constitution of the germinal material in relation to heredity. Carnegie Inst. Wash. Yearbook *34:*284–291.

————, and A. H. Sturtevant, 1944. Genetics of Drosophila. Carnegie Inst. Wash. Yearbook *43:*164–165.

————, A. H. Sturtevant, and H. J. Muller, and C. B. Bridges, 1915. The mechanism of mendelian heredity, Holt, N. Y.: 262 pp.

Moses, M. J., and J. H. Taylor, 1955. Desoxypentose nucleic acid synthesis during microsporogenesis in Tradescantia. Exp. Cell Res. *9:*474–488.

Mühlethaler, K., 1955. The structure of chloroplasts. Intern. Rev. Cyt. *4:*197–220.

Müller, E. W., 1952. A new microscope. Scient. Amer. *185:*58–62.

Muller, H. J., 1914. A new mode of segregation in Gregory's tetraploid Primulas. Amer. Nat. *48:*508–512.

————, 1925. Why polyploidy is rarer in animals than in plants. Amer. Nat. *59:*346–353.

————, 1928. The problem of genic modification. Verhandl. V. intern. Kongr. Vererbungsl. (Berlin, 1927). Zeitschr. ind. Abstam. Vererbungsl., Suppl. 1: 234–260.

————, 1935. A viable two-gene deficiency. Jour. Heredity *26:*469–478.

————, 1938. The remaking of chromosomes. Collect. Net *13:*181–195, 198.

————, 1940. An analysis of the process of structural changes in chromosomes of Drosophila. Jour. Genetics *40:*1–66.

————, 1949. Edmund B. Wilson (1856–1939). Genetics *34:*1–9.

————, 1950a. Radiation damage to the genetic material. Amer. Scientist *38:*33–59, 126, 399–425.

————, 1950b. Evidence of the precision of genetic adaptation. The Harvey Lectures, Series XLIII, C. C. Thomas, Publ., Springfield: 165–229.

————, 1954a. The nature of the genetic effects produced by radiation. In Radiation biology, McGraw, N. Y., *1(1):*351–473.

————, 1954b. The manner of production of mutations by radiation. In Radiation biology, McGraw, N. Y., *1(1):*475–626.

————, I. H. Herskowitz, S. Abrahamson, and I. I. Oster, 1954. A non-linear relation between x-ray dose and recovered lethal mutations in Drosophila. Genetics *39:*741–749.

————, and T. S. Painter, 1932. The differentiation of the sex chromosomes of Drosophila into genetically active and inert regions. Zeitschr. ind. Abstam. Vererbungsl. *62:*316–365.

————, and F. Settle, 1927. The non-functioning of the genes in spermatozoa. Zeitschr. ind. Abstam. Vererbungsl. *43:*285–312.

Müntzing, A., 1936. The evolutionary significance of autopolyploidy. Hereditas *21:*263–378.

————, 1945. Cytological studies of extra fragment chromosomes in rye. II. Transmission and multiplication of standard fragments and isofragments. Hereditas *31:*457–477.

————, 1946a. Different chromosome numbers in root tips and pollen mother cells in a sexual strain of *Poa alpina.* Hereditas *32:*127–129.

————, 1946b. Cytological studies of extra fragment chromosomes in rye. III. The mechanism of non-disjunction at the pollen mitosis. Hereditas *32:*97–119.

————, 1950. Accessory chromosomes in rye populations from Turkey and Afghanistan. Hereditas *36:*507–509.

Nabours, R. K., and F. M. Stebbins, 1950. Cytogenetics of the grouse locust *Apotettix eurycephalus,* Hancock. Tech. Bull., Kansas St. Col. Agric. Exp. Sta., No. 67: 116 pp.

Naithani, S. P., 1937. Chromosome studies in *Hyacinthus orientalis* L. I and II. Ann. Bot. *1:*126–146, 257–276.

Navaschin, M., 1934. Chromosome alterations caused by hybridization and their bearing upon certain general genetic problems. Cytologia *5:*169–203.

Nebel, B. R., 1936. Chromosome structure. X. An x-ray experiment. Genetics *21:*605–614.

————, 1937. Chromosome structure. XII. Further radiation experiments with Tradescantia. Amer. Jour. Bot. *24:*365–372.

————, 1939. Chromosome structure. Bot. Rev. *5:*563–626.

————, 1941. Structure of Tradescantia and Trillium chromosomes with particular emphasis on the number of chromonemata. Cold Spring Harbor Symp. Quant. Biol. *9:*7–12.

Neuhaus, M. J., 1936. Crossing-over between the X- and Y-chromosomes in the female of *Drosophila melanogaster.* Zeitschr. ind. Abstam. Vererbungsl. *71:*265–275.

————, 1937. Additional data on crossing-over between X and Y chromosomes in *Drosophila melanogaster*. Genetics *22:*333–339.

Newcombe, H. B., and J. F. McGregor, 1954. Dose-response relationships in radiation induced mutation. Saturation effects in Streptomyces. Genetics *39:*619–627.

Newton, W. C. F., and C. D. Darlington, 1930. *Fritillaria Meleagris:* chiasma-formation and distribution. Jour. Genetics *22:*1–14.

————, and C. Pellew, 1929. *Primula kewensis* and its derivatives. Jour. Genetics *20:*405–467.

Nichols, C., 1941. Spontaneous chromosome aberrations in Allium. Genetics *26:*89–100.

Nickson, J. J., ed. 1952. Symposium on radiobiology (Oberlin), Wiley, N. Y.: 465 pp.

Noggle, G. R., 1946. The physiology of polyploidy in plants. I. Review of the literature. Lloydia *9:*153–173.

Nordenskiöld, H., 1941. Cytological studies in triploid Phleum. Bot. Not. 12–32.

————, 1945. Cytogenetic studies in the genus Phleum. Acta. Agric. Succanae *1(1):*1–36.

Novitski, E., 1951. Non-random disjunction in Drosophila. Genetics *36:*267–280.

————, 1952. The genetic consequences of anaphase bridge formation in Drosophila. Genetics *37:*270–287.

————, 1954. The compound X-chromosomes in Drosophila. Genetics *39:*127–140.

————, and G. Braver, 1954. An analysis of crossing over within a hetero-zygous inversion in *Drosophila melanogaster*. Genetics *39:*197–209.

Novikoff, A. B., 1955. Histochemical and cytochemical staining methods. In Analytical cytology (R. C. Mellors, ed.), McGraw, N. Y.: 2/1–2/63.

Nygren, A., 1946. The genesis of some Scandinavian species of Calama-grostis. Hereditas *32:*131–262.

————, 1954. Apomixis in the angiosperms. II. Bot. Rev. *20:*577–649.

Oehlkers, F., 1943. Die Auslösung von Chromosomenmutationen in der Meiosis durch Einwirkung von Chemikalien. Zeitschr. ind. Abstam. Verer-bungsl. *81:*313–341.

————, 1953. Chromosome breaks influenced by chemicals. Heredity 6 *(Suppl.):*95–106.

Oksala, T., 1943. Zytologische Studien an Odonaten. I. Chromosomenverhalt-nisse bei der Gattung Aeschna, mit besonderer Berücksichtingung der postreduktionellen Teilung der Bivalente. Ann. Acad. Sci. Fenn. A, *4:*1–65.

O'Mara, J., 1932. Chromosome pairing in *Yucca flaccida*. Cytologia *3:*66–76.

Ostergren, G., 1943. Elastic chromosome repulsion. Hereditas *29:*444–450.

————, 1945. Transverse equilibrium on the spindle. Bot. Not. *1:*467–468.

————, 1947. Heterochromatic B-chromosomes in Anthoxanthum. Hereditas *33:*261–296.

————, 1949a. Equilibria and movements of chromosomes. Proc. 8th Intern. Cong. Genetics Hereditas (Suppl. Vol.): 688–689.

——, 1949b. Luzula and the mechanism of chromosome movements. Hereditas *35:*445–468.

——, 1951. The mechanism of co-orientation in bivalents and multivalents. The theory of orientation by pulling. Hereditas *37:*85–156.

——, and R. Praaken, 1946. Behaviour on the spindle of the actively mobile chromosome ends of rye. Hereditas *32:*473–494.

——, and T. Wakonig, 1954. True or apparent sub-chromatid breakage and the induction of labile states in cytological chromosome loci. Bot. Not. *4:*357–375.

Painter, T. S., 1933. A new method for the study of chromosome rearrangements and the plotting of chromosome maps. Science *78:*585–586.

——, 1934. A new method for the study of chromosome aberrations and the plotting of chromosome maps in *Drosophila melanogaster*. Genetics *19:*175–188.

——, 1939. The structure of salivary gland chromosomes. Amer. Nat. *75:*315–330.

——, 1941. An experimental study of salivary chromosomes. Cold Spring Harbor Symp. Quant. Biol. *9:*47–54.

——, and E. C. Reindorp, 1939. Endomitosis in the nurse cells of the ovary of *Drosophila melanogaster*. Chromosoma *1:*276–283.

Palade, G. E., 1952. The fine structure of mitochondria. Anat. Rec. *114:*427–451.

——, 1953. The fine structure of mitochondria. An electron microscope study. Jour. Histochem. Cytochem. *1:*188–211.

——, 1955. A small particulate component of the cytoplasm. Jour. Biophys. Biochem. Cytology *1:*59–68.

——, and A. Claude, 1949. The nature of the Golgi apparatus. I. Parallelism between intercellular myelin figures and Golgi apparatus in somatic cells. II. Identification of the Golgi apparatus with a complex of myelin figures. Jour. Morph. *85:*35–70,71–112.

——, and P. Siekevitz, 1956. Liver microsomes. An integrated morphological and biochemical study. Jour. Biophy. Biochem. Cytology *2:*171–200.

Panshin, I. B., and V. V. Khvostova, 1938. Experimental proof of the subterminal position of the attachment point of the spindle in chromosome IV of *Drosophila melanogaster*. Biol. Zh. *7:*359–380.

Papazian, H. P., 1952. The analysis of tetrad data. Genetics *37:*175–188.

Patterson, J. T., and W. S. Stone, 1952. Evolution in the Genus Drosophila. Macmillan, N. Y.: 610 pp.

Pavan, C., and M. E. Breuer, 1952. Polytene chromosomes in different tissues of Rhynchosciara. Jour. Heredity *43:*151–157.

Perkins, D. D., 1955. Tetrads and crossing over. Jour. Cell. Comp. Physiol. *45(2):*119–149.

Peterson, P. A., 1953. A mutable *pale green* locus in maize. Genetics *38:*682.

Philip, J., and C. L. Huskins, 1931. The cytology of *Matthiola incana* R. Br., especially in relation to the inheritance of double flowers. Jour. Genetics *24:*359–404.

Pierce, W. P., 1937. The effect of phosphorus on chromosome and nuclear volume in a violet species. Bull. Torrey Bot. Club *64:*345–356.

Pipkin, S. B., 1940a. Segregation and crossing over in a 2–3 translocation in *Drosophila melanogaster*. Univ. Texas Bull. *4032:*73–125.

———, 1940b. Multiple sex genes in the X-chromosome of *Drosophila melanogaster*. Univ. Texas Publ. *4032:*126–156.

———, 1947. A search for sex genes in the second chromosome of *Drosophila melanogaster*, using the triploid method. Genetics *32:*592–607.

Piza, S. de T., 1939. Compartamento dos cromossômios na primeira divisao do espermatocito do *Tityus bahiensis*. Sci. genet. *1:*255–261.

Plough, H. H., 1917. The effect of temperature on crossing over in Drosophila. Jour. Exp. Zool. *24:*147–209.

———, 1921. Further studies on the effect of temperature on crossing over. Jour. Exp. Zool. *32:*187–202.

———, 1941. Spontaneous mutability in Drosophila. Cold Spring Harbor Symp. Quant. Biol. *9:*127–137.

Pollister, A. W., 1939. Centrioles and chromosomes in the atypical spermatogenesis of Vivipara. Proc. Nat. Acad. Sci. *25:*189–195.

———, 1941. Mitochondrial orientations and molecular patterns. Physiol. Zool. *14:*268–279.

———, 1952. Nucleoproteins of the nucleus. Exp. Cell Res., 2(Suppl.):59–70.

———, and C. Leuchtenberger, 1949. The nature of the specificity of methyl green for chromatin. Proc. Nat. Acad. Sci. *35:*111–116.

———, and L. Ornstein, 1955. Cytophotometric analysis in the visible spectrum. In Analytical cytology (R. C. Mellors, ed.), McGraw, N. Y.: 1/3–1/71.

———, and P. F. Pollister, 1943. The relation between centriole and centromere in atypical spermatogenesis of viviparid snails. Ann. N. Y. Acad. Sci. *45:*1–48.

———, and H. Ris, 1947. Nucleoprotein determination in cytological preparations. Cold Spring Harbor Symp. Quant. Biol. *12:*147–157.

Pomper, S., and K. C. Atwood, 1955. Radiation studies in fungi. In Radiation biology, McGraw, N. Y., *2:*431–454.

Pontecorvo, G., 1944. Structure of heterochromatin. Nature *153:*365.

———, 1952. Genetic formulation of gene structure and gene action. Adv. Enzym. *13:*121–150.

———, 1953. The genetics of *Aspergillus nidulans*. Adv. Genetics *5:*142–239.

Powers, L., 1945. Fertilization without reduction in guayule (*Parthenium argentatum* Gray) and a hypothesis as to the evolution of apomixis and polyploidy. Genetics *30:*323–346.

Praaken, R., and A. Müntzing, 1942. A meiotic peculiarity in rye, simulating a terminal centromere. Hereditas *28:*441–482.

Preer, J. R., 1948. A study of some properties of the cytoplasmic factor, "kappa," in *Paramecium aurelia*, variety 2. Genetics *33:*349–404.

———, 1950. Microscopically visible bodies in the cytoplasm of the "killer" strains of *Paramecium aurelia*. Genetics *35:*344–362.

———, and P. Stark, 1953. Cytological observations on the cytoplasmic factor "kappa" in *Paramecium aurelia*. Exp. Cell Res. *5:*478–491.

Preston, R. D., 1952. The molecular architecture of plant cell walls. Wiley, N. Y.: 211 pp.

568 REFERENCES

Prokofieva-Belgowskaya, A. A., 1937. Structure of the Y-chromosome in the salivary glands of Drosophila. Genetics *22:*94–103.

Randolph, L. F., 1928. Chromosome numbers in *Zea Mays* L. Cornell Univ. Exp. Sta. Mem., No. 117.

———, 1941a. Genetic characteristics of the B-chromosomes in maize. Genetics *26:*608–631.

———, 1941b. An evaluation of induced polypoidy as a method of breeding crop plants. Amer. Nat. *75:*347–363.

Rapaport, J. A., 1940. Multiple linear repetitions of chromosome blocks and their evolutionary significance. Jour. Gen. Biol. *1:*235–270.

Ray-Chaudhuri, S. P., and G. K. Manna, 1952. A new type of segregation of the sex chromosomes in the meiotic divisions of the cotton stainer, *Dysdercus koenigii* (Fabr.). Jour. Genetics *51:*191–197.

Redfield, H., 1930. Crossing-over in the third chromosomes of triploids of *Drosophila melanogaster.* Genetics *15:*205–252.

———, 1932. A comparison of triploid and diploid crossing over for chromosome II of *Drosophila melanogaster.* Genetics *17:*137–152.

Rees, H., 1952. Asynapsis and spontaneous chromosome breakage in Scilla. Heredity *6:*89–97.

———, 1953. Centromere control of chromosome splitting and breakage. Heredity *6 (Suppl.):*235–246.

Reitberger, A., 1940. Die Cytologie des pädogenetischen Entwicklungszyklus der Gallmücke *Oligarces paradoxus* Mei. Chromosoma *1:*391–473.

Renner, O., 1917. Versuche über die gametische Konstitution der Oenotheren. Zeitschr. ind. Abstam. Vererbungsl. *18:*121–294.

———, 1921. Heterogamie im weiblichen Geschlecht und Embryosackentwicklung bei den Oenotheren. Zeitschr. Bot. *13:*609–621.

———, 1934. Die pflanzlichen Plastiden als selbstandige Element der genetischen Konstitution. Ber. Math.-Phys. Kl. Acad. Wiss. Leipzig *86:*241–266.

———, 1936. Zur Kenntnis der nicht-mendelnden Bundheit der Laubblätter. Flora, N. F. *30:*218–290.

Resende, F., 1940. Über die Chromosomenstruktur in der Mitose der Wurzelspitzen. II. SAT-Differenzierungen, Spiralbau, and Chromonemata. Chromosoma *1:*486–520.

Revell, S. H., 1953. Chromosome breakage by x-rays and radiomimetic substances in Vicia. Heredity *6 (Suppl.):*107–124.

———, 1955. A new hypothesis for "chromatid" changes. Radiobiology symp. (Liège) Butterworths, London: 243–253.

Rhoades, M. M., 1931. A new type of translocation in *Drosophila melanogaster.* Genetics *16:*490–504.

———, 1933a. An experimental and theoretical study of chromatid crossing over. Genetics *18:*535–555.

———, 1933b. The cytoplasmic inheritance of male sterility in *Zea Mays.* Jour. Genetics *27:*71–93.

———, 1936. A cytological study of a chromosome fragment in maize. Genetics *21:*491–502.

————, 1938. On the origin of a secondary trisome through the doubling of a half-chromosome fragment. Genetics *23*:163–164.

————, 1939. *White sheath-3* (*ws₃*). Genetics *24*:62–63.

————, 1940. Studies of a telocentric chromosome in maize with reference to the stability of its centromere. Genetics *25*:483–520.

————, 1941a. The genetic control of mutability in maize. Cold Spring Harbor Symp. Quant. Biol. *9*:138–144.

————, 1941b. Different rates of crossing over in male and female gametes of maize. Jour. Amer. Soc. Agron. *33*:603–615.

————, 1942. Preferential segregation in maize. Genetics *27*:395–407.

————, 1945. On the genetic control of mutability in maize. Proc. Nat. Acad. Sci. *31*:91–95.

————, 1946. Plastid mutations. Cold Spring Harbor Symp. Quant. Biol. *11*:202–207.

————, 1947. Crossover chromosomes in unreduced gametes of asynaptic maize. Genetics 32: 101.

————, 1950. Meiosis in maize. Jour. Heredity *41*:59–67.

————, 1952. Preferential segregation in maize. In Heterosis, Iowa State College Press, Ames: 66–80.

————, 1954. Chromosomes, mutations, and cytoplasm in maize. Science *120*:115–120.

————, 1955. The cytogenetics of maize. In Corn and corn improvement, Academic Press, N. Y.: 123–219.

————, and A. Carvalho, 1944. The function and structure of the parenchyma sheath plastids of the maize leaf. Bull. Torrey Bot. Club *71*:335–346.

————, and E. Dempsey, 1953. Cytogenetic studies of deficient-duplicate chromosomes derived from inversion heterozygotes in maize. Amer. Jour. Bot. *40*:405–424.

————, and W. E. Kerr, 1949. A note on centromere organization. Proc. Nat. Acad. Sci. *35*:129–132.

————, and B. McClintock, 1935. The cytogenetics of maize. Bot. Rev. *1*:292–325.

————, and H. Vilkomerson, 1942. On the anaphase movement of chromosomes. Proc. Nat. Acad. Sci. *28*:433–436.

Ribbands, C. R., 1941. Meiosis in Diptera. I. Prophase association of non-homologous chromosomes and their relation to mutual attraction between centromeres, centrosomes, and chromosome ends. Jour. Genetics *41*:411–442.

Richards, O. W., 1946. Biological phase microscopy. Cold Spring Harbor Symp. Quant. Biol. *11*:208–214.

Richardson, M. M., 1935. Meiosis in Crepis. II. Failure of pairing in *Crepis capillaris*. Jour. Genetics *31*:119–143.

Rick, C. M., 1940. On the nature of x-ray induced deletions in Tradescantia chromosomes. Genetics *25*:467–482.

————, 1945. A survey of cytogenetic causes of unfruitfulness in the tomato. Genetics *30*:347–362.

————, 1946. The development of sterile ovules in *Lycopersicum esculentum*, Mill. Amer. Jour. Bot. *33*:250–256.

————, and D. W. Barton, 1954. Cytological and genetical identification of the primary trisomics of the tomato. Genetics *39:*640–666.

Riley, H. P., N. H. Giles, Jr., and A. V. Beatty, 1952. The effect of oxygen on the induction of chromatid aberrations in Tradescantia microspores by x-irradiation. Amer. Jour. Bot. *39:*592–597.

Ris, H., 1942. A cytological and experimental analysis of the meiotic behavior of the univalent X-chromosome in the bearberry aphid *Tamalia* (= *Phyllaphis*) *coweni* (Ckll.). Jour. Exp. Zool. *90:*267–330.

————, 1943. A quantitative study of anaphase movement in the aphid Tamalia. Biol. Bull. *85:*164–178.

————, 1945. The structure of meiotic chromosomes in the grasshopper and its bearing on the nature of "chromomeres" and "lamp-brush chromosomes." Biol. Bull. *89:*242–257.

————, 1949. The anaphase movement of chromosomes in the spermatocytes of the grasshopper. Biol. Bull. *96:*90–106.

————, and H. C. Crouse, 1945. Structure of the salivary gland chromosomes of Diptera. Proc. Nat. Acad. Sci. *31:*321–327.

————, and A. E. Mirsky, 1949. The state of the chromosomes in the interphase nucleus. Jour. Gen. Physiol. *32:*489–502.

Roman, H., 1947a. Mitotic non-disjunction in the case of interchanges involving the B-type chromosome in maize. Genetics *32:*391–409.

————, 1947b. Directed fertilization in maize. Proc. Nat. Acad. Sci. *34:*46–52.

Russell, W. L., 1954. Genetic effects of radiation in mammals. In Radiation biology, McGraw, N. Y., *1(2):*825–860.

Sandler, L., and G. Braver, 1954. The meiotic loss of unpaired chromosomes in *Drosophila melanogaster*. Genetics *39:*365–377.

Sansome, F. W., and J. Philp, 1939. Recent advances in plant genetics. Churchill, London: 412 pp.

Satina, S., 1953. Chromosome end arrangements in *Datura inoxia, D. meteloides,* and *D. metel.* Amer. Jour. Bot. *40:*638–646.

————, and A. F. Blakeslee, 1941. Periclinal chimeras in Datura stramonium in relation to development of leaf and flower. Amer. Jour. Bot. *28:*862–871.

————, A. F. Blakeslee, and A. G. Avery, 1940. Demonstration of the three germ layers in the shoot apex of Datura by means of induced polyploidy in periclinal chimeras. Amer. Jour. Bot. *27:*895–905.

Sax, H. J., and K. Sax, 1935. Chromosome structure and behavior in mitosis and meiosis. Jour. Arn. Arboretum *16:*423–439.

Sax, K., 1931. The origin and relationship of the Pomoideae. Jour. Arn. Arboretum *12:*3–22.

————, 1932. Chromosome relationships in the Pomoideae. Jour. Arn. Arboretum *13:*363–367.

————, 1932b. The cytological mechanism of crossing over. Jour. Arn. Arboretum *13:*180–212.

————, 1933. Species hybrids in Platanus and Campsis. Jour. Arn. Arboretum *14:*274–278.

————, 1937. Chromosome behavior and nuclear development in Tradescantia. Genetics *22:*523–533.

————, 1938. Induction by x-rays of chromosome aberrations in Tradescantia microspores. Genetics 23:494–516.

————, 1940. An analysis of x-ray induced chromosomal aberrations in Tradescantia. Genetics 25:41–68.

————, 1941. Types and frequencies of chromosomal aberrations induced by x-rays. Cold Spring Harbor Symp. Quant. Biol. 9:93–101.

————, 1942. The mechanisms of x-ray effect on cells. Jour. Gen. Physiol. 25:533–537.

————, 1943. The effect of centrifuging upon the production of x-ray induced chromosomal aberrations. Proc. Nat. Acad. Sci. 29:18–21.

————, and E. V. Enzman, 1939. The effect of temperature on the frequency of x-ray induced chromosome aberrations. Proc. Nat. Acad. Sci. 25:397–405.

————, and L. M. Humphrey, 1934. Structure of meiotic chromosomes in microsporogenesis of Tradescantia. Bot. Gaz. 96:353–362.

————, and E. D. King, 1955. An x-ray analysis of chromosome duplication. Proc. Nat. Acad. Sci. 41:150–155.

————, E. D. King, and H. Luippold, 1955. The effect of fractionated x-ray dosage on the frequency of chromatid and chromosome aberrations. Rad. Res. 2:171–179.

————, and K. Mather, 1939. An x-ray analysis of progressive chromosome splitting. Jour. Genetics 37:483–490.

————, and C. P. Swanson, 1941. Differential sensitivity of cells to x-rays. Amer. Jour. Bot. 28:52–59.

Schneiderman, H. A., and E. D. King, 1953. Further studies on the effects of carbon dioxide and oxygen on the frequency of x-ray induced chromosome aberrations in Tradescantia. Proc. Nat. Acad. Sci. 39:834–838.

Schrader, F., 1923. A study of the chromosomes in three species of Pseudococcus. Arch. Zellforsch. 17:45–62.

————, 1928. Die Geschlechtschromosomen. Borntraeger, Berlin: 194 pp.

————, 1929. Experimental and cytological investigations of the life cycle of Gossyparia spuria (Coccidae) and their bearing on the problem of haploidy in males. Zeitschr. wiss. Zool. 134:149–179.

————, 1931. The chromosome cycle of Protortonia primitiva (Coccidae) and a consideration of the meiotic division apparatus in the male. Zeitschr. wiss. Zool. 138:386–408.

————, 1935. Notes on the mitotic behavior of long chromosomes. Cytologia 6:422–431.

————, 1936. The kinetochore or spindle fiber locus in Amphiuma tridactylus. Biol. Bull. 70:484–498.

————, 1939. The structure of the kinetochore at meiosis. Chromosoma 1:230–237.

————, 1940. Touch-and-go pairing in chromosomes. Proc. Nat. Acad. Sci. 26:634–636.

————, 1941a. Heteropycnosis and non-homologous association of chromosomes in Edessa irrorata (Hemiptera, Heteroptera). Jour. Morph. 69:587–604.

————, 1941b. The spermatogenesis of the earwig Anisolabis maritima Bon with reference to the mechanism of chromosomal movement. Jour. Morph. 68:123–141.

————, 1947a. Data contributing to an analysis of metaphase mechanics. Chromosoma *3:*22–47.

————, 1947b. The role of the kinetochore in the evolution of the Heteroptera and Homoptera. Evol. *1:*134–142.

————, 1948. Three quarter-centuries of cytology. Science *107:*155–159.

————, 1953. Mitosis: the movement of chromosomes in cell division, Columbia Univ. Press, N. Y.: 170 pp.

————, and S. Hughes-Schrader, 1956. Polyploidy and fragmentation in the chromosomal evolution of various species of Thyanta (Hemiptera). Chromosoma *7:*469–496.

————, and C. Leuchtenberger, 1950. A cytochemical analysis of the functional interrelationships of various cell structures in *Arvelius albopunctatus* (De Geer). Exp. Cell Res. *1:*421–452.

Schultz, J., 1936. Radiation and the study of mutation in animals. In Biological effects of radiation, McGraw, N. Y.: 1209–1261.

————, 1941. The evidence of the nucleoprotein nature of the gene. Cold Spring Harbor Symp. Quant. Biol. *9:*55–65.

————, 1947. The nature of heterochromatin. Cold Spring Harbor Symp. Quant. Biol. *12:*179–191.

————, 1951. The effect of ultra-violet radiation on a ring chromosome in *Zea Mays*. Proc. Nat. Acad. Sci. *37:*590–600.

————, 1952. Interrelations between nucleus and cytoplasm: problems at the biological level. Exp. Cell Res. *2 (Suppl.):*17–44.

————, and H. Redfield, 1951. Interchromosomal effects on crossing over in Drosophila. Cold Spring Harbor Symp. Quant. Biol. *16:*175–195.

Schwartz, D., 1949. The chlorophyll mutants of maize. Bot. Gaz. *111:*123–130.

————, 1951. The interaction of nuclear and cytoplasmic factors in the inheritance of male sterility in maize. Genetics *36:*676–696.

————, 1952. The effect of oxygen concentration on x-ray-induced chromosome breakage in maize. Proc. Nat. Acad. Sci. 38:490–494.

————, 1953a. The behavior of an x-ray-induced ring chromosome in maize. Amer. Nat. *87:*19–28.

————, 1953b. Evidence for sister-strand crossing over in maize. Genetics *38:*251–260.

————, 1954. Studies on the mechanism of crossing over. Genetics *39:*692–700.

————, 1955a. Studies on crossing over in maize and Drosophila. Jour. Cell. Comp. Physiol. *45(2):*171–188.

————, 1955b. Speculations on gene action and protein specificity. Proc. Nat. Acad. Sci. *41:*300–307.

Sears, E. R., 1944. Cytogenetic studies with polyploid species of wheat. II. Additional chromosomal aberrations in *Triticum vulgare*. Genetics *29:*232–246.

————, 1948. The cytology and genetics of the wheats and their relatives. Adv. Genetics *2:*240–270.

————, 1952a. The behavior of isochromosomes and telocentrics in wheat. Chromosoma *4:*551–562.

————, 1952b. Misdivision of univalents in common wheat. Chromosoma *4:*535–550.

————, 1954. The aneuploids of common wheat. Univ. Missouri Res. Bull. *572:*1–58.

————, and A. Camara, 1952. A transmissible dicentric chromosome. Genetics *37:*125–135.

Seiler, J., 1921. Geschlechtschromosomen-untersuchunger an Psychiden. I. Experimentelle Beeinflussung der geschlechtsbestimmenden Reifeteilung bei *Talaeporia tubulosa* Retz. Arch. Zeliforsch. *15:*249–268.

Senn, H. A., 1938. Chromosome number relationships in the Leguminosae. Biblio. Genetica *12:*175–336.

Serra, J. A., 1947. Composition of chromonemata and matrix and the role of nucleoproteins in mitosis and meiosis. Cold Spring Harbor Symp. Quant. Biol. *12:*192–210.

Sharp, L. W., 1934. Introduction to cytology, 3rd ed., McGraw, N. Y.: 567 pp.

————, 1943. Fundamentals of cytology, McGraw, N. Y.: 270 pp.

Sherman, M., 1946. Karyotype evolution: a cytogenetic study of seven species and six interspecific hybrids of Crepis. Univ. Calif. Publ. Bot. *18:*369–408.

Sidorov, B. N., N. N. Sokolov, and I. E. Trofimov, 1935. Forces of attraction of homologous loci and chromosome conjugation. Nature *136:*108–109.

————, N. N. Sokolov, and I. E. Trofimov, 1936. Crossing over in hetero-zygoten Inversionen. Genetica *18:*291–312.

Singleton, J. R., 1953. Chromosome morphology and the chromosome cycle in the ascus of *Neurospora crassa.* Amer. Jour. Bot. *40:*124–144.

Sinnott, E. W., L. C. Dunn, and T. Dobzhansky, 1950. Principles of genetics. McGraw, N. Y.: 505 pp.

Sjöstrand, F. S., 1956a. The ultrastructure of the ground substance of the cyto-plasm. In Fine structure of cells, P. Noordhoff, Groningen: 222–228.

————, 1956b. The ultrastructure of mitochondria. In Fine structure of cells, P. Noordhoff, Groningen: 16–30.

————, and V. Hanzon, 1954. Ultrastructure of Golgi apparatus of exocrine cells of mouse pancreas. Exp. Cell Res. *7:*415–429.

————, and J. Rhodin, 1953. The ultrastructure of the proximal convoluted tubules of the mouse kidney as revealed by high resolution electron microscopy. Exp. Cell Res. *4:*426–456.

Skirm, G. W., 1942. Bivalent pairing in an induced tetraploid of Tradescantia. Genetics *27:*635–640.

Slack, H. D., 1938. Chromosome numbers in Cimex. Nature *142:*358.

————, 1939. Structural hybridity in Cimex L. Chromosoma *1:*104–118.

Slizynska, H., 1938. Salivary gland analysis of the *white-facet* region of *Dro-sophila melanogaster.* Genetics *23:*291–299.

Slizynski, B. M., 1942. Deficiency effects of ultra-violet light in *Drosophila melanogaster.* Proc. Roy. Soc. Edinburgh, B. *61:*297–315.

————, 1945. "Ectopic" pairing and the distribution of heterochromatin in the X-chromosome of salivary gland nuclei of *Drosophila melanogaster.* Proc. Roy. Soc. Edinburgh *62:*114–119.

————, 1950. Partial breakage of salivary gland chromosomes. Genetics *35:*279–287.

Smith, H. H., 1943. Effects of genome balance, polyploidy, and single extra chromosomes on size in Nicotiana. Genetics 28:227–236.

Smith, L., 1942a. Cytogenetics of a factor for multiploid sporocytes in barley. Amer. Jour. Bot. 29:451–456.

———, 1942b. Hereditary susceptibility to x-ray injury in Triticum monococcum. Amer. Jour. Bot. 29:189–191.

Smith, S. G., 1941. A new form of spruce sawfly identified by means of its cytology and parthenogenesis. Sci. Agric. 21:245–305.

———, 1942a. Polarization and progression in pairing-pachytene observations in Neodiprion (Hymenoptera). Can. Jour. Res. 20:368–379.

———, 1942b. Polarization and progression in pairing. II. Premeiotic orientation and the initiation of pairing. Can. Jour. Res., D, 20:221–229.

———, 1949. Evolutionary changes in the sex chromosomes of Coleoptera. I. Wood borers of the genus Agrilus. Evolution 3:344–357.

———, 1952. The evolution of heterochromatin in Tribolium (Tenebrionidae, Coleoptera). Chromosoma 4:585–610.

Sonneborn, T. M., 1943. Gene and cytoplasm. I. The determination and inheritance of the killer character in variety 4 of Paramecium aurelia. Proc. Nat. Acad. Sci. 29:329–338.

Sparrow, A. H., 1942. The structure and development of the chromosome spirals in microspores of Trillium. Can. Jour. Res., D, 20:257–266.

———, 1951. Radiation sensitivity of cells during mitotic and meiotic cells with emphasis on possible cytochemical changes. Ann. N. Y. Acad. Sci. 51:1508–1540.

———, C. L. Huskins, and G. B. Wilson, 1941. Studies on the chromosome spiralization cycle in Trillium. Can. Jour. Res. 19:323–350.

———, M. J. Moses, and R. Steele, 1952. A cytological and cytochemical approach to an understanding of radiation damage in dividing cells. Brit. Jour. Rad. 25:182–189.

———, and F. M. Rosenfeld, 1946. X-ray induced depolymerization of thymus nucleohistone and of sodium thymonucleate. Science 104:245–246.

———, M. L. Ruttle, and B. R. Nebel, 1942. Comparative cytology of sterile intra- and fertile intervarietal hybrids of Antirrhinum majus L. Amer. Jour. Bot. 29:711–715.

Spiess, E., 1950. Experimental populations of Drosophila persimilis from an altitudinal transect of the Sierra Nevada. Evolution 4:14–33.

Stadler, L. J., 1928. Mutations in barley induced by x-rays and radium. Science 68:186.

———, 1941. The comparison of ultraviolet and x-ray effects on mutations. Cold Spring Harbor Symp. Quant. Biol. 9:168–178.

———, 1942. Some observations on gene variability and spontaneous mutation. Spragg Memorial Lectures on Plant Breeding (3rd Series), Mich. State College, E. Lansing, Mich.

———, 1954. The Gene. Science 120:811–819.

———, and H. Roman, 1948. The effect of x-rays upon mutation of the gene A in maize. Genetics 33:273–303.

———, and F. M. Uber, 1942. Genetic effects of ultraviolet radiation in maize. IV. Comparison of monochromatic radiations. Genetics 27:84–118.

Stalker, H. D., 1954. Banded polytene chromosomes in the ovarion nurse cells of Diptera. Jour. Heredity 45:259–272.

Stebbins, G. L., Jr., 1938. Cytological characteristics associated with the different growth habits in dicotyledons. Amer. Jour. Bot. 25:189–198.

―――, 1940. The significance of polyploidy in plant evolution. Amer. Nat. 74:54–56.

―――, 1941a. Apomixis in the angiosperms. Bot. Rev. 7:507–542.

―――, 1941b. Comparative growth rates of diploid and autotetraploid Stipa lepida. Amer. Jour. Bot. 28 (Suppl.):6s.

―――, 1947. The origin of the complex of Bromus carinatus and its phytogeographic implications. Contr. Gray Herb. 165:42–55.

―――, 1949a. Rates of evolution in plants. In Genetics, paleontology, and evolution. Princeton Univ. Press, Princeton, N. J.: 229–242.

―――, 1949b. The evolutionary significance of natural and artificial polyploids in the family Gramineae. Proc. 8th Int. Cong. Genetics: 461–485.

―――, 1950. Variation and evolution in plants. Columbia Univ. Press, N. Y.: 643 pp.

―――, and E. B. Babcock, 1939. The effect of polyploidy and apomixis on the evolution of species in Crepis. Jour. Heredity 30:519–530.

―――, and H. A. Tobgy, 1944. The cytogenetics of hybrids in Bromus. I. Hybrids within the section Ceratochloa. Amer. Jour. Bot. 31:1–11.

―――, H. A. Tobgy, and J. R. Harlan, 1944. The cytogenetics of hybrids in Bromus. II. Bromus carinatus and Bromus arizonicus. Proc. Calif. Acad. Sci. 25:307–322.

―――, and M. S. Walters, 1949. The evolutionary significance of two synthetic allopolyploidy species of Bromus. Port. Acta Biol., Series A. R. B. Goldschmidt Vol: 106–136.

Stedman, E., and E. Stedman, 1947. The chemical nature and functions of the components of cell nuclei. Cold Spring Harbor Symp. Quant. Biol. 12:224–236.

Steffensen, D., 1953. Induction of chromosome breakage at meiosis by a magnesium deficiency in Tradescantia. Proc. Nat. Acad. Sci., 39:613–620.

―――, 1955. Chromosome breakage with a calcium deficiency in Tradescantia. Proc. Nat. Acad. Sci. 41:155–160.

Steinberg, A. G., 1936. The effect of autosomal inversions on crossing over in the X-chromosome of Drosophila melanogaster. Genetics 21:615–624.

―――, 1937. Relations between chromosome size and effects of inversions on crossing over in Drosophila melanogaster. Proc. Nat. Acad. Sci. 23:54–56

―――, and F. C. Fraser, 1944. Studies on the effect of X-chromosome inversions on crossing over in the third chromosome of Drosophila melanogaster. Genetics 29:83–101.

Steinmann, E., and F. S. Sjöstrand, 1955. The ultrastructure of chloroplasts. Exp. Cell Res. 8:15–23.

Stephens, S. G., 1951. "Homologous" genetic loci in Gossypium. Cold Spring Harbor Symp. Quant. Biol. 16:131–142.

―――, 1955. Summary, synthesis, and critique (Symposium on pseudoallelism and the theory of the gene). Amer. Nat. 89:117–122.

Stern, C., 1926. An effect of temperature and age on crossing over in the first chromosome of *Drosophila melanogaster*. Proc. Nat. Acad. Sci. *12:*530–532.

———, 1931. Zytologisch-genetische Untersuchungen als Beweise für die Morgansche Theorie des Factorenaustauschs. Biol. Zbl. *51:*547–587.

———, 1936. Somatic crossing over and segregation in *Drosophila melanogaster*. Genetics *21:*625–730.

———, and D. Doan, 1936. A cytogenetic demonstration of crossing-over between X- and Y-chromosomes in the male *Drosophila melanogaster*. Proc. Nat. Acad. Sci. *22:*649–654.

———, and V. Rentschler, 1936. The effect of temperature on the frequency of crossing over in *Drosophila melanogaster*. Proc. Nat. Acad. Sci. *22:*451–453.

Stern, H., 1955. On the intranuclear environment. Science 121: 144–145.

Stewart, R. N., and R. Bamford, 1942. The chromosomes and nucleoli of *Medeola virginiana*. Amer. Jour. Bot. *29:*301–303.

Stubbe, H., and D. von Wettstein, 1955. Zur Struktur erblich verschiedener Chloroplasten von Oenothera. Protoplasma *45:*241–250.

Sturtevant, A. H., 1915. The behavior of chromosomes as studied through linkage. Zeitschr. ind. Abstam. Vererbungsl. *13:*234–287.

———, 1919. Contributions to the genetics of *Drosophila melanogaster*. III. Inherited linkage variations in the second chromosome. Carnegie Inst. Wash. Pub. *278:*305–341.

———, 1921. Genetic studies on *Drosophila simulans*. I. Introduction: hybrids with *Drosophila melanogaster*. Genetics *5:*488–500.

———, 1925. The effects of unequal crossing over at the *Bar* locus in Drosophila. Genetics *10:*117–147.

———, 1928. A further study of the so-called mutation at the *Bar* locus of Drosophila. Genetics *13:*401–409.

———, 1929. The *claret* mutant type of *Drosophila simulans:* a study of chromosome elimination and of cell lineage. Zeitschr. wiss. Zool. *135:*325–355.

———, 1936. Preferential segregation in triplo-IV females of *Drosophila melanogaster*. Genetics *21:*444–466.

———, 1951a. The relation of genes and chromosomes. In Genetics in the 20th century. Macmillan, N. Y.: 101–110.

———, 1951b. A map of the fourth chromosome of *Drosophila melanogaster*, based on crossing over in triploid females. Proc. Nat. Acad. Sci. *37:*405–407.

———, 1955. Evaluation of recombination theory. Jour. Cell. Comp. Physiol. *45(2):*337–242.

———, and G. W. Beadle, 1936. The relations of inversions in the X-chromosome of *Drosophila melanogaster* to crossing over and disjunction. Genetics *21:*554–604.

———, and G. W. Beadle, 1939. An Introduction to genetics. W. B. Saunders Co., Phila.: 391 pp.

———, and T. Dobzhansky, 1936. Geographical distribution and cytology of "sex ratio" in *Drosophila pseudoobscura* and related species. Genetics *21:*473–490.

————, and T. H. Morgan, 1923. Reverse mutation of the *Bar* gene correlated with crossing over. Science *57:*746–747.

Suomaleinen, E., 1950. Parthenogenesis in animals. Adv. Genetics *3:*193–253.

Sutton, E., 1943a. A cytogenetic study of the *yellow-scute* region of the X-chromosome in *Drosophila melanogaster*. Genetics *28:*210–217.

————, 1943b. *Bar* eye in *Drosophila melanogaster:* a cytological analysis of some mutations and reverse mutations. Genetics *28:*97–107.

Sutton, W. S., 1902. On the morphology of the chromosome-group in *Brachystola magna*. Biol. Bull. *4:*24–39.

————, 1903. The chromosomes in heredity. Biol. Bull. *4:*231–248.

Swann, M. M., 1951. Protoplasmic structure and mitosis. I and II. Jour. Exp. Biol. *28:*417–444.

Swanson, C. P., 1940a. A comparison of chromosomal aberrations induced by x-ray and ultraviolet radiation. Proc. Nat. Acad. Sci. *26:*366–373

————, 1940b. The distribution of inversions in Tradescantia. Genetics *25:*438–465.

————, 1942a. Meiotic coiling in Tradescantia. Bot. Gaz. *103:*457–474.

————, 1942b. Some considerations on the phenomenon of chiasma terminalization. Amer. Nat. *76:*593–610.

————, 1942c. The effects of ultraviolet and x-ray treatment on the pollen tube chromosomes of Tradescantia. Genetics *27:*491–503.

————, 1943a. Differential sensitivity of prophase pollen tube chromosomes to x-rays and ultraviolet radiation. Jour. Gen. Physiol. *26:*485–494.

————, 1943b. Differences in meiotic coiling between Trillium and Tradescantia. Mich. Acad. Sci. Arts Letters *28:*133–142.

————, 1943c. The behavior of meiotic prophase chromosomes as revealed through the use of high temperatures. Amer. Jour. Bot. *30:*422–428.

————, 1943d. Secondary association of fragment chromosomes in generative nucleus of Tradescantia and its bearing on their origin. Bot. Gaz. *105:*108–112.

————, 1944. X-ray and ultraviolet studies on pollen tube chromosomes. I. The effect of ultraviolet (2537 A) on x-ray induced chromosomal aberrations. Genetics *29:*61–68.

————, 1947. X-ray and ultraviolet studies on pollen tube chromosomes. II. The quadripartite structure of the prophase chromosomes of Tradescantia. Proc. Nat. Acad. Sci. *33:*229–232.

————, 1949. Further studies on the effect of infrared radiation on x-ray induced chromatid aberrations in Tradescantia. Proc. Nat. Acad. Sci. *35:*237–244.

————, 1952. The effect of supplementary factors on the radiation induced frequency of mutations in *Aspergillus terreus*. Jour. Cell. Comp. Physiol. *39(1):*27–38.

————, 1955. Relative effects of qualitatively different radiations on the production of chromatid aberrations in air and in nitrogen. Genetics *40:*193–203.

————, and A. Hollaender, 1946. The frequency of x-ray induced chromatid breaks in Tradescantia as modified by near infrared radiation. Proc. Nat. Acad. Sci. *32:*295–302.

————, A. Hollaender, and B. N. Kaufmann, 1948. Modification of the x-ray and ultraviolet induced mutation rate in *Aspergillus terreus* by pretreatment with near infrared radiation. Genetics *33:*429–437.

————, and A. H. Johnston, 1955. Radiation-induced pycnosis of chromosomes and its relation to oxygen tension. Amer. Nat. *88:*425–430.

————, C. S. Rupert, and H. T. Yost, Jr., 1953. Infrared absorption and temperature studies on the buds and chromosomes of *Tradescantia paludosa*. Amer. Jour. Bot. *40:*557–565.

————, and D. Schwartz, 1953. Effects of x-rays on chromatid aberrations in air and in nitrogen. Proc. Nat. Acad. Sci. *39:*1241–1250.

————, and L. J. Stadler, 1955. The effect of ultraviolet radiation on the genes and chromosomes of higher organisms. In Radiation biology. McGraw, N. Y., *2:*249–284.

————, and H. T. Yost, Jr., 1951. The induction of activated, stable states in the chromosomes of Tradescantia by infrared and x-rays. Proc. Nat. Acad. Sci. *37:*796–802.

Swift, H., 1953. Quantitative aspects of nuclear nucleoproteins. Intern. Rev. Cytology *2:*1–76.

————, and R. Kleinfeld, 1953. DNA in grasshopper spermatogenesis, oögenesis, and cleavage. Physiol. Zool. *26:*301–311.

————, and E. M. Rasch, 1955. Nucleoproteins in Drosophila polytene chromosomes. Jour. Histochem. Cytochem. *2:*456–458.

Täckholm, G., 1922. Zytologische Studien über die Gattung Rosa. Acta Hort. Berg. *7:*97–381.

Tatum, E. L., and D. D. Perkins, 1950. Genetics in microorganisms. Ann. Rev. Microbiol. *4:*129–150.

Taylor, B., J. P. Greenstein, and A. Hollaender, 1948. Effects of x-radiation on sodium thymus nucleate. Arch. Biochem. *16:*19–31.

Taylor, J. H., 1949. Chromosomes from cultures of excised anthers. Jour. Heredity *40:*87–88.

Therman-Suomaleinen, E., 1949. Investigations on secondary constrictions in Polygonatum. Hereditas *35:*86–108.

Thoday, J. M., 1953. Sister-union isolocus breaks in irradiated *Vicia faba:* the target theory and physiological variation. Heredity *6 (Suppl.):*299–309.

————, and J. M. Read, 1947. Effect of oxygen on the frequency of chromosome aberrations produced by x-rays. Nature *160:*608.

————, and J. M. Read, 1949. Effect of oxygen on the frequency of chromosome aberrations produced by alpha-rays. Nature *163:*133–134.

Thomas, P. T., 1936. Genotypic control of chromosome size. Nature *138:*402.

Timofeeff-Ressovsky, N. W., K. G. Zimmer, and M. Delbrück, 1935. Über die Natur der Genmutation und der Genstruktur. Nachr. Ges. Wiss. Göttingen, Fachgruppe VI, n.F., *1:*189–245.

Tischler, G., 1950. Die Chromosomenzahlen. W. Junk, Hague: 263 pp.

Tjio, J. H., and A. Levan, 1954a. Some experiences with acetic orcein in animal chromosomes. Ana. Est. Exp. Aula Dei *3(2):*225–228.

————, and ————, 1954a. Chromosome analysis of three hyperdiploid ascites tumors of the mouse. Lunds Univ. Årsskr., N. F. *2:*3–38.

Tobgy, H. A., 1943. A cytological study of *Crepis fuliginosa, C. neglecta,* and their F_1 hybrid, and its bearing on the mechanism of phylogenetic reduction in chromosome number. Jour. Genetics *45:*67–111.

Tobler, M., 1931. Experimentelle Analyze der Genom- und Plasmon-wirkung bei Noosen. IV. Zur Variabilität des Zellvolumens einer Sippenkreuzung von *Funaria hygrometrica* und deren bivalenten Rassen. Zeitschr. ind. Abstamm. Vererbungsl. *60:*39–62.

Troedsson, P. H., 1944. The behavior of the compound sex chromosomes in the females of certain Hemiptera Heteroptera. Jour. Morph. *75:*103–147.

Upcott, M., 1937. Timing unbalance at meiosis in the pollen-sterile *Lathyrus odoratus.* Cytologia, Fujii Jub. Vol.: 299–310.

Vandel, A., 1938. Chromosome number, polyploidy, and sex in the animal kingdom. Proc. Zool. Soc., London, A, *107:*519–541.

Vanderlyn, L., 1948. Somatic mitosis in the root tip of *Allium Cepa*—a review and a reorientation. Bot. Rev. *14:*270–318.

———, 1949. The heterochromatin problem in cyto-genetics as related to other branches of investigation. Bot. Rev. *15:*507–582.

van Overbeek, J., 1935. The growth hormone and the dwarf type of growth in maize. Proc. Nat. Acad. Sci. *21:*292–299.

———, 1938. "Laziness" in maize due to abnormal distribution of growth hormone. Jour. Heredity *29:*339–341.

Vendrely, R., and C. Vendrely, 1948. La teneur du noyau cellulaire en acide désoxyribonucléique à travers les organes, les individus et les espèces animales. Experientia *4:*434–436.

Vincent, W. S., 1955. Structure and chemistry of nucleoli. Intern. Rev. Cytology *4:*269–298.

Visconti, N., and M. Delbrück, 1953. The mechanism of genetic recombination in phage. Genetics *38:*5–33.

von Wettstein, D., 1954. Forwechsel und Teilung der Chromatophoren von *Fucus vesiculous.* Zeitschr. Naturforsch. *9b:*476–481.

———, 1956. Formation of the plastid structures as affected by mutation in the chlorophyll apparatus. In Fine structure of cells. Noordhoff, Groningen: 55–59.

von Wettstein, F., 1928. Über plasmatische Verebung und über das Zusammenwirken von Genen und Plasma. Ber. Deuts. Bot. Ges. *46:*32–49.

Wagner, R. P., and H. K. Mitchell, 1955. Genetics and metabolism. Wiley, N. Y.: 444 pp.

Wald, H., 1936. Cytologic studies on the abnormal development of the eggs of *claret* mutant type of *Drosophila simulans.* Genetics *21:*264–281.

Walker, R. I., 1938. The effect of colchicine on somatic cells of *Tradescantia paludosa.* Jour. Arn. Arboretum *19:*158–162.

Wallace, B., 1953a. Coadaptation and gene arrangements of *Drosophila pseudoobscura.* Intern. Union Biol. Sci. Symp. Genetics Pop. Struc.: 67–94.

———, 1953b. On coadaptation in Drosophila. Amer. Nat. *87*:343–358.

Walters, J. L., 1942. Distribution of structural hybrids in *Paeonia californica*. Amer. Jour. Bot. *29*:270–275.

Walters, M. S., 1950. Spontaneous breakage and reunion of meiotic chromosomes in the hybrid *Bromus Trinii* × *B. maritimus*. Genetics 35:11–37.

———, 1951. Spontaneous chromosome breakage and atypical chromosome movement in meiosis of the hybrid *Bromus marginatus* × *B. pseudolaevipes*. Genetics *37*:8–25.

———, and D. U. Gerstel, 1948. A cytological investigation of a tetraploid *Rhoeo discolor*. Amer. Jour. Bot. *35*:141–150.

Warmke, H. E., 1941. Chromosome continuity and individuality. Cold Spring Harbor Symp. Quant. Biol. *9*:1–6.

———, 1946. Sex determination and sex balance in Melandrium. Amer. Jour. Bot. *33*:648–660.

———, and A. F. Blakeslee, 1940. The establishment of a dioecious race in Melandrium. Amer. Jour. Bot. *27*:751–762.

Warters, M., and A. B. Griffen, 1950. The telomeres of Drosophila. Jour. Heredity *41*:182–190.

Watson, J. D., and F. H. C. Crick, 1953a. Molecular structure of nucleic acids. Nature *171*:737–738.

———, and F. H. C. Crick, 1953b. The structure of DNA. Cold Spring Harbor Symp. Quant. Biol. *18*:123–131.

Watson, M. L., 1955. The nuclear envelope. Its structure and relation to cytoplasmic membranes. Jour. Biophys. Biochem. Cytology *1*:257–270.

Weier, T. E., and C. R. Stocking, 1952. The chloroplast: structure, inheritance, and enzymology. II. Bot. Rev. *18*:14–76.

Weinstein, A., 1936. The theory of multiple-strand crossing over. Genetics *21*:155–199.

Westergaard, M., 1940. Studies on cytology and sex determination in polyploid forms of *Melandrium album*. Dansk. Bot. Arkiv. *10*:1–131.

———, 1948. The relation between chromosomal constitution and sex in the offspring of triploid Melandrium. Hereditas *34*:257–279.

White, M. J. D., 1935. The effect of x-rays on the spermatogonial divisions in *Locusta migratoria* L. Proc. Roy. Soc. B, *119*:61–84.

———, 1936. Chiasma localization in *Mecostethus grossus* L. and *Metrioptera brachyptera*. Zeitschr. Zellforsch. *24*:128–135.

———, 1941. The evolution of the sex chromosomes. I. The XO and X_1X_2Y mechanisms in praying mantids. Jour. Genetics *42*:143–172.

———, 1946a. The evidence against polyploidy in sexually-reproducing animals. Amer. Nat. *80*:610–619.

———, 1946b. The cytology of the Cecidomyidae (Diptera). I. Polyploidy and polyteny in salivary gland cells of *Lestodiplosis spp.* Jour. Morph. 78:201–219.

———, 1946c. The cytology of the Cecidomyidae (Diptera). II. The chromosome cycle and anomalous spermatogenesis in Miastor. Jour. Morph. 79:323–370.

———, 1947. The cytology of the Cecidomyidae (Diptera). III. The spermatogenesis of *Taxomyia taxi*. Jour. Morph. *80*:1–24.

————, 1950. Cytological studies on gall midges (Cecidomyidae). Univ. Texas Publ. *5007:*1–80.

————, 1951a. Cytogenetics of orthopteroid insects. Adv. Genetics *4:*267–330.

————, 1951b. Nucleus, chromosomes, and genes. In Cytology and cell physiology, 2nd ed., Clarendon Press, Oxford: 183–231.

————, 1954. Animal cytology and evolution, 2nd ed., Univ. Press, Cambridge: 454 pp.

Whitehouse, H. L. K., 1942. Crossing over in Neurospora. New Phyt. *41:*23–62.

Whiting, P. W., 1943. Multiple alleles in complementary sex determination of Habrobracon. Genetics *28:*365–382.

————, 1945. The evolution of male haploidy. Quart. Rev. Biol. *20:*231–260.

Whittinghill, M., 1937. Induced crossing over in Drosophila males and its probable nature. Genetics *22:*114–129.

————, 1947. Spermatogonial crossing over between the third chromosomes in the presence of the Curly inversions in *Drosophila melanogaster.* Genetics *32:*608–614.

Wilson, E. B., 1925. The cell in development and heredity, 3rd ed., Macmillan, N. Y.: 1232 pp.

Wilson, G. B., and E. R. Boothroyd, 1941. Studies in differential reactivity. I. The rate and degree of differentiation in the somatic chromosomes of *Trillium erectum* L. Canad. Jour. Res., C, *19:*400–412.

————, and E. R. Boothroyd, 1944. Temperature-induced differential contraction in the somatic chromosomes of *Trillium erectum* L. Canad. Jour. Res., C, *22:*105–119.

Winge, O., 1932. The nature of sex chromosomes. Proc. 6th Intern. Cong. Genetics *1:*343–355.

Witkus, E. R., 1945. Endomitotic tapetal cell divisions in Spinacia. Amer. Jour. Bot. *32:*326–330.

Wolff, S., 1954. Delay of chromosome rejoining in *Vicia faba* induced by irradiation. Nature *173:*501.

————, and K. C. Atwood, 1954. Independent x-ray effects on chromosome breakage and reunion. Proc. Nat. Acad. Sci. *40:*187–192.

————, and H. E. Luippold, 1955. Metabolism and chromosome-break rejoining. Science *122:*231–232.

————, and R. C. Von Borstel, 1954. The effects of pre- and post-irradiation centrifugation on the chromosomes of Tradescantia and Vicia. Proc. Nat. Acad. Sci. *40:*1138–1141.

Wollman, E. L., and F. Jacob, 1955. Sur le mechanismé du transfert de material genetique au cours de la recombinaison chez *Escherichia coli* K12. Compt. rend. acad. sci. *240:*2449.

Wright, S., 1934. Physiological and evolutionary theories of dominance. Amer. Nat. *68:*24–53.

————, and T. Dobzhansky, 1946. Genetics of natural populations. XII Experimental reproduction of some of the changes caused by natural selection in certain populations of *Drosophila pseudoobscura.* Genetics *31:*125–156.

Wycoff, R. W. G., 1949. Electron microscopy: technique and applications, Interscience Publ., N. Y.: 248 pp.

Yost, H. T., Jr., 1951. The frequency of x-ray induced chromosome aberrations in Tradescantia as modified by near infrared radiation. Genetics *36:*176–184.

Zamenhof, S., 1952. Newer aspects of the chemistry of nucleic acids. In Phosphorus metabolism II, Johns Hopkins Univ. Press, Baltimore: 301–328.

Zelle, M. R., and A. Hollaender, 1955. Effects of radiation on bacteria. In Radiation biology, McGraw, N. Y., *2:*365–430.

———, and J. Lederberg, 1951. Single cell isolates of diploid heterozygous *Escherichia coli.* Jour. Bact. *61:*351–355.

Zinder, N. D., 1953. Infective heredity in bacteria. Cold Spring Harbor Symp. Quant. Biol. *18:*261–269.

———, 1955. Bacterial transduction. Jour. Cell. Comp. Physiol. *45(2):*23–49.

———, and J. Lederberg, 1952. Genetic exchange in Salmonella. Jour. Bact. *64:*679–699.

Index